TOLD
UNDER THE
MAGIC UMBRELLA

MODERN TALES OF FANCY AND HUMOR

TOLD
UNDER THE
MAGIC UMBRELLA

Selected by the Literature Committee of the
Association for Childhood Education International

Illustrated by Elizabeth Orton Jones

THE MACMILLAN COMPANY · NEW YORK

TO

THE CHILDREN

WHO LOVE

WONDER, MAGIC AND FUN

ACKNOWLEDGMENTS

FOR permission to reprint the stories included in *Told Under the Magic Umbrella* the Literature Committee of the Association for Childhood Education records its appreciation to the following:

D. Appleton-Century Company, Inc., New York, for "The Ogre That Played Jackstraws," from *The Book of Knight and Barbara* by David Starr Jordan.

Dodd, Mead & Company, Inc., New York, for "Sojo," by Erick Berry, and "The Lost Merbaby," by Mary and Margaret Baker (Copyright, 1927, by Dodd, Mead & Company, Inc.).

Doubleday, Doran & Company, Inc., New York, for "The Saddler's Horse," from *A Street of Little Shops* by Margery Williams Bianco (Copyright, 1932, by Margery Williams Bianco. Permission of Doubleday, Doran & Company, Inc.); "The Bojabi Tree," by Edith Rickert (Copyright, 1923, by Doubleday, Doran & Company, Inc.); "The Lamb That Went to Fairyland," from *The Rainbow Cat* by Rose Fyleman (Copyright, 1923, by Doubleday, Doran & Company, Inc.); "The Bean Boy," from *California Fairy Tales* by Monica Shannon (Copyright, 1926, by Doubleday, Doran & Company, Inc.).

E. P. Dutton & Company, Inc., New York, for "The Merry-Go-Round and the Griggses," from *A Merry-Go-Round of Modern Tales* by Caroline D. Emerson.

Faber & Faber, Ltd., London, for "The Three Apples," from *Michael of Ireland* by Anne Casserley (Permission Harper & Brothers); "The Pixies' Scarf," from *Mustard, Pepper and Salt* by Alison Uttley.

Harcourt, Brace & Company, Inc., New York, for "How to Tell the Corn Fairies," from *Rootabaga Stories* by Carl Sandburg (Copyright, 1922, by Harcourt, Brace & Company, Inc.); "Rocking-Horse Land," from *Moonshine and Clover* by Laurence Housman.

Harper & Brothers, New York, for "Gooseberry Garden," by Lois Lenski; "Living in W'ales," from *The Spider's Palace* by Richard Hughes.

The Harter Publishing Company, Cleveland, for "Sojo," by Erick Berry.

J. B. Lippincott Company, Philadelphia, for "Gissing and the Telephone," from *I Know a Secret* by Christopher Morley.

Little, Brown & Company, Boston, for "The Brownie in the House," from *Seven Peas in a Pod* by Margery Bailey.

Longmans, Green & Company, New York, for "The Musical Box," by Clare Leighton.

Lothrop, Lee & Shepard Company, New York, for "Little Dog and Big Dog," by Maude Lindsay, from *A Story Garden for Little Children.*

The Macmillan Company, New York, for "Ask Mr. Bear," by Marjorie Flack.

Methodist Book Concern, Cincinnati, for "Two Little Shoes," by Carol Ryrie Brink, in *Picture Story Paper.*

William Morrow & Company, Inc., New York, for "Millitinkle," from *Tal, His Marvelous Adventures with Noom-Zor-Noom* by Paul Fenimore Cooper.

John Murray, London, for "George and Angela," by Cicely Englefield.

Thomas Nelson & Sons, New York, for "The Little Old Woman and How She Kept Her Geese Warm," from *The Little Old Woman Who Used Her Head* by Hope Newell.

Oxford University Press, New York, for "The Cobbler's Tale," from *Ragman of Paris* by Elizabeth Orton Jones.

Frederick A. Stokes Company, New York, for "The Pony Tree," by Charlotte Brate (Copyright, 1928, by Frederick A. Stokes Company); "The Three Elevators," from *The Lively City O' Ligg* (Copyright, 1899, by Gelett Burgess); "Elsie Piddock Skips in Her Sleep," from *Martin Pippin in the Daisy Field* by Eleanor Farjeon (Copyright, 1937, by Eleanor Farjeon).

The John C. Winston Company, Philadelphia, for "If You Had a Wish?", by Charles J. Finger.

Erick Berry and *Child Life,* Chicago, for "Sojo."

Carol Ryrie Brink, for "Two Little Shoes."

Emma L. Brock, for "Gingham Lena."

Frances Anne Brown, for "A Happy Christmas Tree."

Alice Crew Gall and Fleming Crew, for "The Song of the Little Donkey."

Louise M. La Fleur and *Child Life,* Chicago, for "Little Duckling Tries His Voice," by Marjorie La Fleur.

Julian Street, for "The Goldfish" (Copyright, 1911, by the Ridgway Company; Copyright, 1912, by Dodd, Mead & Co., Inc.).

The Literature Committee acknowledges its appreciation also to May Hill Arbuthnot, Lula E. Wright, Carol Ryrie Brink, Edwina Fallis, Jennie Milton and Laura M. White for cooperative editorial service, story suggestions and other assistance to the new umbrella book.

FOREWORD

MAKE-BELIEVE is a great resource of childhood. It is a child's first essay in imagination, his attempt to interpret a strange and confusing world in terms of his own understanding and to his own liking. Explanations of the older mind are not always satisfactory; they take too much for granted, and the child mind, insatiably curious, often prefers to invent its own explanations. Young children are apt to have rather tidy minds; they dislike loose ends instinctively; they want to find a reason for everything, and where a reason is not forthcoming they will promptly make one up for themselves, and more often than not their reasoning takes the form of a story. In a word, they are born creators of folklore, a folklore entirely their own and concerned with the familiar things around them.

The modern fairy tale—or fanciful tale, to make a useful distinction—takes full account of this creative instinct. It differs from its long line of predecessors in concerning itself not so much with fantastic elements outside the child's experience as with the more everyday things of his own world. It realizes that magic, like charity, begins best at home.

In this kind of story the child is not only audience, he feels himself almost collaborator. At a certain point in the tale he knows beforehand what is going to happen, because it is the sort of conclusion that he himself would choose. His is the delight of one artist recognizing another artist's master-hand.

The world of fantasy may be a topsy-turvy world, but it is one which children have always found particularly satisfying and logical. Nothing about it can unduly surprise them, since life is so full of surprises anyway and things very seldom turn out to be just what they seem. In an existence where so many things are strange and inexplicable—the transformation of a seed into a flower, the mystery of a lighted match, the fact that some objects float on water, while others for no apparent reason fall to the bottom—why should any one thing seem stranger than another? If a voice can and does come out of a wooden box, it should also come, far more appropriately, from a calico dog. Talking animals are an old convention by no means confined to childhood, and any toy once taken to the heart assumes a character and personality which needs only the lightest touch of fancy to bring it into life and action.

The imaginative story has a function deeper than that of entertainment alone. It shows life from a new angle, like objects seen through a prism. It can open fresh ranges of vision and understanding, rouse the perception of beauty in hitherto disregarded things. It has power through the simple magic of humor to rob childhood of a good many of its fears and bugaboos, for once you have laughed at anything in reassuring company it no longer has power to frighten you, and behind all nonsense there is somewhere a sound sanity. Moreover, it teaches, far more acceptably than the realistic story, sympathy and unselfishness, the value of laughter, and a certain happy tolerance with the foibles and foolishness of other people. In the fairy tale it is usually the over-clever and malicious who get their come-uppings, the humble of heart who inherit the earth.

Imagination, more than any other quality, makes for understanding and a regard for the feelings of others. The child who has learned to look upon his own toys as something more than mere sawdust and stuffing is inclined to have respect for other people's treasures as well as his own and to respect the sentiment that values them; the child who meets frogs and kittens and puppies as individualized characters in his favorite storybook is not likely to be careless and unfeeling towards animals in everyday life. Wonder and mystery are the elements of life and growth all around us. Nothing in any story can actually add to the magic of the world as a child sees it, but it can help him towards new perceptions, fresh discoveries of his own.

Told Under the Magic Umbrella is a collection of modern fanciful tales, widely representative and chosen each for its particular appeal. *Ask Mr. Bear* has long been a nursery classic, forerunner of many delightful tales in which Marjorie Flack shows an unfailing sense of the story needs of young children and of the dramatic elements that most appeal to them. *Two Little Shoes* by Carol Ryrie Brink and Emma Brock's *Gingham Lena* both hinge on the homely magic by which inanimate things take life and personality. Gingham Lena, smudgy, carefree and adventurous, may well stand for the spirit of rag dolls the world over, and, by the way, it is not for nothing that the rag doll, and not her more elaborate sister, figures usually in the best-loved doll stories. Both Gelett Burgess, in *The Three Elevators,* and Caroline Emerson have the grand idea of bringing modern inventions and mechanical devices into line, so to speak, in the child's imaginative world by investing them with personal character. In Caroline Emerson's "Merry-Go-Round of Modern Tales" the car, the steam roller, the telephone, and other familiar objects suddenly decide to take matters into their own hands, with startling results. *The Merry-Go-Round and the Griggses* is one of the best of these irresistibly humorous tales.

Magic and wisdom are the time-honored attributes of the storybook cat. In *The Cobbler's Tale* it takes a cat to hit upon the simple device that makes the King's shoes comfortable. The ten-times granddaughter of this same cat is one of many endearing characters in "Ragman of Paris," the refreshingly droll and genial story by Elizabeth Orton Jones from which this little tale is taken. Hope Newell's *Little Old Woman* is close kin to the wise men of Gotham and has a long ancestry among the more kindly forms of folklore humor. How to keep her geese warm is one of the problems which she solves by a system of patient and simple-minded reasoning. All children love paradoxes, and behind the laughter in this tale they will appreciate a kind of commonsense logic not so far different from their own.

Two of the stories in this volume have an African background, *Sojo* by Erick Berry and *The Bojabi Tree* by Edith Rickert, the latter being an adapted folk tale. African folklore is particularly rich in drama and action; animals play a more important part than humans in its legendry, and its nearness to primitive nature gives it a special interest to children. In "Rootabaga Stories" Carl Sandburg created a whole new folklore almost overnight—tales spontaneous, fresh as the prairie wind and colored through and through with the feeling of the American soil. Told in vigorous homespun prose, they bring to every child a sense of the magic of his own time and country. The Californian fairy tales of Monica Shannon, too, are definitely native in quality; one feels that they have grown directly out of their own environment.

One of the first tests of a good story is that it can be read or told aloud. It must hold its audience. The tales collected under the *Magic Umbrella* have all stood this test successfully, not once but many times.

MARGERY BIANCO

CONTENTS

CONTENTS

ASK MR. BEAR

ONCE THERE WAS a boy named Danny. One day Danny's mother had a birthday.

Danny said to himself, "What shall I give my mother for her birthday?"

So Danny started out to see what he could find.

He walked along, and he met a Hen.

"Good morning, Mrs. Hen," said Danny. "Can you give me something for my mother's birthday?"

"Cluck, cluck," said the Hen. "I can give you a nice fresh egg for your mother's birthday."

"Thank you," said Danny, "but she has an egg."

"Let's see what we can find then," said the Hen.

So Danny and the Hen skipped along until they met a Goose.

"Good morning, Mrs. Goose," said Danny. "Can you give me something for my mother's birthday?"

"Honk, honk," said the Goose. "I can give you some nice feathers to make a fine pillow for your mother's birthday."

"Thank you," said Danny, "but she has a pillow."

"Let's see what we can find then," said the Goose.

So Danny and the Hen and the Goose all hopped along until they met a Goat.

"Good morning, Mrs. Goat," said Danny. "Can you give me something for my mother's birthday?"

"Maa, maa," said the Goat. "I can give you milk for making cheese."

"Thank you," said Danny, "but she has some cheese."

"Let's see what we can find then," said the Goat.

So Danny and the Hen and the Goose and the Goat all galloped along until they met a Sheep.

"Good morning, Mrs. Sheep," said Danny. "Can you give me something for my mother's birthday?"

"Baa, baa," said the Sheep. "I can give you some wool to make a warm blanket for your mother's birthday."

"Thank you," said Danny, "but she has a blanket."

"Let's see what we can find then," said the Sheep.

So Danny and the Hen and the Goose and the Goat and the Sheep all trotted along until they met a Cow.

"Good morning, Mrs. Cow," said Danny. "Can you give me something for my mother's birthday?"

"Moo, moo," said the Cow. "I can give you some milk and cream."

"Thank you," said Danny, "but she has some milk and cream."

"Then ask Mr. Bear," said the Cow. "He lives in the woods over the hill."

"All right," said Danny. "Let's go ask Mr. Bear."

"No," said the Hen.

"No," said the Goose.

"No," said the Goat.

"No," said the Sheep.

"No—no," said the Cow.

So Danny went alone to find Mr. Bear.

He ran and he ran until he came to a hill, and he walked and he walked until he came to the woods and there he met—Mr. Bear.

"Good morning, Mr. Bear," said Danny. "Can you give me something for my mother's birthday?"

"Hum, hum," said the Bear. "I have nothing to give you for your mother's birthday, but I can tell you something you can give her."

So Mr. Bear whispered a secret in Danny's ear.

"Oh," said Danny. "Thank you, Mr. Bear!"

Then he ran through the woods and he skipped down the hill and he came to his house.

"Guess what I have for your birthday!" Danny said to his mother.

So his mother tried to guess.

"Is it an egg?"

"No, it isn't an egg," said Danny.

"Is it a pillow?"

"No, it isn't a pillow," said Danny.

"Is it a cheese?"

"No, it isn't a cheese," said Danny.

"Is it a blanket?"

"No, it isn't a blanket," said Danny.

"Is it milk or cream?"

"No, it isn't milk or cream," said Danny.

His mother could not guess at all. So—Danny gave his mother

a Big Birthday
Bear Hug.

By Marjorie Flack

LITTLE DUCKLING TRIES HIS VOICE

ONCE UPON A TIME fat Little Duckling went on a journey into the Wide World. He wandered along the Barnyard Road, and presently he saw the Kitty Cat.

"Me-ow!" said the Kitty Cat.

"O-o-oh!" cried Little Duckling. "Isn't that a *pretty* sound! I think I'll talk that way!"

But do you suppose Little Duckling could say "Me-ow"?

No indeed!

He tried, but the best he could do was: "Me-e-ack! Me-e-ack!"

And that wasn't pretty at all!

So Little Duckling waddled on and on. After a while he saw Puppy Dog.

"Bow-wow," said Puppy Dog.

"O-o-oh!" cried Little Duckling. "Isn't that a *lovely* noise! I think I'll talk that way!"

But do you suppose Little Duckling could say "Bow-wow"?

No indeed!

5

He tried, but this is the way he sounded: "B-ack! B-ack!" And that wasn't lovely at all!

Then Little Duckling waddled on and on. Soon he saw a Yellow Bird in a tree.

"Tweet-tweet-tweet-tweet tweet!" said Yellow Bird.

"Oh, oh, oh!" sighed Little Duckling. "Isn't that a *sweet* song! I think I'll sing that way!"

But do you suppose Little Duckling could sing "Tweet-Tweet"?

No indeed!

He tried his very best, but all he could say was: "Twack! Twack!"

And that wasn't sweet at all!

So Little Duckling waddled on and on. After a while he met Big Cow.

"Moo-o-o!" said Big Cow.

"O-o-oh!" thought Little Duckling. "Isn't that a *beautiful* roar! I think I'll roar that way!"

But do you suppose Little Duckling could say "Moo-o-o"?

He tried, but all he could manage to say was: "M-ack! M-ack!"

And that wasn't beautiful at all!

Little Duckling was very sad. He could not say "Me-ow" like Kitty Cat. He could not say "Bow-wow" like Puppy Dog. He could not say "Tweet-tweet" like Yellow Bird. He could not say "Moo-o-o" like Big Cow.

He waddled slowly on and on. All at once he saw his own Mother Duck coming toward him along the Barnyard Road.

"Quack! Quack!" cried Mother Duck.

"O-o-oh!" whispered happy Little Duckling to him-self. "That is the prettiest sound in the whole Wide World! I think I'll talk *that* way!"

And he found he could say "Quack! Quack!" very nicely.

By Marjorie La Fleur

TWO LITTLE SHOES

ALL WINTER Sally Lou's two little shoes had carried
her up and down stairs, back and forth to school, and
out to play. They felt very important and proud. For
how could Sally go to school or run errands for Mother
or play hop-scotch without their help? The more
wrinkled and scuffed they grew, the prouder they became.

"We have grown old in Sally Lou's service," said
one to the other. "She could certainly never get along
without us!"

"She changes her stockings every day, and she has
even put away her winter coat," said the other, "but
she could never, never get along without us."

Then one day Mother said: "Sally Lou, I'm going
to take you downtown today." The two little shoes
jumped for joy when they heard Mother speak, and
they cried: "Oh, goody!" and "Hurray!" just as Sally

Lou did. They carried Sally Lou away to get ready, and soon they were trotting side by side to town. Into a great big store they went, and the little shoes were just as much interested in looking at everything as Sally Lou herself. They kept stopping to admire things, and Mother had to hurry them along.

At last they came to the strangest place of all, for it was entirely full of little shoes. Shoe-button eyes gazed at them from all sides, wide-mouthed pumps seemed to smile at them, and one impudent play-shoe stuck out its tongue. Suddenly Sally Lou's shoes began to feel how worn and shabby they looked among all these shining patent leathers and fine new shoes.

"Sally Lou really should have polished us before bringing us into such high society," they said. Then the terrible truth dawned upon them. Sally Lou's Mother was buying her a brand new pair of shoes! The shoe man took them off and cast them aside while Sally Lou tried on pair after pair of darling pumps and sandals and slippers.

"Those flimsy things will never keep her warm," groaned the two little shoes. But nobody paid the slightest attention to them. At last Sally Lou and Mother found a shiny pair of strap slippers that were just what they wanted.

"Oh, may I please wear them?" begged Sally Lou.

"I believe you may," said Mother, "if the gentleman will be so kind as to wrap up the old ones." So Sally Lou's two little shoes were wrapped in a brown paper parcel and carried home. They grumbled a good deal about the string and paper being too tight. But that was not the real trouble with them. Their poor hearts were nearly broken because Sally Lou had put them aside for a pair of slippers. When they got home they were unwrapped and set side by side in Sally Lou's closet.

"Well," said Sally Lou's winter coat, hanging above them, "I see you're here at last. I thought you were never coming."

"How can she skip and play without us?" cried the little shoes. "And won't she catch cold in those silly little slippers?"

"It's spring now," said the winter coat. "We've had our day." The little shoes sighed and flopped dejectedly on the closet floor. But they couldn't help dreaming of the good times they were missing.

And when the summer dresses began talking about the picnic, they couldn't help listening.

"I'm sure she's going to wear me," said the little sleeveless dress, "and it will be such fun!"

"Oh, I do wish she'd choose me," sighed the blue gingham. "There's nothing I like better than a picnic." The two little shoes cuddled closer together.

"We used to go to everything," they whispered. "Oh, how we should like to go to the picnic! But that is all over now."

The night before the picnic the dresses were squabbling and arguing all night as to which was going next day. The new strap slippers, which had been set in the closet for the night, laughed scornfully.

"There is only one thing certain about it," they said, "she is *sure* to wear *us!*"

They were all making so much noise that they didn't hear the patter of the raindrops on the roof. It rained all night. When Sally Lou got up the next morning she began to cry. The dresses all hung limp and dejected. It looked as if there wouldn't be any picnic that day.

But presently they heard Sally Lou laughing and singing again.

"It's clearing! It's clearing!" she sang as she danced up the stairs. "And Mother says I may go, if I'll wear my little old shoes to keep my feet warm and dry. Where are you, little old shoes? We're going on the picnic!" The little old shoes sat up as stiffly as they could, and as soon as Sally Lou put them on they began to dance. Oh! how they danced! They had never been gayer or happier in their lives, or carried Sally Lou through livelier adventures. The weather continued to clear and the picnic was a great success.

And after that the two little shoes never minded being put away in the closet. For they thought:

"Someday Sally Lou will be sure to need us again. If it hadn't been for us, she couldn't have gone on the picnic."

By Carol Ryrie Brink

GINGHAM LENA

ONCE UPON A TIME there was a little boy named Elmer
who had a little sister Selma. They lived with their
father and mother in a white farmhouse with a porch
in the front and a pump under a windmill at the back.
On the farm there were twenty cows and twenty pigs
and some chickens and two dozen big fields that rolled
away over the hills and were covered with wheat and
corn and potatoes. There was a silo and a plow and
other farm things.

Selma had a doll with blue eyes, orange wool hair
and a smudgy nose. Her name was Brin Hilda and her
nose was smudgy because she ate mud pies. Elmer had
a gingham dog called Lena. She ate ants sometimes if
they waited long enough.

One day Selma could not find Brin Hilda anywhere.
She and Elmer looked in the house under the radio

and in the barn under the hay and in the seats of the old black car. They could not find Brin Hilda anywhere.

Selma sat down on one side of the pump and twisted her face up to keep from crying. Elmer put his hands in his pockets and sat down on the other side of the pump and kicked dirt with his bare toes. They could not think where Brin Hilda could be. Gingham Lena sat by the pump, too, and thought and thought.

Oh, Brin Hilda, with your smudgy face, where have you gone and what are you doing?

Then Lena smiled and said to herself, "I'll just go out and find Brin Hilda. She must be somewhere."

So Gingham Lena cocked up one ear and ran over to the chicken yard to ask the chickens.

"Have you seen Brin Hilda?" she cried out.

But the chickens were too busy pecking and clucking to notice anything.

"No, Gingham Lena, we have not seen her," they said.

Lena cocked up her other ear and ran into the barn to ask the horses and cows. But the horses were out in the field working and the cows were far away eating in the pasture.

Then she cocked both ears at once and ran out of the barn again and right into a big gray goose who was peering in at the barn door with her neck stretched way out.

"Have you seen Brin Hilda?" asked Lena.

"No, Gingham Lena," said the goose, "I have not seen her."

And the turkeys in the field had not seen Brin Hilda. And the red squirrel in the tree had not seen her either. Nor had the pigs who were grubbing in the pig yard.

"No, we have not seen her, Gingham Lena," each one of them answered.

Gingham Lena sat down by the pig yard fence and thought and thought.

Oh, Brin Hilda, with your smudgy face, where have you gone and what are you doing?

Then Lena wagged her tail and ran over to the duck pond, where the ducks were cleaning their feathers.

"Have you—" cried Lena, and she slipped in the mud and splashed into the pond. She went bump down to the bottom, but as she was stuffed with cotton, she bobbed up again in a second. The ducks fished her out and set her in the sun to dry.

"Have you seen Brin Hilda?" gasped Lena between the drops that trickled down her nose.

"No, Gingham Lena," said the ducks, "we have not seen her."

Gingham Lena sat in the sun drying and thought and thought about a place where Brin Hilda could be.

Oh, Brin Hilda, Brin Hilda, with your smudgy face, where have you gone and what are you doing?

"Have you asked the scarecrow?" said the ducks. "He sees everything that happens around here."

"Oh, thanks," said Lena, and she raced around the pond through the apple orchard. She ran between the bee hives by the sweet clover field and bumped into one of the hives in her hurry. And all the bees flew buzzing out and chased her. Lena ran as fast as she could with bees sitting on her nose and bees sitting on her tail and everywhere. But when they found she was only cotton, they flew back home.

At last she came to the corn field.

"Have you seen Brin Hilda?" she cried.

But the scarecrow had not seen Brin Hilda anywhere, not for days and days. The last he had seen of her was the bow on her apron one day last week.

Lena ran up and down and back and forth between the corn rows looking, but she could not see a bit of Brin Hilda either. She lay down all tired out and tried to think of a place where Brin Hilda might be hiding.

"I must find her somewhere," said Lena, "or Selma will be crying for lonesomeness."

She thought and thought.

Oh, Brin Hilda, Brin Hilda, with your smudgy face, where have you gone and what are you doing?

Then suddenly she smiled and cocked her ears and wagged her tail and ran off toward the wild-blackberry patch. She jumped over the ditch and dashed along the highway past Nokomis Lake and Yellow Butter Farm, and the white church and the schoolhouse of Blooming Valley. She ran past a gopher sitting by the roadside and under a meadow lark singing on the telegraph wire, and past the field of hazel nut bushes and into the blackberry patch all out of breath. She sniffed around the bushes and scratched her gingham sides on the stickers.

Then she caught sight of someone in a pink bonnet, someone sitting with her back that way.

"Have you seen Brin Hilda," shouted Lena.

She thought she heard someone giggle, but the person in the pink bonnet did not say a word.

Lena started toward her, but one blackberry bramble was holding her on one side and more blackberry brambles were holding her on the other side. Lena jerked this way and that and tore a hole in her gingham.

"Selma has a thimble and she can mend that," said Lena.

And she ran around to peep into the pink bonnet. And there inside of it were Brin Hilda's blue eyes and smudgy nose, as plain as plain could be!

"So that is where you are," said Lena. "You come along home!"

And Gingham Lena ran back through the brambles out of the blackberry patch with Brin Hilda balanced on her back.

She ran along the highway past the schoolhouse and the church of Blooming Valley and past Yellow Butter Farm and Nokomis Lake and over the ditch into the corn field. She bounced past the scarecrow who waved his sleeves at her, through the orchard and around the duck pond between the geese and the turkeys. The pigs squealed and the ducks quacked and the turkeys gobbled and all the birds sang.

Lena dashed toward the pump where Selma and Elmer were sitting. Selma had her hands in her eyes and the tears were running into her mouth. Elmer was throwing stones at the back fence.

Lena pranced up crying, "Here we are, here we are!"

And when they saw who was coming, the children

shouted loudly. Selma hugged Brin Hilda up in her arms and Elmer patted Lena on her cotton head and said, "Good dog, good dog!"

Gingham Lena wiggled herself all over—and they lived happily ever after.

By Emma L. Brock

THE MERRY-GO-ROUND AND THE GRIGGSES

THE MERRY-GO-ROUND whirled round and round and the music played. The horses and the ponies and the zebras rose and fell on their shiny poles as they dashed past. The Griggses watched the merry-go-round and the merry-go-round watched the Griggses. Every last Griggs was there and never had the merry-go-round seen them look so happy and triumphant, and he had seen them every day since he had come to town.

But today was different from any other day. There was joy and excitement in the heart of every Griggs; in the heart of Mary Griggs, aged eleven; in the heart of Tommy Griggs, aged nine; likewise in Betty Griggs, aged seven, and in Billy Griggs, aged five. The same feelings were equally alive in Jennie and Jimmie, the twins, aged four. For today each Griggs held five cents gripped in his right hand. *They were going to ride on the merry-go-round!*

"I'm glad that they got the money together in time," thought the merry-go-round. "It's my last day here. I suppose those bigger two had to earn it for the whole crew. Five, ten, fifteen, twenty, twenty-five, thirty," he counted as he whirled by. "They had to get thirty cents just for one ride. That *is* a lot!"

The merry-go-round felt himself go slowly and more slowly. It was time for him to stop. The people who were riding the horses and the ponies climbed down and the boy jumped off the zebra.

"He seemed to think he could make me go faster by kicking me," complained the zebra. "I'm glad his money is all used up."

"You shouldn't mind things so much," said the merry-go-round comfortingly. "He hasn't hurt your paint any."

Then came the Griggses. They swarmed over the merry-go-round like a drove of monkeys. They tried every horse and they tried every seat before they were satisfied. Mary and Tommy lifted the twins into one of the coaches and told them to sit very still, which they did not do. They hung over the edge and shouted. Tommy mounted a gallant black charger and Mary chose a milk white steed. Betty climbed on to the complaining zebra and Billy upon a brown pony. But Billy very soon fell off and they put him into the coach with the twins.

"All aboard!" whistled the merry-go-round. "Hang on tight. I'm starting!"

The merry-go-round man shut the gates so that no one else could enter. The music began to play. The engine started and away they went.

At first the Griggses sat very still. They hung on as tight as they could and did not say a word. Things felt a little strange and queer to the Griggses. The merry-go-round was disappointed.

"Aren't they going to like me?" A fear crept into the valves of the merry-go-round. "Have they waited a whole week and earned thirty cents and then aren't they going to like me? Oh, dearie me!" sighed the merry-go-round.

But a few turns more and his doubts vanished. The Griggses were becoming accustomed to the new motion and they began to shout to each other. You could hear them even above the music. Round and round they spun. Up and down went the horses. The Griggses became more and more exhilarated.

"I can change horses," shouted Tommy. "Watch me!"

He swung over to the next mount. The others cheered.

"I can ride without holding on," screamed Betty.

"Not for long," said the zebra as she promptly fell off and had to be picked up and put back on again by the merry-go-round man.

The merry-go-round was quite satisfied. Carrying Griggses was a pleasure to him.

But the best of things must end. The merry-go-round had gone as far as he ever went for a five cent fare. The music stopped. The merry-go-round ran slowly and more slowly. The ride was over. The Griggses had no more five cents. They would have to get off!

They climbed down quietly, every last Griggs of them. Even the twins at four knew that "no more" meant *no more* with the Griggses. They did not even cry.

Then a strange thing happened.

"I have been doing just what that merry-go-round man has told me to do ever since I was a child," said the merry-go-round. "To-day for once I'm going to do what I want to do. I don't care if I have given them a five cent ride. I'm not going to stop! *I'm going to keep right on going!*"

So instead of stopping the merry-go-round went faster and faster until he was whirling around as before, with the music playing and the flags flying.

"Stop!" shouted the merry-go-round man as he ran round and round after the merry-go-round; but no good did shouting do him.

"*Stop!*" shouted all the people who were waiting to get on, and they ran round and round the merry-go-round; but no good did shouting do them.

"*Keep on going!*" shouted all the Griggses and that is just what the merry-go-round did do.

The children climbed back to their places. The horses rose higher than they had ever risen before. The music played louder than ever. Never in the days of merry-go-rounds was there such a ride!

When the merry-go-round could run no longer for want of steam and the music could play no longer for want of breath, they both had to stop. Off tumbled the Griggses. They had had five times as much ride as they had expected. The merry-go-round man was very cross but there was nothing to do about that.

The Griggses jumped to the ground, but—they were so dizzy that they could scarcely stand. Indeed, they did not stand long. The twins laughed and sat down heavily. Mary fell over them, while Betty and Billy hung on to the turnstile. The trees and the houses spun round and round. All that the children could do was to sit on the ground and laugh.

The merry-go-round man was worried. Whatever was he going to do with them? He picked them up carefully and put them on their feet and started them off toward home.

"Good-by," they shouted back to the merry-go-round, "and thank you!"

"Don't mention it," chuckled the merry-go-round as he started off with his new load of passengers.

He watched them out of sight. The twins sat down twice and had to be picked up and put on their feet again. And this is the way their tracks looked all the way down the street.

By Caroline D. Emerson

GOOSEBERRY GARDEN

ONCE THERE WAS a beautiful green garden. In the garden there lived a lady, and her name was Mrs. Gooseberry.

And the green grass grew all around.

Now in the beautiful green garden there was a lovely house. In the house there were ever so many windows. In the windows were children peeping out. Their name was Gooseberry, too.

And the green grass grew all around.

Now in the lovely house there was a room with a big, big window. In the window there hung a golden cage. In the cage there was a little green bird. All day long it sang a merry tune.

And the green grass grew all around.

In the garden the Gooseberry children played. Sometimes Mrs. Gooseberry opened the door of the cage and the little green bird flew out. It sat on their shoulders and ate from their hands. It flew above their heads and sang its merry tune. Always at night it flew back into its cage and went to sleep.

And the green grass grew all around.

One morning Mrs. Gooseberry woke up very early. The sun was rising over the hills. All was still. She looked, and what did she see? The little green bird was gone from its cage. The door was unhooked and standing open. The breeze blew in the open window.

And the green grass grew all around.

Mrs. Gooseberry called the children and they all jumped out of bed. The biggest Gooseberry children hunted, the middle-sized Gooseberry children called, the littlest Gooseberry children cried, but the little green bird was gone.

And the green grass grew all around.

At last the Gooseberry children sat down to eat their breakfast. A very sad meal it was. The porridge had lumps, the milk would spill, and the sugar bowl was empty. Worst of all, there was no little green bird to sing its merry tune.

And the green grass grew all around.

The Gooseberry children ran outdoors. "We will find the little green bird," said the biggest Gooseberry child to the littlest. "We will, we will," said all the Gooseberry children together. So they hitched up the pony to the cart and started off at a trot. They drove round and round the garden wall, looking and listening.

And the green grass grew all around.

Now in Gooseberry Garden there was a pond. In the pond there was an island. On the island there was a tree. Mrs. Gooseberry wheeled the baby up and down and back and forth over the little bridge, for his nap, while the children hunted.

And the green grass grew all around.

Soon the children grew tired and the pony grew tired, for they could not find the little green bird. Back through the garden gate they came to ask their mother what they should do next. Mrs. Gooseberry smiled and said: "Perhaps the little green bird is very near. Perhaps it is right here in the garden!"

And the green grass grew all around.

So the Gooseberry children kept on hunting. The first day they looked in the orchard. They climbed up ladders. They shook down apples. They slid down trunks of trees. But no little bird was there.

And the green grass grew all around.

But the children kept on hunting. The second day they looked in the vegetable patch. They lifted up the rhubarb leaves. They shook the tomato branches. They pulled up the cabbages. But no little bird was there.

And the green grass grew all around.

Still the Gooseberry children kept on hunting. The third day they looked in the flower beds. They peered in the rosebushes. They filled their aprons with daisies. They tipped over flower pots. But no little bird was there.

And the green grass grew all around.

At last the Gooseberry children had to give up. The little green bird was really gone. Suddenly they heard a merry tune coming from the island. Over the bridge they ran as fast as they could go. Up, up they looked. In the tree there was a branch. On the branch there was a nest. On the nest there was a little green bird.

And the green grass grew all around.

When they saw the little green bird on the nest, with four baby birds peeping their heads out, they were very happy. They held hands and danced round the tree. And this is the song they sang:

"The bird was on the nest,
  The nest was on the branch,
  The branch was on the limb,
  The limb was on the tree,
  The tree was on the island,
  The island was in the pond,
  The pond was in the garden,
  And the green grass grew all around, around, around,
  And the green grass grew all around."

By Lois Lenski

THE COBBLER'S TALE

A LONG TIME AGO there lived a king who had very big feet. Everybody knew it. And everybody knew that the king never laughed. But who would laugh if he were a king with feet so big that he could have only one pair of shoes?

One day a cobbler was called to the palace. The king took his one pair of shoes from a place called ROYAL SHOE CLOSET.

He said to the cobbler, "The right shoe you must stitch all around, and the left one you must make comfy, for my royal great toe is very tender. Now, mind they be done by tomorrow! A king must not go barefooted for more than a day."

"Very well," said the cobbler. And he took away the shoes.

He stitched and he stitched all around the right shoe. But when he came to the left shoe he began to scratch his head.

"How can I make it comfy?" he thought. And the more he thought the more he scratched his head.

Then his little boy said, "What would happen, sir, if you *didn't* make the king's shoe comfy before tomorrow?"

"Tsck! Both our heads would be chopped off!" said the cobbler, scratching his head again.

The little boy was very much afraid. He ran to the palace. He ran to the guardroom. He ran to the house of the king's best wigmaker. But nobody knew what to do.

The last thing before he went to bed that night, the little boy whispered into the ear of a wise old cat with green whiskers, "Please, my dear, try to think of some way to make the king's shoe comfy!"

Now all wise cats, and perhaps other cats, too, take fur from their own soft coats to make their babies' beds comfy.

The next morning the cobbler stopped scratching his head. "Look!" he cried.

And the little boy jumped out of bed to see.

The king's left shoe was not only lined with fur, but

it held six new kittens, sound asleep. And the wise old cat with green whiskers was very proud indeed.

"Just the thing!" said the cobbler, as he took the kittens out of the shoe and set them down by their wise old mother.

"Just the thing!" said the little boy, for he loved kittens.

"JUST THE THING!" said the king as he sat upon his throne, wearing his fur-lined shoe. And all of a sudden his majesty began to laugh!

Then the first row of courtiers began to smile. The second row began to snicker. The third row began to titter. And the fourth row rolled on the floor.

And the Lord High Chancellor in charge of titles and holidays said, "Let there be a holiday throughout the land because the king is laughing!"

"Three cheers!" shouted the courtiers.

"Let the cobbler who made the king's shoe comfy," continued the Lord High Chancellor, "be made cobbler to all France."

The courtiers shouted again.

So the cobbler became a famous man. But after that the wise old cat with green whiskers, and her six new kittens, too, lived with the cobbler and the little boy, and ate the best they had. For it was she who had saved their lives by making the king's shoe comfy.

By Elizabeth Orton Jones

THE LAMB THAT WENT TO FAIRYLAND

THERE WAS ONCE a fairy who took a great fancy to a tiny white lamb. He really was a dear little creature, and I don't wonder she fell in love with him. She used often to come and visit with him in the meadow where he lived with his mother, and she was very anxious to take him to a fairy party some evening.

The little lamb was shy. "What do you do at the parties?" he asked.

"Oh, dance mostly," said the fairy.

But the little lamb explained that he didn't know how to dance.

"I will soon teach you," said the fairy.

So she came every evening when her day's work was done and showed the little lamb how to dance, and he soon learned to skip about quite nicely.

At last a day came when the fairy took him off to the party, but his mother made him promise to come back the next morning. She knew the ways of fairies.

He enjoyed himself tremendously.

All the fairies admired him very much. They thought his coat so beautifully white and soft; they loved his little black nose and quaint woodeny legs. He gave them all rides on his back in turn (even the Fairy Queen had one), and when the time for dancing came he did very well indeed and astonished them all with his pretty steps. When he left, the Fairy Queen presented him with a garland of daisies. "They are fairy flowers," she said. "They will never fade, and so long as you wear them you will remain young."

When the lamb got home he had great tales to tell about his happy adventures, so that he became quite a celebrity and everyone made such a fuss over him that he got rather proud and silly, and after a very short time would hardly speak to his friends.

Of course this vexed them very much, and the wicked old rat who lived in the mill-pond and was always ready to do anyone an ill turn, suggested a way to pay him out for his pride. "While he is asleep I will gnaw through his gay garland that he is so proud of," she said, "and when he goes out walking he will lose it." All of which happened just as she planned. And so the foolish lamb lost his fairy garland and grew older like any other lamb.

His friend the fairy did not come to see him for some time. She was very busy helping on the spring things, and had no time for visiting. When she did come again she was very disappointed to find that the lamb had grown into quite a good-sized sheep, fat and comfortable. His wool was no longer downy and white, and he had entirely forgotten how to dance.

"Where is your magic garland?" said the fairy. And he had to confess he had lost it.

The fairy went back to her friends. She really did not feel that a big solemn sheep would be very welcome at their revels. But every year in the early spring when the new lambs are born, their mothers tell the story of the lamb that was invited to Fairyland, and they all go skipping about in the meadows practicing their dancing steps.

Each of them hopes that he may one day find the magic garland, and never grow old and staid, and be able to go a-visiting to Fairyland. After all, it must be lying about somewhere; so if you find it, you will know what to do with it, won't you? But be sure to give it to a lamb with a black nose. They're so much the prettiest.

By Rose Fyleman

LITTLE DOG AND BIG DOG

ONCE UPON A TIME there were two dogs who were great friends. One of them was small and one of them was large, and they were called Little Dog and Big Dog all the days of their lives, and had no other names.

Little Dog barked at everything he saw. He barked at the cat and he barked at the kittens; he barked at the cow and he barked at the calf; he barked at his own shadow; and he even barked at the moon in the sky with a "Bow-wow-wow!" and a "Bow-wow-wow!"

Big Dog had a very loud bark, "Bow-wow!" "Bow-wow!" but he barked only when he had something to say. And everybody listened to him.

Now one day as the two dogs sat together in the sunshine, Big Dog said to Little Dog:

"Come, let us go to see our friend, the king."

Little Dog thought this was a splendid plan, and they started at once.

Big Dog walked along the road with his tail curled over his back, and his head held high. "There is no need of haste," he said, but Little Dog thought there must be.

"I shall get there first," he called, as he scampered ahead, but presently he came back as fast as he had gone.

"Oh, Big Dog, Big Dog," he said, "we cannot go to see the king."

"Why not?" asked Big Dog. "Has he gone away from home?"

"I know nothing about that," answered Little Dog, who was almost out of breath, "but a little farther on there is a great river, and we can never get across."

But Big Dog would not turn back. "I must see this great river," he said, and he walked on as quietly as before. Little Dog followed him, and when they came to the river Big Dog jumped in, splish! splash! and began to swim.

"Wait, wait," cried Little Dog, but Big Dog only answered, "Don't be afraid."

So in jumped Little Dog, splish! splash! too, for he did not want to be left behind. He was terribly frightened, but he paddled himself along with his four feet just as he saw Big Dog doing, and when he was safe across the river, which was not half so wide as he had thought, he barked at it as if he had never been afraid at all.

"Bow-wow-wow-wow! You cannot keep us from the king," he said, and he was off and away before Big Dog had shaken the water from his coat. But in less time than it takes to tell it, Big Dog spied him running back, with his tail hanging down and his ears drooping.

"Oh, Big Dog, Big Dog!" he cried. "We cannot go

to see the king, for in the wood yonder there is a bear, and she will eat us both for her supper. I heard her say so myself."

Then Big Dog made haste to the wood, barking loudly:

"Bow-wow! Bow-wow! I am not afraid! I am not afraid!" and when the bear heard him she ran to her home as fast as she could.

"I can eat honey for my supper," she said; and the two dogs saw no more of her.

Now by this time Little Dog had run so fast and barked so much that he was tired. "I do not want to go to see the king," he said; and he lay down in the road and put his head between his two front paws.

But Big Dog said, "I smell a bone," and Little Dog jumped up in a hurry again. Sniff! Sniff!—where could it be? The two dogs put their noses close to the ground and followed the scent till they came to the turn of the road; and there sat a charcoal burner eating his supper of bread and mutton chops by his fire.

Little Dog wanted to run up and beg for something, but Big Dog would not go with him. "It is more polite to wait," he said; and he sat down on the other side of the road. Little Dog sat down beside him, and they waited and waited; but at last the man finished his chops and threw the bones to the dogs, which was just what Big Dog had hoped he would do. Oh, how good they tasted!

"Where shall we sleep tonight?" asked Little Dog when he had eaten his share.

"Oh, never fear," answered Big Dog, "we will find

a place"; and when they had gone on their way they very soon came to a house in the wood. The door was open, and Big Dog put his head inside to see if anybody was at home. Nobody lived there, however, but a barn swallow, so the dogs went in and lay down to rest on some hay in the corner.

"We must be off early," said Big Dog; but when they woke up the next morning the door was fastened tight; for the wind had blown by in the night and slammed it into its place. When Big Dog saw this he was in great distress.

"Oh, Little Dog! Little Dog!" he cried. "I fear we can never go to see the king, for the door is closed, and there is no one to open it."

"But we can go through the hole under the door," answered Little Dog; and when Big Dog looked, there, sure enough, at the bottom of the door, where a board had rotted away, was a hole just large enough for a little dog to creep through. Little Dog put his nose through and his head through, and then wriggle, wriggle, he was out and barking merrily.

"Come on, Big Dog," he called; but Big Dog could not go. He could not even get his head through the hole.

"You must go on alone," he said to Little Dog, "and when you have come to the king's palace, and have told him about me, perhaps he will send me aid."

But Little Dog did not wait until he reached the king's palace to ask for help. "Bow-wow-wow-wow! Listen to me," he barked, as he ran down the road. "Big Dog, my friend, is shut up in the house in the wood, and cannot go to see the king. Bow-wow-wow-wow!"

At first there were only birds to hear him, but presently he saw a woodcutter with an ax on his shoulder.

"Bow-wow-wow-wow! Listen to me," barked Little Dog. "Big Dog, my friend, is shut up in the house in the wood and cannot go to see the king. Bow-wow-wow-wow!" But the woodcutter did not understand a word he said.

"Whew! whew!" he whistled, which meant, "Come, little doggie, follow me"; but Little Dog had no time to play.

He hurried on as fast as he could, and by and by he met the woodcutter's wife going to town with a basket of eggs on her arm. "Bow-wow-wow-wow! Listen to me. Big Dog, my friend, is shut up in the house in the wood, and cannot go to see the king," barked Little Dog. But the woodcutter's wife did not understand a word he said.

"You noisy little dog," she cried. "You have startled me so that it is a wonder every egg in my basket is not broken," and she shook her skirts to get rid of him.

"Nobody will listen to me," thought Little Dog, as he scampered on, but just then he spied a little boy with a bundle of sticks on his back. He was the woodcutter's little boy; and—do you believe it?—he understood every word that Little Dog said, and followed him to the house.

When they drew near they heard Big Dog calling for help:

"Bow-wow! Bow-wow! Come and let me out. Come and let me out."

"Bow-wow! We are coming," answered Little Dog.

"We are coming," said the woodcutter's little boy; and the very next minute Big Dog was free.

The king's palace was not far from the wood, and the two dogs were soon at their journey's end. The king was so pleased to see them that he made a great feast for them, and invited the woodcutter's little boy because he was their friend.

After the feast Big Dog and Little Dog were sent home in the king's own carriage; and all the rest of their lives they were even better friends than before they went traveling together.

By Maude Lindsay

SOJO

SOJO WAS ALWAYS sleepy. He woke up sleepy in the
morning. He yawned all day long. He dropped asleep
over his lunch; he slept halfway through his dinner.
And if you'll believe it, he went to sleep when he should
have been working.

One morning his Mammy called him early to get up
and go down to the pool and bring back water for the
cabbages. That, if you haven't guessed it, was on a
Monday morning. Sojo rubbed his eyes and ate his
breakfast and took his bowl and went down to the pool.

Pretty soon he lay down and began to finish his sleep.
When he woke up, he heard something sper-lashing and
sper-loshing in the water. Sojo yawned and rubbed his

eyes; and there, right in the very middle of the pool, was a quite small Elephant, a-squirting water over his back from a quite small trunk.

"It must be fun to do that," said Sojo, yawning politely behind his hand.

"Not very," said the quite small Elephant. "It's too easy," and he squirted a trunkful of water into the bushes.

"Look here," said Sojo suddenly. "I know a place that would be just loads of fun to squirt water on. It's quite near here, too."

"Is that so?" asked the quite small Elephant eagerly. "Where is this place?"

But Sojo shook his head sleepily. "You wouldn't be interested," he decided after a moment; and he flopped back on the grass again and closed his eyes. The quite small Elephant was silent a moment. Then he squirted another trunkful of water into the bushes. Sojo opened one eye, ever so little.

The quite small Elephant came nearer.

"Hi!" he said. "What would you take to show me this place? I've been doing this every day for a whole week."

Sojo opened both eyes and sat up. "Oh, I wouldn't take anything for it. You're a friend of mine, and I'd be glad to show it to you. Mind you, it's a good game, but a sort of difficult one. I don't even know if you could do it. The game," he explained, getting to his feet, "is to take a trunkful of water from here— Follow me."

With the quite small Elephant carrying a trunkful of water, Sojo went along the path to the garden where the cabbages grew.

"You see, this is the game," explained Sojo. "You spray the water ve-ry carefully over the cabbages. If you spray it too hard and root up a cabbage, you lose a point. And if you don't bring enough water and the cabbages dry up, you lose the game. But if you bring four trunkfuls a morning every morning and make this place a nice swimmy marsh, it's a beautiful game."

"That does sound fun," said the quite small Elephant gratefully. "Like this?" and he sent out the water from his trunk in a long wish-h, whoo-o-sh all over the cabbages.

Sojo watched with his head on one side. "Not bad for a first try. But it's only fair."

"I think I could do better next time," said the quite small Elephant anxiously. And he could. And he did. Sojo leaned against a tree; and when the Elephant had used up the fourth trunkful of water, he woke up again.

"That was very good indeed," he said. "And no doubt you'll do better tomorrow."

"Please, can't I do just one more?" asked the Elephant.

But Sojo shook his head. "Oh, no. Four tries every morning is all you can have. That's the rule of the game. Now come back tomorrow and see how much better you can do."

"Well, thank you tremendously!" cried the quite small Elephant, and went away.

And Sojo slid down to the foot of the tree to finish his sleep. When his Mammy came to wake him, she certainly was surprised to see how nicely her cabbages had been watered.

Next morning Sojo's Mammy called him to get up and husk the corn. She said, "Take the corn down to the wide flat stone by the pool and pound the husks away." And that, if you haven't guessed it, was on a Tuesday morning.

Sojo rubbed his eyes and ate his breakfast. He took the corn in a basket down to the wide flat stone and sat down to look at it. Pretty soon he rolled over and began to finish his sleep.

When he woke up, he saw straight ahead of him in the pool two e-normous nostrils, and two little pricky pink ears, and two small twinkly black eyes.

"Hi there, Hippo!" said Sojo, and he got to his feet and began to pound the corn with a long flail.

Pretty soon he felt a cool breath on his shoulder; and the Hippo sighed, "What are you doing there? Can't I do that, too?"

Sojo shook his head and kept right on pounding the corn with his flail. "This is just a game; you wouldn't be interested," he said.

"How do you know I wouldn't be interested?" asked the Hippo crossly. "I can do that as well as you can. Just let me try," and he started to shove Sojo off the rock. But Sojo was firm.

"No, it's a very difficult game; and you have to play it just so. Now run along and don't bother me."

The Hippo watched a little longer. Then he said,

"What would you take to let me play at that game, too?
I bet I'd be good at it."

Sojo sighed and stopped pounding the corn. "If you
want to play it, you walk round and round the rock,
stamping on the corn. And when it's all stamped out,
you blow on it, very gently, and blow all the husks into
the water. And if you leave any husks, you lose a point;
and if you blow away any corn, you lose the game. It's
difficult, and I don't even know if you could do it."

"Oh, I could do it all right," said the Hippo in his
big breathful voice. And he could. And he would. And
he did. His four big flat feet were four times as big as
Sojo's two feet and the flail. And he pounded out all
the dry corn. And his breath was four times as strong
as any little breeze and he blew away all the chaff into
the water.

Sojo had lain down under a tree; and when he woke
up, the Hippo said, "Now that's done. What do I do
next?"

"You help me put it all in a basket, so. And I'll take
it home. And the next time I play this game I'll let you
know so that you can come and play it, too," said Sojo;
and he went home, yawning, to his Mammy.

And she certainly was surprised to see how well her
corn had been pounded.

Next morning Sojo's Mammy called him to get up
and dig her a new garden. She said, "Get up. I want a
garden dug down beyond the cabbages." And that, if
you haven't guessed it, was on a Wednesday morning.

Sojo rubbed his eyes and ate his breakfast. He took
his hoe and went down beyond the cabbages to dig the

new garden. He sat down under a tree and looked at what he had to do, and pretty soon he rolled over and began to finish his sleep.

When he woke up, he heard the funniest grunting and sk-uff-ulufuling in the underbrush. So he yawned and sat up, and straight ahead of him was a dark snout and two bright black eyes poking out through the brush. And then a little bristly black Pig with two shiny white tusks followed the snout.

"Hi there, little black Pig!" said Sojo; and he got to his feet and began to dig busily with his hoe.

Pretty soon the little bristly black Pig asked, "What are you doing there? Can't I do that, too?"

Sojo shook his head and kept right on digging with his hoe. "This is just a game; you wouldn't be interested," he said.

"How do you know I wouldn't be interested?" asked the little bristly black Pig snappily. "I could do it as well as you could. Just you let me try."

But Sojo was firm. "No. It's a very difficult game, and you have to play it just so. Now run along and don't bother me."

The little Pig watched for a while longer; and then he said, "What would you take to let me play at that game, too? I bet I'd be good at it."

Sojo sighed and stopped digging with his hoe. "Oh, I wouldn't take anything for it. You're a friend of mine, but I don't know if you could do it," and he laid down his hoe and sat down under a tree.

But the little black Pig could. And he would. And he did. He began to dig with his tusks. He shoved and he pushed and he grunted and he scrabbled, and he went down one row of the garden. His two tusks were twice as sharp as Sojo's hoe and much, much faster. And he went down another row of the garden. And pretty soon he had finished it all.

Sojo had lain down under a tree; and when he woke up, the little bristly black Pig asked, "Now that's done. What am I to do next?"

"That's all there is," said Sojo. "But you played it very well. Come and play again sometime," and he went home, yawning, to his Mammy.

And she certainly was surprised to see how well her new garden had been hoed.

Next morning Sojo's Mammy called him to get up and cut the grass on the path to the road. She said, "The grass on the path to the road is too long to walk through." And that, if you haven't guessed it, was on a Thursday morning.

Sojo rubbed his eyes and ate his breakfast. He took his sickle and went off along the path to the roadway. He cut a few feet of grass, and then he sat down under a tree to look at what he had to do and began to finish his sleep.

When he woke up, he saw a white animal with black spots and two long black horns, eating the grass on the pathway.

"Hi there, Goat!" said Sojo; and he got to his feet and began to cut the grass with his sickle. After he had cut a little more, he began to gather it up, piece by piece, blade by blade, and bind it together into a small bundle.

"What's that you're doing?" asked the Goat, very interested.

"Oh," said Sojo. "I'm just going to cut and collect all the grass along this path. It's the finest grass in the country, you know. And so we cut it every week and put it away."

"The finest grass, you say?" asked the Goat. "Why, I never knew that!" and he came closer to nibble along the edges of the path.

"Hi," said Sojo, and he shook his head at the goat. "That's my grass."

"Well, but look here. Can't I eat even a little of it?" asked the Goat.

"M-m. Maybe a little," said Sojo. "But you be careful not to eat too much," and he yawned and lay down under a tree. When he woke up, the Goat was gone.

But the path which Sojo was going to cut was cropped as clean as the middle of the road. Not a blade of grass was in sight. Sojo went home, yawning, to his Mammy.

And she certainly was surprised to see how well her path had been cut.

Next morning Sojo's Mammy called him to get up and go fishing. She said, "Bring me a lot of fish for my dinner. Because I like fish." And that, if you haven't guessed it, was on a Friday morning.

Sojo rubbed his eyes and ate his breakfast. He took his fishing lines and his fishing rods and went down to the river. He stuck his fishing rods in the ground and put bait on his hooks and threw the lines into the river.

Then he sat down under a tree, and pretty soon he rolled over and began to finish his sleep.

When he woke up, he saw a huge bird a-sitting on a sandbar in the middle of the river catching fish. The huge bird had a big fish-basket of skin right underneath his beak; and every time he caught a fish, he'd pop it into the basket.

Sojo sat up and wriggled his fish lines. But there was nothing on any of them. Not one single, solitary fish.

Then he yawned and called out to the huge bird, "Hi, Pelican! Good fishing?"

"Splendid!" said the Pelican, tossing a fish into the air and catching it in his fish-basket beak. "Too good, in fact."

"How's that?" asked Sojo.

"Well, you see," the Pelican shifted his weight from one great flat foot to the other great flat foot, "I've eaten all I can hold, and my basket is full, and still I keep on catching fish. But if I put them back into the water, they'll swim away and warn the others about me so I won't be able to catch any tomorrow."

"Well," said Sojo, "you're a friend of mine. Perhaps I can manage to help you out and take some of those fish off your hands. That is—off your beak. Just, of course, as a very special favor."

"Oh, would you?" asked the Pelican, very pleased.

And Sojo could. And he would. And he did. He took two catfish and a dogfish, some mudfish and three eels. And he put them all on a stick together and went home, yawning, to his Mammy.

And his Mammy certainly was surprised to see all the fish he had brought home.

Next morning Sojo's Mammy said, "It's a nice warm

day, so take the hammock and go out and rest under a tree. I've never known you to work so hard." And that, if you haven't guessed it, was on a Saturday.

So Sojo took his hammock and went out and sat under a tree. Overhead was a little red Bird sitting on a branch.

"Hi, little red Bird!" said Sojo. "Sing me a song."

The little red Bird broke into a string of notes, then cocked his head on one side. "How's that?" he asked eagerly.

"Well enough," said Sojo, yawning politely behind his hand. "Sing some more."

So the little red Bird sang some more notes. "How's that?" he asked again, cocking his head on one side.

"It's good," Sojo nodded. "But since you ask me, I think it's too short. A really good song lasts a long time. It goes on and on and on. I'm afraid you couldn't sing a real song."

"I could, too," said the little red Bird crossly; and he settled down on his branch to sing a long time.

Sojo yawned and got up to tie one end of his hammock to the tree. But the rope wasn't long enough to reach to the next tree. So he sat down again.

Pretty soon he opened his eyes and saw two bright black eyes shining in the grass. It was a very short piebald Python—oh, a very short one, and ab-so-lute-ly harmless.

"Look here, Sojo," whispered the very short piebald Python in a very secret piebald Python whisper. "You've given games to all the other animals. What's the matter with making up a game for me?"

"There's only one game left," said Sojo. "And you're much too small to play it," and he closed his eyes again.

"Oh, pu-please, Sojo!" begged the very small piebald Python, stretching himself to his very fullest piebald Python length. "Pu-pu-pu-pl-eee-ease!"

"Oh, all right," agreed Sojo kindly. "But I wouldn't bother with this for anyone else, because I really do need sleep." And he got up and stretched out the hammock as near as it would go to the second tree.

"Now, here's the idea. You climb that tree, so. And loop yourself through the end of the hammock, so. And catch your tail between your teeth. Now you pull and stretch, pull and stretch. And if you stop, you lose a point. But if you drop the hammock"—and Sojo looked anxious—"you lose the game. See?"

"I see," said the very short piebald Python with his mouth full of very short Python tail. "And what happens next?"

"Well, I wouldn't do it for any of the others, because I really do need sleep," said Sojo, politely yawning behind his hand. "But I'll climb into the hammock. Like this. And keep pressing downward with my back. Like this. And help you to stretch and grow."

And when Sojo's Mammy came out to see if he was resting, she found the little red Bird still singing overhead. And Sojo in the hammock was getting lots of rest. She certainly was surprised to see how well he was doing.

By Erick Berry

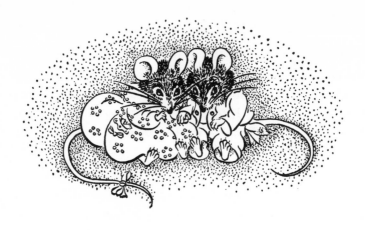

GEORGE AND ANGELA

ONCE UPON A TIME there was a little mouse and she had seven children. They were Seraphine, Gertrude and Angela, Albert, Edward, Henry and George—and George was a bit of a pickle.

Every evening, when Cook had shut up for the night and Puss was safely away down the garden, the little mouse and her family would creep out of the hole in the larder floor, which was their home, to spend the night feeding and playing.

There was always plenty to eat, for, as the little mouse used to say, while she handed round morsels of cheese, juicy lettuce leaves or nice crusty bits of bread, "Cook is such a thoughtful woman!"

When they had eaten enough, they would rush around the larder, sliding down anything sliddery, chasing each other round the bottles and tins and learning to take cheese out of a trap without getting caught.

They had a merry time, feeding and playing, till the larder grew gray in the morning light, when the little

mouse would call, "Bedtime! Come along, children!"
Then they all hurried down the hole in the larder floor
(which was their home), before Cook came down to
her work and Puss was let in from the garden.

Now George didn't like going to bed—I told you he
was a bit of a pickle.

"It's always the same," he complained to Angela one
morning as they snuggled together in their cozy nest of
chewed string, paper and hair, "it's always the same,
just when things are getting really interesting—BED-
TIME!" He leaned forward and whispered in Angela's
ear, "I'm going to stay out tomorrow—and *so are you!*"

"Oo-er!" said Angela (she was never *very* original).

The next morning when the first rays of the sun
peeped through the larder window the little mouse began to collect her family as usual.

"Albert!" called the little mouse, sitting up on her
tail, the better to see what they were all doing.

Albert stopped admiring his whiskers in the polished
surface of the tea caddy and hurried to his mother.

"Edward!"

Edward slid gracefully down the meat cover and
landed at the little mouse's feet.

"Seraphine! Gertrude!"

Seraphine and Gertrude, who were skipping with
their tails, ran up together.

Angela slipped behind the milk jug.

"Henry!" called the little mouse.

Henry, who was partial to onions, scuttled out from
under the vegetables.

"Angela! George!"

Angela squeezed still tighter behind the milk jug, and George (who *was* a bit of a pickle) crouched under a fine new Dutch cheese the mice had only started that night.

The larder grew lighter.

"Angela! George!" cried the little mouse anxiously. "Dear, dear, where can those children be?"

Albert, Edward and Henry suggested that perhaps they had already gone home, so the little mouse, very worried and fidgety, hurried her family down to see.

The larder grew quiet and much lighter.

Upstairs Cook's alarm clock started ringing. Puss came silently along the garden path and sat on the steps by the milk bottles.

George slipped out from under the cheese and peeped over the edge of the plate.

"Angela!" he whispered—he *was* a pickle—"Angela, if we made the hole in this cheese a little bit bigger, we could sit inside all cozy and just eat and sleep . . . eat and sleep . . . eat and sleep . . ."

"Oo-er!" said Angela. . . . I told you she wasn't very bright.

The two little mice worked hard, nibbling and scratching and pushing the cheese away with their tiny front paws.

Cook stretched and yawned and started to dress. Puss stretched and yawned and started to wash.

The larder grew lighter and lighter. . . .

Presently the hole in the cheese was quite big, and first George and then Angela squeezed inside.

"Don't push so!" cried George.

"I'm not pushing," squeaked Angela. "It's the cheese!"

"Phoof! The cheese!" snorted George—but Angela was right.

The two fidgety little mice had started the cheese rolling and now it went, bumpety, bumpety, bumpety— off the plate, over the edge of the shelf—BUMP—right down onto the larder floor, where it settled at last— with the hole underneath!

The two little mice inside in the dark sat and blinked.

"George!" squeaked Angela. "We can't get out!"

Cook came downstairs, let Puss in from the garden, took up the milk and started her day's work.

The larder was now quite light and the larder door stood open just a crack.

Puss nosed round the kitchen till she came to the larder, where she put her nose to the crack of the door and sniffed; then, very soft and slinky, she squeezed through with her whiskers twitching.

Cook began to be busy with a broom.

Inside the cheese two little mice crouched down and shivered.

Puss fixed her eyes on the cheese and crept nearer and nearer; then she put out a velvet paw and patted it, very gently.

The cheese rocked backwards and forwards.

"Oh, George!" squeaked Angela.

George said nothing, but his eyes stuck out of his head like two little black beads.

Puss patted the cheese again, while her nose twitched greedily; the cheese rocked more and more. . . .

This looks as though the story were going to end badly; but—and, mind you, if it hadn't been for this it certainly would have—but just as Puss was remembering how delicious young mouse tasted, Cook came into the larder.

"Here! Hi!" she cried. "Whatever are you doing with my cheese? *I'll* teach you to roll my cheeses about. Shoo, Phwf. Phwft!" and Puss was chased out of the larder at the end of a broom.

The cheese rocked right over.

"Run!" squeaked George, and even Angela didn't need to be told twice.

The two little mice were out of that cheese and down the hole in the larder floor (which was their home) before you could say Jack Robinson. Though why anyone should ever *want* to say Jack Robinson I never could think.

The little mouse was very pleased to see George and Angela, but very cross when she heard what they had been doing.

"You will both go to bed early for a week," she told them severely. And I'm sure you will agree that it was no more than they deserved.

They never stayed out late again.

By Cicely Englefield

THE LITTLE OLD WOMAN AND HOW
SHE KEPT HER GEESE WARM

ONCE UPON A TIME there was a Little Old Woman. She
lived in a little yellow house with a blue door and two
blue window boxes. In each of the window boxes there
were yellow tulips.

All around her house was a neat blue fence. Inside
the fence was the Little Old Woman's soup garden. She
called it a soup garden because she raised vegetables in
it, to cook in her soup. She raised carrots, potatoes,
turnips, garlic, cabbages, and onions.

The Little Old Woman was very poor. If she had not
been so clever, she probably could not have made ends
meet. But she was a great one for using her head. She
always said, "What is the good of having a head if you
don't use it?"

So, as you will see, she managed to get along very
well.

One cold winter night the Little Old Woman was out
in the barn putting her geese to bed. She gave them

some corn and took off their little red coats. Then she brushed each little coat with a whisk broom and carefully shook out the wrinkles.

As she was folding the coats in a neat pile, she thought:

"My poor geese must be very cold at night. I have my cozy fire and my feather bed. But they have not even a blanket to keep them warm."

After the geese had eaten their corn, they began to go to roost.

"Honk, honk!" said the big gander, and he hopped up on the roost.

"Honk, honk!" said the gray goose, and she hopped up on the roost.

"Honk, honk!" said all the other geese, and they hopped up on the roost.

Then the Little Old Woman closed the barn door and went into the house. When she went to bed, she lay awake worrying about the geese. After a while she said to herself:

"I cannot sleep a wink for thinking how cold the geese must be. I had better bring them in the house where it is warm."

So the Little Old Woman dressed herself and went out to the barn to fetch the geese. She shooed them off the roost and put on their little red coats. She picked up two geese, and tucking one under each arm, she carried them into the house.

When the Little Old Woman had brought all the geese into the house, she said to herself:

"Now I must get them ready for bed again."

She took off their little red coats and gave the geese some corn. Then she brushed each little coat with a whisk broom and carefully shook out all the wrinkles.

As she was folding the coats in a neat pile, she thought:

"It was very clever of me to bring the geese into the house. Now they will be warm, and I shall be able to sleep."

Then the Little Old Woman undressed herself again and went to bed.

After the geese had eaten their corn, they began to roost.

"Honk, honk!" said the gander, and he hopped up on the foot of the Little Old Woman's bed.

"Honk, honk!" said the gray goose, and she hopped up on the Little Old Woman's bed.

"Honk, honk!" said all the other geese, and they tried to hop up on the foot of the Little Old Woman's bed.

But it was not a very big bed, and there was not enough room for all the geese to roost. They began to fight. They pushed and shoved each other. They hissed and squawked and flapped their wings.

All night long the geese pushed and shoved each other. All night long they hissed and squawked and flapped their wings.

They made so much noise that the Little Old Woman did not sleep a wink.

"This will never do," she said. "When they were in the barn, I did not sleep for thinking how cold they must be. When they are in the house, I cannot sleep because they make so much noise. Perhaps if I use my head I shall know what to do."

The Little Old Woman tied a wet towel around her forehead. Then she sat down with her forefinger against her nose and shut her eyes.

She used her head and used her head, and after a while she knew what to do.

"I will move the roost into the house," she said. "The geese will have the cozy fire to keep them warm. Then I will move my bed out into the barn. My feather bed will keep me warm, and I will not be worrying about the geese. They will not keep me awake with their noise. I shall sleep quite comfortably in the barn."

The Little Old Woman moved the roost into the house, and she moved her bed out into the barn.

When night came again, she brought the geese into the house. After she had fed them some corn, she took off their little red coats. Then they all hopped up on the roost, and the Little Old Woman went out to the barn to sleep.

Her feather bed kept her as warm as toast. She was not worried about the geese, because she knew that they were warm too. So she slept as sound as a top all night long.

By Hope Newell

THE PONY TREE

THERE WAS ONCE a little boy whose name was Jimmie.

He had a sister, Joan, but Joan had gone to spend a week with her grandmother!

His two dearest friends who lived right next door were Susan Sill and Nellie Nelson.

The dearest wish of these children, since the day the circus came to town, was for a pony, and a little yellow cart, and red harness—just like the clown had!

Every day Jimmie said to his Mother, "I do want a little pony. Please!"

And every day Mother said, "Darling, if I bought you a pony, I wouldn't have enough money to buy spinach and carrots and prunes for you, and shoes for you to go to school!"

So Susan and Nellie and Jimmie thought and thought about it.

Bye and bye Susan said, "Maybe, if we were good, the fairies would bring us a pony."

So the children were good. They were very good.

They ran errands for their mothers.

They knew all the answers in school!

They kept their clothes clean!

One night after they had been good three whole days, something happened!

Jimmie was lying in bed, looking up at the moon.

Suddenly, right out of the moon came a fairy!

He said, "Jimmie, you have been good, and I have brought a present for you. It is a seed. Plant it in your garden."

And the fairy flew away.

And what do you think Jimmie did?

Well, he got right out of bed in his bare feet and ran down to the garden.

And in a hole, in the middle of the lawn, Jimmie planted the seed and patted it down. Then he went back to bed.

In the morning Jimmie said, "Oh, Mother, a fairy gave me a seed and I planted it in the garden."

But Mother said, "Darling, you only dreamed it."

Sometimes Jimmie thought maybe his mother didn't believe in fairies.

Jimmie said to his father, "Father, I planted a seed that a fairy gave me, in the lawn," and his father laughed and said:

"What an imagination that child has!" And he went on shaving.

Sometimes Jimmie was sure Father didn't believe in fairies!

As soon as breakfast was over Jimmie went out and told Susan and Nellie all about it—and weren't they glad!

They all ran to the garden and there—what do you suppose?

Right out of the ground where Jimmie had planted the seed a plant was growing.

Mother said, "It is a weed, you must pull it up right away. Father won't like it!"

But the children begged so hard that finally she said they might leave it. And she sent them all to school.

But in school, oh my! Susan could not keep her mind on her lessons!

She looked out of the window and thought of the Fairy Seed.

She did not hear the teacher! It was all quite, quite dreadful!

The moment school was out, Susan and Jimmie and Nellie raced for home, and—what do you think? The plant had grown into a tree, and it had three blossoms on it!

The children stood and looked and looked.

Even Mother was surprised.

The children did not want to go in to lunch, and so Jimmie's mother gave them three bowls of bread and milk under the tree.

Pretty soon in the center of each flower they could see something forming. At first there were just two little points, but very soon they knew that they were—ears!

Then they saw that the ears were attached to something. It was a tiny pony head!

And then it was school time. The children wept but they had to go.

That afternoon Jimmie was so naughty that the teacher had to make him stand in the corner.

And when the teacher asked Susan to spell "kitten," Susan said, "P-o-n-y."

After school, they thought they would never get home!

Their feet were so heavy.

But when they got there—what do you think?

From each blossom was growing a pony! And from between the leaves on the tree were growing little yellow wagons and red harnesses!

Just think!

Jimmie cried, "Oh, Mother, may I pick a pony?"

Mother looked worried and said, "Oh, I'm afraid they aren't ripe yet. It would be very bad to pick a pony before it is ripe."

So the children waited and it was well they did, for as each pony grew larger it grew heavier, and bent down its branch more and more until finally its feet touched the ground.

Nellie had called in the other children from the block.

And now they were all standing around watching.

So Susan picked a black pony, and he seemed very glad to see her and licked her face!

Nellie picked a white pony, and kissed him on the nose.

And Jimmie picked a brown pony and hugged him.

The children harnessed the ponies to the carts and gave all the children rides, up and down the street.

And after that, I guess those fathers and mothers believed in fairies!

By Charlotte Brate

THE THREE ELEVATORS

THERE WAS ONE immense building in the City o' Ligg; it was twenty-seven stories high! At the end of the main corridor, which was a gorgeous affair, paved with marble and walled with malachite, there was a shaft, in which lived three elevators.

One of these elevators was very, very strong. One was very, very swift. One was neither very strong nor very swift, but it made up for it by being very, very clever, as you shall see.

The strong elevator was used chiefly for carrying up heavy pieces of merchandise, and was not fitted up so beautifully as the others. The swift one was an "Express Elevator," and did not stop till he got to the twentieth story. If you wanted to go to a floor between that and the ground floor, you had to take the one in the middle of the three, which was the clever elevator.

At night, after the power was turned off, the three elevators rested, side by side on the ground floor, at the end of the corridor. It was then that they used to gossip over the day's work, and the strong one would brag of the heavy cases he had lifted; the swift one would boast of how he had made the trip to the roof in two minutes many and many a time, and could do it in 1 :46, if necessary, with a good elevator boy; and the clever one did not say much, but she would lead the others on, and keep them talking.

One day the swift elevator, who always made the last trip, dropped down to the floor, as the electric lights were turned off, in great excitement.

"What do you think?" he said. "A great, stupid house has crawled on top of this building; it is a ten-story house, too!"

"Heavens! Do you suppose we'll have to make thirty-seven-story trips now? That is too much of a good thing!" said the strong elevator.

"I am afraid we shall," said the clever one, "unless we can do something about it, in a hurry!"

"What can we do?" cried the other two.

"Well," said the clever one to the swift one, "if you could only go fast enough—"

"Oh, no fear, *I* can go fast enough; you wait!" said the swift elevator, shaking her annunciator drops.

"Or if you were a little stronger," continued the one in the center, as she looked slyly at the heavy freight car.

The strong one rattled his rope with his chuckles.

"Well, I think you can trust *me!*"

"Well, then, perhaps we can do it," said the clever little elevator.

"But *how?*" inquired the other two.

"Why, it's only necessary to push the house off; and it doesn't matter whether you shoot up fast and knock it off with a jerk, or go up slowly—the way old freightie does—and push it off by main force; it's all the same, as long as the house falls off. I'm not very strong, and I'm not very swift, but I can see the way it ought to be done, easily enough."

Then the other two consulted together. "Let *me* try first!" said one, and "No, let *me* try first," said the other, till they had to appeal to the middle one to decide which should have the honor of the first trial.

"Let the express go first," said the clever one, "and if he can't do it, then the goods elevator may try it."

So the express elevator drew a long breath and braced himself against a floor. *"Go!"* cried the others. He shot up like a bullet out of a gun, so fast and so hard that he drove up and up, right into the house on top of the building, where there was no shaft, and tore a hole, ten stories high, clear through it. But his speed was so great that he flew through the house, high into the air, and then fell down, *smash!* on the roof of the house, and was killed.

"Now, it is your turn," said the clever one, smiling wickedly.

The strong freight car took a tight hold on his rope, and crawled slowly up, story by story, till he had reached the top of the shaft, at the twenty-seventh floor. There he rested a few minutes to get his breath. Then he put his head against the house, and exerted all his strength in a mighty effort. He pushed and pushed; but though he lifted the whole house up about twenty feet, he could do no more.

Then he shouted down the shaft to the other: "Come on and help! It's heavier than I thought, and I can't hold it much longer! Come quickly!"

"I'm right here!" said the clever elevator, who had stolen up the shaft after him. "I'll help."

But instead of helping, that sly little car crawled out of the hole the swift elevator had made, and crept along the roof of the building in the space left by the other's holding up the house. It was lucky for her that the stupid freight elevator could not see; for if he had dropped the house, it would have crushed her flatter than a pancake. She was a little frightened, but she got safely to the edge, and dropped to a roof near by, and lay there laughing to her own naughty little self.

The strong elevator held up the house as long as he could, and then let it drop with a groan.

"Why didn't you push more?" he said. But when he came down and found that the clever one was gone, he didn't know what to make of it at all. He was a very dull machine, and he never knew what a fool the sly one had made of them both.

But the clever little car stayed up on the roof in the sun watching the lively City o' Ligg all day, and slept all night, thanking her ropes that she didn't have to work any more, and didn't have to obey an ignorant elevator boy who would stop her with a jerk, and start her with a jounce. And unless she has been taken away and made into a streetcar, she is there yet!

By Gelett Burgess

A HAPPY CHRISTMAS TREE

AN EVERGREEN TREE grew in the front yard near the porch of a large farmhouse. Every Christmas it was decorated with gay colored lights. They shone in the farm windows at night. They sparkled and danced across the lawn for people who passed by to see. Everyone thought the little Tree was very beautiful. But he was not happy. He wanted to be loaded from top to bottom with Christmas gifts like the Christmas tree inside the window of the big house.

"Twinkling lights are not enough," the Evergreen Tree said. "I am not a real Christmas Tree with real Christmas gifts. I am only a pretend."

Then a bright idea flashed into the small Tree's mind. "If I could only travel—I could see the way with my gay lights," he said. "Then I might find some Christmas toys to put on my branches."

Suddenly something happened—

There was a terrific sound—

Rumble....

Rumble....

Rumbling....

Something shook the earth very hard. Then it shook the earth gently. Then very hard again! There was a rushing sound of wind. The big farmhouse rattled its windows. The Snow Man in the path near the house shivered and shook. He shook until—

he lost his hat—

he lost the pipe out of his mouth—

he lost his coal buttons.

And the small Evergreen Tree shook! He shook until his gay Christmas lights blinked—

and blinked—

and blinked.

"Oo—oo—oo—" went the wind blowing around the Evergreen Tree. It tore at his branches. It pushed and pulled. It tugged at his roots. It blew snow all over him.

"What—is—happening? What—is—happening—to me?" called out the small Evergreen Tree.

"Why, it's an earthquake," shouted the Snow Man. "Look out there. Hold on tight. You are moving."

"I can't hold on," said the Tree. "I never—moved— before in my life."

"Well, you're moving now," replied the Snow Man.

And sure enough. Out of the snow came the roots of

the little Evergreen Tree and he was off! He caught his breath. Then he was glad. "I—am—to—have—my —wish," he called to the Snow Man and started out of the yard.

"Merry Christmas to you," shouted the Snow Man as he shivered and shook in the path near the big house.

"Merry Christmas," shouted back the Tree, almost out of breath.

Twinkle, twinkle, twinkle
   and
      Jingle, jingle, jingle,
went his lights as down, down the road went the Evergreen Tree. Faster and faster behind him blew the wind.

Soon the Tree was out of sight of the big farmhouse and the Snow Man.

"Oo—oo—oo—" cried the wind.

Tramp, tramp, tramp,
   Jingle, jingle, jingle
     and
       Twinkle, twinkle, twinkle,
went the Evergreen Tree.

On and on he went right down through the middle of the road. At last the wind pushed him up to a Store on the edge of the town. There were many, many toys in the Store window, so—

With all his gay lights twinkling, the Evergreen Tree opened the door of the Store and rushed in.

"Store," called out the Evergreen Tree, "will you give me some of your toys to make me a real Christmas Tree?"

"Well, I might let you have some, for I can't sell any more before Christmas. But where did you come from?" replied the Store.

"It's a long story," answered the Tree. "Every year at Christmas time, I have been shining in the yard of a big farmhouse, and every year I have wanted presents hanging on my branches for children. But this year something strange happened. Didn't you feel the earthquake?"

"I certainly did," said the Store. "All my toys came tumbling and dancing off my shelves in a hurry."

"Well, that is how I got here. The earthquake started me off," said the Evergreen Tree.

Then the Store began to take toys down from his shelf. He even tied them on the Tree. And soon a drum, a Teddy Bear, a rocking horse, two dolls, a doll carriage and some picture books were hanging from the branches of the Evergreen Tree.

"Thank you, Store," said the Evergreen Tree. "Now I feel like a real Christmas Tree!" And out of the Store the Tree danced down the roadway to the other end of the town.

There stood a house among some trees and it was very dark. Not a candle gleamed in any one of its windows. The Evergreen Tree walked up to the door and knocked.

"Woof—woof! Woof—woof!" barked a little dog. "What do you want at this hour of the night?"

"I am a Christmas Tree," said the voice outside, "May I come in?"

The little dog opened the door very quickly.

"Have you any dog biscuit on your branches?" he asked.

"I am sorry," said the Evergreen Tree. "I never thought of dog biscuit. But I do have oranges and candy."

"I never eat them," said the little dog. "Have you any bones?"

"I never thought of bones, either," replied the Tree. "But I have

    a doll,

      a Teddy Bear,

        a drum,

          and a rocking horse!"

"Well, I don't play with toys," barked the little dog. "You had better try another house." And with a snort he pushed the door shut.

The Evergreen Tree went on down the road. The toys rattled and rattled against his branches. His gay lights flickered and sparkled.

By and by he came to another house. It was very dark but the Tree could see smoke curling out of its chimney.

"I'll try this house," the Tree said to himself. So he walked up to the door and knocked.

"Miew! Miew! Miew!" came a faint voice from within. A pussy cat inside stretched herself before the fire and came to the door.

"What do you want at this hour of the night?" asked the pussy cat crossly.

"I am a Christmas Tree," said the voice outside.

The pussy cat opened the door very quickly. "Have you any pink mice on your branches?" she inquired.

"I am sorry," said the Evergreen Tree, "I haven't any, but I have oranges and candy."

"Well, I never eat them. Haven't you any catnip balls?"

"Catnip balls! I never thought of catnip balls, but I have

    a Teddy Bear,

      a drum,

        and a rocking horse."

"Well, those toys are not for me. They must be for some boy or girl." Then the pussy shut the door. She yawned and went back to stretch herself out again in front of the fire.

So the Evergreen Tree walked on. And he walked and he walked until he came to another house. It was a very dark house, but one tiny candle shone through the window. Surely, he thought, there must be boys and girls living here.

So he walked up to the door and knocked.

Now in this house there lived a little old man and a little old lady. They had been sitting by the fire and wishing they had some Christmas toys for their grandchildren. But they were very poor and couldn't buy any. And while they were sitting there wishing, they had fallen asleep.

The little old man was snoring loudly. Snore! snore!

The little old lady was snoring gently. Snore! snore!

The Evergreen Tree knocked again, louder this time—

Knock!

Knock!

Knock!

The little old lady woke up with a start. She poked the little old man.

"Somebody is knocking at the door," she said. "Who can it be at this hour of the night?"

The little old man opened the door quickly. In walked the Tree, his lights gleaming and his toys rattling and jingling.

"Where did you come from?" asked the little old lady.

"Well, it's a long story," answered the Tree. "But that earthquake started me off and here I am. Do you know any boys and girls who need Christmas presents?"

At this the little old lady clapped her hands for joy. "Oh, I do—I do! Our grandchildren, Nancy and Charles, live next door," she said. "We have been wishing for a tree for them but we have no money to buy one."

"Thank you," said the Tree, as he went out of the door, "I'll hurry over." Across the snow the Tree went to the next door. He didn't stop even to knock. He walked straight in and stood himself up in a corner.

Then he gave himself a gentle shake to straighten out the toys that had tangled up in his branches.

Jingle, jingle, tingled the toys.

Blink, blink, blink, went the Evergreen Tree's lights.

The Evergreen Tree stood very still. His lights shone on the clock on the mantel. They were sleepy.

Twinkle, twinkle, twinkle!

Blink, blink, blink, nodded the lights.

The clock struck one—two—three. There was not a sound in the house.

The clock struck four. Still there was not a sound in the house.

The clock struck five.

Surely someone will wake up soon, thought the Evergreen Tree. It's time to build the fires so the house will be warm.

Then the clock struck six.

A stair creaked, then another—

Creak! Creak! they went.

Someone was up. The Christmas Tree waited.

Creak-crack!

Creak-crack!

Footsteps came down, down the stairs, nearer and nearer.

Father hurried into the room and over to the big stove. He built a crackling fire. Then he hurried out of the room. He did not see the Christmas Tree.

The stairs creaked—

Creak-crack!

Creak-crack!

Mother hurried into the room. She laid some clothes on chairs near the stove so they would be warm for Nancy and Charles. Then she hurried out to the kitchen. She did not see the Christmas Tree, either.

Again the stairs creaked—

Creak-crack!

Creak-crack!

The children are coming now, thought the Tree as

he stood very straight and still. The footsteps came nearer. The stair door opened. There stood Nancy and Charles in their pajamas.

Nancy ran shivering over to the big iron stove.

Charles ran after her.

"Here are our clothes," said Nancy. "Mother has them warming for us by the fire."

They sat down on the bench to put on their clothes. They stretched their toes out toward the crackling fire.

"Oh, look!" said Nancy, "we have new stockings."

"There is something big and round in mine," exclaimed Charles.

"There is something big and round in mine, too," exclaimed Nancy.

"It's a big, red apple," laughed Charles.

"It's a big, red apple," laughed Nancy.

("Wait until they see me," chuckled the Tree to himself.)

Nancy and Charles reached for their shoes.

"There is a stick of candy in my shoe," sang out Nancy.

"There is a stick of candy in my shoe, too," sang out Charles.

("Wait until they see me!" chuckled the Tree to himself again.)

"Maybe there is something in my coat pocket," shouted Charles. He put his hand in but there was nothing there.

"I'll look in my apron pocket," exclaimed Nancy. But when she put her hand in, it came out empty.

("Now is the time," chuckled the Tree. "I'll shake myself.") And he did.

Rattle! Rattle! Rattle!
went all the Tree's toys.

Jingle! Jingle! Jingle!
went all his bells.

Twinkle! Twinkle! Twinkle!
went all his lights together.

Nancy caught Charles by the arm. She held on tight to him. They looked at each other. They looked at the Tree. For a minute they could not speak at all. Then they ran toward the gay lights. They danced around the Tree shouting—

"A Christmas Tree!

A Christmas Tree!

A really, truly Christmas Tree."

Mother heard the children shouting. Father heard them shouting, too. They came running in from the kitchen. They saw the children dancing around the Tree. They could hardly believe their eyes.

Father caught Charles up in his arms and danced around the Tree. Nancy ran to her mother.

"Mother! Mother!" she cried. "Come dance with me." And round and round the Tree they danced together.

Suddenly the door opened. Grandma and Grandpa walked in.

"Come and dance with us!" shouted Charles.

"Come and dance with us!" shouted Nancy.

And they all danced around the Christmas Tree—

Grandfather, Grandmother, Father, Mother, Nancy and Charles.

But the happiest time of all for the Evergreen Tree was when the children took off their presents. Then it was that he knew that he was a real Christmas Tree at last.

There were the two dolls and the doll carriage for Nancy . . . the drum, the Teddy Bear, and the rocking horse for Charles . . . and bright colored picture books for both.

"Dear me," said the Christmas Tree to himself, "I have liked Christmas always but I have never had such a happy Christmas before in all my life."

By Frances Anne Brown

GISSING AND THE TELEPHONE

IN THE HOUSE where Gissing lived there was a speaking tube in the hall upstairs. This speaking tube was a great joy. When children blew in it it made a loud whistling squeal down in the kitchen. Done suddenly, it often startled cooks and cats half out of their wits. It sounded like the squeak of a mouse as big as a police dog. But like many amusing jokes this got overdone. And so, to prevent the speaking tube becoming a nuisance, it was agreed that it was a private magic telephone to Santa Claus, and must not be used except in the week before Christmas. Santa Claus, like everyone else, does not care to be bothered with unnecessary telephone calls. Like many other wise people he does not allow his number to be listed in the book, and only tells it to his intimate friends.

But, of course, in the week before Christmas everyone is so busy that a little extra squeaking in the kitchen does not matter.

Now Gissing, arriving in the house as a very small puppy, heard so much about this Santa Claus telephone that he really believed it. He heard the children making their plans, and writing out lists, and then blowing in the mouthpiece until it squawked, and announcing down the tube their desires for Christmas. He wished very much that he, too, could telephone to Santa Claus and tell what he wanted. But he felt bashful about doing it, and a little ashamed because he did not understand very well just what Christmas was. He heard all the children talking about it, and he tried to pick up some information by listening, but he did not learn anything definite. You know how it is: when everyone else seems to know about something that you yourself don't understand, you don't like to admit your ignorance. You listen carefully, hoping you'll overhear some remark that will explain what it's all about.

Gissing spoke in a casual way to the others, hoping to lead them into saying something that would help him to know what was going to happen. He would say, "Christmas will be fun, won't it!" or some such innocent thing. But their replies, though enthusiastic, did not help much. In his heart he was lonely because he felt there was some great secret that they knew and he didn't. "Oh, I wish someone would tell me what Christmas is," he said to himself. "Is it something to eat? Is it something to wear? Is it a game? Is it a person? And who is this mysterious Santa Claus?"

One day so much happened that Gissing felt more sure than ever that Christmas was going to be something very important. It was even a little frightening. From early morning the house was full of movement and hullabaloo. Tin horns were blown, there was a crackling of paper parcels being unwrapped, and the living room was so crowded with children playing with new toys that he retired under the dining-room table. Even there he was not safe, for by chance he squatted on the electric bell, and after many visits made to the front door he was found and moved off. There were smells of balsam and evergreen, and a whiff of brandy from the kitchen. Most alarming of all, the pudding caught fire and was carried in blazing. It was all very puzzling to a puppy, and Gissing lay under the couch feeling wistful. Everyone seemed too occupied to play with him, and he began to think that it was all because he had never talked into the magic telephone.

After supper things quieted down a bit. The children were got to bed early. The grown-ups, exhausted by picking up so much paper and string, sat down to rest. Gissing saw his chance. With great labor he pulled his toy box into the upstairs hall and stood on it so he could reach the speaking tube. He blew into it, and heard it squeal at the other end. Then he said, just as he had heard the children do, "Give me North Pole 1." To his great surprise he heard a deep voice coming back to him through the tube. "Santa Claus speaking," it said.

Santa Claus had had a long day. He had just got home, very tired after delivering toys all over the world. He was so tired that even before putting away the sleigh and the reindeer he had come into his house to sit down for a few moments and smoke a pipe. Everything was ready for a quiet evening. His slippers were warming in front of the fire; on the mantel a thermos jug of hot cocoa was waiting for him. He had left the door open to remind himself that he still had to go out and stable his reindeer for the night.

Santa was a little annoyed when the telephone rang. He believed that he had earned his ease. He was intending to rest his feet a bit, and then, with a happy feeling, he was going to tear off the 25 on the calendar pad that hung on the wall.

"Who is it?" he asked.

"This is Gissing," said a small and rather frightened voice that sounded very far away. "You know, Gissing in the Roslyn Estates. At Mr. Mistletoe's house."

Of course Santa knew about the Roslyn Estates, but he had never heard about Gissing, who was still so young that his name had not been entered on the lists. Santa gets the names and addresses of all the dogs from the Town Hall in Manhasset, where the dog licenses are registered. However, he answered very kindly.

"Yes, Gissing," he said. "How are you?"

"Well, I'm fine," said Gissing, "but I thought I'd better tell you what I want for Christmas."

It was on the tip of Santa's tongue to say, a little crossly, "But Christmas is over. You're too late." But he could guess from the trembly sound of Gissing's voice that there must be some misunderstanding.

"All right, Gissing," he said in an encouraging voice. "What is it?"

"What have you got?" asked Gissing eagerly.

Santa Claus almost laughed. Gissing, even when he was a small puppy, was always rather impudent. Santa looked at his shelves. There were only a few toys remaining, now that all that year's Christmas presents had been delivered.

"Well," said Santa patiently, "I have a toy schooner, a train, a doll, a rubber ball, a rake, a pail and shovel, a football, a white china cat, a paint-box, and a toy automobile."

Gissing was so excited he could hardly hold all those ideas in his head.

"Would you mind, please, repeating the list?" he asked politely.

Santa repeated, smiling to himself.

"I think I would like a white china cat," said Gissing. He wanted very much to ask for the toy automobile also, but he restrained himself.

Santa Claus sighed at the thought of going all the way back to the Roslyn Estates that night. He was rather angry at Mr. Mistletoe for not having properly instructed Gissing about Christmas and told him the date. But he did not want anyone to be disappointed.

"Very well," he said. "You hang up your stocking, and the cat will be there in the morning. Merry Christmas!"

"Here's looking at you," replied Gissing. It was a phrase he had heard the grown-ups say, and it was the only thing he could think of at the moment. He pulled his toy box back into the nursery, quietly, so that no one would know what he had been up to, got out his largest stocking, and went to bed.

Santa Claus had a cup of hot cocoa, and gave some to the reindeer, who were peevish at having to go out again. But with such a light load to carry, the sleigh sped swiftly. Across the snowy curve of the world the red sleigh went flashing. Great gauzes of daffodil yellow rippled and flickered in the dark blue, the wonderful Northern Lights. A brilliant star burned steadily right above the Pole, the North Star, the true Christmas Star. You can find it easily in the sky (unless you live south of the Equator) because the two stars in the end of the Dipper point straight to it.

It was the quietest night of the year, the night when all the children go to sleep at once because they are tired out with toys and excitements. Santa and the reindeer soon got over their irritation at having to go out again. It was very peaceful, even better than the hurry of Christmas Eve.

When Gissing woke up the next morning, there was the china cat. And not only the cat. Because Gissing's request had been so modest, Santa had brought along all the toys that were left—the schooner, the train, the doll, the ball, the rake, the pail and shovel, the football, the paint-box, and the aunbile.

It wasn't until Gissing was much older that he learned that Santa Claus had made a special trip, all the way from the North Pole to the Roslyn Estates. And that was why Gissing himself, when he grew up and went on a long adventure, was careful to get home on Christmas Eve, so that his puppies wouldn't be disappointed.

By Christopher Morley

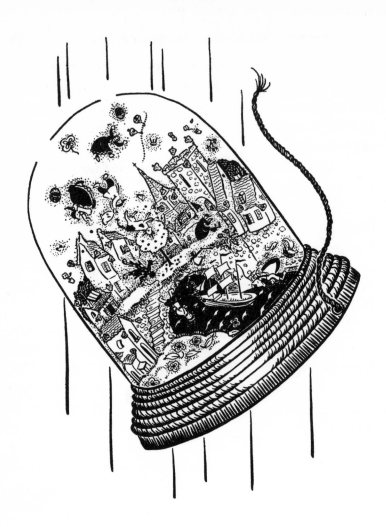

THE MUSICAL BOX

ONCE UPON A TIME there was a very happy Little French Town. It was so happy that it did not mind being kept in a Glass Case. In fact, it was glad, for no Dust could get at it and the People's Clothes were always bright in color.

The Houses were painted in gay colors—red, and orange and green and yellow.

The Sun always shone and the Sky was always blue and there were big Blue Flowers on the River Bank near the Sailing Ship.

And a beautiful little Cherry Tree with crimson Fruit was planted halfway across the Bridge.

Every day Somebody pulled a String under the Little Town and then the Bells of the Town rang and all the People crossed the Bridge. There are some People you are sure to see—there's the Miller with his Sack of Flour and the Women going to Market with large Baskets on their arms.

There's the Blind Beggar and his Black Dog; and the Priest hurrying to the Church, always carrying a Red Umbrella.

Look over the Bridge and you'll see the Laundress washing clothes in the River near the Sailing Ship. The Waves are very white. And then, of course, we were forgetting the Little Girl with the Pail, driving the black and white Cow in front of her, to be milked.

It's such a happy Little Town when the Bells ring that one wishes one were living there oneself.

But one day a fearful thing happened. Someone forgot to pull the String, and so the Bells could not ring and the People could not cross the Bridge.

For months the People waited, but always in vain.

It was terrible. NOBODY COULD MOVE!

The Miller stood by the crooked Steps near the Bridge with his Sack on his shoulder. "Oh, dear," he groaned, "I'm getting old. This Sack gets heavier and heavier. My shoulders ache till I would drop—if I only could!

"BUT I CANNOT MOVE!"

The Women were going to Market. They had Ducks to buy and Cheeses and Salad and Wine. "Oh, dear," they sighed. "We shall be late. All the best things will have gone. Come, let's hurry!"

BUT THEY COULDN'T MOVE!

The Blind Beggar shouted to his Black Dog. "Here, Tootoo, move along, can't you! If we're not at the Church Door before the Wedding Party there'll be no bone for you tonight."

But Tootoo's nose was glued to a stone.

The Priest tried to hurry across the Bridge to the Church, but his feet would not pass the patch of Dandelions by his right boot. He read the marriage service to the Dandelions, but could go no further.

IT WAS VERY STRANGE!

And then, of course, there was the Soldier on the Fort. His duty was to walk round and round, and if he could look down and watch the Laundress he was happy. But for months he had not seen her. He stood with his back to her.

AND HE COULD NOT MOVE!

For Months the Little Town in the Glass Case was left on the Shelf. And nobody came, until . . .

One morning Somebody was careless
     and
        it
           fell
              down!

In the Little Town there was a terrible Thunderstorm. First the Earth shook and then it rocked. Windows were flung open and smashed. Loud Rumbles were heard from the River. The Ship trembled and began to toss. The People shivered with fear. The Earth shook and rocked more. But the worst was yet to come. . . . The whole Town was flung into Space and hurled down

    and down

        and down.

The Little Girl left her Cow and jumped over the Bridge into the Ship, while the Soldier on the Fort was carried down through the air to the Riverside—where he fainted among the Blue Flowers.

As for the Market Women, they got so muddled up with their Baskets and their Petticoats that they forgot all about the marketing.

But then a wonderful thing happened. The Bells of the Town began to peal, louder and louder, till they filled the whole place with Music and Joy.

They filled the People with Joy, too, so that they forgot the terrible Earthquake and laughed and moved.

The Priest took one leap forward right over the Dandelions with his Red Umbrella in the air.

The Miller flung his Sack away and danced and sang.

The Blind Beggar's Dog ran off and stole a Duck from the Market Place, while the Soldier, when he recovered, found himself beside the Laundress. They were so happy and the Blue Flowers opened and grew tall to look at them!

And then what happened?

Somebody heard the Music and saw the Little Town
in the Glass Case lying on the Floor and put it back on
the Shelf.

And after that,
Every day,
They pulled the String
That made the Music;
And the People walked across the Bridge
And Everybody lived happily ever after.

THE MORAL

Now you know the sort of thing
That will befall a Little Town
If you forget to pull the String
Or let the Box come tumbling down.
Even the Heavenly Stars may fail
And Lilies sulk beneath the ground,
Learn then the Moral of this Tale:
'TIS MUSIC MAKES THE WORLD GO ROUND!

By Clare Leighton

THE OGRE THAT PLAYED JACKSTRAWS

ONCE THERE WAS a terrible giant ogre, and he lived in a huge castle that was built right in the middle of a valley. All men had to pass by it when they came to the king's palace on the rock at the head of the valley. And they were all terribly afraid of the ogre, and ran just as fast as they could when they went by. And when they looked back as they were running, they could see the ogre sitting on the wall of his castle. And he scowled at them so fiercely that they ran as fast as ever they could. For the ogre had a head as large as a barrel, and great black eyes sunk deep under long bushy eyelashes. And when he opened his mouth, they saw it was full of teeth; and so they ran away faster than ever, without caring to see any more.

And the king wanted to get rid of the ogre, and he sent his men to drive the ogre away and to tear down his castle. But the ogre scowled at them so savagely that their teeth began to fall out, and they all turned back and said they dare not fight such a horrid creature. Then Roger, the king's son, rode his black horse Hurricane up against the door of the ogre's castle, and struck hard against it with his iron glove. Then the door opened and the ogre came out and seized Roger in one hand and the great black horse in the other and rubbed their heads together, and while he did this he made them very small. Then he tumbled them over the wall into the ogre's garden. And they crawled through a hole in the garden fence and both ran home, Roger one way and Hurricane the other; and neither dared tell the king nor anyone else where he had been, nor what the ogre had done to him. But it was two or three days before they became large again.

Then the king sent out some men with a cannon to batter down the walls of the ogre's castle. But the ogre sat on the wall and caught the cannon balls in his hand and tossed them back at the cannon, so that they broke the wheels and scared away all the men. And when the cannon sounded, the ogre roared so loudly that all the windows in the king's palace were broken, and the queen and all the princesses went down in the cellar and hid among the sugar barrels, and stuffed cotton in their ears till the noise should stop. And whatever the king's men tried to do, the ogre made it worse and worse.

And at last no one dared to go out into the valley beside the ogre's castle, and no one dared look at it from anywhere, because when the ogre scowled all who saw him dropped to the ground with fear, and their teeth began to fall out, and when the ogre roared there was no one who could bear to hear it.

So the king and all his men hid in the cellar of the castle with the queen and the princesses, and they stuffed their ears full of cotton, and the ogre scowled and roared and had his own way.

But there was one little boy named Pennyroyal, who tended the black horse Hurricane; and he was not afraid of anything, because he was a little boy. And the little boy said he would go out and see the ogre and tell him to go away. And they were all so scared that they could not ask him not to go. So Pennyroyal put on his hat, filled his pocket with marbles and took his kite under his arm, and went down the valley to the castle of the ogre. The ogre sat on the wall and looked at him, but the little boy was not afraid, and so it did the ogre no good to scowl. Then Pennyroyal knocked on the ogre's door, and the ogre opened it and looked at the little boy.

"Please, Mr. Ogre, may I come in?" said Pennyroyal; and the ogre opened the door, and the little boy began to walk around the castle looking at all the things. There was one room filled with bones, but the ogre was ashamed of it, and did not want to let the little boy see it. So when Pennyroyal was not looking, the ogre just changed the room and made it small—so that instead of a room full of bones it became just a box of jackstraws. And the big elephant he had there to play with he made into a lap-elephant, and the little boy took it in his hand and stroked its tiny tusks and tied a knot in its trunk.

And everything that could frighten the little boy the ogre made small and pretty, so that they had great times together.

And by and by the ogre grew smaller and smaller, and took off his ugly old face with the long teeth and bushy eyebrows and dropped them on the floor and covered them with a wolf-skin. Then he sat down on the wolf-skin and the little boy sat down on the floor beside him, and they began to play jackstraws with the box of jackstraws that had been a room full of bones. The ogre had never been a boy himself, so jackstraws was the only game he knew how to play. Then the elephant he had made small snuggled down between them on the floor. And as they played with each other, the castle itself grew small, and shrank away until there was just room enough for them and their game.

Up in the palace, when the ogre stopped roaring, the king's men looked out and saw that the ogre's castle was gone. Then Roger, the king's son, called for Pennyroyal. But when he could not find the boy, he saddled the black horse Hurricane himself and rode down the valley to where the ogre's castle had been. When he came back he told the king that the ogre and his castle were all gone. Where the castle stood there was nothing left but a board tent under the oak tree, and in the tent there were just two little boys playing jackstraws, and between them on the ground lay a candy elephant.

That was all. For the terrible ogre was one of that kind of ogres that will do to folks just what folks do to him. There isn't any other kind of ogre.

By David Starr Jordan

THE THREE APPLES

EVERY SUMMER the apple tree which grew in the Old Apple Woman's garden was covered thickly with apples; and as the summer days passed, these apples grew big and red and ripe, and at last fell one by one to the ground. Then the Apple Woman would come out and gather them up, and store them away until the time came when she could carry them to the fair and sell them.

But once, when the Old Apple Woman thought that all her apples were safely stored away, she went out to have a last look at her tree, and there she saw, right at the very tip-top, round and red against the sky, three apples still remaining. The Old Apple Woman stood and looked at them, and she saw that they were bigger and riper than any of the other apples, and she at once began to plan how she could get them.

"I must consult Marley about this matter," said the Apple Woman to herself.

Marley was the Apple Woman's hen. She was not at all clever, but in some ways she was very sensible, and she always had a very kind heart.

When Marley heard what the Apple Woman had to tell, she turned her head from side to side, looking at the Apple Woman, first with one round yellow eye and then with the other.

"We must not leave the apples on the tree," she said, "or the birds will come and eat them. On the other hand, you cannot climb the tree for them, because you know that your joints are stiff with rheumatism. But my joints are not stiff, and I have, moreover, a strong pair of wings, which you have not, so I will fly up to the tip-top of the tree where the apples are, and I will shake the bough until they fall."

"What a clever idea! You are a wonderful hen, Marley," said the Old Apple Woman joyfully, and they both went out. The Apple Woman stood under the tree, holding her apron to catch the apples as they fell, and Marley flew up to the tip-top of the apple tree.

But the bough on which the apples grew was slender and weak, and, on the other hand, Marley was heavy and fat; so when Marley alighted on the branch it gave way under her so far and so suddenly that Marley, much alarmed, flew off into the air, cackling with fright, and flapped her way down to the grass at the Old Woman's feet. But the apples still hung, red and ripe, at the tip-top of the apple tree.

"You did not get the apples, Marley," said the Apple Woman, much disappointed.

Marley was too much upset to answer. She walked up and down on the grass, cackling from sheer nervousness.

"You did not get the apples," repeated the Apple Woman.

"Apples?" clucked Marley. "What are three apples compared to my life? I might as well have broken my neck."

"That would have been dreadful," said the Apple Woman soothingly.

"It would have been very dreadful," replied Marley, looking at the Old Apple Woman, first with one yellow eye and then with the other.

"But since you have not broken anything," said the Apple Woman, "cannot you think of some other plan for reaching those three apples at the tip-top of the tree?"

"I cannot think of any other plan," said Marley shortly.

Then suddenly the Apple Woman began to smile and nod her head.

"But I have myself thought of a plan," she said. "I remember that the Leprechaun left his long ladder here the other day, because he said he was too tired to carry it home, and he has not yet come to fetch it. I will lean the Leprechaun's ladder against the tree, and though my joints are stiff with rheumatism, I am sure I shall be able to climb as high as those three red apples."

But Marley was offended, because she thought the Apple Woman had not made enough fuss over her, so she answered in a cold indifferent way:

"Yes, yes! I dare say you will be able to climb as high as the apples. I am now going to rest for a little. I do not feel at all well."

And Marley went into the house and shut the door.

The Apple Woman found the Leprechaun's long ladder, and she leaned it against the apple tree, and began to climb up—very slowly, because of her rheumatism. When she reached the top she stepped right off the ladder onto a bough of the tree, and putting up her hand, she found that she could just reach the apples. She pulled them, one by one, and put them into her great pockets, and then she turned to step back on the ladder again, intending to climb down as she had climbed up.

But a dreadful thing had happened while the Apple Woman was standing on the bough of the apple tree, pulling the apples. For the Leprechaun had come to fetch his ladder, and carry it home; and when he came up to the Old Apple Woman's house, he saw his ladder leaning against the tree; but he did not see the Apple Woman, who was hidden among the leaves.

"Why, here is my ladder," he said to himself, "and why should I disturb the Apple Woman and her good hen Marley by knocking at the door and asking for it? I will simply take my ladder and carry it away."

So he took it up and carried it away, and the Leprechaun was just out of sight when the Apple Woman turned round and found that the ladder was gone. She could scarcely believe her eyes.

"Marley!" she screamed. "Help! Marley! Come quick!"

Marley came running out when she heard the Apple Woman calling, but when she saw what had happened she could do nothing but cry and beat her wings in despair.

"What shall I do?" cried the Apple Woman. "Here I am on the tip-top of this terrible apple tree, and if I try to get down I shall certainly fall! Must I sit here for always and always and always?"

But Marley could only cry louder and beat her wings harder.

Now just then Michael happened to be passing near, and when he heard such a noise coming from the Apple Woman's house, he ran up to see what it was all about.

"Why do you cry so, Marley?" he said. "And why do you beat your wings?"

"How can I help it?" replied Marley. "Do you not see that the Old Apple Woman is on the tip-top of the apple tree, and cannot get down? She climbed up by the Leprechaun's long ladder, and when she turned to climb down again, the ladder was gone."

Michael thought very hard for a few minutes. Then he said:

"The Old Woman who keeps the goats has also a

long ladder. It is rather too heavy for me to carry alone, but if Teig the dog and the Eldest Goat were to help to carry it, we could bring it here and lean it against the tree, and if the Apple Woman climbed up by one long ladder, she could climb down by another."

"Oh, Michael," cried Marley and the Apple Woman together, "go quickly and fetch the ladder."

So Michael went, and before long he and Teig the dog and the Eldest Goat had brought up the ladder, and they leaned it carefully against the tree and held it steady while the Apple Woman climbed down.

When the Apple Woman was once more standing safely on the grass, she and her hen Marley cried with joy. Then the Apple Woman took the three big red apples out of her pockets and she gave them to Michael, and Teig the dog, and the Eldest Goat, one apple to each, as a reward for their kindness in helping her.

So Michael and Teig the dog and the Eldest Goat were happy, too.

By Anne Casserley

THE BOJABI TREE

I. Robin Rat

In the land of All-the-Beasts there was a GREAT HUN-GER. Some of the animals who were so HUNGRY were
Tabby Tiger
  Bruno Bear
    Katy Crocodile
     Robin Rat
      Pinky Pig
       Giddy Goat
        Tommy Tortoise
and many more—more than you could ever count in a year.

They ran around the wood, here and there and everywhere, eating roots and twigs and any old scraps they could find. But still they were HUNGRY.

One day they came to a Big Tree full of fruit. But

they could not eat it, for they did not know what it was.

They sat down in a circle round the tree, and said, "What can we do?"

When they had thought a while, they said, "Let us send Robin Rat up the river to Leo, our King, and ask him what the fruit is and whether we may eat it."

Robin Rat was young and spry. He scuttled up the tree and brought down one of its fruit to show King Leo.

It was a DELICIOUS-looking fruit!

It looked like an

APPLEORANGEPEARPLUMBANANA

but it smelled like a

BANANAPLUMPEARORANGEAPPLE.

Then Robin Rat scuttled down to the river bank and climbed into his little canoe.

All the day and all the day he paddled

and paddled

and PADDLED

up the river.

And the Great Red Sun dropped behind the trees.

Then he found King Leo on the bank, all ready to receive visitors. He was wearing his crown tipped on the back of his head because he felt happy. He smiled at Robin Rat as pleasant as you please, and asked him to stay to supper.

After supper they curled up and went to sleep. There was nothing else to do, you see.

In the morning King Leo said politely, "What can I do for you, my small friend?"

Then Robin Rat answered, "Please tell us, King Leo,

what is the name of this tree and whether we may eat the fruit of it. We are all SO HUNGRY!"

King Leo looked at the fruit that was like an

APPLEORANGEPEARPLUMBANANA

and he sniffed at the fruit that was like a

BANANAPLUMPEARORANGEAPPLE.

Then he said, "It is a good fruit. You may eat it. The name of the tree is

BOJABI."

Then Robin Rat hung his cap over his right ear and climbed into his little canoe.

All the day and all the day he paddled down the great river.

And all the way he was thinking how much he could eat of that

DELICIOUS fruit.

And at night he came home.

All the Beasts were waiting for him on the shore. He came up, whisking his paddle *this* way and *that* way through the water, just to show how well he could do it.

"What is it, Robin Rat?" said All the Beasts. "Tell us the name!" they roared and howled and grunted and whined and shrieked and squealed, each in his own PARTICULAR voice.

"Oh!" said Robin Rat. "I knew it a while ago, but now I have clean forgotten."

Then All the Beasts stepped into the water and upset Robin Rat's little canoe.

They SPLASHED and they

SPLUTTERED and they

SP-L-ANKED

Robin Rat.

Squeaksqueaksqueaksqueaksqueak!

Nobody heard a word more from *him* that day.

II. PINKY PIG

But now All the Beasts were HUNGRIER STILL.

They sat in a circle round the tree and thought a while.

Then they said, "Let us send Pinky Pig to King Leo to ask the name of the tree. But, Pinky Pig,

"DO NOT FORGET IT!"

Pinky Pig trotted away home—

　　trip-trap, trip-trap, trip-trap.

He put on his best blue coat and buttoned it up, though it squeezed him a little.

Then he trotted—trip-trap, trip-trap, trip-trap— down to his little rowboat and took his oars to row up the big river.

All the day and all the day he rowed

　　　　　　and he rowed

　　　　　　and he ROWED

up the big river.

And the Great Red Sun dropped behind the trees.

Then he found King Leo on the bank, all ready to receive visitors. His crown was a little crooked because he had put it on in a hurry when he saw Pinky Pig coming.

He smiled politely but he did not invite Pinky Pig to stay to supper.

"What can I do for you, my plump friend?" he asked.

Pinky Pig showed him the fruit that looked like an

APPLEORANGEPEARPLUMBANANA

and smelled like a

BANANAPLUMPEARORANGEAPPLE,

and said, "Please, King Leo, we must know the name of this tree or we cannot eat the fruit. Please be so kind as to tell us."

Then King Leo said,

"I have told Robin Rat.

"I will tell you.

"The name of the tree is

BOJABI!

"Do not forget it."

Pinky Pig trotted back to his rowboat—trip-trap, trip-trap, trip-trap.

All the night and all the night he rowed—he rowed —and he ro-o-owed until the oars—dropped—from— his—hands—and the big river took the boat down itself.

Pinky Pig curled up under the seat. And this is the sound that came from the boat:

H-r-r-r-umph

  h-h-r-r-r-*umph*

    h-h-h-r-r-r-r-UM-MPH!

In the morning Pinky Pig sat up and rubbed his eyes. He was at home. All the Beasts stood on the river bank looking at him. "What is it, Pinky Pig? Tell us the name!" they whistled and snarled and squealed and shrieked and whined and grunted and howled and roared, each in his own PARTICULAR voice.

"I know it," said Pinky Pig. Then he yawned.

"I knew it last night," he said, "but—ah—ah—I— must—have—been—asleep, and—ah—for—got—ten— it."

That is the way he talked when he was yawning.

Then All the Beasts jumped into the water and smashed Pinky Pig's boat and his oars.

They PLUNGED about and

                PUNCHED poor Pinky Pig and

                POUNDED him until he went

plop—plop—into the water.

SQue-e-e-e-e-e-E-E-E-E-E-E-E-AL!

He ran home with the water running off him and making little puddles here and there.

Nobody heard a word more from *him* that day.

III. GIDDY GOAT

But now All the Beasts were HUNGRIER and HUN-GRIER. They could have eaten nails if there had been any nails in the Great Wood.

They sat in a circle round the tree and thought a while.

Then they said, "Giddy Goat is older than Pinky Pig, and wiser than Robin Rat. Let us send him to King Leo to ask the name of the tree, so that we may eat the fruit of it before we starve. But, Giddy Goat,

"DO NOT FORGET IT!"

"A-rashum!" said Giddy Goat. He was afraid of catching cold. Away he ran—ker-lipp, ker-lipp—to his house to get a big woolly muffler to wear on the river. He wrapped it three times round his neck and tucked it neatly under his beard.

Then he ran—ker-lipp, ker-lipp—down to his little sailboat on the river.

All the day and all the day he sailed
> and he sailed
> and he SAILED

up the big river.

And the Great Red Sun dropped behind the trees.

Then he found King Leo on the bank, *not* ready to receive visitors. His crown was on straight and he looked very CROSS.

"Whatdoyouwant?" he snapped—just like that.

"A-rashum!" said Giddy Goat. "I beg your Majesty's pardon. I have a cold coming on."

He showed King Leo the fruit that looked like an

> APPLEORANGEPEARPLUMBANANA

and smelled like a

> BANANAPLUMPEARORANGEAPPLE,

and said, "If you would be so very kind, King Leo, to tell us the name of this tree, so that we may know whether we may eat the fruit of it . . ."

Then King Leo said,

"I have told Robin Rat.

"I have told Pinky Pig.

"I will tell you.

"But I will not tell ANYBODY ELSE.

"The name is

> BOJABI.

"DO NOT FORGET IT!"

"A-rash-oo!" said Giddy Goat, and he skipped away —ker-lipp, ker-lipp—to his sailboat.

All the night and all the night he sailed
> and he sailed
> and he SAILED.

All the way he was remembering the name, and he remembered it very well.

He sailed so fast that he got home in the early, early morning.

And all the way, when he wasn't remembering the name, he was sneezing:

"A-tchoo! A-rashum! A-tchoo!"

All the beasts were waiting for him—rows and rows of them. Those in the back rows looked over the shoulders of those in the front rows, or climbed on their backs.

They pushed and jostled one another until they had upset Giddy Goat's sailboat. Ker-splash!—he went into the river.

Such a sight as he was when they pulled him out! His long hair was full of water. His beard was full of water. His eyes were full of water. His beautiful new muffler was full of water.

When the animals crowded round him to ask the name of the tree, he shook himself so that the water flew in their faces, and ran away home—ker-lipp, ker-lipp—with a most dreadful

A-TCHOO!

His wife made him go to bed. And not one word could anyone get from him all that day but "A-tchoo! A-rashum! A-TCHOO!"

IV. TOMMY TORTOISE

By this time All the Beasts were so HUNGRY that they sat round the tree and cried.

You see, there was no one else who had a boat.

"What shall we do?" they wailed and howled and buzzed and grunted and groaned and sobbed and lamented, each in his own most PARTICULAR voice.

Then Tommy Tortoise, who had been lying asleep in the sun, opened one eye, and said, "What is all this fuss about? Haven't you found out the name of this tree YET?"

They said they had not and cried harder than ever.

"Oh, well," said he, "if that's all, I'll go and get it for you."

"YOU!" snarled Tabby Tiger.

"You! You!" grunted Bruno Bear.

"You!" snapped Katy Crocodile, biting her word off short.

"You-u-u-u!" trumpeted Elizabeth Elephant.

"You! You! You!" chattered Mimi Monkey.

You never heard such a noise—not even at the circus —as there was when they all said this, each in his own PARTICULAR voice.

"Yes, me—I mean *I,*" said Tommy Tortoise in his little, thin voice.

Then he crawled slowly home, trailing one foot after the other, as some boys do on their way to school.

He found his mother knitting stockings and rocking the baby.

"Hssh!" said Mrs. Tortoise. "He's just dropping off."

"Mother," said Tommy Tortoise. "How can I remember the name of that tree if I go up the river to get it?"

"Tommy," said Mrs. Tortoise, "do you remember

how you used to go to school with all the other little
tortoises and learn things?"

"Yes," said Tommy.

"Nine times one makes nine,

"Nine times two makes eighteen,

"Nine times three makes twenty-seven—"

He said the Nines table because anybody can say the
Tens, and he wasn't sure about the Elevens.

"Hsh!" said Mrs. Tortoise. "That will do. You will
wake the baby.

"But I will tell you how to remember." She whispered in his ear.

Then she said, "Now, Tommy, whatever happens to
you, mind your manners. Remember to bow to King
Leo and to speak to him so politely that he will know
you have been well brought up."

"Yes, Mother," said Tommy Tortoise.

Then he put on his cap with the red tassel, and he
went down to the river. He had no boat; so he had to
swim.

All the day and all the day he swam

and he swam

and he SWAM.

When he was tired swimming, he would turn over on
his shell and float with all his legs kicking in the water,
just as the baby kicks in his bath.

And the Great Red Sun dropped behind the trees.

When Tommy Tortoise reached King Leo's home,
King Leo was NOT curled up comfortably wearing his
crown and ready to receive visitors. He was standing on
the river bank waving his tail. His big head was wag-

gling *this* way and *that* way, and he was not smiling
AT ALL.

Before Tommy could speak a word, or even make his
best bow, King Leo said:

"R-R-R-R-R-R-R-R-R-R-R-R-R-R-R-R-R! S-s-cat! S-scamper!
S-scat! S-skedaddle!

"I told Robin Rat.

"I told Pinky Pig.

"I told Giddy Goat.

"I WILL NOT TELL YOU

that the name of the tree is bojabi.

"R-R-R-R-R-R-R-R-R-R-R-R-R-R-R-R-R!"

"Bojabi," whispers Tommy Tortoise to himself, and
jumps—ker-lump—into the river again.

All the night and all the night he swam

　　　　　　　and he swam

　　　　　　　and he SWAM.

But it was easy work to let the big river carry him on its
back.

All the night and all the night he made up a little
song and sang it, like this:

> "O Robin Rat, what shall we eat?
> 　　Bojabi—bojabi—bojabi.
> O Pinky Pig, so fat and neat,
> 　　Bojabi—bojabi—bojabi.
> O Giddy Goat, so fast and fleet,
> 　　Bojabi—bojabi—bojabi.
> O Humpy Hippo, hard to beat,
> 　　Bojabi—bojabi—bojabi.
> O Bruno Bear, with clumsy feet,

Bojabi—bojabi—bojabi.
O Katy Crocodile, here's a treat,
Bojabi—bojabi—bojabi.
O Tommy Tortoise, of Puddle Street,
Bojabi—bojabi—bojabi.
O All the Beasts, come quick and eat
Bojabi—bojabi—bojabi."

And THAT was what his mother had told him to do.

All the Beasts were lying on the bank of the river. Far away they heard the little, thin voice of Tommy Tortoise singing his song. They pricked up their ears, looking *this* way and *that* way as they listened.

And presently Tommy Tortoise came crawling up through the mud.

"What is it?" they cried, each in his own PARTICULAR voice. You would have thought that all the circuses in the world were there.

"Bojabi," said Tommy Tortoise, and crawled away home without another word.

That night All the Beasts had bojabi for their supper.

But Tommy Tortoise had cream with his.

After that All the Beasts in that wood were never hungry. They could always eat bojabi.

They made Tommy Tortoise their king. "For," they said, "if he could remember the name of the bojabi tree, he can do anything."

As far as I know he is king of All the Beasts in the Great Wood today.

—Adapted from an African Folk Tale.
By Edith Rickert

LIVING IN W'ALES

ONCE THERE WAS a man who said he didn't like the
sort of houses people lived in, so he built a model village. It was not really like a model village at all, because the houses were all big enough for real people to
live in, and he went about telling people to come and
live in W'ales.

There was also living in Liverpool a little girl who
was very nice. So when all the people went off with the
man to live in W'ales, she went with them. But the
man walked so fast that presently some of them got left
behind. The ones who were left behind were the little
girl, and an Alsatian dog, and a very cross old lady in
a bonnet and black beads, who was all stiff, but had a
nice husband, who was left behind too.

So they went along till they came to the sea; and in
the sea was a whale. The little girl said, "That was what

he meant, I suppose, when he talked about living in W'ales. I expect the others are inside: or, if not, they are in another one. We had better get in this one."

So they shouted to know if they might come in, but the whale didn't hear them. The nice husband said that if that was what living in W'ales meant, he would rather go back to Liverpool; but the horrid old lady said, "Nonsense! I will go and whisper in its ear."

But she was very silly, and so instead of whispering in its ear she went and tried to whisper in its blowhole. Still the whale didn't hear; so she got very cross and said, "None of this nonsense, now! Let us in at once! I won't have it, do you hear? I simply won't stand it!" and she began to stir in his blowhole with her umbrella.

So the whale blew, like an enormous sneeze, and blew her right away up into the sky on top of the water he blew out of his hole, and she was never seen again. So then the nice husband went quietly back to Liverpool.

But the little girl went to the whale's real ear, which was very small and not a bit like his blowhole, and whispered into it, "Please, nice whale, we would so like to come in, if we may, and live inside." Then the whale opened his mouth, and the little girl and the Alsatian dog went in.

When they got right down inside, of course, there was no furniture. "He was quite right," said the little girl. "It is certainly not a bit like living in a house."

The only thing in there was a giant's wig that the whale had once eaten. So the little girl said, "This will do for a doormat." So she made it into a doormat, and the Alsatian dog went to sleep on it.

When he woke up again he started to dig holes; and, of course, it gave the whale most terrible pains to have holes dug by such a big dog in his inside, so he went up to the top of the water and shouted to the Captain of a ship to give him a pill. On board the ship there was a cold dressed leg of mutton that the Captain was tired of, so he thought, "That will make a splendid pill to give the whale." So he threw it to the whale, and the whale swallowed it; and when it came tobogganing down the whale's throat the Alsatian dog, who was very hungry, ate it, and stopped digging holes; and when the dog stopped digging holes the whale's pain went away. So he said "Thank you" to the Captain. "That was an excellent pill."

The Captain was very surprised that his pill had made the whale well again so soon; he had really done it only to get rid of the cold mutton.

But the poor little girl wasn't so lucky as the Alsatian dog. *He* had a doormat to sleep on, and something to eat. But there was no bed, and the little girl couldn't possibly sleep without a bed to sleep on; and she had nothing to eat—and this went on for days and days.

Meanwhile the whale began to get rather worried about them. He had swallowed them without thinking much about it; but he soon began to wonder what was happening to them, and whether they were comfortable. He knew nothing at all about little girls. He thought she would probably want something to eat by now, but he didn't know at all what. So he tried to talk down into his own inside, to ask her. But that is very difficult; at any rate, *he* couldn't do it. The words all came out instead of going in.

So he swam off to the tropics, where he knew a parrot, and asked him what to do. The parrot said it was quite simple, and flew off to an island where there was a big snake. He bit off its head and bit off its tail, and then flew back to the whale with the rest of it. He put most of the snake down the whale's throat, so that one end just came up out of its mouth.

"There," he said, "now you have a speaking tube. You speak into one end of the snake, and the words will go down it inside you."

So the whale said "Hello" into one end of the snake, and the little girl heard "Hello" come out of the other. "What do you want?" said the whale. "I want something to eat," said the little girl. The whale told the parrot, "She wants something to eat. What do little girls eat?"

"Little girls eat rice pudding," said the parrot. He had one, in a big glass bowl; so he poured it down the snake too, and it came down the other end and the little girl ate it.

When she had eaten it she caught hold of her end of the snake, and called "Hello!" up it.

"Hello!" said the whale.

"May I have a bed?" said the little girl.

"She wants a bed," the whale said to the parrot.

"You go to Harrod's for that," said the parrot, "which is the biggest shop in London," and flew away.

When the whale got to Harrod's, he went inside. One of the shopwalkers came up to him and said, "What can I do for *you,* please?" which sounded very silly.

"I want a bed," said the whale.

"Mr. Binks, BEDS!" The shopwalker called out very loud, and then ran away. He was terribly frightened, because there had never been a whale in the shop before.

Mr. Binks the Bed Man came up and looked rather worried.

"I don't know that we have got a bed that will exactly fit you, sir," he said.

"Why not, silly?" said the whale. "I only want an ordinary one."

"Yes, sir," said the Bed Man, "but it will have to be rather a large ordinary one, won't it?"

"Of course not, silly," said the whale. "On the contrary, it will have to be rather a small one."

He saw a very nice little one standing in a corner.

"I think that one will just about fit me," he said.

"You can have it if you like," said the Bed Man. "But I think it's you who are the silly to think a little bed like that will fit you!"

"I want it to fit me *inside,* of course," said the whale, "not *outside!* . . . Push!" and he opened his mouth.

So they all came and pushed, and sure enough it just did fit him. Then he ate all the pillows and blankets he could find, which was far more than was needed really, and when it all got down inside, the little girl made the bed and went to sleep on it.

So the whale went back to the sea. Now that the little

girl and the Alsatian dog both had had something to eat and somewhere to sleep, they said:

"The man was right, it really is much more fun living in W'ales than living in houses."

So they stayed on.

P.S. The parrot went on feeding them, not always on rice pudding.

By Richard Hughes

THE SADDLER'S HORSE

I WONDER how many of you who read this story have ever seen a cigar-store Indian?

I don't mean in pictures, or in someone's collection of old-fashioned curiosities, but a real one, all carved and painted and standing just where he should stand, on the sidewalk outside the cigar-store door. Not so many years ago a cigar-store Indian used to be quite an every-day sight, almost as common as a barber's pole. And as for saddler's horses, many a town that really was a town used to have one, and very proud they were of him.

I don't know where all the cigar-store Indians have

gone to. Perhaps they are living somewhere, here and there, in private families. Perhaps they have all migrated in a body to the great open spaces, or wherever it is that Wooden Indians do go. Certainly one does not see them any more on the sidewalk, kindly offering one a cigar or a pinch of snuff, as they used to do.

But I do know of one place where there is still a Saddler's Horse.

He is very big and tall, painted all over a pleasant varnishy dapple gray, and he stands outside what is still the saddler's store—though it sells other things as well nowadays—in the open space near the railroad station, just two minutes' walk from Mr. Murdle's store. All day long he stands there and dreams.

He dreams of the old days when there were no airplanes and no gas pumps; when the railroad station was very much smaller and the big hotel had not yet been built, nor the concrete highway; when it took country folk a whole day, instead of an hour, to get to town and back, and they drove in spring-top buggies and buckboards and farm wagons, and instead of parked cars by the sidewalk edge there were horses, long rows of them, tied in the shade to hitching posts under the big elm trees.

In those days the feed store and the hardware store and the saddler's were quite the most important stores in town. And the Saddler's Horse, standing out there with the very newest style of shiny harness buckled on his back for every passer-by to admire, would gaze down his nose at the country horses switching their tails under the elms, and feel that he was very, very superior.

But times have changed. There are gas pumps now instead of hitching posts. Automobiles and trucks go up and down the street; very few teams pass by, and the Saddler's Horse rarely sees a buggy at all. But still he stands there, all day long, watching the traffic go past, and at six o'clock, when the train whistle blows, the saddler wheels him indoors and puts him to bed for the night.

Just across the street is an antique shop. It happened that one day, not very long ago, the storekeeper came across a Wooden Indian. I don't know where he found him, but he brought him home, together with a grandfather clock and an old bureau and a print of a little girl hugging a kitten, and he stood him out on the sidewalk just beside the shop door.

As soon as the Wooden Indian saw the Saddler's Horse, and as soon as the Saddler's Horse caught sight of the Wooden Indian, they began to shout to each other across the street. The Saddler's Horse was very pleased. He hadn't seen a Wooden Indian for years and years. It was just like old times come back again.

"Hello," said the Indian. "What are you doing there? I haven't seen a horse like you for ages!"

"Oh, I live here," said the Saddler's Horse. "I'm the oldest person in this town! I've been here longer than the Town Hall itself."

"Well, well," said the Wooden Indian. "Times have surely changed, haven't they? None of these nasty automobiles when *we* were young! I don't like them, and I don't like the gas pumps, either. Things used to be much better. You and I are losing our jobs now. I've lost mine

already. Antiques, that's what they call us nowadays!
Still, I've spent the last five years in a barn, and it feels
good to stand out on the sidewalk again and see the
folks passing. I've always been used to an outdoor life,
and I like it. But tomorrow I suppose someone will
come along and buy me, and then there'll be an end of it
all—"

Just then a big truck passed by. It made so much noise
that neither of them could hear the other speaking.

"*That's* what I complain of!" said the Saddler's
Horse, when it had passed. "All that noise, and it shakes
one to pieces! Yes, the old times were much better."

"Tell you what," cried the Wooden Indian as soon as
he could make himself heard once more. "Suppose you
and I take a trip together? We might never get the
chance again! Everyone should have a good gallop once
in his life. They think we are back numbers, here, but
we'll show them! Come along!"

He hopped across the street, right between the automobiles, and made one spring to the back of the Saddler's Horse. The Saddler's Horse had no time even to
think; he just threw up his head and snorted, and off
they went! Out ran the antique dealer, out ran the saddler, waving his arms and shouting, but it was too late.
The Saddler's Horse and the Wooden Indian were off
together, and nothing could stop them!

First they galloped by the railroad station, dodging
in and out among the jitneys and busses and parked
cars; then up the hill, round the corner by the Post
Office and into Main Street. Everyone turned and
stared. Little boys yelled, shopkeepers ran to their door-

ways, old ladies dropped their parcels and screamed.
People shouted:

"It's a circus parade!"

"It's a new advertisement!"

"It's a wild Indian gone crazy!"

And among all the shouting and excitement the saddler and the antique dealer ran puffing and panting
along, shouting: "Stop them! Stop them!"

But no one could stop them.

Down Main Street they galloped, right through all
the traffic. The policeman ran out and blew his whistle
at them, but they dashed straight by him. Past the
cinema, past the bank and Town Hall, and when they
came to the tall Stop and Go sign on the corner the
Saddler's Horse jumped clear over it. Then his great
hoofs thundered over the bridge, and they were gone.

The townsfolk were left staring.

"Did you ever hear of such a thing!" they gasped.
The old gentlemen mopped their foreheads, and the old
ladies picked up their parcels again. "The idea of tearing along like that!" they cried indignantly. "Something ought to be done about it!" And as for the traffic
cop, he was as red in the face as a beetroot, and he
shouted and waved at the automobiles as if it were all
their fault.

The little boys craned their necks down the street.
They were still hoping to see the rest of the circus
parade.

Before long the news had gone out over the whole
countryside. Startled motorists pulled up at wayside gas

stations, telling of great hoofs that had thundered behind them along the highway, of a huge gray horse that
had flashed by in a cloud of dust and disappeared. Up
and down the state roads, far and wide, motor-cycle
cops went whizzing past, looking everywhere for a
crazy Indian on a big gray horse.

Meantime, many miles away in a green meadow by
the roadside, the Wooden Indian and the Saddler's
Horse had stopped to rest.

"That was a grand ride!" said the Wooden Indian as
he slid off.

"It was!" panted the Saddler's Horse.

"Didn't we give them a scare?" said the Wooden Indian.

"We did!" puffed the Saddler's Horse.

To tell the truth, he was beginning to feel a bit tired,
and was quite glad to stop galloping for a while and
just rest quietly in the deep grass. It had been grand
while it lasted, but now, all at once, his wooden limbs
began to tremble and his wooden back began to ache.
Tomorrow, he knew, he would be terribly stiff in all his
joints. After all, when one is as old as the Saddler's
Horse, and has never galloped before in one's life, one
is bound to feel it!

Just then, somewhere in the distance, a train whistle
blew; a long, plaintive note. The Saddler's Horse gave
a start. He thought all at once of the sidewalk and the
trees and the railroad station, the familiar street that he
had gazed on for so many years. Six o'clock . . . at this
very moment, perhaps, the saddler was stepping out of

the doorway in his apron, ready to wheel him back into the cool, dark store to sleep for the night.

"Don't you think," said the Saddler's Horse in a rather shaky voice, "that we ought to be turning back now?"

"Back?" said the Wooden Indian. "I'm not going back! You can go if you want to, I shall stay here for the rest of my life and live in the woods!"

The Saddler's Horse looked doubtfully at the meadows, at the tall dark woods behind, and the sky already deepening to sunset.

"Well . . . good-by!" he said at last.

"Good-by!" said the Wooden Indian.

Slowly and stiffly the Saddler's Horse began to limp back along the dusty highroad toward town. Every once in a while he turned his head to gaze back. There in the middle of the field, grown each moment smaller and smaller, he could see the Wooden Indian standing, waving his arms, clear and distinct against the sunset.

The saddler felt not at all cheerful that evening as he stood in his doorway, staring across the street. For one thing, he was afraid that at any moment the policeman might come and arrest him, because of all the disturbance that had occurred. He had talked it over with the antique dealer and they had both decided that the wisest thing was to say nothing about it. Still, one never knew.

Besides, he really did miss the Horse. He was proud of him, and they had lived together so long that he was like an old friend. All these years the saddler had wheeled him out every morning, and wheeled him in to bed every night, and now goodness alone knew where he was or what had happened to him!

When the six o'clock whistle blew, the saddler had all he could do to keep from bursting into tears.

But next morning, when he opened the store door, his heart gave a great jump.

"Bless me!" cried the saddler.

For there in his old place on the sidewalk stood the Saddler's Horse, gazing down his nose at the automobiles just as usual. He looked a little dusty and perhaps a bit shaky on his legs, and of all strange things there was a burdock caught in his long tail! But otherwise he was none the worse. There he stood and there he stands to this day, perfectly contented, for he has never tried to run away again. You may see him yourself, any time between eight and six, if you happen to be passing by.

And as for the Wooden Indian, no one has ever set eyes on him again.

By Margery Williams Bianco

HOW TO TELL CORN FAIRIES
IF YOU SEE 'EM

IF YOU HAVE ever watched the little corn begin to
march across the black lands and then slowly change

to big corn and go marching on from the little corn moon of summer to the big corn harvest moon of autumn, then you must have guessed who it is that helps the corn come along. It is the corn fairies. Leave out the corn fairies and there wouldn't be any corn.

All children know this. All boys and girls know that corn is no good unless there are corn fairies.

Have you ever stood in Illinois or Iowa and watched the late summer wind or the early fall wind running across a big cornfield? It looks as if a big, long blanket were being spread out for dancers to come and dance on. If you look close and if you listen close you can see the corn fairies come dancing and singing—sometimes. If it is a wild day and a hot sun is pouring down while a cool north wind blows—and this happens sometimes— then you will be sure to see thousands of corn fairies marching and countermarching in mocking grand marches over the big, long blanket of green and silver. Then, too, they sing, only you must listen with your littlest and newest ears if you wish to hear their singing. They sing soft songs that go pla-sizzy pla-sizzy-sizzy, and each song is softer than an eye-wink, softer than a Nebraska baby's thumb.

And Spink, who is a little girl living in the same house with the man writing this story, and Skabootch, who is another little girl in the same house—both Spink and Skabootch are asking the question, "How can we tell corn fairies if we see 'em? If we meet a corn fairy how will we know it?" And this is the explanation the man gave to Spink who is older than Skabootch, and to Skabootch who is younger than Spink:

All corn fairies wear overalls. They work hard, the corn fairies, and they are proud. The reason they are proud is because they work so hard. And the reason they work so hard is because they have overalls.

But understand this. The overalls are corn gold cloth, woven from leaves of ripe corn mixed with ripe October corn silk. In the first week of the harvest moon coming up red and changing to yellow and silver the corn fairies sit by thousands between the corn rows weaving and stitching the clothes they have to wear next winter, next spring, next summer.

They sit cross-legged when they sew. And it is a law among them that each one must point the big toe at the moon while sewing the harvest moon clothes. When the moon comes up red as blood early in the evening they point their big toes slanting toward the east. Then toward midnight when the moon is yellow and halfway up the sky their big toes are only half slanted as they sit cross-legged sewing. And after midnight when the moon sails its silver disk high overhead and toward the west, then the corn fairies sit sewing with their big toes pointed nearly straight up.

If it is a cool night and looks like frost, then the laughter of the corn fairies is something worth hearing. All the time they sit sewing their next year clothes they are laughing. It is not a law they have to laugh. They laugh because they are half-tickled and glad because it is a good corn year.

And whenever the corn fairies laugh then the laugh comes out of the mouth like a thin gold frost. If you should be lucky enough to see a thousand corn fairies sitting between the corn rows and all of them laughing, you would laugh with wonder yourself to see the gold frost coming from their mouths while they laugh.

Travelers who have traveled far, and seen many things, say that if you know the corn fairies with a real knowledge you can always tell by the stitches in their clothes what state they are from.

In Illinois the corn fairies stitch fifteen stitches of ripe corn silk across the woven corn leaf cloth. In Iowa they stitch sixteen stitches, in Nebraska seventeen, and the farther west you go the more corn silk stitches the corn fairies have in the corn cloth clothes they wear.

In Minnesota one year there were fairies with a blue sash of corn-flowers across the breast. In the Dakotas the same year all the fairies wore pumpkin-flower neckties, yellow four-in-hands and yellow ascots. And in one strange year it happened in both the states of Ohio and Texas the corn fairies wore little wristlets of white morning glories.

The traveler who heard about this asked many questions and found out the reason why that year the corn fairies wore little wristlets of white morning glories. He said, "Whenever fairies are sad they wear white. And this year, which was long ago, was the year men were tearing down all the old zigzag rail fences. Now those old zigzag rail fences were beautiful for the fairies because a hundred fairies could sit on one rail and thousands and thousands of them could sit on the zigzags and sing pla-sizzy pla-sizzy, softer than an eye-wink, softer than a baby's thumb, all on a moonlit summer night. And they found out that year was going to be the last year of the zigzag rail fences. It made them sorry and sad, and when they are sorry and sad they wear white. So they picked the wonderful white morning glories running along the zigzag rail fences and made them into little wristlets and wore those wristlets the next year to show they were sorry and sad."

Of course, all this helps you to know how the corn fairies look in the evening, the night time and the moonlight. Now we shall see how they look in the day time.

In the day time the corn fairies have their overalls of corn gold cloth on. And they walk among the corn rows and climb the corn stalks and fix things in the leaves and stalks and ears of the corn. They help it to grow.

Each one carries on the left shoulder a mouse brush to brush away the field mice. And over the right shoulder each one has a cricket broom to sweep away the crickets. The brush is a whisk brush to brush away mice that get foolish. And the broom is to sweep away crickets that get foolish.

Around the middle of each corn fairy is a yellow belly belt. And stuck in this belt is a purple moon shaft hammer. Whenever the wind blows strong and nearly blows the corn down, then the fairies run out and take their purple moon shaft hammers out of their yellow belly belts and nail down nails to keep the corn from blowing down. When a rain storm is blowing up terrible and driving all kinds of terribles across the corn-field, then you can be sure of one thing. Running like the wind among the corn rows are the fairies, jerking their purple moon shaft hammers out of their belts and nailing nails down to keep the corn standing up so it will grow and be ripe and beautiful when the harvest moon comes again in the fall.

Spink and Skabootch ask where the corn fairies get the nails. The answer to Spink and Skabootch is, "Next week you will learn all about where the corn fairies get the nails to nail down the corn if you will keep your faces washed and your ears washed till next week."

And the next time you stand watching a big cornfield in late summer or early fall, when the wind is running across the green and silver, listen with your littlest and newest ears. Maybe you will hear the corn fairies going pla-sizzy pla-sizzy-sizzy, softer than an eye-wink, softer than a Nebraska baby's thumb.

By Carl Sandburg

THE LOST MERBABY

ONCE UPON A TIME there were a fisherman and his wife who lived in a little stone house by the sea. It was only a tiny house, but that was no matter, for it was so neat and pretty that no one could wish it to be different. There was a creeper climbing on the wall, and a pot of flowers in each little window; and in the little kitchen there was a tall old clock, and a dresser with rows of blue platters, and there were two chairs and a round table and a carved oak settle, and by the fireside was a wooden cradle.

But the cradle was empty.

"A baby would be so troublesome," said the fisherman's wife. "How should I keep my little house neat and clean with a baby to mind?"

"A baby may be very well in its way," said the fisherman, "but we are happier as we are."

Every day the fisherman set the sails of his boat and went out to sea, and every day his wife went busily about

133

and about the little house. And when her work was done she took her knitting and sat beside the door. She would watch the clouds wandering across the sky, and the waves breaking on the sand, and the sea-gulls wheeling above the cliffs, and then at last she would see the little boat come sailing into the bay, and she would run down to the beach to wave a welcome to the fisherman as soon as he should be near enough to see it.

"Who could be happier than we?" said they.

Now not so very far away there was another little home, but it could not be seen from the fisherman's house however hard one looked, for it lay under the sea. It was only a sandy hollow among the rocks, but it was set about so prettily with sea-weeds that it could not be bettered; and in the hollow lived four little mermaids and a merbaby.

The little mermaids loved the merbaby dearly, but for all that they often found her a great deal of trouble.

"Oh dear!" they would sigh, "how glad we shall be when she is grown up! She is sure to want us if we swim far away; and see how she plays with our sea-weeds and spoils them, and how she disturbs the sand in our little hollow when we have taken care to make it smooth. She is the most beautiful merbaby that could be," said they, "but she is rather a nuisance sometimes."

Now it happened one day that they found a round basket, such as the fishermen use, floating on the waves.

"Here is a cradle for our baby!" cried they. "When we want to play we can lay her inside and the waves will rock her to sleep."

So they took the basket and stopped up the holes and

lined it with sea-weed, and then they put the baby inside. The baby laughed and crowed with delight, and the mermaids swam to their home in the hollow among the rocks. They tidied the sea-weed and smoothed the sand upon the floor, and when they swam back to the cradle and peeped inside the baby was fast asleep.

"See how useful a cradle can be!" they cried. "Now we can swim away to play, for she will not need us for a long, long time."

But the little mermaids had forgotten all about the wind and the tide, and while they were gone the basket was carried far away. It was carried so far that at last it came to the foot of the cliffs near the fisherman's house, and there it rolled over and the merbaby slipped into a rock pool among the anemones.

When the fisherman came sailing home he saw something shining at the foot of the cliffs, and as soon as he had brought his boat to land he went to find out what it could be. And it was the merbaby's hair shining like polished gold in the sun.

"Good lack!" cried the fisherman. "What have we here?"

The merbaby was very tired of being all alone and it held out its little arms and cried to be taken up.

What was there left for the fisherman to do but to lift the baby from the pool and hurry home with it as fast as he could?

The fisherman's wife was just as surprised as he. She took the baby in her arms and hushed it and sang to it and coaxed the smile back into its face.

"How it laughs and crows!" cried she. "Look! its

eyes are the color of the sea, and what a dear little tail it has! It is nearly as beautiful as a real baby."

Then they pulled out the wooden cradle and put the baby inside, and there it lay crooning happily to itself. The fisherman's wife kept running to look at it and sing to it, and the baby laughed to see her and tangled its tiny hands in her hair; and the fisherman brought it shells for toys and threaded them in a chain.

That was all well enough, but away under the sea things were not going well at all. The little mermaids had come back from their playing and were looking everywhere for the baby.

"Have you seen our baby?" they asked the plaice who were lying almost buried in the sand.

The largest plaice flicked the sand off itself, for it is not polite to speak to anyone with only your eyes show- ing. "I have not seen any merbabies for quite a long time," it said, "but that may be because I only see things that are above me on account of my eyes. Perhaps you have noticed my eyes are both on one side of my head," he said proudly; "we are not like other fishes."

"Our baby was in a cradle," explained the little mer- maids. "It was only a round basket, but it rocked up and down on the waves and sent her to sleep as well as a real cradle could have done."

"Something that might have been your cradle floated overhead a little while ago," said the plaice. "That is the way it went. Now, if my eyes had been one on each side of my head I should never have seen it."

Away swam the little mermaids, but no sign of the merbaby could they find.

Presently they met a porpoise. "Have you seen our baby?" they asked, and told him all the tale.

"This is very sad business," said the porpoise. "Come with me and we will see what can be done."

So they swam away together and asked all the fishes they met for news of the merbaby. Not one of them had seen her, but they were so sorry for the little mermaids that they all joined in the search.

The fisherman stood at the door of his house. "There is no wind," said he. "But look how strangely the sea is tossing!"

How could he know the waves were made by the mermaids and fishes as they looked for the lost baby?

"Let us look for her in the rock pools under the cliffs," said the little mermaids.

The lobsters came out of their holes to see what was wanted.

"We have lost our baby," said the mermaids. "We used to think she was only a nuisance, but now she is lost we are sure we can never be happy until she is found." And they told them all about it.

The lobsters waved their legs in surprise. "How strange to mind losing a baby!" said they. "We never take any notice of our own."

The eldest lobster drew his claws thoughtfully among his feelers. "There is a nasty wicker thing over there that might be your baby's cradle," said he. "It looks too much like a lobster trap for my taste, but as you are not lobsters perhaps you will not mind going near it."

Away went the little mermaids, and among the rocks

they found the basket they had used for a cradle. But there was no baby in it.

A big crab came sidling toward them.

"You look as unhappy as though you had just cast your shells," he said. "What can be the matter?"

Then the mermaids told their sorrowful tale all over again and the crab was very sad for them. He went up and down the rock pools explaining what had happened to everything he met, to the fishes and the shrimps and the sea-horses and the whelks, but not one of them could tell him anything.

At last he came to the anemones. "Have you seen the merbaby?" he asked.

"How could we see it?" asked the anemones. "We have no eyes."

"How dreadful to have no eyes!" exclaimed the crab, popping his own in and out with horror at the thought.

"It is not dreadful at all," said the anemones. "We have dozens of feelers and they are much more sensible than eyes, we think."

"But I can't help being sorry for you," said the crab. "Why, even if the mermaids' baby was here you could not see her, and she is worth seeing, they say. Her hair is golden yellow and her eyes are the color of the sea."

"What does it matter what color hair may be as long as it is hair?" said the biggest anemone crossly. "There is a piece twisted around one of my feelers now and it is most uncomfortable."

The crab brought the mermaids to look. He twiddled his eyes in great excitement. "See what I have found!" cried he.

One of the mermaids gently untangled the hair, and it was so fine and so shining that it could have belonged to no one but a merbaby.

"Our baby has been here," said they, "but where can she be now?"

The puffins came waddling along to see what was the matter. They looked very wise indeed when they heard all there was to be told.

"Now we come to think of it . . ." began one.

"We don't think often, you know," said the others, "But when we do we think to some purpose."

"When we come to think of it," said the first puffin again, "we saw the fisherman pick a merbaby from that very pool where you were talking to the anemones."

"Oh, tell us what he did with her!" cried the little mermaids.

"He took it home, of course," said the puffins. "Your baby is not lost now because we have told you where she is."

And they waddled away.

"Alas!" cried the mermaids. "We are scarcely any better off than when we did not know where to find her. The fisherman's house lies far beyond the reach of the waves and we can only go where the waves can carry us."

Then the mermaids lifted themselves out of the water. "Sea-gulls! Sea-gulls!" they cried. "Fly to the fisherman's house and tell us what has become of our baby."

So the sea-gulls flew across the sand and round and round the fisherman's house.

"Surely there is a storm coming," said the fisherman, "else why should the gulls fly so near and cry so loudly?"

How could he know they had come to see what was done with the merbaby?

"The fisherman has put the baby in the cradle and his wife is tending it as though it was their own," said the sea-gulls when they came back. Then the little mermaids began to weep and sigh. "If they grow to love our baby they will never give her to us again," they sobbed.

"How the sea moans tonight!" said the fisherman. "There is surely a storm coming."

But when the merbaby heard it she began to wail and would not be comforted. "Hush, hush!" soothed the fisherman's wife and ran to pick the baby out of the cradle, but the baby only wailed the more pitifully.

"It is the moaning of the sea that distresses her," said the fisherman's wife. "I could almost weep myself for the sorrowful sound of it." And she shut her window.

How could she know the baby cried because she knew the sound was the mermaid's weeping?

Now, as was only to be expected, the news of the merbaby spread among the fisherfolk, and they one and all made some excuse to come tapping at the fisherman's door.

The fisherman's wife showed the baby proudly. "Look what beautiful eyes she has!" she would say. "And see her tiny hands and the shining of her hair!"

"Yes! yes!" said the fisherfolk, "but it is a great pity that she has a tail."

"It is a very beautiful tail," said the fisherman's wife.

"And there are so many people with feet that to have a tail is to be quite distinguished."

"A tail will be very awkward when she grows up," said the fisherfolk shaking their heads. "Why don't you put her back in the sea?"

"How cruel that would be!" cried the fisherman's wife. "She is far too tiny to care for herself. Besides, we love her too much to part with her now."

So the merbaby lay from day to day in the wooden cradle and cooed and crooned to itself. The fisherman would leave the mending of his nets to play with it, and his wife sang it gay little songs as she went about her work and ran to kiss its tiny hands and cover it with caresses.

"How could we think a baby was too much trouble!" cried they. "A baby is the loveliest thing in the world."

But the little mermaids in their home among the rocks had no heart to tend the sea-weeds, nor to smooth the sand upon the floor and make all neat and tidy; they had no heart to talk to the fishes, nor to play as they had done before.

"How could we think our baby a trouble?" cried they.

"Perhaps some day the fisherman's wife may tire of her," said the eldest.

So every day they swam to the foot of the cliffs. "Sea-gulls! Sea-gulls!" they cried. "Fly away and bring news of our baby!"

And every day the sea-gulls told how the fisherman's wife was fondling the baby as though it were her own.

"Alas! Alas!" wept the little mermaids. "We shall never see our baby again."

And every day when the merbaby heard the sound of their crying it began to wail and would not be comforted.

Then the fisherman would shake his head and ponder. " 'Tis strange," said he, "the moaning of the sea is as the sound of someone weeping."

His wife, too, would ponder on the strangeness as she tried to hush the baby's crying, and she pondered so long that in the end she could not help but find the truth.

"Hark!" cried she. "The baby weeps in answer to the sound. It is no moaning of the waves we hear, but the sorrowing of those who have lost her."

Then she lifted the baby from the cradle and kissed it on this cheek and that, and ran with it to the shore. There sat the little mermaids weeping, and when they saw the fisherman's wife they held out their arms.

"Give us our baby!" cried they. "We cannot play nor sing nor be happy till we have her again."

"Sorrow no more. Here is your baby," said the fisherman's wife, and she kissed it over and over and gave it to them.

But when she came back to the little house and saw the empty cradle she fell to weeping as sadly as ever the little mermaids had done.

"It is my turn to sorrow now," said she.

And the fisherman could find no words to comfort her, for he was as sad as she.

But the little mermaids were happier than they had ever been before, and they swam up and down with the baby to tell all the sea-creatures of their good fortune and to thank them for their help.

"You look much happier than you did," said the crabs," but, "It is rather hard to understand family life," said the puffins. "We think a great deal of our babies, but of course they are much nicer than mer-babies because they have down and feathers."

"And wings," added the sea-gulls. "We cannot imagine what use arms can be."

The anemones shut up as soon as the mermaids came near. "We are glad you have found the baby, since it pleases you so much," said they. "But do take her away or we shall get hair all over us again."

The fishes looked at the merbaby very curiously. "Her tail is very fine," they said, "but a fin or two would improve her."

"Or having both her eyes on one side of her head," said the plaice.

"But of course if you are satisfied with her there is nothing more to be said," added the porpoise, and waved his flipper as he swam away.

The little mermaids hugged and kissed their baby. "Fancy thinking she is not perfect!" they cried. "Only the fisherman and his wife know how to love her as we do, and now they are sorrowful because we have taken her back again."

So sometimes they swam to the little bay and called, and the fisherman's wife would hear them and come running to the edge of the sea. Then the mermaids would give her the baby, and she would sit on the rocks to play with it and fondle it.

"It is so lonely now that the cradle is empty," she would sigh for sympathy. "We will come again soon," said they.

But one day when they swam to the bay, though they called and called, the fisherman's wife did not come running out to greet them.

"What can have befallen her?" they asked one another.

Then they lifted themselves out of the water. "Sea-gulls! Sea-gulls!" they cried. "Fly away across the sand and tell us why the fisherman's wife does not hear us calling."

So the sea-gulls flew round and round the little house as they had done before.

"You need not sorrow longer for the loneliness of the fisherman's wife," said they. "There is another baby in the cradle; it has feet instead of a tail and its eyes are the color of the sky, but she does not seem to mind, nor does the fisherman. They have not heard you call because they are too happy to hear anything but their own joy."

Then the little mermaids swam back to the hollow among the rocks.

"Now we can be happy all day long," said they, "for there is no one left lonely and sorrowing. And some day we will go again to the bay and the fisherman's wife will show us her baby and we will love it next to our own."

By Margaret Baker

THE SONG OF THE LITTLE DONKEY

COLUMBUS, a small gray donkey, was being made ready for a journey. He stood very still while his master put his bridle on him and hitched him to the shafts of the cart, but when at last his little bell was fastened to his bridle he shook his head, so that the bell sent forth a series of tinkling notes. Columbus liked this sound: it made him feel cheerful.

"Just a minute now and we'll be off," his master said to him. "But first I have to load the cart." Columbus moved his ears back and forth to show he understood, and then shut his eyes while he waited.

But though his eyes were shut, he knew just what was happening. His master was carrying chairs from the house and putting them onto the cart. They were fine, dark chairs, so beautifully polished that they looked like satin, and Columbus knew that when the word to start was given he must walk very carefully, so that these chairs would not joggle against each other and get marred and scratched.

Several times each year the little donkey and his master made a journey from the small house by the side of the road, to a great city not far away. The cart was always filled with chairs when they started and always empty when they returned, for Columbus' master was such a fine cabinet-maker that he never had any trouble at all in selling the things he made.

And chairs were the things he liked best to make. "They are so friendly," he told Columbus, "for they are always inviting us to sit down and rest. And they provide a seat at the table when mealtime comes. The world would be a dreary place without chairs."

The old cabinet-maker often talked like this to his donkey, because he lived alone and had no one else to talk to. And Columbus always listened politely. The cabinet-maker and his donkey were good friends and got along well together, but there was one thing about which they could *not* agree and that was—roads. Each time they started to the city, the old cabinet-maker wanted to go straight along and get there as soon as possible. But Columbus wanted to explore, and always tried to turn in at the lanes and byways, because he felt sure he would find something there that was new and interesting.

Whenever he did this his master would give the lines a jerk and say: "No, no, Columbus. We have no time now to discover new places. We must get to town so that I can sell my chairs." And Columbus would have to give up the lanes and byways and go straight along.

Today, when the cart was loaded, the old cabinet-maker climbed into the driver's seat and picked up the lines as he always did. "Giddap!" he said, making a little clucking noise, and Columbus opened his eyes, shook a few tinkles from his bell and trotted off.

The old cabinet-maker turned his head for a last look at his house. "It's a funny thing," he told his little donkey, "the way I feel today. I love my home better than any place on earth. I love the hills around it; I love Butterfly Brook that runs just behind it; and I love the trees and flowers that grow beside it. I don't like cities and never did—they are too crowded. But today I am glad to be going to the city. I am lonesome for the sound of children's voices. I want to hear them laugh and watch them play. Maybe it's because it's spring that I feel like this. Maybe the spring has got into my blood."

Columbus put his ears back and listened. There was a glad note in his master's voice that he had never heard before, and it made the little donkey so happy that he opened his mouth and sang. At least he *meant* it for singing, though really it was not so very musical.

"You understand how I feel, don't you, old fellow?" laughed the cabinet-maker. "Well, I'll tell you something else. Today, after I sell my chairs, I am going to find some place where children are playing, and we are going to stop and watch them, you and I. We are going to watch them even though it makes us late in getting back to Butterfly Brook."

Columbus tried to pay attention to what his master was saying, but his mind wandered. For just ahead he saw a shady lane running off from the highway. It was an inviting lane and the little donkey hastened his steps.

He would turn in there, he thought, and have a look at it. Surely on a day like this, when the air smelled so good and the grass was so green, his master would not mind stopping for a little while.

But when he turned toward the entrance to the lane his master gave the usual jerk on the lines. "Not today, Columbus," he said. "Someday when we have more time I'll let you explore all you want to; but not now." And so, once again, the little donkey had to go straight along.

"Here's the place we'll stop first," the old cabinet-maker said, when they had reached the city and traveled along one of its wide streets until they came to a handsome house. Columbus stopped obediently and looked around him.

The house stood well back on a beautiful lawn, and was surrounded by great trees and beds of blooming flowers. It looked even more inviting than the shady lane, he thought, and he wished he could go in and nibble some grass. But around this lawn was a high iron fence and there seemed to be no way of getting through it.

"Stand still, Columbus," the cabinet-maker told him, "and I'll go and ring the bell, there by the gate. I hope there's someone at home."

Climbing down from the cart, he pushed the bell, and at once a tall servant hurried forward.

"Good morning," said the old cabinet-maker. "If your master is at home, I should like to show him some chairs."

The tall servant looked at the cabinet-maker, and

then at Columbus, and then at the cart. "My master is at home," he said, "but I don't believe you had better try to sell him anything today. He's not in a very good humor."

"Oh, that doesn't matter," the cabinet-maker answered. "He will be in a good humor when he sees my chairs."

The tall servant opened the gate. "Very well," he said. "You may drive your little donkey up to the house. You'll find my master on the front porch, but don't blame *me* if he's cross with you."

Columbus could scarcely believe it when the cabinet-maker took him by the bridle and led him through the gate. He was going into the beautiful yard after all, he thought, and at once he started for the flower beds.

"Keep your donkey off the grass!" shouted the tall servant. And he sounded so stern that Columbus knew it was no use; he would have to go straight along.

"Good morning," said Columbus' master to the man who was sitting on the porch. "I am the cabinet-maker of Butterfly Brook, and I should like to show you my chairs."

"I don't want to see them," growled the man on the porch. "I have no use for any more chairs, because I live alone."

"I live alone, too," the cabinet-maker told him, "but I like to have lots of chairs around me. Chairs are good friends."

"Hump!" growled the man again. "I don't care for friends."

"That's too bad," said the cabinet-maker, shaking his

head and looking off across the wide lawn to where a fountain sparkled in the sunshine. "I should think you'd want to have someone to enjoy all this beauty with you. This yard would be a fine place for children to play in."

"Children!" shouted the man, jumping to his feet. "They would trample my grass and pick my flowers and throw stones in my fountain! They're a nuisance, children are. Look there," he went on, pointing across the lawn to the side fence. "See those children? They come here every day and stare at me and my lawn, but I never let them in."

The old cabinet-maker looked at the children pressing their faces against the fence. "Dear, dear," he said sadly. "I don't see how you have the heart to keep them out. One reason I came to town today was to see children. I wanted to watch them play, and to hear them shout and laugh."

The cabinet-maker's voice was so sad that Columbus stopped admiring the soft green grass, and shook his little bell as hard as he could, to make things sound more cheerful. And when he did this, the children outside the yard broke into peals of laughter.

"Do it again, little donkey. Shake your bell again!" they cried.

Columbus not only shook his bell again for them, but he moved his ears back and forth and, after a moment, he lifted his head and sang as he had done that morning on the road.

At this, the children laughed so hard that their voices were like hundreds of silver bells all being rung at the same time.

The man on the porch leaned forward and listened to them. "Well, I declare," he said. "That sounds pretty, doesn't it?"

"Children's laughter is the prettiest sound in the world," the old cabinet-maker told him. "Why won't you let them come into your yard and play for a while? They won't hurt anything, and it will make them so happy that they will laugh a great deal. You'd like that, wouldn't you?"

"I believe I would," the man on the porch said slowly. "Somehow it sounds like spring, and makes me happier than I have been in years."

As he finished speaking he touched a bell on the table beside him. "Open the gates and invite the children in," he said when the tall servant appeared. "And then go and tell the cook to prepare a great deal of food —cookies and other things that children like. We'll have lunch out here on the lawn. And don't forget to fetch some food for the little donkey."

The old cabinet-maker tried to tell the man on the porch how fine he thought this was, but his words were drowned by the shouts and laughter of the children as they came trooping through the gate.

"Thank you for letting us in," they called. "We think you have the loveliest house and lawn in the world!"

"Do you?" said the man, smiling in spite of himself. "Well, make yourselves at home. There's a little stream at the back of the lawn that you might like to wade in."

"A stream! A stream!" cried the children, dashing away. "We're going to wade in a stream!"

When they had gone, the man on the porch turned to

the old cabinet-maker. "I have changed my mind about your chairs," he said. "I am going to buy all of them— for the children to sit on when they eat their lunch. Unload them from the cart, and turn your little donkey loose to graze on my lawn. He ought to have some pleasure, too."

Columbus could scarcely wait until his master unhitched him. And when this was done he walked off across the lawn, nibbling as he went. Nothing like this had ever happened to him before, and he was so happy that he kicked his heels to show how glad he was to be alive on this fine spring morning.

And a fine spring morning it was for everyone. The children played leap frog and tag and blind-man's buff, while the two men sat on the porch and watched them. They rode Columbus up and down the garden paths and, at last, they all sat down to such a luncheon as they had never eaten before.

When they had eaten all they could hold, they gathered round the master of the house to thank him and say good-by. "I'm glad you have had a good time," he told them. "But don't thank *me* for it. The thanks belong partly to the cabinet-maker of Butterfly Brook, and partly to the springtime. But mostly they belong to the little donkey, Columbus. He made you laugh, and your laughter made me happy. And so I let you in."

"Thank you, Columbus!" shouted the children, patting the little donkey. "Thank you ever so much."

"Listen," said the master of the house, holding up his hand for quiet. "I have just had a wonderful idea. Each day, from now on, I shall leave my gate open so that you can come into the yard and play. And whenever the cabinet-maker and his little donkey come to town, we will have lunch on the lawn as we did today."

At this, the children jumped up and down and clapped their hands and the old cabinet-maker went over and put his arms about Columbus' neck and gave him a big hug.

When the last child had scampered out through the great iron gates, Columbus' master hitched him to the donkey cart, said good-by to the man on the porch, and started off toward home, feeling happier than he ever had before.

The little donkey was happy too. It had been a wonderful day for him, and he shook his bell gaily as he trotted along over the country roads. But after a while he slackened his pace. And then he came to a full stop. He had reached the shady lane that he had so long wanted to explore. What if he went in there now? he wondered. Would his master stop him?

"All right, Columbus," the old cabinet-maker said with a laugh. "You deserve a little treat as a reward for the way you behaved today. You made a good many people happy because you sang at just the right time. So go ahead and enjoy yourself. Butterfly Brook will be there when we get back."

Without waiting a moment, Columbus crossed the road and turned in at the shady lane. And this time there was no jerk on the lines to stop him!

By Alice Crew Gall and Fleming Crew

THE GOLDFISH

THE FIRST THING Mrs. Harman saw when she opened the nursery door was the cat crouched upon the table, tense and motionless, watching Peter, the goldfish, in his glass bowl.

"Shoo! You're a bad cat! Shoo!" she cried, stamping her foot.

The cat shot her a quick, guilty glance, and was gone like a shadow through the doorway.

"Shoo!" cried Mrs. Harman after her, and turned to her son.

"You shouldn't let the cat in here, Don. She'll get Peter."

Seven-year-old Don was seated on the floor struggling with a shoe lace.

"Now—" he began, "now—I didn't see her, Mother. I've been tying my laces. Mother, will you telephone for Craig to come over and play? You know I was dis-

appointed yesterday and day before, and— Will you,
Mother?"

"Have you spotted today?" asked Mrs. Harman.

"A little jelly spot at lunch. It was very little, and—
now—I didn't spot at breakfast."

"Very well," said Mrs. Harman, "I'll see if Craig
can come."

But Craig could not come and for the third successive
day Don was disappointed.

"You see it's near Christmas, dear," the mother explained, "and all the boys are busy."

"I'm not busy," Don told her wistfully.

"I'll tell you what you can do." Mrs. Harman spoke
brightly. "You can write a letter to Santa Claus. Won't
that be fun? It's only three weeks to Christmas, and
he'll be wondering what you want."

"I don't know what I want." His tone was listless.

"Snow shoes?" she suggested.

"Oh, I don't know."

"A sled?"

Don brightened. The sled gave him an idea.

"I know what. I want a brother. Not a little one. A
regular brother. Big, you know, with lots and lots of
teeth."

"They're hard to get in those large sizes," Mrs. Harman said, "and it's so near Christmas they must be
pretty well picked over. The best plan is to write to
Santa about it. Here's paper with lines, and a nice sharp
pencil."

Don sat down at his little desk and in a round laborious hand began to write. The letter, when completed, ran uphill and down and read as follows:

> Dear Santy
>   i am well i hope you are well i would like a boy with teeth the biggest one you can spair for a brother
>
>   yours truly
>   D Harman

The paper, originally white, was changed to gray in the process of writing, and smudges had somehow been communicated to Don's face and hands.

"Now," said his mother, "we'll send it."

"Do you think he'll get it tonight?"

"He ought to."

They moved to the fireplace; Mrs. Harman touched a match to the letter and they watched it burn to a black, wavering crisp, and disappear.

That night Mrs. Harman told her husband she was worried about Don.

"He needs boys to play with," she said.

"There seem to be plenty of boys in the neighborhood," Mr. Harman replied.

"Yes, but they're not his age. Craig is Don's age but he lives almost a mile away, and Don doesn't see much of him except at school. I was thinking—" She sighed and broke off.

"What were you thinking, dear?"

"I was thinking of little Fred, your sister Helen's boy. He's just three months older than Don, you know."

"Isn't he getting on all right at Aunt Henrietta's?"

"I suppose so. But your Aunt Henrietta is growing old, and—well, it's not as if he had a father and a mother."

"Look here, Sallie," her husband said, "you've got something in your mind. What is it? Do you feel that we ought to—" He did not finish the question, for his wife was nodding at him, smiling.

Meanwhile, up in the nursery, Don was eating his supper and his nurse was watching every mouthful.

"Will you never learn to be a little gentleman?" she demanded. "Look at your napkin. One mass of jelly. I'll have to show it to your mother. A big boy like you, and Christmas so near, too!"

"I don't care," said Don, defiantly.

"One mass of jelly," she repeated. "I'll certainly have to show it to your mother." So saying, she took the offending napkin from the boy's neck and left the room.

"I don't care!" he said again, and moved slowly over to the table where, with chin on hands, he sat and gazed at Peter, the goldfish, in his bowl.

He was not thinking of the bowl; he was not staring into it as the cat had stared, but through it at something far beyond—just what, I do not know. Nor do I know how long he sat there gazing beyond the glass and the water and the weeds and the little castle and even Peter himself. It may have been a long time or a short time, but whether it was long or short his attention was at last attracted by a tiny squeaky sound.

He listened and the sound grew plainer. Somehow it

suggested words—words which at first seemed to come from so far away you couldn't understand them. Then suddenly he realized that the sound was coming from inside the goldfish bowl.

Don looked at Peter. He was not swimming now, but was lying motionless, nose pressed against the glass, staring out into the nursery. His mouth was moving. It opened and shut, opened and shut, and the squeaky little sound continued.

Don leaned forward and turned one ear to the bowl. The sound grew plainer.

"Is that you, Peter?"

"Yes! Yes! Yes! Yes!" the little squeak responded instantly.

"Don't talk so fast," said Don. "What do you want?"

"Help me out!"

"All right," said the boy, but when he dipped his hand into the water, Peter darted to his castle.

"Not like that! You'll drown me!"

"You can't drown a fish."

"Have you ever been a fish?" asked Peter sharply.

"Of course not."

"Then what do you know about it?"

"I'm a boy, and a boy knows more than a fish."

"He thinks he does!" As Peter spoke, four round bubbles issued from his mouth and followed one another to the surface, where they broke with a chuckling sound: "Ha-ha-ha-ha!"

Don did not like to be laughed at by grown-ups, let alone fish.

"If that's how you're going to talk," he said, "I won't help you."

"Wait a minute! I want to tell you something. Will you promise not to tell?"

"Yes, what?"

"Put your ear close."

Don hesitated. "No tricks, now! If you jump up and nip my ear, or yell in it, or anything like that, I'll grab you out and have you cooked."

Peter looked shocked. "I wouldn't think of playing tricks on you," he said. "May I float belly-up if I would."

"Well, go ahead, then."

"I'm ashamed to tell it." The little fish looked very red. "It happened through my messy way of eating. They all warned me—my mother, my aunt, my nurse —but I—"

"Your nurse? Fish don't have nurses."

"That was before I *was* a fish. It was when I was a boy."

"Were you a boy?" Don was hardly able to believe his ears.

"Yes."

"What happened to you?"

"Spilling did it—spilling food on my napkin and the tablecloth."

"A fish hasn't napkins and tablecloths."

"Of course not; that's just it," said Peter. "That's how I happened to become a fish. They told me I didn't deserve a napkin on a lap. They told me I ought to be

kept in water. But I never dreamed I'd come to this."
A little groan came from the bowl.

"Don't you like to be a fish?" asked Don. "You don't
have to go to school."

"Swimming was fun at first," said Peter, "but I'm
awfully tired of it. The bowl's so round—one side just
like another. And when my nose tickles I miss my hands
terribly. Really there's nothing as nice as being a boy
with hands and a clean white napkin and a lap."

"I wish I could get you out," said Don, "but you'd
flip around on the table and die, wouldn't you?"

"Yes, there's only one way to turn me back into a
boy."

"How?"

"Another boy must do it for me. He has to keep his
napkin clean for a week."

"A whole *week?*" Don gasped.

"Only a week. After that I'll be his brother. I can
make box kites, and we could dig caves, and keep rabbits, and get some garter snakes, and some—"

"I'll try!" exclaimed Don. "I'll try like everything!"

"Oh, thanks!" said Peter. "I can't tell you what it's
going to mean to me!" He looked through the other side
of the bowl at the calendar on the wall. "This is the
seventeenth. You begin tomorrow morning. You only
have to keep your napkin clean until the twenty-fourth,
and then—why, my scales! That will be Christmas Eve!
How jolly!"

"If I should spot just once," Don asked, "would that
spoil everything?"

Peter quivered.

"Don't speak of such a thing!" he begged. "And remember, you are not to breathe a word of what I've told you. If you tell, the whole thing will be—"

"There you are!" cried the nurse, appearing in the doorway. "You're supposed to be in bed. Now, I'll have to tell your mother."

Don turned and blinked at her. Then he arose, shuffled over to his bed, slipped out of his bathrobe and tumbled in.

The week dragged along. The Christmas preparations, the mysterious packages, the crackling of wrapping paper Don heard through the closed door of his mother's room—none of these things occupied his mind as they had the year before. His thoughts were fixed on the tremendous task of freeing Peter. Somehow, somehow he must manage to keep his napkin spotless for a week. He must!

At first he thought the safest plan would be to go without meals altogether; but when he tried it Nurse scolded, and besides he got hungry. His one idea when he sat down to eat was to keep from splattering and spilling. When there was meat with gravy he cut it into little pieces with the utmost care, never allowing his knife or fork to slip. He spread his apple sauce and jelly very thin upon his bread and butter, and saw to it that none was hanging to the edges. He pushed his glass of water or milk far back from the table's edge, and when he drank he took the smallest swallows. As for cereals, eggs and soft, custardy desserts, he ate such little spoonfuls that Nurse could not believe her eyes, and wondered "what ailed the child."

To his surprise he found the task less difficult as meals and days went by. There were little tricks, he learned, to keep from making spots, and the more you practiced them the better you got. But as the work grew easier, responsibility increased. It would be awful to dribble something on his napkin after having kept it clean three days . . . four days . . . five days.

When Nurse was absent from the room he would go to Peter's bowl and whisper reassuring words; but Peter never spoke again, although he looked at Don with sad, appealing eyes, especially during meals.

At breakfast on the seventh day Peter was plainly nervous. At luncheon he was more excited still. And when night came his fins and tail were all a-quiver as he gazed through the glass wall.

This made it hard for Don. He tried not to watch Peter. At lunch he made a slip with some potato but caught it in his hand before it reached his napkin. As this occurred, a great big bubble rose like a sigh from Peter's mouth.

Having safely disposed of the last spoonful of custard, Don gave a joyful cry. He removed his napkin, and raised it like a fair white banner.

"Look!" he cried. "A whole week, and not a single spot!"

"Now, I do declare!" exclaimed the nurse, who thought he was showing it to her. "How good little boys do get when Christmas is coming. It shows what you can do. Look at it, all clean and white! I'll have to show it to your mother." She took the napkin and left the room.

Don placed his elbows on the table, rested his chin in his hands, and gazed intently at the goldfish bowl.

"Peter!" he whispered softly.

But Peter only swam about, as much a goldfish as he ever was.

Don was disappointed. He had hoped the thing would happen after supper, while Nurse was there. He had imagined Peter rising from the water, changing shape, and dropping off his scales—until he stood a full-fledged boy. How Nurse's eyes would bulge! But though this didn't happen, Don never lost his faith; he only sat there wondering how and when the change would come.

"There you are!" cried the nurse, appearing in the doorway. "You're supposed to be in bed. Now, I'll have to go and tell your mother."

Don skipped over to the bed and leaped in.

"You such a big boy," Nurse went on, "and this Christmas Eve, and your stocking hanging in the living room! I'll really have to tell your mother." She was muttering and puttering around the nursery as he fell asleep.

"Shoo! Shoo! You bad cat!" It was Mrs. Harman's voice.

Don turned over in his bed and squinted at the early morning light.

"Merry Christmas, dear!"

"Merry Christmas, Mother!" He sat up suddenly and stared with wide eyes at the goldfish bowl.

"Why, Peter's gone!" he cried, jumping out of bed.

"Never mind that now," said his mother. "You must hurry down and see all the lovely things Santa left in the living room. Get into your bathrobe and slippers. Hurry, son!"

As she spoke Don heard a motor in the driveway. Then the slam of the front door and his father's voice in the hall below.

"Dad! Dad!" he shouted, rushing down the stairs.

On the bottom step he stopped abruptly. There, holding tightly to his father's hand, stood another boy, a boy just Don's size. He grinned, and as he did so Don saw that he had lots and lots of teeth.

The two stared at each other for a moment. Then Don moved slowly forward.

"We can make box kites," he said, "and dig caves, and keep rabbits and—"

"And garter snakes," put in the other boy.

—Condensed by Permission of the Author

By Julian Street

THE BEAN BOY

IN THE YEARS between this and that, there lived a little boy named String, because he used strings for shoelaces: a red string in one shoe and a green string in the other. Now, String lived in a Lima bean field. And when the Lima beans were green he picked them, put them in sacks, and took sackfuls of green Lima beans into town to sell, so he was called the Bean Boy.

One morning, when the town looked yellow and dusty as a Chinaman sitting in the sun, String stopped at the Governor's Palace to leave a sack of green Lima beans for the Governor's little daughter, who had ordered large, flat beans in her soup. She was called Dulce because, although her eyes were dark and sad, her smile was sweet and gaudy as a dulce.

Now, Dulce was leaning out of the palace window watching for her sack of large, flat beans, when the Bean Boy came whistling into the patio of the palace, tripping over his red and green shoestrings, always coming undone. Dulce ran downstairs, fetching a pan, so the Bean Boy could dump out his sack of big, flat beans. Then the Bean Boy sat down to tie up his green and red shoestrings. By this time, the Governor's little daughter had stopped smiling, so String noticed how sad and dark her eyes looked.

"It must be nice," she said, "to live in a bean field and bring sacks of beans into town."

"It is nice. And I am always finding things on the way in and out."

"What kind of things?" asked Dulce eagerly.

"Oh, tree toads and moonstones and old Spanish pesos and Indian beads and kelp for dress-up helmets."

At that the Governor's little daughter smiled her gaudy smile.

"Maybe," she asked, "maybe you can find my dream for me?"

"Maybe I can," said the Bean Boy.

"I dreamed," Dulce said, "that my father was not a governor any more and didn't need to worry about revolutions. I dreamed that he was an organ-grinder man, with a tiny tomboy monkey from Central America."

The Bean Boy nodded. "I know. And you went with him, walking through bean fields, singing 'Maria Mia.'

And people filled your cup with pennies. And you made a bonfire every night, popping stacks of corn."

"Yes, yes, and my father didn't worry any more about revolutions. Just think, he didn't need to worry about revolutions."

Dulce opened her sad eyes wide open. "But I only dreamed it once. Now, do you think you can find my dream again for me?"

"Of course." And the Bean Boy took a moonstone, an Indian bead, a tree toad, and an old Spanish coin out of his pocket, spreading them on the tile floor in front of Dulce.

"Of course," said the Bean Boy. "I can find anything on my way in and out."

"Then," said Dulce, "I intend to marry you when you grow up tall."

At that the Bean Boy went whistling away, tying up the green and red strings, always coming undone.

Next morning at sunup, String was picking big, flat beans and putting them into sacks, when a Goblin came hurrying up a bean row and tipped his bean-leaf cap, stuck round with oak holly berries, green and red ones.

"Could you possibly spare two good-sized beans this morning?" the Goblin inquired politely. "The finest baby of our king will be christened in sixteen minutes, and I find myself without a christening present."

The polite Goblin bowed as best he could, for he was a thick little person. He had a wide, cheerful mouth and looked hearty in his seaweed suit.

The Bean Boy was red with surprise.

"Two beans, you want two beans!" he kept saying.

"If you can spare them, please," said the polite Goblin.

"Fill your cap," String told him. And he helped the Goblin pick eight or ten fine Lima beans.

"While you are here," the Bean Boy said hurriedly, "I wish you would tell me where to find the dream of the Governor's little girl, Dulce."

The polite Goblin bowed in spite of his girth. "Certainly," he said, "all dreams are kept in the Cave of Yawns down by the sea, two leagues south, two leagues west. And there you are. But remember not to yawn in the cave. For every time anyone yawns, the cave gets bigger and bigger, opening up at the end. And if you go to sleep in there, you will never wake up. Then," asked the Goblin, "who will pick the beans, put them in sacks, and take sacksful of Lima beans into town?"

He went away, looking surprised at his own question.

At that the Bean Boy hurried off, going two leagues south, two leagues west. And there he was at the Cave of Yawns down by the sea. There were dark chests along the walls of the cave. Rich, hand-carved chests, out of which the Sandman was selecting dreams. He stood at the farthest end of the cave, throwing a handful of sand into his bag and then a dream. Just like that—a handful of sand and then a dream. "Whoo, whoo," called the Bean Boy, but when the Sandman looked up the Bean Boy yawned.

The cave opened up at the end just as the polite Goblin said it would. The Sandman was leagues farther away now than he had been before.

The Bean Boy began to feel sleepy now. His hands went to sleep, his feet went to sleep, and every step pricked like pins and needles. Then the Bean Boy yawned again, and the cave opened up at the end, just as the polite Goblin said it would. The Sandman and the rich, hand-carved chests were so far away now they looked like dots on a dotted line. Then the Bean Boy's ears went to sleep. After that his nose went to sleep. But he said to himself, "Even though I feel all over like a pincushion, I must keep my two eyes awake and walk with my feet asleep until I can nudge the Sandman and get Dulce's dream for her."

So the Bean Boy walked with his feet asleep, his hands asleep, his ears asleep, and his nose asleep. But the jolt of tripping over his shoestrings kept his eyes awake, until he nudged the Sandman.

"Please," he said stifling an enormous yawn, "may I have Dulce's dream?"

"What was it like?" asked the Sandman. "And about how long?"

"Hurry," cried the Bean Boy, "I'm going to yawn again."

"Did it have a monkey and an organ grinder in it and a song called 'Maria Mia'?"

"Yes, yes." The Bean Boy's eyes were closing. But he tripped over his shoestrings and opened them again with a terrible effort.

"It's an old dream," said the Sandman, "almost worn out, so I suppose you may as well have it." He shook the dream out, sticking his finger through the holes. The Bean Boy's eyes closed again. He shook himself, saying, "My hands are asleep, my feet are asleep, and so are my nose and ears, but though I feel like a pin-cushion all over, I must keep my eyes open." So he opened his eyes. The Sandman handed him the old, tattered dream, and the Bean Boy ran from the cave with his feet asleep, his hands asleep, his ears asleep, and his nose asleep. He was really asleep all over, except that his eyes were awake from the jolt of tripping over his shoestrings, a red string in one shoe and a green string in the other.

Next morning, before dawn, the little boy started for town with his bean sacks and the old dream, which looked as if it were falling to pieces. When he came near the gates of the town, he heard guns. At that, sol-diers came out, singing lustily, "Maria Mia." The Bean Boy went into town. The palace was in ruins, and there on some stones sat the Governor and Dulce.

"We have had another revolution," Dulce told the Bean Boy, who noticed how sad and dark her eyes were.

Just then a soldier came running up and spoke low to the Governor.

"Your Excellency must go away at once in disguise!"

Whereupon the Bean Boy handed Dulce the old worn dream.

And so it happened that the Governor disguised him-self as an organ-grinder man, owning a tiny tomboy monkey from Central America. He and Dulce and the Bean Boy wandered up and down the world joyously, making bonfires every night and popping stacks of corn. After they had wandered from one end of the world to the other, the Bean Boy married Dulce one night by a big campfire, and they inherited great stretches of bean fields, where they lived happily for years and years and years and years.

By Monica Shannon

THE BROWNIE IN THE HOUSE

O PROVIDENCE!

When all the world was young and green,
And babies grew, the rocks between,
    And slumbered in the shade;
Then fox and hen and cat and mouse;
All dwelt together in one house,
    And had one serving maid.—
O Providence, O Providence, why must such pictures
    fade?

In those good days the brownie-men
Were digging gold in every glen,
    And slept on every bough;
For her who kept her house aright

They washed and scrubbed and made things bright,
    I cannot tell you how.—
O Providence, O Providence, where are the brownies
    now?

IN THOSE DAYS, when the fox and the cock were bosom
friends, there lived a man at the edge of the green forest
who had one fair daughter, and no child else. The
mother was dead some time since, and the father and
daughter lived all alone, but for all that they prospered
exceedingly, and life was for them as smooth as new
butter. There was a sound enough reason for all this:
there was a brownie in that house, and to say that is
almost as much as to clink the money between one's
fingers.

The daughter got out of bed at four o'clock, and
baked and brewed and spun and sewed; the father went
out into the wood and gathered faggots, and came back to
his own dooryard and planted turnips. Every night the
daughter took a fresh bowl, and put steaming porridge
in it, with a lump of butter as big as a goose egg floating
on the top, and set it by the hearth; in the morning she
found the pans scoured so that she could see her face in
them, the good bread was ready for the oven, and the
yarn was piled in heaps for the weaver; the faggots
were trimmed, and the turnips were gathered and
washed and left in a basin. And the bowl was empty on
the hearth. So they had padded pockets and light
hearts; but Luck lays no eggs if her throat is cut, and
so the man found out. You shall hear:

One time the farmer went to the town to trade, and
was gone three days and a day; when he came back, he

had a wife with him, and a new daughter to boot, for he had married a widow with a daughter of her own. The woman was as gentle as a breeze in summer, and the stepsister was a good-looking body, and pleasant-spoken enough, but from that day there was nothing but curdled cream in that house. The daughter worked as hard as ever, but she got no help from the stepsister, who sat with her hands folded and counted the flies on the wall. And as for the bowl on the hearth: scraps from the kitchen with a lump of fat on top were good enough for any brownie—that was what the stepmother said.

After that, when the daughter came into the kitchen at four o'clock, she found the pans rusted and black, the good bread flat and lumpy, and the yarn tangled and torn; the faggots were scattered on the floor, and the turnips were left where they were gathered. So the poor girl had to work twice as hard as ever she had before, with no more thanks than the bees gave the bear when they found him stealing honey; but she cared less for that than she did for the good brownie, who was cheated of his due as the luck of the house.

Well, the time came when the daughter could stand it no longer; so one night at the first cock-crow, when all the household was asleep, she went into the kitchen and poked the fire into a blaze, for she was going to make porridge for the brownie, say what they might.

"Tut! tut!" says one among the ashes, "and what do you here, troublemaker?" And out pops the brownie in his red cap, with ashes in his whiskers and his furry ears.

"Hush!" says the daughter of the house; "tongues were made for other things besides talking! I crave your pardon for disturbing your rest, but I have porridge to make." The brownie cut a caper, as merry as a red leaf in the October wind; and the maiden took a blue bowl, and after she had mixed the porridge, she put it in the bowl with a wooden spoon and a lump of butter as big as a goose egg, and set it in the ingle. Then she was all for hurrying away without a look over her shoulder, for the good little people have no love of those who spy upon them; but the brownie waved his wooden spoon at her, and snorted, that being the only sound he could make, since his mouth was crammed with porridge.

"Come back!" says he presently; "that is an ill master who gives a horse nothing but straw. Look you, if a traveler passes by this way, and offers you aught from his store, do you make free to ask for that which pleases you."

So the maid thanked the brownie as gravely as if he had given her a ring with rubies in it; but then, she had not put chips in that basket in hopes of finding them turned into guldens—so she was perfectly satisfied.

The next day the pans were scoured so that one would have said they were golden, the good bread was sweet and freshly kneaded, and the yarn was rolled in skeins ready for the weaving; the faggots were trimmed, and the turnips were washed and left in a basin. And the bowl was empty on the hearth. The daughter put it away and said nothing about it; and every night thereafter she crept into the kitchen and set the porridge in the ingle.

Well, it was but a short time afterward that the house-father must needs stumble over a pile of faggots and sprain his ankle; and now the daughter must go to town and do the trading, for the other two were needed at home. So off she set with a basket on her arm, as neat and fresh as a meadow daisy; and while she was gone the stepsister was to do the work she attended to when she was at home.

Dear me! what a stir Lazy-bones made about it! She did no more than peel the turnips and wash the pots, but the cat by the fire could have done as well, and with less grumbling. The turnips were boiled to shreds, the cloth was set on the table awry, and the pots were hung on the first nail she saw, with streaks of grease and soot upon them.

That night, about the first cock-crow, the stepsister woke with a squeak, for she thought somebody was pinching her. Sure enough, her arms were the color of blackberries and smoke, and they kept on growing darker and darker and sorer and sorer, for the pinches came as fast and thick as raindrops in a thunderstorm. She rolled out of bed, and laid about her smartly with her shoe, but all to no avail; and suddenly there came a noise from the kitchen that sounded as if a regiment of soldiers were fighting with bayonets. Such a clashing and rattling was never heard since the last time the hill opened and showed the little men of the mountains hammering at their forges.

The stepsister crept to the kitchen door and peered

in. There was the brownie on the table, with his red cap all askew, hurling the dirty pots about, and laughing like a mad March hare. "Ah, there you are, Soggyhead," says he; "now perhaps you will be washing the pots clean, since I have been good enough to get them down for you!"

The stepsister was all for saying no, but there are times when wisdom leads to courage, as the fox said when he jumped through the back window of the henhouse as the farmer came in at the door. Willy-nilly, she picked up the dirty pans and set about scouring them, for whenever she stopped to rest, the pinches began again harder than ever. By the time the red sun came marching over the hill, the last pan was scoured, but the brownie had swung himself up on the smoke-jack, and gone up the chimney, so that all Lady Heavy-foot had for her labor was a pair of dirty hands and hollows under the eyes. And here was the daughter home from the town, and tapping at the door.

Three days thereafter, there came a traveler with a pack to the door of the house on the green forest-edge. He was dressed in a dusty brown jerkin, and ragged woolen hose, and his cloak was as much protection against the weather as a bit of gossamer; but his face was brown and keen, and there was that in it which made the daughter of the house think to herself, "Oh, if only the saints would send me such a one!"

And was there a bite and a sup for a foot-weary man? That was what the traveler asked. The stepmother looked askance at his ragged clothes, but at last she said yes, there was, and set before the traveler a bowl of broken bits that were about to be thrown to the dogs.

"Is there no better than that, sister?" said the daughter of the house.

"Suppose there is?" said the stepsister; "it is not my place to wait on beggars."

So the daughter waited until the stepmother had gone, and then she took away the bowl of scraps. She went over to the bin where the flour was, and took a bit of the brown flour, and a drop of water, and began to stir them together; and the more she stirred the whiter it got. So then she poked up the fire, and set the cake over it; and it puffed up, light and toothsome, and fit for a Prince's eating. This she offered to the traveler, with a cup of milk and a square of cheese.

"Thanks is a thin word when the heart is full," says the traveler. "Is there nothing I can give you out of my poor store?" And he opened the pack.

Hi! you should have seen the stepsister's eyes stand out then! For the pack was full of jewels and gold, and rings and chains and armlets without number. But the daughter shook her head at them.

"I am free to ask for what I want," says she to herself, "but I have no right surely to any of these, for by them the traveler earns his bread, and he has need of them." So at last all she asked for was the bit of brown cord that was hanging about his neck.

The traveler took off the cord, and on the end of it was a little rusty key; he threw it over her head, and the key was rusty no more, but as bright as the King's crown. "That is the key to the treasure house of joy," says he, "and you and I will go and find the door of it together."

"But is there nothing for me?" said the stepsister.

"Take what you like," says the traveler. Well, the sister looked and looked, and fingered one thing after another; and at last she seized a great ring with red fiery stones in it, and put it on. Behold! it was changed to a gray toadstool, that grew tight to her finger, and could not be got off; and she wore it all the days of her life.

"Nothing for nothing," said the traveler. So then he took the daughter by the hand, and they went out of the door together; the sun was warm upon their faces, for it was the first of summertime.

But after that time the brownie was never seen in that house any more, and they had no more good fortune than a cricket in the winter snow. And have you never seen a brownie? Well, do you get up at four o'clock, and bake and brew and spin and sew, and perhaps if you come into the kitchen at the first cock-crow some night, you will find him swinging on the smoke-jack.

By Margery Bailey

ROCKING-HORSE LAND

LITTLE PRINCE FREEDLING woke up with a jump, and sprang out of bed into the sunshine. He was five years old that morning, by all the clocks and calendars in the kingdom; and the day was going to be beautiful. Every golden minute was precious. He was dressed and out of his room before the attendants knew that he was awake.

In the ante-chamber stood piles on piles of glittering presents; when he walked among them they came up to the measure of his waist. His fairy godmother had sent him a toy with the most humorous effect. It was labeled, "Break me and I shall turn into something else." So every time he broke it he got a new toy more beautiful than the last. It began by being a hoop, and from that it ran on, while the Prince broke it incessantly for the space of one hour, during which it became by turn—a top, a Noah's ark, a skipping-rope, a man-of-war, a box of bricks, a picture puzzle, a pair of stilts, a drum, a trumpet, a kaleidoscope, a steam-engine, and nine hundred and fifty other things exactly. Then he began to grow discontented, because it would never turn into the same thing again; and after having broken the man-of-war he wanted to get it back again. Also he wanted to see if the steam-engine would go inside the Noah's ark; but the toy would never be two things at the same time, either. This was very unsatisfactory. He thought his fairy godmother ought to have sent him two toys, out of which he could make combinations.

At last he broke it once more, and it turned into a kite; and while he was flying the kite he broke the string, and the kite went sailing away up into nasty blue sky, and was never heard of again.

Then Prince Freedling sat down and howled at his fairy godmother; what a dissembling lot fairy godmothers were, to be sure! They were always setting traps to make their god-children unhappy. Nevertheless, when told to, he took up his pen and wrote her a nice little note, full of bad spelling and tarradiddles, to say what a happy birthday he was spending in breaking up the beautiful toy she had sent him.

Then he went to look at the rest of the presents, and found it quite refreshing to break a few that did not send him giddy by turning into anything else.

Suddenly his eyes became fixed with delight; alone, right at the end of the room, stood a great black rocking-horse. The saddle and bridle were hung with tiny gold bells and balls of coral; and the horse's tail and mane flowed till they almost touched the ground.

The Prince scampered across the room, and threw his

arms around the beautiful creature's neck. All its bells jangled as the head swayed gracefully down; and the Prince kissed it between the eyes. Great eyes they were, the color of fire; so wonderfully bright, it seemed they must be really alive; only they did not move, but gazed continually with a set stare at the tapestry-hung wall, on which were figures of armed knights riding to battle.

So Prince Freedling mounted to the back of his rocking-horse; and all day long he rode and shouted to the figures of the armed knights, challenging them to fight, or leading them against the enemy.

At length, when it came to be bedtime, weary of so much glory, he was lifted down from the saddle and carried away to bed.

In his sleep Freedling still felt his black rocking-horse swinging to and fro under him, and heard the melodious chime of its bells, and, in the land of dreams, saw a great country open before him, full of the sound of the battle-cry and the hunting-horn calling him to strange perils and triumphs.

In the middle of the night he grew softly awake, and his heart was full of love for his black rocking-horse. He crept gently out of bed: he would go and look at it where it was standing so grand and still in the next room, to make sure that it was all safe and not afraid of being by itself in the dark night. Parting the door-hangings he passed through into the wide hollow chamber beyond, all littered about with toys.

The moon was shining in through the window, making a square cistern of light upon the floor. And then, all at once, he saw that the rocking-horse had moved from the place where he had left it! It had crossed the room, and was standing close to the window, with its head toward the night, as though watching the movement of the clouds and the trees swaying in the wind.

The Prince could not understand how it had been moved so; he was a little bit afraid and, stealing timidly across, he took hold of the bridle to comfort himself with the jangle of its bells. As he came close, and looked up into the dark solemn face, he saw that the eyes were full of tears and, reaching up, felt one fall warm against his hand.

"Why do you weep, my Beautiful?" said the Prince.

The rocking-horse answered, "I weep because I am a prisoner, and not free. Open the window, Master, and let me go!"

"But if I let you go I shall lose you," said the Prince. "Cannot you be happy here with me?"

"Let me go," said the horse, "for my brothers call me out of Rocking-Horse Land; I hear my mare whinnying to her foals; and they all cry, seeking me through the ups and hollows of my native fastness! Sweet Master, let me go this night, and I will return to you when it is day!"

Then Freedling said, "How shall I know that you will return; and what name shall I call you by?"

And the rocking-horse answered, "My name is Rollonde. Search my mane till you find in it a white hair; draw it out and wind it upon one of your fingers; and as long as you have it so wound you are my master; and wherever I am I must return at your bidding."

So the Prince drew down the rocking-horse's head;

and searching the mane, he found the white hair, and wound it upon his finger and tied it. Then he kissed Rollonde between the eyes, saying, "Go, Rollonde, since I love you, and wish you to be happy; only return to me when it is day!" And so saying, he threw open the window to the stir of the night.

Then the rocking-horse lifted his dark head and neighed aloud for joy, and swaying forward with a mighty circling motion rose full into the air, and sprang out into the free world before him.

Freedling watched how with plunge and curve he went over the bowed trees; and again he neighed into the darkness of the night, then swifter than wind disappeared in the distance. And faintly from far away came a sound of the neighing of many horses answering him.

Then the Prince closed the window and crept back to bed; and all night long he dreamed strange dreams of Rocking-Horse Land. There he saw smooth hills and valleys that rose and sank without a stone or a tree to disturb the steel-like polish of their surface, slippery as glass, and driven over by a strong wind; and over them, with a sound like the humming of bees, flew the rocking-horses. Up and down, up and down, with bright manes streaming like colored fires, and feet motionless behind and before, went the swift pendulum of their flight. Their long bodies bowed and rose; their heads worked to give impetus to their going; they cried, neighing to each other over hill and valley, "Which of us shall be first? Which of us shall be first?" After them the mares with their tall foals came spinning to watch, crying also among themselves, "Ah! which shall be first?"

"Rollonde, Rollonde is first!" shouted the Prince, clapping his hands as they reached the goal; and at that, all at once, he woke, and saw it was broad day. Then he ran and threw open the window and, holding out the finger that carried the white hair, cried, "Rollonde, Rollonde, come back, Rollonde!"

Far away he heard an answering sound; and in another moment there came the great rocking-horse himself, dipping and dancing over the hills. He crossed the woods and cleared the palace-wall at a bound, and floating in through the window, dropped to rest at Prince Freedling's side, rocking gently to and fro as though panting from the strain of his long flight.

"Now are you happy?" asked the Prince as he caressed him.

"Ah! sweet Prince," said Rollonde, "ah, kind Master!" And then he said no more, but became the stock-still, staring rocking-horse of the day before, with fixed eyes and rigid limbs, which could do nothing but rock up and down with a jangling of sweet bells so long as the Prince rode him.

That night Freedling came again when all was still in the palace; and now as before Rollonde had moved from his place and was standing with his head against the window waiting to be let out. "Ah, dear Master," he said, as soon as he saw the Prince coming, "let me go this night also, and surely I will return with day."

So again the Prince opened the window, and watched him disappear, and heard from far away the neighing of the horses in Rocking-Horse Land calling to him. And in the morning, with the white hair round his finger, he called, "Rollonde, Rollonde!" and Rollonde neighed and came back to him, dipping and dancing over the hills.

Now this same thing happened every night; and every morning the horse kissed Freedling, saying, "Ah! dear Prince and kind Master!" and became stock-still once more.

So a year went by, till one morning Freedling woke up to find it was his sixth birthday. And as six is to five, so were the presents he received on his sixth birthday for magnificence and multitude to the presents he had received the year before. His fairy godmother had sent him a bird, a real live bird; but when he pulled its tail it became a lizard, and when he pulled the lizard's tail it became a mouse, and when he pulled the mouse's tail it became a cat. Then he did very much want to see if the cat would eat the mouse, and not being able to have them both he got rather vexed with his fairy godmother. However, he pulled the cat's tail and the cat became a dog, and when he pulled the dog's tail the dog became a goat; and so it went on till he got to a cow. And he pulled the cow's tail and it became a camel, and he pulled the camel's tail and it became an elephant, and still not being contented, he pulled the elephant's tail and it became a guinea-pig. Now a guinea-pig has no tail to pull, so it remained a guinea-pig, while Prince Freedling sat down and howled at his fairy godmother.

But the best of all his presents was the one given to

him by the King his father. It was a most beautiful horse, for, said the King, "You are now old enough to learn to ride."

So Freedling was put upon the horse's back, and from having ridden so long upon his rocking-horse he learned to ride perfectly in a single day, and was declared by all the courtiers to be the most perfect equestrian that was ever seen.

Now these praises and the pleasure of riding a real horse so occupied his thoughts that that night he forgot all about Rollonde, and falling fast asleep dreamed of nothing but real horses and horsemen going to battle. And so it was the next night too.

But the night after that, just as he was falling asleep, he heard someone sobbing by his bed, and a voice saying, "Ah! dear Prince and kind Master, let me go, for my heart breaks for a sight of my native land." And there stood his poor rocking-horse Rollonde, with tears falling out of his beautiful eyes on to the white coverlet.

Then the Prince, full of shame at having forgotten his friend, sprang up and threw his arms round his neck, saying, "Be of good cheer, Rollonde, for now surely I will let thee go!" and he ran to the window and opened it for the horse to go through. "Ah! dear Prince and kind Master!" said Rollonde. Then he lifted his head and neighed so that the whole palace shook; and swaying forward till his head almost touched the ground, he sprang out into the night and away toward Rocking-Horse Land.

Then Prince Freedling, standing by the window, thoughtfully unloosed the white hair from his finger, and let it float away into the darkness, out of sight of his eye or reach of his hand.

"Good-by, Rollonde," he murmured softly, "brave Rollonde, my own good Rollonde! Go and be happy in your own land, since I, your Master, was forgetting to be kind to you." And far away he heard the neighing of horses in Rocking-Horse Land.

Many years after, when Freedling had become King in his father's stead, the fifth birthday of the Prince his son came to be celebrated; and there on the morning of the day, among all the presents that covered the floor of the chamber, stood a beautiful foal rocking-horse, black, with deep-burning eyes.

No one knew how it had come there, or whose present it was, till the King himself came to look at it. And when he saw it so like the old Rollonde he had loved as a boy, he smiled, and, stroking its dark mane, said softly in its ear, "Art thou, then, the son of Rollonde?" And the foal answered him, "Ah, dear Prince and kind Master!" but never a word more.

Then the King took the little Prince his son, and told him the story of Rollonde as I have told it here; and at the end he went and searched in the foal's mane till he found one white hair, and, drawing it out, he wound it about the little Prince's finger, bidding him guard it well and be ever a kind master to Rollonde's son.

So here is my story of Rollonde come to a good ending.

By Laurence Housman

IF YOU HAD A WISH?

IN THE OLD DAYS, and very good days they were (this was in France long ago), there was a fisherman, and never did hard-working, cheerful fellow have worse luck. If a storm blew up it was his nets that were carried away. If he caught no fish the market would be good, and if he caught a good haul there would be no market at all. Yet he was a cheerful soul who never complained, even when his wife, a sour-tempered woman, scolded and frowned.

"I see nothing to smile for," she would say when he came home empty-handed. "You bring nothing with as merry a look as if you had a boatful."

"Why not sing?" he would reply. "The longer the bad luck lasts, the nearer we are to good, since nothing lasts forever."

"Bah!" she would say. "Every time you come home a fool enters the house."

"Well, well!" said he, trying to calm her, "with health and hope a man is lucky, and I have both in plenty."

One day his luck changed. There had been much talk of a certain big fish which had been seen often, and the rich man of that place offered a purse of gold to the one who would catch it. Then, wonder of wonders! what should be but that it leaped into the poor fisherman's boat. So he cleaned it, put it on a wooden dish, thrust a lemon in its mouth to make it look beautiful, and started through the forest to carry it to the rich man's house. On his way he came upon a poor man, in clothes so ragged that they could hardly hold together, sitting under a tree, groaning sadly.

"Now what ails you?" asked the good-hearted fisherman.

"What should it be but hunger?" was the answer. "I have eaten nothing for many days, and here you come with a fish big enough for three men with something left over. Luck is with you."

"That may well be," answered the fisherman, "yet my bread has not been buttered always on both sides, nor has it always fallen into the honey when I dropped it."

"If luck knocks at a man's door, he ought to share it with the luckless," grumbled the other.

"I was taking the fish to the rich man's house," the fisher explained.

"So you are one who shares his luck with the lucky and lets the hungry go famished," said the other, and groaned piteously.

"Not so," was the reply. "But I must say that some seem born to have the gold, and others to hold an empty purse, and—"

The beggar interrupted with, "Say no more. I may die famished."

"Now, friend," said the good-hearted fisher, "if you are in such a bad case, why, the fish is yours for the asking." So saying, he laid the fish at the beggar's feet.

Thereupon the ragged man stood up and clapped the fisher on the shoulder in high delight. "Never yet," said he, "did a good deed go unrewarded. This moment you shall have your wish granted. What is it?"

"Well," said the fisherman, "that is hard to decide."

"Wish in half a minute," said the other.

"There are so many things—" said the fisher.

"You have less than half a minute," warned the ragged man.

"Well, then, for the rest of today let me have everything I can wish for," said the fisherman.

"You are a clever fellow," answered the beggar. "It shall be so. But look to it that you choose well, and that you think of others. Until midnight, then, you may wish, and what you wish shall come to be."

With that the ragged man went his way carrying the fish, and the fisher turned his steps toward his cottage, busy with his thoughts. Presently he became aware that the wind was cold and the way long, so, without thinking, he said to himself, "Now I wish I was home and on my stool in front of a blazing fire, with a good supper on the table."

No sooner had he said the words than he found himself on his stool before the fire, and his wife sprawling in the corner and saying hard things to him, for she had been sitting in that very place.

"What silly jokes are these?" she asked, believing he had come in quietly and pushed her off the stool. "A pretty way to do! Did I not say that every time you come home a fool enters the house?"

"Peace, good woman," he replied, "I did but wish thoughtlessly, as the beggar warned me against, but I see that wishes may be dangerous, and I did not think of others."

So he told her the tale of the fish and the stranger, and how both of them might wish, and how the gift would end at midnight, wherefore they had better get busy and be thoughtful in their wishing. For a long time they argued, trying to decide, and at last, remembering the warning that he should consider others, the man said, "Well, there's one thing that can do no harm. I wish that every neighbor in this village had a house twice as large, with the finest of furniture and the best the world has to eat and drink."

The words were hardly spoken when a great uproar arose. The two ran to the window to look, and beheld a strange sight. Where had been neat cottages, each with its garden, were now buildings they had never seen before. Houses had spread to crowd one another. Some had grown so as to crowd trees sideways. They had elbowed one another, and were crooked, or bent, or partly tilted upwards to get room. So the people were much disturbed, and many were running about crying that the place was surely bewitched.

Those who were at supper found strange foods before them, since the fisher had wished the best that the world had, and there were foods of which they knew nothing. Some found boiled camel's meat on their dishes, some seal fat and whale meat, some turkey, some roast monkey, some Turkish sherbet, some haggis, and some found the fish on their forks and on the way to their mouths changed to meats they had never dreamed of and did not like. Tables, chairs, beds that they had used for a lifetime had vanished, and in their place were strange furnishings, silks, velvets, plush, seal skin or Eskimo furs. So every man, woman, and child was comfortless.

"Now see what you have done!" cried the woman. "Here is every one rich, with great houses when they put them in order, and we are in our old cottage, the poorest of the poor, fool that you are."

"I did but wish for the welfare of others," said the astonished fisherman, very miserably. "It begins to look as if with wishing comes grieving."

"Not with me," said his wife. "Hear this. I wish that this cottage was ten times as big, with furniture to match."

With that there came a strange groaning, and rumbling, and creaking, and cracking; and the room spread and spread, high and wide, so that it became great as a church. The man had been standing with his back to the fire, looking at his wife who sat on the stool, but suddenly found himself at a mighty scorching fire that promised to set fire to his clothes. He moved to one side in a hop, and, so doing, fell over a tree trunk a yard high and twenty feet long that had been a log for the fire. Then he heard his wife's voice screaming, and, looking up, saw her perched on the grown stool twenty feet in the air, in a state of terror lest she might fall. Above her head, on rafters sixty feet high, hung great hams the size of pigs, sausages too that would have killed a man had they fallen on him. So the fisherman had much trouble climbing the leg of the stool and teaching his wife to clamber down, for while he might have wished, he forgot. They could not reach the shelves, or see out of the window, or unlatch the door; and the bed was like a rich man's barn for bigness, while the fireplace was a fearful flaming cave near which they dared not go for the strong wind.

Then they saw the cat!

It was a monstrous creature whose head stood higher than theirs, with green glaring eyes and terrible whiskers, with a body like a tiger's, and long white teeth. And it came to both of them to remember that the cat was hungry. Across the floor crept the great beast, its eyes glaring, its tail waving fearfully from side to side. Then it crouched, ready to spring.

"Wish something!" cried the woman in great fear, clinging to her husband.

"Oh! I wish we were in the middle of the table," said he. Immediately they found themselves in the middle of a great bowl of fish stew, warm and waist deep, a sticky pond all of ten feet across. Slowly they waded to the edge, and the man helped the woman out, then climbed out himself, to find he was on what looked like a great plain, with a mighty loaf of bread, and knives and forks twice a man's length, and two mugs with rims as high as their heads. Also there was the cat on the table's edge, looking at them greedily. Full of fear they looked down at the floor, a dizzy height, then back at the cat which was creeping toward them.

Suddenly the fisher remembered his gift, not carefully or with thought, and wished they were on the mantel. So they found themselves there safe for a moment, but a moment only, for the cat gave a leap and sailed across the sixty-foot gap between the table and the mantel-shelf to land close to them. They might have wished themselves outside, or wished themselves big, or wished the cat dead; but they did not. They were too excited, and too nervous, and too fearful to think of anything except getting out of reach of the dreadful creature.

"I wish we were on the rafters," cried the man in great distress, and at once they were there, looking down in great fear at what had been their comfortable hearth, now so far away. Their clothes were wet and heavy with fish stew. They were tired. They were miserable. But they were safe from the cat in the corner where the rafters joined the wall.

Then came a new thing to distress them. From a black hole, that smelt horribly, there shone evil, red eyes. Then out of the dark reached a pincer-like pair of claws, then first one and then another long, thin, hairy leg; and out from the dark came a great spider as big as a platter. It stood a moment looking at them, swaying back and forth, then slowly advanced. With a scream the woman turned and fled along the rafter, the man following; nor did they stop though the way seemed long, until they came to a great rope, as thick as they were tall, that held one of the hams, and over which they had to climb.

"These wishes are terrible," wailed the woman, wringing her hands. "If ever things get right again I shall nevermore wish, but be satisfied with what I do."

"How can things ever be right again?" asked the man. "Everything is wrong. Our neighbors are ruined. We are undone. We shall perish if things are not right at midnight."

"With wishing comes grieving," said the woman.

"Alas! I wish we were all in a far-off land, where things are right, with our neighbors, where we could all begin again."

And that is how there came to be very contented people in Gaspé. For of a sudden, they and their neighbors found themselves in this good land where fish is plentiful, and where fields are green, and where men know that if they cannot make the thing they wish for, then they must wish for that which they themselves can do.

By Charles J. Finger

MILLITINKLE

MILLITINKLE used to be just like any other donkey. She could not talk, she was not white, and she did not have pink ears with little golden bells in the tops of them. She worked hard for her master, carrying heavy loads and making long journeys. And everything he told her to do, Millitinkle did.

One time this man and his donkey were traveling up in the mountains. For days and days they had been making their way along narrow trails and over high passes. At last they got so far up in the mountains that soon they would be going down the other side. There they stopped at the foot of a cliff one night to sleep. The man put up his tent; and, as was his custom, he turned out Millitinkle to eat such grass as she could find. After doing this, he rolled up in his blanket and went to sleep.

In the night it started to snow. But the man knew nothing about it, for he was asleep. It snowed and snowed. In the morning when the man woke up he started to go out of the tent, and a lot of snow fell in on him. He thought, "I am lost. There is no hope for me now. My donkey has probably been frozen to death. And I shall not be able to move from here until the snow melts. What a fool I was to leave the donkey outside." With much trouble he pushed his way out of the tent and climbed up on a snow drift. Everywhere he looked, in every direction, he could see nothing but snow. It was so deep that it was over his head. He called to Millitinkle, but she did not come. At last he gave up, went back into the tent, and made up his mind to wait. There was nothing else he could do. But his heart was sad, and he wept over the horrible fate that had befallen his donkey.

Now, when the snow began to fall, Millitinkle was a long way from her master. She had not found much to eat near by, so she had wandered down the mountainside in search of grass. She was busy grazing when the storm started. Before she realized what a bad storm it was, the snow was already so deep that she could hardly lift one leg after the other. Fright seized her. She turned this way and that way in hopes of being able to move. She brayed for help. But the wind carried her voice down the mountain instead of toward the tent. All the time the snow was falling fast and heavy. The more the donkey struggled, the deeper in she got. Finally the snow covered her over completely and she felt nice and warm. "This is not so bad," she thought. "I'll rest for a while and then burrow along. I might as well travel under the snow as on top. It's warm, and there's no wind down here." So she rested and slept a little: and afterwards she began to kick and paw and make a tunnel for herself underneath the snow.

In this way she traveled for some distance, always down hill, for that was the easiest way to go. Behind her she left a long tunnel where the snow had been pushed aside and trampled down. On she went and on. She was thinking that soon she would get out, when the snow in front of her fell away, and she found herself in a cave. The walls were all of ice, and a dim light shone through them. The floor was ice too, very smooth and very slippery. Millitinkle looked around at herself; she was pure white. The snow had changed her color, and no amount of licking or shaking would change it back. This rather pleased her. She said to herself, "Now I'll be different from all other donkeys. None of them are as white or as beautiful as I am. My master won't know me when he sees me again." Then she started off at a trot down through the cave, wondering what she was going to find.

This cave that Millitinkle came into was the entrance to the palace of the Snow Queen. There the Snow Queen lived alone with all the snow fairies whose task it was to make the snow-flakes and scatter them during a storm. But the donkey did not know this. She trotted on and on, until she found herself at the door of a big room. The room was lit up with a wonderful white light that seemed to come from nowhere. From the ceiling hung long icicles that glittered and sparkled with every color of the rainbow. The walls were of ice, but as clear and pure as crystal. In the middle of the room was a high throne made of blocks of ice. On this sat the Snow Queen. She was all dressed in white fur, and on her head she wore what seemed to be a diamond crown. But it was really made of beautifully cut pieces of ice. When she saw Millitinkle at the door, she said, "What are you doing here? Neither man nor animal has ever found his way here before. Come in and let me see you."

Millitinkle trotted in and made a low bow before the queen. The queen, seeing what a beautiful animal the donkey was, said, "In all my life I have never seen a white donkey. You must stay with me. I will keep you and feed you well. Will you stay?"

Millitinkle brayed and tried to make herself understood. But it seemed impossible to make the queen see what she was trying to say. At last the donkey stood there in silence and looked sadly at the floor.

The queen said, "I see what's the matter. You can't talk. Eat this, and you'll be able to." She handed Millitinkle a small cake all covered with white frost. As soon as the donkey swallowed it, she was able to speak just like a human being. Then Millitinkle told the queen all about what had happened. And when the queen heard the story, she said, "I will send you back to your master. But first you must stay a month with me. I am all alone here. And I want you for a friend. You stay a month: then you can go to your master."

Millitinkle asked, "Do you think he will be all right?"

"I know he will," said the queen.

So Millitinkle agreed to stay a month with the Snow Queen. She lived in the palace and had a happy life.

During this month the donkey learned many things she had not known before. The Snow Queen took her from room to room and showed her the snow fairies at work. They were little white people with silver wings. All day they worked hard making snow-flakes. They made them in many shapes and in many sizes. When they were made, they put them in little baskets that seemed to be woven out of frozen cobwebs. Then, when the queen wished to have a storm anywhere, the fairies flew forth with their baskets and scattered the flakes in the wind. All this Millitinkle saw. Also she met some ice fairies. These were almost without color; they could hardly be seen. But they had a wonderful power. For wherever they touched water with their feet, that water turned into ice. All of these people lived in the palace. They were very happy and very busy. And they all loved their queen.

In return Millitinkle told the queen many things about the world of men. To these the Snow Queen always listened with a great deal of interest, for she had never heard about them before. She came to like the donkey more and more. And she dreaded the day when the animal would have to leave.

One night, while they were eating together at a silver table, a fairy came in and said, "I have been to the man's tent. He is very lonely. All day long he sits and sighs for his donkey. In this way he cannot live much longer."

The queen said, "He won't have to wait many days more. His time is nearly up."

Millitinkle was sad and said, "It isn't fair that I should stay from him. Hadn't I better go?"

But the queen insisted that the donkey stay, saying, "If you go now, you will be sorry; for your master could not find you in the snow. When the month is up, I'll give you something to make you more beautiful than you are now. Then you can go, and your master will have no trouble finding you."

So Millitinkle said no more. But she wondered what the queen meant by her words.

Finally the month was up, and the time came for the donkey to leave. She said to the queen, "Today I shall go away. You have been very kind to me and have treated me well. Now that I'm going, tell me what you are going to give me."

The queen said, "Come over here with me, where this red light from the icicle shines on the wall. You must do just as I tell you."

They walked over to the wall, and the queen made Millitinkle kneel down so that just her ears were shaded by the red light. Then she took a long, silvery icicle, and lightly touched the top of each ear. She said, "Now you have pink ears. Your master will be able to see you in the snow." But Millitinkle, who could not see her own ears, did not know whether the queen spoke the truth or not. "One thing more I want to do for you before you go," continued the queen. "I am going to give you a present to remember me by." And in the top of each of the donkey's ears she put a little golden bell. Then she said, "Now you can go. You are in every way the most beautiful donkey in the world. I wish you could stay with me forever."

Millitinkle thanked the queen for all she had done, saying, "I won't forget you. If I didn't have a master, I'd be glad to stay here. But I can't stay away from him any longer. Every time I think of you I'll do this." And the donkey shook her ears, and the bells went, "Tinkle, tinkle, tinkle."

So the queen and the donkey bade each other goodby, and Millitinkle went off by the same way she had come. Out through the cave she trotted and down through the tunnel she had made in the snow. There, when she came to the end, she stopped to rest.

While she rested, the sun shone on the snow above her, and the snow melted. It melted enough so that her pink ears stuck out. And when she wagged them, the bells went "Tinkle, tinkle, tinkle." Her master, who was sitting in the tent, heard this sound. He got up to look out, and he saw the pink ears. With a jump he was up and running through the snow. He thought, "What can those two pink things be? There's just a chance that they may be the ears of my donkey. Poor Millitinkle, she's frozen! That's why her ears are pink." He pushed his way on to where the donkey was. Just as he came near enough to see things clearly, Millitinkle stuck her head out of the snow and said, "Hello. Come help me!"

"Who is that?" said the man, for he could not believe that it was the donkey that spoke.

"Millitinkle," said the donkey. "Help me out, and I'll tell you how I learned to talk."

"Are you still alive?" asked the man, who was so surprised that he really did not know what he was saying.

"Of course I am," said Millitinkle. "But I'll freeze if you leave me here much longer."

Then the man dug the donkey out. And she told him about the wonderful things that had happened to her: How she got her pink ears. And why she had bells in them. And the man thought of nothing but how glad he was to have his donkey back. Together they made their way up to the tent. By the next day the snow had melted enough so that they could go on their journey. They were happy; they talked to each other; and they became the best of friends in the world.

By Paul Fenimore Cooper

THE PIXIES' SCARF

ONCE UPON A TIME there was an old woman who went out to pick whortleberries on Dartymoor. She carried a tin can in one hand and a basket in the other, and she meant to fill them both before she returned home.

Behind her came a little boy, her young grandson, Dicky, who had asked her to take him with her across the great windy moor. The old woman's eyes were on the ground, on the low green bushes which spread in a web for miles, but the little boy stared about him at the birds in the air, and the white clouds in the sky, and the great black tors like castles rising from the heather and grass.

"Grandmother, where does those birds come from?" he asked, but Mrs. Bundle shook her head.

"Never mind the birds, Dicky. Pick the worts. There's lots of worts here. 'Tis blue with 'em," and she stooped and gathered the little bloomy whortle-berries with her gnarled old fingers, stripping them from the bushes, and dropping them into her can with a rattle like beads falling in a box.

So Dicky turned his head from the blue sky and the flittering birds, and looked at the rounded bushes, like dark-green cushions. Dartymoor was more full of lovely things even than the sky, he thought, as he looked down. He crammed his red mouth with berries, and put a handful in his own little basket. Then he knelt down to look at the scurrying beetles and ants and the long-legged spiders which hurried about their business in the green and scarlet leaves.

Suddenly his attention was caught by a wisp of rain-bow color, hanging on a twiggy branch of one of the bushes. He thought at first it was a spider's web, blue and green and gold; but when he picked it up he found it was woven silk, fine as the gossamer sacks which hang in the grasses, shimmering as the dewdrops in the grass.

"What have you got there?" asked old Mrs. Bundle, as she saw him twist the rag round his finger and hold it up to the sun.

"It's a pretty something I've found," said Dicky, going up to her and showing the scrap of silk.

"Drop it, Dicky, drop it! It's maybe something belonging to the Wee Folk."

She lowered her voice to a whisper and looked round as if she expected to see somebody coming.

"It's a pixie-scarf you've found, I reckon," she whispered. "Put it back. It doesn't do to touch their things. They don't like it."

She waited till he dropped the little scarf and then she went on gathering the berries, muttering to herself.

Dicky turned round and looked at the scarf. He couldn't bear to leave it, so he whisked it up again and slipped it in his pocket. Nobody would know, he told himself. He would take it home with him.

He wandered on, picking the ripe berries, following the little old woman, staring and whistling, forgetting the little silken scarf; but as he ruffled the bushes with stained purple hands, and drew aside the tiny leaves, he was surprised to see far more things than he had ever imagined before. Down in the soil he saw the rabbits in their holes, playing and sleeping, or curled in their smooth dwelling houses. He saw the rocks and the little streams and trickles of water flowing underground. Like a mirror was the ground and he watched the hidden life beneath it. Many things were there, deep down, a rusty dagger, a broken sword blade, and he wandered on, staring at the secrets he discovered.

"Grandmother," he called. "See here. Here's something under the grass," but the good old woman saw nothing at all except heather and whortleberries and the short sweet grass.

"Saints preserve us!" she cried, when Dicky scrabbled away the soil and brought up a broken crock of ancient coins. "How did you know they were there?" she asked.

"I seed 'em," said he.

She fingered the money and rubbed it on her torn skirt, but Dicky turned away. He didn't care about it. A new feeling had come to him, and he stood very still, listening, waiting.

The scent of the moor flowed to him, wild thyme and honey and moss in wet places. He could hear the countless bells of the purple heather ringing like merry church chimes, and the wind in the reeds sang like a harp, whilst the deep, dark bogs sighed and moaned.

"I won't touch these," said old Mrs. Bundle, and she threw the coins away into the bog, but Dicky only laughed, for he heard new music as they fell and were sucked down to the depths. The earth itself seemed to be whispering, and the stream answered back, speaking to the bog and the emerald mosses.

"Get on with your picking," scolded Mrs. Bundle. "You asked me to bring you with me a-worting, and here you are, finding queer things as ought to be hid. Whatever's took you, Dicky Bundle!"

But Dicky's eyes were wide with wonder, and he took no notice of his grandmother. Up in the trees were voices talking, two blackbirds were arguing, and he heard every word they said. A robin called: "Come here! Take no notice of those people below. Come here!" and a tom tit swung on a bough and chattered to its friend, the linnet.

More than that, he could hear the low reedy voices of the worms in the stream's banks, and understand their language as they murmured on and on with placid talk of this and that, and pushed their way among the grasses.

Then came the shrill whisper of fishes in the water, and he leaned over the peaty stream to see who was there. Flat round eyes stared back at him, and the fishes swam under a rock as his shadow fell on them. A king-fisher darted past, and Dicky heard its chuckle of glee as it dived and snatched up a weeping fish.

He would have stayed there all night, crouched on the stream's edge, hearkening to the talk of the creatures, listening to the music of the wild moorland, looking at the hidden life which was visible to his eyes, but his grandmother pulled his arm and shook him.

"Didn't you hear me? Dick Bundle! Come away home. My basket and pail are full to the brim, but you've only got a tuthree! Shame on you for a lazy good-for-nothing little boy."

Dicky was bewildered, and he followed her meekly along the road to the cottage down in Widdicombe, listening to voices all the way.

When they got home his grandmother emptied her fruit into the great brass pan, and soon there was a humming and bubbling as the jam simmered over the fire. Dicky took off his coat and hung it up behind the door, and when the scarf was away from him the little voices of the mice in the wainscot and birds in the garden ceased. The cat purred and he no longer knew what she said. The buzzing flies in the window lost their tiny excited voices; the spider in the corner was dumb.

"It's gone very quiet," said Dicky to his grand-mother.

"Quiet? It's the same as usual. You go and fill the kettle and put it on ready for tea. Then wash your hands and face. No wonder you didn't find many ber-ries. You ate 'em all."

Mrs. Bundle was indignant with her grandson, and when the two sat down to their tea, she thought of her son, Dicky's father, away in America, earning his liv-ing far from the village he loved. She must bring Dicky up to be a good boy, worthy of that father. She sighed, and looked at her grandson, and shook her head wear-ily. It was hard with her old bones to have to deal with a lazy young sky-gazer like Dicky.

"Now you can go out and play," she told Dicky when the meal was finished and the table cleared. "I shall make my jam ready for selling to customers, and maybe we shall get enough money to buy you a pair of shoes, for you sadly need them."

Dicky went out to Widdicombe Green and played at marbles with the other boys. Then Farmer Vinney let him take his brown mare to the stable, and Farmer Deacon asked him to catch a hen that had gone astray. So he was busy with this and that, until the moon came up over the hills and the stars shone in the night sky, and the great tors disappeared in the shadows.

Then Dicky went indoors for his supper of bread and milk. He went upstairs to the little room with a

crooked beam across the ceiling and he said his prayers and got into his wooden bed. Old Mrs. Bundle
came up to look at him and tuck in the clothes.

"Now go to sleep, Dicky. I've brought your jacket
upstairs, ready for morning. Go to sleep, and God bless
you, my dear."

But Dicky wasn't sleepy at all, and he lay with his
eyes wide open staring at the moon over the moor and
the tall tower of the church across the Green. After
a time he heard a high silvery bell-like voice, calling
and calling; as clear and fresh it was, just as if the
stars were speaking to one another.

"Dick Bundle! Dick Bundle!" cried the tiny voice.
"Give me back the scarf."

"Dick Bundle! Dick Bundle!" echoed a hundred
little voices, pealing like a chime of fairy bells, ringing like a field of harebells all swaying in the wind.

Dick sprang out of bed and looked through the window. In a rosebush in the narrow garden below, holding a glow-worm in his hands, sat a little man and
Dicky knew he was a pixie. He saw the little creature's
pointed cap, and his thin spindly legs, crossed as he
squatted among the roses, and he caught the green glint
of the pixie's eyes.

Behind were many more pixies, crowds of them,
perched on the garden wall, clambering in the flower-
beds, running across the grass, each one carrying a
glow-worm and calling "Dick Bundle" in its shrill
tinkling voice.

"Give us back the scarf," they sang.

"Come and fetch it," called Dick Bundle through

the window, and he went to his jacket pocket and took the wisp of rainbow silk and held it dangling at the window.

How beautiful it looked! It was quite different with the moon shining upon it, and it moved like a shimmering fish, and glittered in his hands.

"Oh! Oh! Oh!" sang the pixies. "There it is! There it is! Give it back!"

"Come and fetch it," said Dicky again, for he wanted to try to catch one of the little men.

"We can't come in because you said your prayers," they replied, and others echoed: "Prayers. Prayers. No, we can't come in," and their voices wailed and squeaked.

"You come down to us," invited the first pixie, who seemed to be the leader. "You bring it to us, Dick Bundle."

"No," replied Dick. "I can't do that," and he folded the scarf and drew it through his fingers. "I mustn't go out in the night, or I should catch rheumatics like my Granny."

He looked at his fingers and they were shining with light where the scarf had touched them. Yes, it was too lovely a thing to lose!

"Throw it down to us, Dicky boy," wheedled the nearest pixie. "It belongs to our Queen, and she has been hunting it all day."

"How did you know it was here?" asked Dicky. "I've never had it out of my pocket until now."

"The birds and the fishes and the rabbits all knew you heard their voices, for you stopped to listen, and no human can understand what the other world says. Only the pixies know. So when they told us a boy had hearkened to their talk as they spoke to one another, and had found old coins lost under the ground, and had bent his head to listen to the heather bells and the gossamer harps in the bushes, then we knew you must have found the scarf. For it gives eyes and ears to those who are blind and deaf."

"I'm not blind or deaf," protested Dicky.

"Yes, you are. You can see nothing without the scarf. Throw it back to us, for you can't keep it. We shall torment you till we get it."

"What will you give me for it?" asked Dicky.

"A carriage and pair," said the pixie.

"Show it to me first," said Dicky.

Then a tiny carriage rolled across the garden path, and it was made out of a cunningly carved walnut shell, drawn by a pair of field mice. The carriage was lined with green moss, and the coachman was a grasshopper with a whip of moonshine.

"I can't get into that," Dick complained. "That's no good to me."

He watched the little carriage bowl along into the shadows.

"What else will you give me?"

"A suit of armor," suggested the pixie.

"Show me first," said Dicky, and he leaned low, expecting to see a grand iron suit like the knights of old wore.

A little man staggered along the wall under the window, carrying a suit of shining armor, and the plates were made of fishes' scales, all blue and silver, and the helmet was adorned with a robin's feather.

"No, I couldn't wear that," said Dicky. "What else have you got?" He twisted the little scarf and waved it before the throng of agitated pixies, who wailed, "Oh! Oh! Oh!" as they gazed at it and held out their skinny arms for it.

"I'll give you a fine dress for your grandmother," said the pixie. He brought out of the rose tree a little crinolined dress made of a hundred rose petals.

"My grannie's too stout for that," laughed Dicky. "What else can you give me?"

The pixies scratched their heads with vexation. They didn't know what to give the great human boy who leaned from the window under the thatched roof. All their belongings were far too small for such a giant, they whispered to one another.

Then one of them had a thought. "A bag of marbles," said he.

Now Dicky was the champion marble player of Widdicombe-on-the-Moor, and he thought if he got some pixie marbles he might be the best player on the whole of Dartymoor.

Surely a pixie marble would capture every other, for there would be magic in it!

"Show them to me," said Dicky, eagerly.

The little man dragged a brown sack up the wall, and emptied the marbles in a shining pile. Green as grass in April, blood-red, snow-white, and blue as the night sky they shone, each one sparkling in the moonlight.

He held out his hand for the sack, and dropped the scarf from the window, but he took care to grasp the sack before he let the scarf flutter down, for he had heard of the tricky way of pixies, who outwit humans whenever it is possible. But they were so eager to get their precious scarf, they never even snatched at the bag. With excited happy cries, queer fluting songs, and chuckles like a flock of starlings at evening, they clasped the scarf. Then singing, whistling, shouting, and waving their glow-worms, they ran away, and Dick could see the tiny lights disappear in the distance.

He put the little brown sack under his pillow, and crept into bed, for suddenly he was very tired and sleepy.

The next morning his grandmother aroused him, and he got ready for school.

"What have you got in that queer bag, Dicky?" asked Mrs. Bundle, as Dicky stuffed it in his pocket. He brought it out reluctantly and showed it to her.

"Don't throw them away, Grannie. They're pixie marbles," said Dick, frightened that he would lose his new possession.

"Pixie marbles? They are pixie rubies and emeralds and I don't know what!" cried his grandmother, holding up the glittering gems to the sunlight.

"You mustn't take them away," said Dicky, sulkily. "I am going to take them to school to play marbles."

"These will buy all of the marbles in the world, Dicky," said Mrs. Bundle. "Now we shall be rich as rich. We will build a neat little house, and have an orchard, and keep a few cows and a horse or two."

"And some pigs?" asked Dicky, quickly.

"Yes, pigs and hens and ducks, too. Yes, all of those and more besides. Perhaps we will have a donkey."

"And a new pair of boots for me and a dress for you, Grannie?" asked Dicky.

"Yes, boots and a dress and a suit of good clothes, my child. Then I will write to your father and bring him home, for we must have him to help with the farm, mustn't we?"

"Yes, oh yes," shouted Dicky, flinging his arms around her. "And we'll live on Devonshire junket and cream, shall we Grannie?"

"Maybe we will," she replied. "I think we can manage it."

She trickled the jewels through her fingers, and tried to calculate their worth. Days of poverty were over; she could sit and rest in her old age, and help others, poor as herself. Yes, the pixies had brought fortune to her cottage.

But Dicky Bundle went running off, lest he should be late for school. In his pocket was one of the gems, a smooth round blood-red stone. It made a famous marble, and never missed its aim, so that Dicky became the champion player of all the boys on Dartymoor. That was more important than riches to him, and he took care to tell nobody, where his marbles came from, lest it, too, should be sold, for money isn't everything.

By Alison Uttley

ELSIE PIDDOCK SKIPS IN HER SLEEP

ELSIE PIDDOCK lived in Glynde under Caburn, where
lots of other little girls lived too. They lived mostly on
bread-and-butter because their mothers were too poor to
buy cake. As soon as Elsie began to hear, she heard the

other little girls skipping every evening after school in the lane outside her mother's cottage. SWISH-SWISH! went the rope through the air. TAPPITY-TAP! went the little girls' feet on the ground. MUMBLE-UMBLE-UMBLE! went the children's voices, saying a rhyme that the skipper could skip to. In course of time, Elsie not only heard the sounds, but understood what they were all about, and then the MUMBLE-UMBLE turned itself into words like this:

> "ANdy
> SPANdy
> SUGARdy
> CANdy,
> FRENCH
> ALmond
> ROCK!

Breadandbutterforyoursupper'sallyourmother'sgot!"

The second bit went twice as fast as the first bit, and when the little girls said it, Elsie Piddock, munching her supper, always munched her mouthful of bread-and-butter in double-quick time. She wished she had some Sugardy-Candy-French-Almond-Rock to suck during the first bit, but she never had.

When Elsie Piddock was three years old, she asked her mother for a skipping-rope.

"You're too little," said her mother. "Bide a bit till you're a bigger girl, then you shall have one."

Elsie pouted and said no more. But in the middle of the night her parents were awakened by something going SLAP-SLAP! on the floor, and there was Elsie in her nightgown skipping with her father's braces. She skipped till her feet caught in the tail of them, and she tumbled down and cried. But she had skipped ten times running first.

"Bless my buttons, Mother!" said Mr. Piddock. "The child's a born skipper."

And Mrs. Piddock jumped out of bed full of pride, rubbed Elsie's elbows for her, and said: "There-a-there now! Dry your tears, and tomorrow you shall have a skip-rope all of your own."

So Elsie dried her eyes on the hem of her nightgown; and in the morning, before he went to work, Mr. Piddock got a little cord, just the right length, and made two little wooden handles to go on the ends. With this Elsie skipped all day, scarcely stopping to eat her breakfast of bread-and-butter, and her dinner of bread-and-butter. And in the evening, when the school-children were gathered in the lane, Elsie went out among them, and began to skip with the best.

"Oh!" cried Joan Challon, who was the champion skipper of them all, "just look at little Elsie Piddock skipping as never so!"

All the skippers stopped to look, and then to wonder. Elsie Piddock certainly *did* skip as never so, and they called their mothers to come and see. And the mothers in the lane came to their doors, and threw up their hands, and cried: "Little Elsie Piddock is a born skipper!"

By the time she was five she could outstrip any of them: whether in "Andy Spandy," "Lady, Lady, Drop

Your Purse," "Charley, Parley Stole Some Barley," or whichever of the games it might be. By the time she was six her name and fame were known to all the villagers in the county. And by the time she was seven, the fairies heard of her. They were very fond of skipping themselves, and they had a special Skipping-Master who taught them new skips every month at the new moon. As they skipped, they chanted:

"The High Skip,
The Sly Skip,
The Skip like a Feather,
The Long Skip,
The Strong Skip,
And the Skip All Together!

"The Slow Skip,
The Toe Skip,
The Skip Double-Double,
The Fast Skip,
The Last Skip,
And the Skip against Trouble!"

All these skips had their own meanings, and were made up by the Skipping-Master, whose name was Andy-Spandy. He was very proud of his fairies, because they skipped better than the fairies of any other county; but he was also very severe with them if they did not please him. One night he scolded Fairy Heels-o'-Lead for skipping badly, and praised Fairy Flea-Foot for skipping well. Then Fairy Heels-o'-Lead sniffed and snuffed, and said, "Hhm-hhm-hhm! There's a little girl in Glynde who could skip Flea-Foot round the moon and back again. A born skipper she is and she skips as never so."

"What is her name?" asked Andy-Spandy.

"Her name is Elsie Piddock, and she has skipped down every village from Didling to Wannock."

"Go and fetch her here!" commanded Andy-Spandy.

Off went Heels-o'-Lead, and poked her head through Elsie's little window under the eaves, crying: "Elsie Piddock! Elsie Piddock! There's a Skipping Match on Caburn, and Fairy Flea-Foot says she can skip better than you."

Elsie Piddock was fast asleep, but the words got into her dream, so she hopped out of bed with her eyes closed, took her skipping rope, and followed Heels-o'-Lead to the top of Mount Caburn, where Andy-Spandy and the fairies were waiting for them.

"Skip, Elsie Piddock!" said Andy-Spandy, "and show us what you're worth!"

Elsie twirled her rope and skipped in her sleep, and as she skipped she murmured:

"ANdy
  SPANdy
  SUGARdy
  CANdy,
  FRENCH
  ALmond
  ROCK!
Breadandbutterforyoursupper'sallyourmother'sgot!"

Andy-Spandy watched her skipping, with his eyes as sharp as needles, but he could find no fault with it, nor could the fairies.

"Very good, as far as it goes!" said Andy-Spandy, "Now let us see how far it *does* go. Stand forth, Elsie and Flea-Foot, for the Long Skip."

Elsie had never done the Long Skip, and if she had had all her wits about her she wouldn't have known what Andy-Spandy meant; but as she was dreaming, she understood him perfectly. So she twirled her rope, and as it came over jumped as far along the ground as she could, about twelve feet from where she had started. Then Flea-Foot did the Long Skip, and skipped clean out of sight.

"Hum!" said Andy-Spandy. "Now, Elsie Piddock, let us see you do the Strong Skip."

Once more Elsie understood what was wanted of her; she put both feet together, jumped her rope, and came down with all her strength, so that her heels sank into the ground. Then Flea-Foot did the Strong Skip, and sank in the ground as deep as her waist.

"Hum!" said Andy-Spandy. "And now, Elsie Piddock, let us see you do the Skip All Together."

At his words, all the fairies leaped to their ropes, and began skipping as lively as they could, and Elsie with them. An hour went by, two hours, and three hours; one by one the fairies fell down exhausted, and Elsie Piddock skipped on. Just before morning she was skipping all by herself.

Then Andy-Spandy wagged his head and said: "Elsie Piddock, you are a born skipper. There's no tiring you at all. And for that you shall come once a month to Caburn when the moon is new, and I will teach you to skip till a year is up. And after that I'll wager there won't be a mortal or fairy to touch you."

Andy-Spandy was as good as his word. Twelve times during the next year Elsie Piddock rose up in her sleep with the new moon, and went to the top of Mount Caburn. There she took her place among the fairies, and learned to do all the tricks of the skipping-rope, until she did them better than any. At the end of the year she did the High Skip so well that she skipped right over the moon.

In the Sly Skip, not a fairy could catch her, or know where she would skip to next; so artful was she that she could skip through the lattice of a skeleton leaf, and never break it.

She doubled the Skip Double-Double, in which you only had to double yourself up twice round the skipping-rope before it came down. Elsie Piddock did it four times.

In the Fast Skip, she skipped so fast you couldn't see her, though she stood on the same spot all the time.

In the Last Skip, when all the fairies skipped over the same rope in turn, running round and round till they made a mistake from giddiness, Elsie never got giddy, and never made a mistake, and was always left in last.

In the Slow Skip, she skipped so slow that a mole had time to throw up his hill under her rope before she came down.

In the Toe Skip, when all the others skipped on their

tip-toes, Elsie never touched a grass-blade with more than the edge of her toe-nail.

In the Skip against Trouble, she skipped so joyously that Andy-Spandy himself chuckled with delight.

In the Long Skip, she skipped from Caburn to the other end of Sussex, and had to be fetched back by the wind.

In the Strong Skip, she went right under the earth, as a diver goes under the sea, and the rabbits, whose burrow she had disturbed, handed her up again.

But in the Skip like a Feather she came down like gossamer, so that she could alight on a spider-thread and never shake the dew-drop off.

And in the Skip All Together, she could skip down the whole tribe of fairies, and remain fresh as a daisy. Nobody had ever found out how long Elsie Piddock could skip without getting tired, for everybody else got tired first. Even Andy-Spandy didn't know.

At the end of the year he said to her: "Elsie Piddock, I have taught you all. Bring me your skipping-rope, and you shall have a Prize."

Elsie gave her rope to Andy-Spandy, and he licked the two little wooden handles, first the one and then the other. When he handed the rope back to her, one of the handles was made of Sugar Candy, and the other of French Almond Rock.

"There!" said Andy-Spandy. "Though you suck them never so, they will never grow less, and you shall therefore suck sweet all your life. And as long as you are little enough to skip with this rope, you shall skip as I have taught you. But when you are too big for this rope, and must get a new one, you will no longer be able to do all the fairy skips that you have learned, although you will skip better in the mortal way than any other girl that was ever born. Good-by, Elsie Piddock."

"Aren't I ever going to skip for you again?" asked Elsie Piddock in her sleep.

But Andy-Spandy didn't answer. For morning had come over the Downs, and the fairies disappeared, and Elsie Piddock went back to bed.

If Elsie had been famous for her skipping before this fairy year, you can imagine what she became after it. She created so much wonder that she hardly dared to show all she could do. Nevertheless, for another year she did such incredible things that people came from far and near to see her skip over the church spire, or through the split oak-tree in the Lord's Park, or across the river at its widest point. When there was trouble in her mother's house or any house in the village, Elsie Piddock skipped so gaily that the trouble was forgotten in laughter. And when she skipped all the old games in Glynde, along with the little girls, and they sang:

"ANdy
SPANdy
SUGARdy
CANdy,
FRENCH
ALmond
rock!
Breadandbutterforyoursupper'sallyourmother'sgot!"

Elsie Piddock said: "It aren't all *I've* got!" and gave them all a suck of her new skipping-rope handles all round. And on the night of the new moon, she always led the children up Mount Caburn, where she skipped more marvelously than ever. In fact, it was Elsie Piddock who established the custom of New-Moon-Skipping on Caburn.

But at the end of another year she had grown too big to skip with her little rope. She laid it away in a box, and went on skipping with a longer one. She still skipped as never so, but her fairy tricks were laid away with the rope, and though her friends teased her to do the marvelous things she used to do, Elsie Piddock only laughed, and shook her head, and never told why. In time, when she was still the pride and wonder of the village, people would say: "Ah, but you should ha' seen her when she was a littling! Why, she could skip through her mother's key-hole!" and in more time, these stories became a legend that nobody believed. And in still more time, Elsie grew up (though never very much), and became a little woman, and gave up skipping, because skipping time was over. After fifty years or so, nobody remembered that she had ever skipped at all. Only Elsie knew. For when times were hard, and they often were, she sat by the hearth with her dry crust and no butter, and sucked the Sugar Candy that Andy-Spandy had given her for life.

It was ever and ever so long afterwards. Three new Lords had walked in the Park since the day when Elsie Piddock had skipped through the split oak. Changes had come in the village; old families had died out, new families had arrived; others had moved away to distant parts, the Piddocks among them. Farms had changed hands, cottages had been pulled down, and new ones had been built. But Mount Caburn was as it always had been, and as the people came to think it always would be. And still the children kept the custom of going there each new moon to skip. Nobody remembered how this custom had come about, it was too far back in the years. But customs are customs, and the child who could not skip the new moon in on Caburn stayed at home and cried.

Then a new Lord came to the Park; one not born a Lord, who had grown rich in trade, and bought the old estate. Soon after his coming, changes began to take place more violent than the pulling down of cottages. The new Lord began to shut up foot-paths and destroy rights of way. He stole the Common rights here and there, as he could. In his greed for more than he had got, he raised rents and pressed the people harder than they could bear. But bad as the high rents were to them, they did not mind these so much as the loss of their old rights. They fought the new Lord, trying to keep what had been theirs for centuries, and sometimes they won the fight, but oftener lost it. The constant quarrels bred a spirit of anger between them and the Lord, and out of hate he was prepared to do whatever he could to spite them.

Amongst the lands over which he exercised a certain power was Caburn. This had always been open to the people, and the Lord determined, if he could, to close it.

Looking up the old deeds, he discovered that, though the Down was his, he was obliged to leave a way upon it by which the people could go from one village to another. For hundreds of years they had made a short cut of it over the top.

The Lord's Lawyer told him that, by the wording of the deeds, he could never stop the people from traveling by way of the Downs.

"Can't I!" snorted the Lord. "Then at least I will make them travel a long way round!"

And he had plans drawn up to inclose the whole of the top of Caburn, so that nobody could walk on it. This meant that the people must trudge miles round the base, as they passed from place to place. The Lord gave out that he needed Mount Caburn to build great factories on.

The village was up in arms to defend its rights.

"Can he do it?" they asked those who knew; and they were told: "It is not quite certain, but we fear he can." The Lord was not quite certain either, but he went on with his plans, and each new move was watched with anger and anxiety by the villagers. And not only by the villagers; for the fairies saw that their own skipping-ground was threatened. How could they ever skip there again when the grass was turned to cinders, and the new moon blackened by chimney-smoke?

The Lawyer said to the Lord: "The people will fight you tooth and nail."

"Let 'em!" blustered the Lord; and he asked uneasily: "Have they a leg to stand on?"

"Just half a leg," said the Lawyer. "It would be as well not to begin building yet, and if you can come to terms with them you'd better."

The Lord sent word to the villagers that, though he undoubtedly could do what he pleased, he would, out of his good heart, restore to them a footpath he had blocked if they would give up all pretensions to Caburn.

"Footpath, indeed!" cried stout John Maltman, among his cronies at the Inn. "What's a footpath to Caburn? Why, our mothers skipped there as children, and our children skip there now. And we hope to see our children's children skip there. If Caburn top be built over, 'twill fair break my little Ellen's heart."

"Ay, and my Margery's," said another.

"And my Mary's and Kitty's!" cried a third. Others spoke up, for nearly all had daughters whose joy it was to skip on Caburn at the new moon.

John Maltman turned to their best adviser, who had studied the matter closely, and asked: "What think ye? Have we a leg to stand on?"

"Only half a one," said the other. "I doubt if you can stop him. It might be as well to come to terms."

"None of his footpaths for us," swore stout John Maltman. "We'll fight the matter out."

So things were left for a little, and each side wondered what the next move would be. Only the people knew in their hearts that they must be beaten in the end, and the Lord was sure of his victory. So sure that he had great loads of bricks ordered; but he did not begin building for fear the people might grow violent, and perhaps burn his bricks and destroy his property. The only thing he did was to put a wire fence round the top of Caburn, and set a keeper there to send the people round it. The people broke the fence in many places, and jumped it, and crawled under it; and as the keeper could not be everywhere at once, many of them crossed the Down almost under his nose.

One evening, just before the new moon was due, Ellen Maltman went into the woods to cry. For she was the best skipper under Mount Caburn, and the thought that she would never skip there again made her more unhappy than she had ever thought she could be. While she was crying in the dark, she felt a hand on her shoulder, and a voice said to her: "Crying for trouble, my dear? That'll never do!"

The voice might have been the voice of a withered leaf, it was so light and dry; but it was also kind, so Ellen checked her sobs and said: "It's a big trouble, ma'am; there's no remedy against it *but* to cry."

"Why yes, there is," said the withered voice. "Ye should skip against trouble, my dear."

At this Ellen's sobs burst forth anew. "I'll never skip no more!" she wailed. "If I can't skip the new moon in on Caburn, I'll never skip no more."

"And why can't you skip the new moon in on Caburn?" asked the voice.

Then Ellen told her.

After a little pause the voice spoke quietly out of the darkness. "It's more than you will break their hearts, if they cannot skip on Caburn. And it must not be; it must not be. Tell me your name."

"Ellen Maltman, ma'am, and I do love skipping. I can skip down anybody, ma'am, and they say I skip as never so!"

"They do, do they?" said the withered voice. "Well, Ellen, run you home and tell them this. They are to go up to the Lord and tell him he shall have his way and build on Caburn, if he will first take down the fence and let all who have ever skipped there skip there once more by turns, at the new moon. *All,* mind you, Ellen. And when the last skipper skips the last skip, he may lay his first brick. And let it be written out on paper, and signed and sealed."

"But, ma'am!" said Ellen, wondering.

"No words, child. Do as I tell you." And the withered voice sounded so compelling that Ellen resisted no more. She ran straight to the village, and told the story to everybody.

At first they could hardly swallow it; and even when they had swallowed it, they said: "But what's the sense of it?" But Ellen persisted and persisted; something of the spirit of the old voice got into her words, and against their reason the people began to think it was the thing to do. To cut a long story short, they sent the message to the Lord next day.

The Lord could scarcely believe his ears. He rubbed his hands, and chortled at the people for fools.

"They've come to terms!" he sneered. "I shall have the Down, and keep my footpath too. Well, they shall have their Skipping Party; and the moment it is ended, up go my factories."

The paper was drawn out, signed by both parties in

the presence of witnesses, and duly sealed; and on the
night of the new moon, the Lord invited a party of his
friends to go with him to Caburn to see the sight.

And what a sight it was for them to see; every little
girl in the village was there with her skipping-rope,
from the toddlers to those who had just turned up their
hair. Nay, even the grown maidens and the young
mothers were there; and the very matrons, too, had
come with ropes. Had they not once as children skipped
on Caburn? And the message had said "All." Yes, and
the others were there—others they could not see: Andy-
Spandy and his fairy team, Heels-o'-Lead, Flea-Foot,
and all the rest were gathered round to watch with
bright fierce eyes the last great skipping on their precious ground.

The skipping began. The toddlers first, a skip or so
apiece, a stumble and they fell out. The Lord and his
party laughed aloud at the comical mites, and at another time the villagers would have laughed too. But
there was no laughter in them tonight. Their eyes were
bright and fierce like those of the fairies. After the toddlers the little girls skipped in the order of their ages,
and as they got older, the skipping got better. In the
thick of the school-children, "This will take some time,"
said the Lord impatiently. And when Ellen Maltman's
turn came, and she went into her thousands, he grew
restive. But even she, who could skip as never so, tired
at last; her foot tripped and she fell on the ground with
a little sob. None lasted even half her time; of those
who followed some were better, some were worse than
others; and in the small hours the older women were

beginning to take their turn. Few of them kept it up for half a minute; they hopped and puffed bravely, but their skipping days were done. As they had laughed at the babies, so now the Lord's friends jibed at the babies' grandmothers.

"Soon over now," said the Lord, as the oldest of the women who had come to skip, a fat old dame of sixty-seven, stepped out and twirled her rope. Her foot caught in it; she staggered, dropped the rope, and hid her face in her hands.

"Done!" shouted the Lord; and he brandished at the crowd a trowel and a brick he had brought with him. "Clear out, the lot of you! I am going to lay the first brick. The skipping's ended!"

"No, if you please," said a gentle withered voice, "it is *my* turn now." And out of the crowd stepped a tiny tiny woman, so very old, so very bent and fragile, that she seemed to be no bigger than a little child.

"You!" cried the Lord. "Who are *you?*"

"My name is Elsie Piddock, if you please, and I am a hundred and nine years old. For the last seventy-nine years I have lived over the border, but I was born in Glynde, and I skipped on Caburn as a child." She spoke like one in a dream and her eyes were closed.

"Elsie Piddock! Elsie Piddock!" the name ran in a whisper round the crowd.

"Elsie Piddock!" murmured Ellen Maltman. "Why, mum, I thought Elsie Piddock was just a tale."

"Nay, Elsie Piddock was no tale!" said the fat woman who had skipped last. "My mother Joan skipped with her many a time, and told me tales you never would believe."

"Elsie Piddock!" they all breathed again; and a wind seemed to fly round Mount Caburn, shrilling the name with glee. But it was no wind, it was Andy-Spandy and his fairy team, for they had seen the skipping-rope in the tiny woman's hands. One of the handles was made of Sugar Candy, and the other was made of French Almond Rock.

But the new Lord had never even heard of Elsie Piddock as a story; so laughing coarsely once again, he said: "One more bump for an old woman's bones! Skip, Elsie Piddock, and show us what you're worth."

"Yes, skip Elsie Piddock," cried Andy-Spandy and the fairies, "and show them what you're worth."

Then Elsie Piddock stepped into the middle of the onlookers, twirled her baby rope over her little shrunken body, and began to skip. And she skipped as never so!

First of all she skipped:

"ANdy
SPANdy
SUGARdy
CANdy,
FRENCH
ALmond
ROCK!
Breadandbutterforyoursupper'sallyourmother'sgot!"

And nobody could find fault with her skipping. Even the Lord gasped: "Wonderful! Wonderful for an old woman!" But Ellen Maltman, who *knew,* whispered: "Oh, mum! 'tis wonderful for *any*body! And oh, mum, do but see—she's skipping in her sleep!"

It was true. Elsie Piddock, shrunk to the size of seven years old, was sound asleep, skipping the new moon in with her baby rope that was up to all the tricks. An hour went by, two hours, three hours. There was no stopping her, and no tiring her. The people gasped, the Lord fumed, and the fairies turned head-over-heels for joy. When morning broke the Lord cried: "That's enough!"

But Elsie Piddock went on skipping.

"Time's up!" cried the Lord.

"When I skip my last skip, you shall lay your first brick," said Elsie Piddock.

The villagers broke out into a cheer.

"Signed and sealed, my Lord; signed and sealed," said Elsie Piddock.

"But hang it, old woman, you can't go on forever!" cried the Lord.

"Oh, yes, I can," said Elsie Piddock. And on she went.

At midday the Lord shouted: "Will the woman never stop?"

"No, she won't," said Elsie Piddock. And she didn't.

"Then I'll stop you!" stormed the Lord, and made a grab at her.

"Now for a Sly Skip," said Elsie Piddock, and skipped right through his thumb and forefinger.

"Hold her, you!" yelled the Lord to his Lawyer.

"Now for a High Skip," said Elsie Piddock, and as

the Lawyer darted at her, she skipped right over the highest lark singing in the sun.

The villagers shouted for glee, and the Lord and his friends were furious. Forgotten was the compact signed and sealed—their one thought now was to seize the maddening old woman, and stop her skipping by sheer force. But they couldn't. She played all her tricks on them: High Skip, Slow Skip, Sly Skip, Toe Skip, Long Skip, Fast Skip, Strong Skip, but never Last Skip. On and on and on she went. When the sun began to set, she was still skipping.

"Can we never rid the Down of the old thing?" cried the Lord desperately.

"No," answered Elsie Piddock in her sleep, "the Down will never be rid of me more. It's the children of Glynde I'm skipping for, to hold the Down for them and theirs forever; it's Andy-Spandy I'm skipping for once again, for through him I've sucked sweet all my life. Oh, Andy, even you never knew how long Elsie Piddock could go on skipping!"

"The woman's mad!" cried the Lord. "Signed and sealed doesn't hold with a madwoman. Skip or no skip, I shall lay the first brick!"

He plunged his trowel into the ground, and forced his brick down into the hole as a token of his possession of the land.

"Now," said Elsie Piddock, "for a Strong Skip!"

Right on the top of the brick she skipped, and down underground she sank out of sight, bearing the brick beneath her. Wild with rage, the Lord dived after her. Up came Elsie Piddock skipping blither than ever—but the Lord never came up again. The Lawyer ran to look down the hole; but there was no sign of him. The Lawyer reached his arm down the hole; but there was no reaching him. The Lawyer dropped a pebble down the hole; and no one heard it fall. So strong had Elsie Piddock skipped the Strong Skip.

The Lawyer shrugged his shoulders, and he and the Lord's friends left Mount Caburn for good and all. Oh, how joyously Elsie Piddock skipped then!

"Skip Against Trouble!" cried she, and skipped so that everyone present burst into happy laughter. To the tune of it she skipped the Long Skip, way out of sight. And the people went home to tea. Caburn was saved for their children and for the fairies, forever.

But that wasn't the end of Elsie Piddock; she has never stopped skipping on Caburn since, for Signed and Sealed is Signed and Sealed. Not many have seen her, because she knows all the tricks; but if you go to Caburn at the new moon, you may catch a glimpse of a tiny bent figure, no bigger than a child, skipping all by itself in its sleep, and hear a gay little voice, like the voice of a dancing yellow leaf, singing:

"ANdy
SPANdy
SUGARdy
CANdy,
FRENCH
ALmond
rock!

Breadandbutterforyoursupper'sallyourmother'sgot!"

By Eleanor Farjeon

TOLD
UNDER THE
MAGIC UMBRELLA

Compiled by the Literature Committee

of the

ASSOCIATION FOR CHILDHOOD EDUCATION *

DOROTHY W. BARUCH, *Whittier College*

JEAN BETZNER, *Teachers College, Columbia University*

FRANCES KERN, *National College of Education*

ANNIE E. MOORE

ELOISE RAMSEY, *Wayne University*

KATHERINE REEVES, *New York State College of Home Economics, Cornell University*

MARTHA SEELING, *Roslyn Heights Public Schools*

MARY REED WOOD, *Trenton Public Schools*

MARY LINCOLN MORSE, *Chairman*

* The Association for Childhood Education became The Association for Childhood Education International in 1946.

A MESSAGE TO GROWN-UPS BY WAY OF EXPLANATION

Told Under the Magic Umbrella has been compiled by the members of the Literature Committee of the Association for Childhood Education as a fourth volume in the series of umbrella books for young children. Its companion volumes are *Told Under the Green Umbrella,* a collection of folk and fairy tales; *Told Under the Blue Umbrella,* a compilation of stories, real and nearly real; and *Sung Under the Silver Umbrella,* an anthology of verse. To supplement the previous umbrella books, and with them to cover the complete field of the literary needs of children, *Told Under the Magic Umbrella* specializes in stories that are both modern and fanciful.

As members of the Literature Committee, we set no limitations to the period covered by the word "modern," yet we found many more than a majority of the stories we had selected as childlike, and for both story and fancy, written in the near-by present and in the language of present-day life. This seems an evidence of the growing art in story writing for the children of today. Surely some of the stories we have chosen will, in the future, take their places among the lasting tales of yesterday.

Our Committee, at long distance, carried on an interpretative discussion. We tried to analyze back of our stories what we believed fancy to be. Broadly speaking, it was taken to mean any departure from conceded reality out into the realm of the unreal. In its simplest form it endowed characters not possessing it with the power of speech. Here a hen may talk, yet otherwise remain thoroughly henlike in character. Or again, we thought of fancy as giving to story characters the ability to act not in keeping with their own acts but with those of human beings—as when a hen markets, cooks, lives like a human being. Still further, departure from the factual was taken to involve the supernatural or superhuman or for characters and events to transcend all reality. Such tales involve fairies, witches, ogres, transformations, charms and the like. Out of this analysis we evolved a definition which we look back on (as has many another such working group as ours) with dissatisfaction. Our definition was bare bones but no more; there was no song of a nightingale in it. We leave any further defining of what we believe fantasy is, to our stories—to them and to Mrs. Bianco's Foreword.

That the field of fancy is as wide as it is varied, and is limited only by the capacity for such in human beings, was evidenced even by the differing personal reactions of our committee members to our included stories. Some of us did or did not like definite tales; but, we added, children like them—or some of them at least. On the whole, the range of stories in *Told Under the Magic Umbrella* should, we think, possess the human variety sought by and satisfying to children of divergent tastes. We regret that some of our unanimously selected stories were not available for use:

Wanda Gag's "Millions of Cats" and Hugh Lofting's "The Story of Mrs. Tubbs" are representative of such.

The stories secured for use in *Told Under the Magic Umbrella* have been arranged from the simpler ones on. Though many of them seem to reach most securely into the imaginative interests of children in the second, third and fourth grades, there are some for younger children. They suggest use with a child wherever their story and fancy fit.

No story, as story, or invested with fancy as such, not receiving a majority vote has found its way into *Told Under the Magic Umbrella*. By majority choice also, our essayist, Margery Williams Bianco, was chosen; our illustrator, Elizabeth Orton Jones, selected; and our dedication—"To the Children Who Love Wonder, Magic, Fun"—adopted. This says what we unanimously want it to say—to wonder, magic, fun our magic umbrella is consecrated. We chose our book title and agreed that its cover carry the magic color red.

In another section devoted to acknowledgments, the committee registers its appreciation to the many publishers who released for our use stories held by them. For stories suggested by other than committee members, for the editorial service of association members, and for the original publication privilege of stories generously contributed, the committee records its gratitude.

No explanation as to how *Told Under the Magic Umbrella* took its present shape would be complete without a tribute to the steady cooperation of Doris S. Patee, Children's Book Editor of our publisher, The

Macmillan Company. Miss Patee has served as adviser to each step in the preparation of our fourth umbrella. For its attractive format she alone is responsible.

In conclusion it is the hope of the members of the Literature Committee of the Association for Childhood Education that, assisted by Mrs. Bianco's foreword and the illustrative art of Miss Jones, the stories in our magic umbrella may carry children's imaginations out beyond the land of conceded reality into the realm of a joyous and spirited fancy. Here unaccountable things happen—a bear may whisper of a mother's birthday present in a little boy's ear, or, on Caburn one may catch, at the new moon, a glimpse of a tiny bent figure, no bigger than a child, skipping all by itself in its sleep. One may even hear a gay little voice, like the voice of a dancing leaf, singing:

> "ANdy
> SPANdy
> SUGARdy
> CANdy,
> FRENCH
> ALmond
> ROCK!

Breadandbutterforyoursupper'sallyourmother'sgot!"

MARY LINCOLN MORSE, *Chairman*

1939

INTERNATIONAL CHEMICAL SERIES

LOUIS P. HAMMETT, PH.D., *Consulting Editor*

★ ★
★

A HISTORY OF CHEMISTRY

A Selection of Titles from the

INTERNATIONAL CHEMICAL SERIES

Louis P. Hammett, Ph.D., *Consulting Editor*

(Photo. by Notman)

PROFESSOR F. J. MOORE

(Reproduced by permission from the photograph by Notman of Cambridge, Mass.)

(Frontispiece)

ROBERT BOYLE
1627–1691

A HISTORY
OF CHEMISTRY

by F. J. MOORE, PH. D.
Late Professor of Organic Chemistry
in Massachusetts Institute of Technology

Revision Prepared by

WILLIAM T. HALL
Associate Professor of Analytical Chemistry
in the Massachusetts Institute of Technology

Third Edition

McGRAW-HILL BOOK COMPANY, INC.
NEW YORK AND LONDON
1939

PREFACE TO THE THIRD EDITION

In preparing the third edition of *A History of Chemistry*, numerous changes have been made throughout. In previous editions of this book, the attempt was made merely to tell the story down to the present time, and little attention was paid to the work of living scientists because it was felt that the student would learn such things from modern texts in the various fields of chemistry. Chemistry, however, has become so broad that it is extremely difficult for any one to keep in touch with all the progress that is being made. For that reason, the work of prominent chemists in the various fields is discussed down to the present time with the hope of showing that today additions to our knowledge are taking place at a rate never before equaled.

Probably no two chemists will agree perfectly concerning the most notable facts or men of a single decade, and, when it comes to covering the entire history of chemical knowledge and theories in a short text, the difficulties are much greater. Tilden, in his *Famous Chemists*, gives biographies of only about twenty scientists in nearly 300 pages. Thorpe's *Essays in Historical Chemistry* covers eighteen topics in 571 pages, but Partington's *A Short History of Chemistry* mentions no less than 416 men in 373 pages. This excellent book by Partington has proved helpful in deciding what names should be added in making the present revision. Concerning early chemistry, considerable information has been obtained from Read's *Prelude to Chemistry*, which is published in very attractive form and is interesting from cover to cover.

Books like Kopp's *Geschichte der Chemie*, Bugge's *Das Buch der grossen Chemiker*, and Ostwald's *Grösse Männer* are valuable sources of information, and one cannot but admire the authors' painstaking thoroughness. It seems, however, that these books sometimes neglect chemists who lived in countries other than Germany. This is, of course, quite natural, for most of us are

vii

more familiar with work that has been published in our own language, and few of us can read Italian, Russian, Spanish, Portuguese, Chinese, and Japanese. The history of chemistry shows clearly that centuries ago knowledge concerning chemical facts was common to several civilizations. Today, with the much more rapid interchange of ideas and materials, most new ideas develop almost simultaneously in several countries, and the literature is full of discoveries (and they really are discoveries!) of facts that are known in other countries or are being published elsewhere. As a rule there are brilliant scientists in Italy, in Russia, or in Japan who are doing similar work to that which is being published in Germany, England, or France, but the English-speaking world is less likely to know about them.

In the German books on the history of chemistry, which have been either directly or indirectly the sources of much information in all books on the subject, the work of American chemists has been neglected. The fact that American chemists have repeatedly won awards, such as the Nobel prizes, shows clearly that chemistry in the United States today is keeping pace with that of other countries. This is not entirely due to the fact that many Americans have studied abroad, but rather to the fact that there has always been an interest in chemistry in America since the early colonial days. More attention in this book is, therefore, paid to the story of American chemistry than is customary in short histories.

When physical chemistry began to develop strongly toward the end of the nineteenth century, many of us felt that organic chemistry had had its day, and some still feel that organic chemistry has received altogether too much attention in the histories of chemistry. Since, however, the organic chemists have learned to take advantage of the laws of physical chemistry, their work has progressed more rapidly than ever.

Physical chemistry is now so inseparably united with every other branch of chemistry that it is hard to discuss it by itself. In preparing the revision it was noticed that many chemists could be mentioned equally well in the chapters on Inorganic Chemistry since 1860, Radioactivity, and The Rise of Physical Chemistry. In the attempt to make a separation, there were so many difficulties encountered that finally all three chapters were merged into one. This makes a very long chapter, some of which has been set in small type for the sake of economy of space.

The originals for most of the new illustrations were kindly loaned by the *Journal of Chemical Education*, which has published the pictures in sets that sell for a reasonable price. In reading the proof, valuable assistance has been received from Professor Tenney L. Davis, who has offered valuable suggestions and whose knowledge of the history of chemistry is very extensive.

WILLIAM T. HALL.

CAMBRIDGE, MASS.,
  August, 1939.

PREFACE TO THE FIRST EDITION

This volume is the outgrowth of a series of talks which the author has for several years given to his students at the Institute of Technology, the hearers being members of the senior class specializing in chemistry, and hence familiar with its more important facts and principles. The lectures have dealt in a direct informal way with the fundamental ideas of the science; their origin, their philosophical basis, the critical periods in their development, and the personalities of the great men whose efforts have contributed to that development.

Put in book form the material has inevitably been somewhat expanded, and just as inevitably its presentation has assumed a more formal tone, without, it is hoped, losing all its spontaneity. Here, as before, the person addressed is the more mature student of chemistry, though it is believed that few portions of the book will present serious difficulties to the general reader. The aim has been to emphasize only those facts and influences which have contributed to make the science what it is today; hence such topics as the chemical achievements of the ancients and the history of alchemy have been compressed beyond the point which the tastes and inclinations of the writer might alone have dictated. In the discussion of later work, also, the claim of a topic for consideration has been not its practical but its historical importance. It has been asked, not whether the work was itself of value, but did it contribute a new fundamental idea. For this reason, to cite a single instance, the work of Werner on the metal-ammonias has been discussed at some length, while that of Emil Fischer on the sugars has been dismissed with a single word. Some modern topics, also, like the work of Werner just mentioned, or that of Bragg upon X-ray spectra, have been treated in considerable detail because they lie outside the field familiar to most undergraduates.

Little attention has been paid to questions of priority. A great discovery is usually preceded by a multitude of earlier observations, the sum total of which may even include all the fundamental facts involved. Hence arise the familiar troubles encountered by the conscientious student when he attempts to learn who invented the steam engine or who really discovered America. We can, however, save ourselves most of these difficulties if we reflect that from the historical standpoint the discoverer of a great truth is usually the one through whose efforts it first becomes available to the race.

A word may not be out of place concerning the illustrations. These have been reproduced from many sources, and have been selected entirely for their historical interest without regard to their artistic merit. It will therefore occasion no surprise that they differ greatly among themselves in the latter respect. Thanks are especially due to Professor Derr of the Institute for placing at the disposal of the author his unusual skill and knowledge of photography, and also to several publishers who have kindly permitted the use of copyrighted material.

The value of the historical method for studying every department of human thought is now so universally recognized that it requires no emphasis, but to the younger student of chemistry it may not be superfluous to point out that, by observing the errors and misunderstandings of the past, we learn to avoid errors in our own thinking; by acquaintance with the way in which great men have solved problems, we are assisted in solving problems of our own; by observing the different aspects presented by the same facts in the light of successive theories, we acquire an insight obtainable in no other way into the nature, limitations, and proper function of all theories. Finally, as we study how man's knowledge of nature has broadened and deepened with the years, we acquire a better understanding of the trend of thought in our own times, and of the exact bearing of each new discovery upon the old but ever recurring problems of the science. At no period has the development of chemistry been more rapid or more interesting than it is today, and the author indulges the hope that even this brief sketch of its history may assist the reader to follow that development with a fuller appreciation of its significance, for, after all, we study the past that we may understand the present and judge wisely of the future.

MASSACHUSETTS INSTITUTE OF TECHNOLOGY,   F. J. MOORE.
    April, 1918.

CONTENTS

F. J. MOORE

Forris Jewett Moore was born in Pittsfield, Massachusetts, on June 9, 1867, and died at Cambridge, Massachusetts, on November 20, 1926. His boyhood days were spent in Claremont, New Hampshire, where he lies buried with others of his family.

In 1889, he was graduated from Amherst College, where his interest in chemistry had been awakened by Elijah Paddock Harris. As a student in college, Moore was especially interested in the study of philosophy and was disposed to do his major work in that field, but the strong personality of Harris led him to choose eventually the field of chemistry. After graduation, Moore taught this subject for one year at Amherst. The next year he went to Germany and studied at Heidelberg under Gatterman and Victor Meyer, receiving the degree of Ph. D. It was there that he became acquainted with Miss Emma Tod of Edinburgh, who was studying music and the German language. In 1892, they were married in Scotland.

Upon completion of his studies in Germany, Moore served a year as an instructor at Cornell. At the World's Fair in Chicago in 1893, he made many chemical analyses. In the fall of 1894, he came to the Massachusetts Institute of Technology as assistant in analytical chemistry. He was later made professor and remained there until 1925, when he retired because of ill health.

Ostwald in his *Grösse Männer* and in the biographical sketches which he wrote for Bugge's *Das Buch der grossen Chemiker* repeatedly states that eminent men usually fit into one of two classes. There is the romantic type of man, represented by those who show great brilliance at an early age and do their best work before they are thirty. Chemists of this type show great promise as students, publish the results of a brilliant research soon after graduation from the university and rarely do anything remarkable after reaching the forties. Then there is the classic type, in which the man matures slowly, constantly

xvii

learns from experience and often does some of his very best work in his declining years. Moore belonged to the latter class. All his life he was a student, and his ability as a teacher, as a chemist, as a philosopher and as a historian ripened with the lapse of time.

A list of Moore's publications arranged in chronological order follows:

1. A Method of Isolating Aromatic Sulfo Acids, *Dissertation*, Heidelberg, 1893.

2. Cleavage of a Sulfo Group by a Reducing Agent, *Ber.*, Vol. 33, pp. 2014–2015 (1900).

3. Some Derivatives of *p*-Sulfocinnamic Acid (with L. A. Salinger), *J. Am. Chem. Soc.*, Vol. 25, pp. 622–629 (1903).

4. Piperonal and Hydrogen Chloride: A Two-component, Three-phase System, *J. Am. Chem. Soc.*, Vol. 28, pp. 1188–1190 (1906).

5. Benzoyl-*p*-bromophenylurea: A By-product in the Preparation of Benzbromamide (with Miss A. M. Cedarholm), *J. Am. Chem. Soc.*, Vol. 28, pp. 1190–1198 (1906).

6. The Colored Salts of Schiff's Bases: A Contribution to Our Knowledge of Color as Related to Chemical Constitution; I, The Hydrochlorides of Bases Formed by Condensing *p*-Aminodiphenylamine with Aromatic Aldehydes (with R. D. Gale), *J. Am. Chem. Soc.*, Vol. 30, pp. 394–404 (1908).

7. The Colored Salts of Schiff's Bases; II, The Hydrochlorides of Bases Formed by Condensing *p*-Aminodiphenylamine with Aromatic Aldehydes (with R. G. Woodbridge, Jr.), *J. Am. Chem. Soc.*, Vol. 30, pp. 1001–1004 (1908).

8. The Colored Salts of Schiff's Bases; III, The Salts of Bases Formed by Condensing *m*-Aminodiethylaniline with Aromatic Aldehydes, *J. Am. Chem. Soc.*, Vol. 32, pp. 382–388 (1910).

9. Note on the Preparation of Benzophenonimide Derivatives, *Ber.*, Vol. 43, pp. 563–565 (1910).

10. *Outlines of Organic Chemistry*, John Wiley and Sons, 1910, 1914, 1924.

11. *Experiments in Organic Chemistry*, John Wiley and Sons, 1911.

12. Recent Synthetic Studies in the Tannin Group, *J. Ind. Eng. Chem.*, Vol. 6, pp. 450–452 (1914).

13. The Periodides of Acid Amides and Their Addition Products with Metallic Salts: Substances of Exceptionally High Molecular Weights (with Ruth M. Thomas), *J. Am. Chem. Soc.*, Vol. 36, pp. 1928–1937 (1914).

14. Constitution of Xanthogallol (with Ruth M. Thomas), *J. Am. Chem. Soc.*, Vol. 39, pp. 974–1011 (1917).

15. Hydrogen Peroxide as a Reagent in the Purine Group; I, Cyanuric Acid as an Oxidation Product of Uric Acid; Its Probable Identity with Tetracarbonimide (with C. S. Venable), *J. Am. Chem. Soc.*, Vol. 39, pp. 1750–1755 (1917).

16. Hydrogen Peroxide as a Reagent in the Purine Group; II, Action of Hydrogen Peroxide upon Uric Acid (with C. S. Venable), *J. Am. Chem. Soc.*, Vol. 40, pp. 1099–1120 (1918).

17. Hydrogen Peroxide as a Reagent in the Purine Group; III, Allantoxanic Acid as an Oxidation Product of Uric Acid (with Ruth M. Thomas), *J. Am. Chem. Soc.*, Vol. 40, pp. 1120–1132 (1918).

18. *History of Chemistry*, McGraw-Hill Book Company, Inc., 1918.

19. Constitution of the Secondary Products in the Sulfonation of Cinnamic Acid (with Ruth M. Thomas), *J. Am. Chem. Soc.*, Vol. 44, pp. 367–369 (1922).

20. Hydrogen Peroxide as a Reagent in the Purine Group; IV, Action of Hydrogen Peroxide upon Certain Phenyl Substituted Uric Acids (with Elizabeth Gatewood), *J. Am. Chem. Soc.*, Vol. 45, pp. 135–145 (1923).

21. Renewed Study of the Sulfonation of Cinnamic Acid: A Proof That the Secondary Product Is *m*-Sulfocinnamic Acid and the Action of Sodium Bisulfite on Cinnamic Acid Derivatives (with G. R. Tucker), *J. Am. Chem. Soc.*, Vol. 49, pp. 258–266 (1927).

22. Unsymmetrical Phenanthridones; I, The Synthesis of 2-Nitro and 7-Nitrophenanthridone (with E. H. Huntress), *J. Am. Chem. Soc.*, Vol. 49, pp. 2618–2624 (1927).

It would lead us too far into the realm of organic chemistry to discuss the scientific value of this work, but those best fitted to judge have been impressed with the thoroughness and the patient attention to minute details. Moore never made a statement without first testing it from various angles.

The dates of the publications show that in the ten years following his research work at Heidelberg, Moore published little. During this period he was teaching analytical chemistry to beginners. He, together with another instructor and a single assistant, was handling large classes of more than one hundred twenty-five students. The laboratory was kept open from 8:30 until 5 and Moore was accessible to students during more than six hours every day. No student ever found him too busy to give instruction and there was rarely an hour during the week when he was free from interruption. For three hours nearly every afternoon, he went slowly from bench to bench in the laboratory, leaving with every student a kindly word of encouragement or advice. To the students in qualitative analysis, he would usually suggest some additional confirmatory test and would show how to make it. Laboratory tests were often recommended in order to teach the worker how to reason correctly from laboratory data. Dr. Richard C. Tolman has said that

Moore was the first teacher who taught him how to think and use his imagination.

In addition to this class work, there were other reasons why Moore did little research during these ten years. He was called upon to teach qualitative and quantitative analysis, although his interest was in another field. He was a good analyst and an excellent teacher of analytical methods, but he did not like routine analytical work. He himself carried out in the laboratory every procedure that he taught and personally analysed the samples that he gave to his students.

Physically, he was never robust and strong enough to do both research and active teaching. Moreover, because of his intense interest in organic chemistry, he was spending a great deal of time reading the scientific journals. Fischer's work on the sugars and on the proteins was, as he sometimes put it, "as interesting and exciting as a novel." He was especially interested in the work of Becquerel, the philosophic writings of Ostwald, and the theoretical speculations of G. N. Lewis.

In 1912, Moore was made professor of organic chemistry at the Massachusetts Institute of Technology and placed in charge of the department; here he felt more at home. His lectures were so fascinating that students sometimes heard the entire course a second time of their own volition and without any academic credit. In 1910–1911 he was lecturer in organic chemistry at Harvard and again in 1917–1918 and in 1918–1919.

He was a member of the Deutsche Chemische Gesellschaft as well as of the American Chemical Society and was appointed a fellow of the American Academy of Arts and Sciences and a member of the National Research Council.

Most of us who worked with Moore regarded him as the ideal teacher and all regarded him as a friend. Many illustrations could be given of his kindly acts. He took a fatherly interest in the careers of his assistants, and during the last years of his service at M.I.T. he always had at least one assistant working for him whose salary was not paid out of the Institute funds. It was characteristic of Moore never to seek praise or to ask monetary reward.

His interests were not limited to chemistry and to his teaching. Many subjects attracted him and he read books on astronomy, navigation, yachting, chess, mathematics, and theoretical chemistry, as well as on organic chemistry. He had a good knowledge of the classics and of French and German literature. His broad general knowledge combined with his outstanding ability as a chemist, his sense of humor, and his friendly interest made him a remarkable teacher—beloved and respected.

A HISTORY

OF

CHEMISTRY

CHAPTER I

CHEMISTRY AMONG THE ANCIENTS

A practical knowledge of many important chemical operations must have preceded the dawn of connected history. The preparation of wine and vinegar, the arts of pottery, elementary metallurgy, glassmaking, and dyeing are referred to as familiar processes in the earliest human records. Those who practiced these arts in ancient times, however, recognized no bond of union between the various pursuits, and would themselves have been astonished if they had been classified together. The dyer, the potter, or the worker in metals either inherited his craft or acquired skill through years of apprenticeship to some successful master. In either case the practical rules of procedure must have been handed down in the form of oral tradition since the artisan class was practically illiterate. From the number and variety of the industries successfully carried on, the sum total of knowledge of chemical phenomena involved in them must have been considerable, but we have no records of the details, and what we know of these early conditions depends upon the chance allusions of contemporary writers or upon the products unearthed by archaeological research.

Mankind has probably existed on this earth for at least 250,000 years, but our definite knowledge of history begins at about 3500 B.C. Early mankind has been classified into various periods of development, such as the Stone Age, the Bronze Age and the Iron Age, according to the prevalent use of stone, bronze, and iron implements, but no definite dates can be given for dis-

1

tinguishing these ages, and, in many respects, the American Indian can be regarded as having been living in a Stone Age when America was discovered.

Gold was probably the first metal known as it occurs in an uncombined state in the sand of some rivers. Gold ornaments have been found, together with polished-stone implements, in excavations in Egypt and in Mesopotamia, which date from the latter part of the Stone Age (the Neolithic Age).

Both gold and silver ornaments have been found that date back to the Stone Age in Egypt. At first, silver appears to have been rarer than gold and was valued more highly up to 3000 B.C., and perhaps later. Copper figures have been found dating back to 3000 B.C., and a spout of a vessel dating from that period or earlier has been found to contain nearly pure antimony. Bronze was in use at 2500 B.C., when lead and iron were also known. The American Indians prepared copper objects from native copper, but it is probable that early Egyptian copper was obtained by reducing the mineral malachite ($Cu_2CO_3(OH)_2$) in charcoal fires. Mercury was known to the Egyptians at 1500 B.C., and ancient Hindu and Chinese literature show references to this element, although it does not appear to have been recognized as a metal. In fact, the word *metal* merely meant something that came from the mines.

Glazed pottery and glass date from the predynastic period in Egypt (before 3400 B.C.), but the manufacture of glass on a large scale did not begin in Egypt until about 1370 B.C. The alkali used in its manufacture was *natron* ($Na_2CO_3.10H_2O$), which was incorrectly translated *niter* in the English Bible. The blue dye *indigo* was used by the Egyptians prior to 2000 B.C. The scriptural account of certain experiences of Noah makes it clear that the preparation of intoxicating beverages at least preceded the writing of Genesis.

The science of chemistry has been regarded as the outcome of man's attempts to make gold and to explain its occurrence. In China and in Egypt gold was regarded as a magic medicine from very remote times. There were expert goldsmiths as early as 3000 B.C., and in the valley of the Euphrates, Sumerian metal workers practiced their craft at least 500 years earlier. The early Egyptians became very skillful in arts, such as metallurgy, enameling, glass tinting, extraction of vegetable oils, and dyeing, and Egypt, or *Khem*, the country of the black soil, has been called the motherland of chemistry. This area of the "black country" became to the Arabs *al Khem*, and from this our word alchemy is probably derived.

The reputed Egyptian origin of chemistry is encouraged by many references in early alchemistic writings to *Hermes Trismegistus*. Hermes, the thrice great, was a legendary character who was a ruler of Egypt, a poet, and a philosopher. He is the equivalent of the Egyptian ibis-headed Thoth and is sometimes identified with Athotis of 3400 B.C. According to an oft-repeated legend, the Precepts of Hermes were engraved on an emerald stone. The emerald tablet is not really chemistry but represents a doctrine of cosmology which was very much like certain Chinese theories and had to do with the action of the sun (sulfur) and the moon (mercury). Later workers read alchemical ideas into it and in alchemical literature some 36,000 writings have been attributed to Hermes.

The main end of alchemy was the search for the *elixir* and the *philosophers' stone*. These were assumed to have the power of creating eternal youth and would turn base metals into gold.

It is quite possible that China is really the original home of alchemy. Ideas that are characteristic of alchemical writings appear in Chinese literature as early as the third century B.C. Chinese alchemy is closely related to Taoism, a system of philosophy and religion. Ko Hung, A.D. 281–361, writes of the three goals of alchemy: (1) the preparation of real gold from base metal, (2) the preparation of gold, either natural or artificial but always genuine gold, in an edible form in order that one might attain immortality by eating it, and (3) the chemical preparation of other less efficacious medicines of immortality.

Some hold that alchemy filtered into China from Egypt, Mesopotamia, or India, and others claim that alchemy reached China as a result of trade with Arabs. But it is just as likely that alchemy really started from the philosophy of Taoism and spread westward from China. At an early period, the Chinese sought to prepare an elixir of life and a similar idea was prevalent in India at A.D. 1000. The Hindus, like the Chinese, associated medicinal gold with longevity, or even immortality.

There is no evidence of alchemy in Europe before the eighth century A.D., but the first known work devoted entirely to alchemy is a Chinese treatise of A.D. 142.

Alchemical reasoning was deductive and based on the assumption that all matter resulted from the combination or interaction of two first principles and on the existence of a transmuting agent, which was known under many names, such as *philosophers' stone, elixir vitae, grand magisterium, magistery* or *elixir, red tincture.* All matter was alike in being composed of an active constituent and a sluggish one. Mercury and sulfur were often regarded as these constituents.

The Greek Philosophers.—Although the origin of alchemy cannot be assigned to a definite time and place, it is clear that practical chemistry prevailed in Alexandria, Egypt, at about the beginning of the Christian era, and during the Alexandrian age (306 B.C.–A.D. 642) the description of chemical transformations became permeated with Greek philosophy and the Egyptian belief in magic. At this time, the Egyptian knowledge of metallurgy and other arts became fused with the mystical philosophies of the Neoplatonists and the Gnostics. The former regarded matter as the principle of unreality or evil, and the latter cared little for the phenomena of the sensible world. The equivalent of the English word *chemistry* (chemia) first appears in an edict of the Emperor Diocletian, in A.D. 296, in which the Egyptian books on the subject were ordered to be burned. Plutarch at about A.D. 100 explains its origin from the old name for Egypt and its black soil. The scholarly Greeks had no first-hand knowledge of chemical transformations. Their social position kept them out of touch with those who might have given them practical information, and the whole atmosphere of the age discredited experiment as it discredited manual labor. Pure thought was alone held worthy of the philosopher, and by its means the Greeks made wonderful advances in mathematics and metaphysics. It was not surprising, therefore, that with no other guide they should have approached the problems of natural science with ill-founded confidence. Here, however, the costly experience of later centuries was destined to show that thinking that is not constantly checked by experiment leads only to unreliable results.

In spite of all this the great Greek philosophers exercised unbounded influence upon their contemporaries, and their ideas held sway throughout the Middle Ages. Indeed, it is not difficult to detect some Greek influence upon scientific thinking even in the twentieth century. For this reason, their opinions must be considered at least in outline here.

Thales.—The first of the Greek philosophers of whom we have any record is Thales of Miletus who is supposed to have lived between 640 and 546 B.C.[1] He left no writings that have come down to us, and we are indebted to Aristotle for most of what we know concerning him, as well as concerning several others of the earliest thinkers. He is best remembered among chemists for his statement that water is the origin of all things, but we can hardly be justified in receiving this statement in a literal sense. We have to recall that philosophers have always delighted in pointing out the ephemeral character of all things temporal, and this general condition of flux and change is well symbolized by water. If we add that Thales, as the inhabitant of a small island, was doubtless well acquainted with the sea and had some realization of its teeming life, we see that he may well have grasped the idea that all life must have had its rise there.

Anaximenes (560–500 B.C.) held that air is the fundamental substance, whereas earth was designated as an element by several philosophers. It seems to depend upon how certain passages are interpreted whether the priority should be according to Xenophanes, Pherecydes, Empedocles, or even Anaximander. In all cases we probably have to do with essentially poetic symbols.

Heraclitus.—Perhaps a little more consideration should be given to Heraclitus of Ephesus (536–470 B.C.), who maintained that fire is the primordial substance. Here again the word fire was doubtless used as a symbol of the transitory, and this philosopher was apparently the first Western thinker to teach systematically that the senses are unreliable and that all things, even those which seem most permanent, are really moving pictures made up by our minds from a series of constantly succeeding

---

[1] The reader will understand that most of these ancient dates may well be in error by a decade or more.

states.   The firelight is apt to promote reflection, and one who
attentively watches a candle or gas flame may reach some
important conclusions, even if he knows very little about the
mechanism of combustion.   A flame has many of the attributes
of a rigid body, such as form, position, temperature, and inertia,
yet it must be made up of constantly changing units whose
entrance into it and departure from it no eye is able to perceive.
Why then may not all our world be a "flame picture" without
permanency or enduring substance?   Such conceptions are common enough in later thought.   They did not serve to advance the
knowledge of chemistry among the ancients.

Heraclitus taught that nature strives toward opposites and
brings harmony from them and not from likes, just as the artist
mixes together the unlike colors to achieve likeness to the original.

Pythagoras, the famous Greek mathematician, lived in the
sixth century B.C.   Although he left no writings, he founded in
the Greek cities of southern Italy a school which was much like
a fraternity or secret society, and which, because of political tendencies, ultimately aroused sufficient hostility to cause its
destruction.   The Pythagoreans held that the cosmos had its
origin and interpretation in number; alchemy derived its mystical
relationships partly from the Pythagoreans and partly from
the Cabala, a system of theosophy developed largely by Jewish
rabbis and scholars during the Middle Ages, which assumed that
every letter, number or even accent in the Scriptures had some
mystical meaning.

The Eleatic School, founded by Xenophanes of Kolophon
(570–480 B.C.), taught that matter is continuous and, since the
universe is full of matter, there is no motion and we only *think*
that things move.   Zeno of Elea (b. 489 B.C.) was a prominent
master of this school.   Leucippus (or Leukippos) was a Greek
philosopher who lived at about this time, but all his writings
are lost, and his very existence has been doubted although
Aristotle (384–322 B.C.) states that Leucippus argued against the
Eleatic School and was the real founder of the atomic theory.
The atomic theory was adopted and extended by Democritus.

Empedocles.—Empedocles (490–430 B.C.) combined the ideas
of his predecessors and was apparently the first to speak of the
"four elements," earth, air, fire, and water.   These he supposed

to act upon each other under the influence of love and hate (attraction and repulsion). He seems to have associated a genuine chemical sense with these expressions, for he is said to have stated that flesh and blood are made up of equal quantities of the four elements, whereas bones are made of one-half fire, one-fourth earth, and one-fourth water. Such a statement in itself goes far to show the irresponsible rashness and self-confidence with which the philosophers of this age were wont to approach the discussion of things concerning which they knew nothing. Because coupled with the authority of great names this did untold harm in later centuries.

Democritus (or Demokritos) (about 460–370 B.C.) was one who had much to do with the development of ideas that led, about twenty centuries later, to the present atomic theory of chemistry. He is said to have been an experimenter and wonder worker. He was one of the most famous and acute thinkers of antiquity, but only a few fragments of his writings remain extant. He taught, according to Aristotle, that atoms are hard and have form, size, and weight. They are invisible, because so small, and have no color, taste, or smell. They are in ceaseless motion, and the universe can be regarded as an immense vacuum in which a vast concourse of atoms moves under the impulse of blind fate. From the time of Democritus, there has always been belief in some sort of an atomic theory. It was adopted as an atheistic theory by the school of Epicurus (340–270 B.C.) whose writings were codified early in the first century B.C. by the Roman Lucretius who wrote a long poem *De Rerum Natura* which gives a good idea of the old Greek atomic theory. To this Lucretius adds that the atoms move in straight lines through space and from time to time swerve for some unknown reason and collide with one another. This same idea is to be found in modern theory concerning the composition of matter.

Dialecticians have always been fond of discussing whether or not matter is infinitely divisible. To one type of mind natural phenomena seem most intelligible when matter is thought of as flowing and continuous so that, however often divided, each fragment is still in its turn divisible. Other minds find it more natural to assume that when subdivision has reached a certain point, a particle is obtained that cannot be further divided, at least without losing the properties of the substance. Such persons are prone to account for the properties of the mass by the qualities of its component particles, and to explain changes in the mass by motion or interaction of the particles. Today we distinguish definitely between the so-called *thermodynamic* and *kinetic* schools of thought and find them mutually helpful and supplementary. Democritus seems to have been the first of the kinetic school to formulate its point of view definitely, and so his fundamental conceptions have considerable interest for us. Like Leucippus, he thought of all things as made up of *atoms*, to which he gave this name because they could not be further subdivided. He also stated that they were absolutely small, full, incompressible, without pores, and homogeneous. Indeed, he assigned them properties not unlike those of the "mathematical point." He permitted them to differ, however, in form, position, and magnitude. Their properties could account in some measure for the properties of larger masses— thus, according to Democritus, water is a liquid because its atoms are smooth and round and can easily glide over each other. A solid like iron, on the other hand, must be made up of atoms that are hard and rough. Democritus indulged in many speculations in order to account for the first formation of bodies from the atoms and some of his other ideas are extremely interesting. He states, for example, that the function of respiration is to introduce new atoms into the body and to remove old ones. Like many of his contemporaries, Democritus praised experiment as a valuable guide to knowledge, but as we have no record that he ever tried any experiments, we must consider what he said as merely a "good resolution" which suffered the ordinary fate of such things. The spirit of the time was entirely against it.

For the love and hate of Empedocles, Democritus substituted fixed laws and believed that all phenomena could be explained by a purely mechanical system and not by means of providence or an intelligent cause working with a definite end in view. He believed in the existence of the soul but had a mechanical conception of it and thought it composed of round, smooth, and very mobile atoms. The soul atoms exercised different effects in different organs of the human body. The head was the seat of reason; the heart, of anger; and the liver, of desire. Life, he believed, was maintained by the inhalation of fresh atoms to replace those lost by exhalation. He taught the doctrine of the three contraries—*knowledge, will,* and *power*—and the balancing principle of *restraint.* Much that we know of him came to us by tradition. He traveled considerably, and in a visit to Babylonia and Egypt he is said to have been initiated into a secret order of priesthood in which one of the sayings of the inducting priest was, "It is necessary to know in order to dare, to dare in order to want, and to be silent in order to have empire."

Plato (about 428–348 B.C.) was one of the most important of the early Greek philosophers. At about 387 B.C., he founded the *Academy* as an institute for the systematic pursuit of philosophical research. He presided over it for the rest of his life and made it the recognized authority in mathematics and law. Plato wrote philosophy in the form of dialogues, but much of our knowledge concerning Plato's views about science and metaphysics have come to us through Aristotle. Plato thought that Nature was developed upon a mathematical plan and that the ultimate realities must be sought in mathematics. In this respect his ideas were very similar to those of Pythagoras. The Platonic theory of number was inspired by thought which has since brought forth abundant fruit in science, but at Plato's time it was to a large degree premature.

Aristotle.—There is little record of what Socrates and Plato thought concerning natural phenomena. Aristotle (384–322 B.C.), however, gave no little attention to such matters and his ideas were destined to have great weight for many centuries. He distinguished between *matter* in a substance and what he called the *essence.* This difference may be the same distinction which later thinkers have drawn between the substance and the sum of its attributes. Without entering into a fruitless metaphysical discussion of this point, or raising what Huxley calls the "geometrical ghost" of a substance without attributes, we may say that what Aristotle called a substance he subdivided into essence and matter. The meaning of these terms may be made clearer by an example. He held that individuals of the same species consisted of the same essence but different matter, and in this way he was able to account for the persistence of the species in spite of the mortality of the individual. So far as the matter itself was concerned, he adopted the four elements of Empedocles, and so the essence came naturally to be regarded as a fifth element —hence the term *quintessence*. It should be emphasized that Aristotle did not accept these elements of Empedocles in a very literal sense. He rather considered them as certain combinations of attributes which in more manifold combination produced the natural properties. The fundamental attributes selected do not impress us now as universal or particularly well chosen. They were heat and cold, wetness and dryness. Fire was that which was at the same time hot and dry, water, wet and cold. Similarly earth was cold and dry, while air was warm and moist. Doubtless because of the striking antitheses involved, this classification became extremely popular and later alchemistic writings abound in diagrams representing it. For our part we cannot fail to see that it deals less with elements in the modern chemical sense than with abstract qualities. This again was in the spirit of the times. Where we should say that a certain clay, for example, was red because it contained an oxide of iron, the ancient Greeks would seem to have been satisfied with the explanation that it contained "redness." Of course we constantly use such figures in common speech; we say of a brave man that he has much courage, but in so doing we recognize clearly that the term is only an abstraction derived from the contemplation of many courageous people. The Greeks do not seem, however, to have realized very clearly the source of their abstractions, and so commonly assigned to them an independent existence; sometimes personifying, and even deifying, them, as their mythology shows us. In consequence we shall find abstract qualities confused with elements for many centuries.

Archimedes and Eratosthenes.—We may read in Aristotle that, when a mine is no longer worked, the ore grows again to its original dimensions, and that a barrel full of ashes will still hold as much water as an empty one. That Aristotle, who was unquestionably one of the greatest thinkers of all time, should have been willing to pass on unverified and untested statements of this kind is an adequate commentary upon the "scientific spirit" of the age in which he lived. It is never possible, however, to do justice by sweeping generalizations which condemn a whole epoch. In Archimedes (287–212 B.C.) and in Eratosthenes (276–194 B.C.), we find men who must have worked in the modern spirit. An account of what they did is unnecessary here since their work was in no sense chemical, but Eratosthenes made a surprisingly accurate calculation of the circumference of the earth, and Archimedes made fundamental discoveries in mechanics and hydrostatics. We owe to the latter the discovery of the principles underlying the determination of specific gravity, as well as of the lever. He designed a "screw" for lifting water, and numerous other less known mechanical appliances, all in addition to much fundamental work in geometry.

Pliny.—No account of science among the ancients would be complete without some word about Pliny the Elder (A.D. 23–79) to whom we are indebted for much of what we know concerning the practical scientific attainments of his contemporaries. Pliny enjoyed the friendship of the emperors Titus and Vespasian. He was an earnest and tireless student and a voluminous writer. The best known of his works is the *Natural History* which originally comprised fully 160 books, though but 31 have come down to us. In his preface the author claims to furnish 20,000 facts compiled from 2,000 books. He transcribes, of course, much that is traditional, visionary, and inexact, but we get through him valuable hints concerning the knowledge of his day and some details of chemical industries as practised at that time. Pliny was prefect of the Roman fleet at the time of the eruption of Vesuvius that overwhelmed Herculaneum and Pompeii, and he lost his life by approaching the volcano to get a closer observation and to assist refugees. A full account of these facts is given in one of the most interesting letters of his nephew, Pliny the Younger, while another letter pays a fine tribute to the uncle's character and industrious habits.

Galen (A.D. 129–199) of Pergamos was a celebrated Greek physician who is regarded as the father of experimental medicine. He wrote some 500 treatises and applied Aristotle's ideas to medicine. In healthy bodies he taught that there were four humors (blood, phlegm, bile, and black bile), which should be in equilibrium. Disease is caused by a preponderance of an element and is cured by the opposite. Anaxagoras (450 B.C.) had similar ideas.

The Greeks of the classical period recognized substances which we now know as oxides of copper, iron, and zinc, sulfates of iron and copper, sulfides of arsenic and mercury, gold amalgam, white-lead (basic lead carbonate), dyes, and various vegetable and animal products. The Greek treatises contain considerable practical information concerning, fusion, calcination, solution, filtration, crystallization, sublimation, distillation, and various methods of heating by the open fire, lamps, sand baths, and water baths. Astrology was associated with chemistry. The sun, moon, Saturn, Jupiter, Mars, Venus, and Mercury were associated, respectively, with gold, silver, lead, tin, iron, copper, and mercury, and the astronomical symbols of these heavenly bodies were used to represent these elements or alloys. The usage was not always uniform, however.

Literature

The titles to be found under this heading at the close of each chapter are intended to assist the reader who wishes to become more familiar with a particular period. The lists make no claim to completeness and, indeed, have been intentionally limited to works known to be reasonably accessible.

One who desires to get into vital touch with the development of the science must, of course, study original papers in the pages of the journals, and it is fortunate that so many of the less accessible of these have now been reprinted. The more casual reader, on the other hand, will frequently prefer a somewhat abridged résumé by a competent hand.

It is assumed for example, that only specialists will care to learn the views of the ancients on scientific matters by a study of their writings in the original. The following two books, however, treat quite comprehensively the development of chemical science both among the ancients and in the medieval period:

HOEFER: *Histoire de la chimie*, Paris, 1842.

KOPP: *Geschichte der Chemie*, Braunschweig, 1843.

The point of view of a writer in 1843 was, of course, quite different from our own, but this difficulty hardly makes itself felt in the study of the development of the science down to Lavoisier.

Pliny's *Natural History* is available in an English translation by Bostock and Riley, 6 vols., Bohn's Classical Library, London, 1893.

The Story of Early Chemistry, by J. M. Stillman, New York, 1922, 539 pages, deals with the development of the science from the earliest times up to and including the work of Lavoisier. It can be heartily recommended to the layman as the most satisfactory introduction to the study of ancient and medieval chemistry. It is charmingly written, perfectly intelligible even to those with only slight knowledge of chemistry, and it gives to the medieval period a sense of unity and continuity hardly equaled in any other treatise.

Die Entwicklung der chemischen Technik bis zu den Anfängen der Gross-industrie, by Gustav Fester, Berlin, 1923, 211 pages, traces the development of chemical industry from the earliest times to the beginning of the nineteenth century. It is particularly timely because modern research tends to show more and more clearly that at least up to the time of Boyle more important advances in chemistry were made by the artisans than by the philosophers.

A History of Magic and Experimental Science during the First Thirteen Centuries of Our Era, by Lynn Thorndike, New York, 1923, 2 vols., 782 and 984 pages, can be heartily recommended to the thoughtful reader who wishes to make a real study of the history of science. Beginning with a thorough analysis of Pliny's *Natural History*, it takes up in great detail and with extensive and interesting quotations the work of all prominent writers on the two subjects within the period covered. The scientific reader will probably be surprised to see how closely allied the two fields once were, and how slowly they became disentangled. The author is a historian and not a laboratory experimenter, and his personal interest in the history of magic evidently outweighs that in experimental science, but this makes the book all the more interesting, because it illuminates from a new angle the mental attitude of many men whose names have always stood high in the history of science.

More recent papers and books on the early history of chemistry are:

DAVIS: *Ambix*, **1**, 109 (1937); *Isis*, **18**, 213 (1932); **25**, 327 (1936); **28**, 73 (1937); *J. Chem. Ed.*, **11**, 517 (1934); **12**, 5 (1935); **13**, 103, 215 (1936); *Proc. Am. Acad. Arts Sci.*, **70**, 221 (1935); *Sci. Monthly*, **43**, 551 (1936).

HOPKINS: *Alchemy, Child of Greek Philosophy*, New York, 1934.

PARTINGTON: *A Short History of Chemistry*, New York, 1937.

PARTINGTON: *Origins and Development of Applied Chemistry*, London. 1935.

READ: *Prelude to Chemistry*, New York, 1937.

CHAPTER II

CHEMISTRY IN THE MIDDLE AGES—ALCHEMY

If the chemist today wishes to look up anything in current chemical literature, his task is a relatively easy one. The chemical societies of the United States, England, and Germany each publish abstracts of nearly every paper on chemistry that is published anywhere in the world. These abstracts are published as promptly as possible in the three great abstract journals known as *Chemical Abstracts, British Chemical and Physiological Abstracts*, and *Chemisches Zentralblatt*. The annual and decennial indexes are especially helpful to the busy chemist. If, however, the chemist desires to trace chemical knowledge to its source, difficulties soon begin to appear. It isn't long before we reach the period where there were no abstract journals and if we try to look up some of the references we are lucky if we can find the book or journal in our library. After we get to about the time of the American Revolution we find that some of the treatises are written in Latin and we begin to find that the German, the French, and even the English are not easy to understand. And the chemical knowledge of the eighteenth century was certainly not expressed in the language of today. In the study of alchemy, we are bothered by a veil of secrecy and mysticism. The early alchemists deliberately tried to write vaguely, they pretended that their knowledge was very old, but so mystical that the average man could never hope to understand it; and they further pretended that what they wrote was handed down in some mysterious way from some person who lived centuries ago. We cannot believe half the things we read in the early chemical writings, and sometimes the work described is attributed to a person who may never have lived at all. Up to the beginning of the Christian era, we find no indication of the existence of chemistry, as such, in Europe.

Intellectual Decline in the Middle Ages.—The civilization of Greece in the time of Pericles or of Rome in the time of Augustus was intellectually upon an extremely high plane, and the minds of educated men were at least as free from prejudice and superstition as they are today.

When, however, the Roman Empire lost military and political power and the governments of its provinces and vassal states became constantly more effete and corrupt, the moral and mental tone of the community was lowered at the same time, and with the decay of manners crept in mental indolence and inefficiency. Finally, when the weakness of the empire invited the cupidity of the barbarian hordes, their conquests smothered intellectual life altogether, and we can record little constructive scientific work or scientific thinking until the revival of learning in the fifteenth century. The unsettled conditions of the times rendered a life devoted to study impossible except in the monasteries, and even here intellectual freedom was so hampered by an inflexible dogmatic theology that the desire for intellectual activity could find expression in little save the copying of manuscripts or the hair-splitting futilities of the scholastic philosophy.

During this period the sciences fared even worse than art and letters, because, with the possible exception of mathematics and astronomy, they had made a much poorer start. We have, however, to take account of new conditions and a new point of view.

Alchemy.—The slow progress of science among the ancients was due to the divorce of theory and practice. Those who did the work and those who did the thinking were entirely out of touch. In the Middle Ages, on the other hand, the theories were indeed evolved by the same men who did the experimenting, but these were frequently persons of inferior mentality, whose work was usually poor and whose thinking was apt to be slovenly when it was not actually dishonest.

From the chemist's standpoint, the most important intellectual symptom of this time is the rise and spread of alchemy. By this we commonly understand the pretended art of changing the baser metals into gold. Such a definition suggests quackery and self-seeking, and there is no question but that many alchemists were no better than common cheats, especially in later times. We should make a grievous mistake, however, if we condemned all so sweepingly or imagined that a vulgar cupidity was the only impulse that started men upon the quest for the philosopher's stone. The literature of alchemy is full of turgid rhetoric and mystic symbolism, but through it all runs the idea that the change of the base into the noble has not only a chemical but a moral significance and that he who discovers the "stone of the ancient sages" will also reap another reward in the enrichment of his mind and the elevation of his character. Furthermore we all remember how our first acquaintance with chemical transformations ministered to our taste for the marvelous, which, after all, is not so far from a true scientific interest. In short, since alchemy was the only chemistry in those days, we can readily see that men pursued it for many motives then as now. Schiller has well said: "To one man science is a sacred goddess to whose service he is happy to devote his life; to another she is a cow who provides him with butter." So it was with alchemy.

Relation of Alchemy to Science.—Perfect clearness is also necessary on another point which is sometimes misunderstood. We must remember that there was nothing inherently absurd in the problem which the alchemists set themselves. It is the essential nature of chemical change that one substance with certain properties disappears while another with different properties takes its place, and there was nothing in the knowledge of the times from which one had the right to conclude that it was any more impossible to obtain gold from lead, than to obtain lead itself from litharge or mercury from cinnabar. In fact, the recent preparation of helium from radium puts the logic entirely on the side of the alchemists. Chemistry is an experimental science, and the only way to find out whether it is practicable to get gold from lead is to try it. We owe it to the alchemists to acknowledge that they did try it, with crude means, it is true, but with endless patience and much needless repetition. The pity of it is that all their efforts were so wasted by secrecy that they could show few results of value in a whole thousand years.

Origin of Alchemy.—Although Egypt is generally regarded as the birthplace of alchemy, it has recently been shown that similar ideas were developed in China at early times. Chinese philosophers studied minerals, like cinnabar, in the hope of finding the philosophers' stone. Since it was believed that eating from gold plates caused a long life, they sought to produce gold from other materials. The aims of these early Chinese writers were very similar to those of the later Greek, Arab, and medieval alchemists. Their ideals were closely related to the magical and fantastic side of the Taoist religion, and in the early Chinese writings there is the same confusion of ideas of spirit and matter that characterizes alchemy.

Concerning the composition of matter, the Chinese believed, prior to 600 B.C., that matter was composed of water, fire, wood, gold (metal) and earth. Allegorical meanings were also attributed to these five elements with reference to the five virtues, five colors, five tones, five tastes, and five seasons of the year. Thus *wood* might represent the spring of the year, the east, or a sour taste; *gold*, the autumn, north, or a salty taste; *fire*, summer, the west, or a bitter taste; *water*, winter, the south, or an astringent taste; *earth*, the season between summer and winter, the center, or a sweet taste.

The first authentic alchemistic literature outside of China is associated with the Arabs. Many of the writings appeared under false names. Alchemy like modern chemistry, had its theories, although these were often vague and subject to interpretations suiting the whims of the interpreter. The chief physical theory was that of the four elements, or simple bodies, which was usually ascribed to Aristotle to whom it descended through Plato from Empedocles. The same idea was recognized in Egypt, India, and China at about 1500 B.C. According to Hopkins, alchemy received from Greece belief in (1) hylozoism, (2) the macrocosm and the microcosm, (3) astrology, and (4) animism. According to hylozoism, all Nature is like man, alive and sensitive. The macrocosm (sun and stars) is guided by the same laws as the earth (the microcosm). According to animism, all events are caused by some spirit.

Zosimos, of Panopolis in Upper Egypt, seems to be the first of a number of voluminous Egyptian writers on alchemy. He probably lived at about A.D. 350–420. Little of his own work remains, but we have its essential characteristics from all subsequent alchemistic writings. They are characterized by a bombastic mysticism, apparently written in a kind of religious ecstasy, and although they contain numerous chemical recipes, these are couched in unintelligible language and alternated with high-sounding invocations. Nevertheless, in all this meaningless jargon we are sometimes refreshed by phrases which show genuine insight and by flashes of real humor.

The traditional view among historians has been that these earliest books represent materials that had been handed down orally for some time by the Egyptian priests and that may have had something to do with their religious ritual. The eminent French chemist Berthelot was of a different opinion. He gave much study to the so-called *Leiden Papyrus*, which was originally found in a tomb in Thebes. On translation this proved to be a book of workshop recipes, in which, among other things, there are directions for so mixing and coloring metals as to imitate gold for the manufacture of cheap jewelry. There is no thought here of transmutation, but Berthelot believed that a goldsmith who had become expert in such arts might, in the absence of all chemical standards, deceive himself into the belief that he had actually effected a transmutation. Such a discovery would be highly profitable, and the finder would be apt to pass on the secret only in terms that could not be easily understood. In this way, as others guessed, experimented, copied, and wrote directions in their turn, a literature like that of alchemy might spring up.

Zosimos distinguished between *bodies* (usually metals) and *spirits* (vapors of arsenic, sulfur, and mercury). The spirits were assumed to be bound to the bodies by affinity but could be liberated by suitable methods. The word *tutia*, an old name for zinc oxide, is derived from a Persian word that means *smokes* and refers to the fact that zinc oxide is evolved as white smoke when zinc ores are roasted with charcoal. The Alexandrian chemists almost discovered gases. Zosimos describes the burning of limestone to make lime as resulting from the taking on of a spirit from the fire. Zosimos describes many chemical operations, such as dissolving, filtration, fusion, sublimation, and distillation. As a Gnostic, Zosimos believed that knowledge rather than faith was the key to salvation.

Throughout the first five centuries of the Christian era, we find constant proof of the desire to obtain knowledge of the invisible world. In these early writings knowledge of Egyptian metallurgical and other arts is blended with the mystical philosophies of the Neoplatonists. Zosimos apparently regarded the tinted imitation silver and gold as really superior in color and purity to that of native silver or gold.   It was capable of imparting the yellow seed of the ferment to other metals, and this doctrine seems to lie behind the alchemistic idea of multiplication by the philosopher's stone or tincture.   The sun and moon of Hermes were the same as the positive sulfur and negative mercury principles of Zosimos and Geber.

Zosimos gave a celebrated "formula of the crab" which, by unintelligible symbols, was supposed to embody the secret of transmutation and was probably a cipher used by Egyptians for making imitation gold.   These early writings embody a curious mixture of chemical facts merged with ecstatic visions, descriptions of apparatus and injunctions to keep things secret. Thus in writing about the philosopher's stone, Zosimos writes, "Receive this stone, which is not a stone, a precious thing which has no value, a thing of many shapes which has no shape, this unknown which is known to all"; and "The quintessence is dear and glorious to him who knows it, vile to him who is ignorant of it, finite and specific for the one, infinite and indeterminate for the other."

Alchemistic Traditions.—Whatever the facts, if we were to accept the traditions of the alchemists themselves concerning the origin of their art, we should come to very different conclusions.   Some of their accounts ascribed it to the days of communion between men and angels in the period before the Flood, and numbered most of the patriarchs, including Adam himself, in the ranks of the alchemists.   This, of course, was meant to play upon the human tendency, stronger then than now, to value everything in proportion to its antiquity.   The same influence led some alchemists to forego fame and ascribe their own writings to the ancient philosophers, Democritus being a favorite.

Alchemistic tradition also has much to say of a certain Hermes Trismegistus (probably connected in some way with Thoth the Egyptian god of wisdom, who also was represented as carrying a rod entwined by serpents).   Concerning the dates and places of residence of this Hermes there is no agreement, but one tradition has it that he inscribed upon an emerald the most essential secrets of alchemy and presented this jewel to Sarah, the wife of Abraham.   After many vicissitudes the stone was

lost, but the traditional wording of the inscription has come
down to us and is worthy of a place here because alchemists in
general seem to have taken Hermes as a model in style and clearness.   We also pay tribute to his name when we speak of sealing
a vessel hermetically.

THE EMERALD TABLET

It is true and without falsehood, certain and most true, that which is
above is even as that which is beneath.   And that which is beneath
is even as that which is above, for accomplishing the miracles of one
thing.

And as all things were from one by the meditation of one, so all things
were born from this one thing by adoption.

Its Father is the Sun, its Mother is the Moon.   The wind carried it
in its belly.   Its nurse is the earth.   This is the father of all the knowledge of the whole world.   Its virtue is unimpaired if it should be turned
toward the earth.

You will separate the earth from the fire, the subtle from the compact,
gently, with great skill.   It ascends from Earth to Heaven, then descends
again to Earth and receives the force of those above and those below.

Thus you will possess the glory of the world whole and all obscurity
will flee from you.

This is the strong strength of all strength, because it will overcome
every subtle thing, and penetrate every solid.

So the World was created.

There will be wonderful adaptations of which this is the mode.

Therefore am I called Hermes Trismegistos having three parts of the
philosophy of the whole world.

It is finished, what I have said concerning the operation of the Sun.

Fundamental Ideas of the Alchemists.—Language of this kind
is hardly capable of expressing any rational idea, but, judging by
their clearer writings, the alchemists seem to have held that there
was a certain *materia prima* which was present in all things
though always contaminated by impurities.   These they hoped
to remove by processes of purification, especially by fire (calcination, sublimation, or distillation), and in this way they expected
to obtain the *essence* or *tincture* which was apparently identical
with the *philosophers' stone*.   Once obtained, this was expected
to work wonders of many kinds.   It would change the baser
metals to gold by contact, it would heal all diseases and even

regenerate the character of the fortunate discoverer. In addition to the *materia prima*, which may have been originally derived from the "quintessence" of Aristotle, the alchemists generally recognized the four other elements which he had accepted, although they frequently added or substituted others of their own, particularly mercury, sulfur, and salt. Here, however, they were always careful to point out that they did not refer to the substances commonly known under these names, but rather to the mercury, sulfur, and salt "of the sages." Mercury seems to have stood for the metallic and also the volatile character in general, and the mechanism of transmutation was frequently referred to as "fixation of the mercury." In the same way, sulfur represented the properties of combustibility, whereas salt stood for the salty or earthy properties, notably resistance toward fire. It must be remembered, however, that all these terms were constantly used in the most reckless and inconsistent way, as the following selection from a book purporting to be written by a certain Basilius Valentinus abundantly shows:

That there can be no perfect generation or resuscitation without the cooperation of the four elements, you may see from the fact that when Adam had been formed by the Creator out of earth, there was no life in him until God breathed into him a living spirit, then the earth was quickened into motion. In the earth was the salt, that is the body; the air that was breathed into it was mercury or the spirit, and this air imparted to him a gentle and temperate heat which was sulfur or fire. Then Adam moved, and by his power of motion showed that there had been infused into him a life-giving spirit. For as there is no fire without air so neither is there any air without fire.[1] Water was incorporated with the earth. Thus living man is a harmonious mixture of the four elements; and Adam was generated out of earth, water, air and fire; out of soul, spirit and body; out of mercury, sulfur and salt.

The recipes and directions in alchemistic books laid great weight upon the phases of the moon, the position of the planets, and the utterance of appropriate incantations, and this need not surprise us when we recall that in these early times no means were available by which such essential conditions as temperature and pressure could be regulated. Furthermore, the materials

[1] The writer had evidently made the important observation that there is "no fire without air," but the last half of the sentence shows how much he preferred a striking antithesis to any fact of observation.

employed could seldom have been pure, or even uniform. When we add that there were no analytical methods by which materials could be tested, we see that the results of experiments must frequently have seemed utterly capricious, and it was natural that weight should be laid upon trifling and irrelevant circumstances.

The planets caused especial trouble. From early times the "seven planets" had been associated with the "seven metals" and in writing, the same astronomical signs were commonly employed for both. The sun stood for gold, the moon for silver, Jupiter for tin, Saturn for lead, Mars for iron, Venus for copper, and Mercury for the metal of the same name. It followed naturally that when a metal was to be acted upon chemically in a certain way, its "patron planet" must be rightly situated.

Practical Achievements of the Alchemists.—In spite of these handicaps, the world gradually did accumulate scientific information. The tendency to heat, distill, and combine all obtainable substances in order to obtain the philosophers' stone had the practical result that many important reactions were observed and many important compounds prepared. Unfortunately the alchemists were so unwilling to use intelligible language in the description of their discoveries that most of these remained unfruitful.

The idea of the elixir of life was thought by Liebig to have originated in the thirteenth century of the Christian era, but T. L. Davis has shown that it was familiar in China in the second or third century. Wei Po-yang in the second century wrote a treatise on the preparation of "the pill of immortality" and there is the interesting story of the time when he, with three of his disciples and a dog, tried out a carefully prepared "medicine" on the dog. The dog promptly died, and Wei Po-yang was so discouraged that he felt he was ashamed to go back and tell of the failure. So he and one of the disciples took some of the medicine and fell dead. The other two disciples then went off to fetch an undertaker, but in their absence Wei Po-yang recovered and with the aid of more medicine joined the immortals together with his friend and the dog.

Attempts to trace alchemy as far back as possible led some of these early writers to assume that even Adam had a knowledge of the elixir which enabled him to reach a ripe age.   The French name for a hot-water bath is *bain-Marie,* and tradition has it that Marie (or Miriam in English) the sister of Moses knew about alchemy and invented the bath.

Chemistry in Arabia.—In A.D. 640 Egypt was overrun by Arabs.   They were brave but ignorant.   They found books in Egypt on how to make gold and cure ills, which they had translated into Arabic, and for a century a stream of books poured into the Mohammedan world through Greece.   In this way Egyptian knowledge reached Europe in the form of Latin translations from Arabic works, and some have thought that the Arabs were the originators in chemistry.   Of the early writers, the most important were Jabir ibn-Haijan, Razi, also called Rhases or Rhazes, and Avicenna, also called ibn-Sina.

The full name of Jabir, rarely used, is Jabir ibn-Haijan, and in the later Latin writings he is usually called *Geber* or Giaber. Geber, according to tradition, is the founder and greatest representative of alchemy and probably lived at about A.D. 720–800.   The place of his residence is uncertain, but his numerous works brought him great fame in the Middle Ages. Some of these are still extant in Arabic, while certain Latin treatises purporting to be translations of Geber are preserved in European libraries.   The latter books date from about the thirteenth century, and Berthelot, after comparing them with the Arabic writings of Geber, came to the conclusion that they were the work of another hand and had been attributed to Geber in order to enhance their prestige.   It is interesting to note that Berthelot found the Latin works superior from the chemical point of view.   This writer is called the *pseudo Geber*.   He was probably a cleric well versed in science.

Geber lived in Bagdad under Caliph Harun-al-Rashid, whose fictitious glory is depicted in the *Arabian Nights*.   Geber made experiments, but his writings are full of unintelligible mysticism. His chief aim was to prepare the magical transmuting *tincture, elixir,* or *powder of projection*.   He postulated the formation of mercury and sulfur by exhalations in the interior of the earth, and by the combination of these elements in different proportions and in varying degrees of purity, the metals and minerals were supposed to be obtained.

Al Razi or Rhases (A.D. 886–925) was a skillful and practical Persian physician and has been called the Persian Boyle. He is frequently referred to in alchemical literature. He described "the Stone" as triangular in essence, square in quality. He, as well as Geber and Avicenna, described the practical achievements of alchemy.

Avicenna (A.D. 980–1036) was a famous physician and has been called the Aristotle of Arabians. He was willing to tell the world the secret of the *Magisterium*. He probably made no experiments himself, and in his interesting books he at times seemed to doubt the possibility of transmutation. Later, Paracelsus burned the works of Galen (a famous physician) and of Avicenna in a brass pan, with the aid of sulfur and potassium nitrate, in his first lecture and then expressed the hope that these authors were in like circumstances.

These men taught the theory, the germ of which was also taught by Aristotle, that metals are composed of mercury and sulfur. Their information may have come from Mesopotamia, Syria, or even China. The association of metals with the planets was introduced into Arabian alchemy probably from Babylonian astrology.

Prominent Alchemists.—Other noted men claimed as alchemists are Vincent de Beauvais, Albertus Magnus, Roger Bacon, and Ramon Lull. Extensive treatises on alchemy are commonly ascribed to these men, but the best modern opinion holds that these are spurious.

Vincent de Beauvais (1190–1264) was a Domincan monk who wrote an encyclopedia, the *Speculum Naturale*, with a section on alchemy which was mostly derived from Latin translations of Arabic works.

Albertus Magnus (1193–1280), sometimes called *Doctor Universalis*, was one of the most important and best representatives of alchemy. He was the wisest man and greatest German scholar of that time and was distinguished as a priest, monk, scientist, philosopher, mystic, and astrologer, as well as alchemist. He has been called the Aristotle of the Middle Ages because of his wisdom and his work in arranging and systematizing the writings of the famous Greek. He was Bishop of Regensburg in 1260, was a friend of Thomas Aquinas, and is mentioned by

Dante. He wrote a great deal, but many of his reputed writings are undoubtedly forgeries. As a monk he wandered about from place to place and practiced some alchemy. He thought that metals were all more or less pure mercury and sulfur. To him the liquid and yet metallic mercury represented water and earth, whereas sulfur represented the volatile and combustible (fatty) material. He had the idea that all matter was composed of a prime material. In describing the relation between sulfur and the metals, he spoke of the attraction of sulfur to metals, indicating ideas concerning chemical affinity. He defined flame as ignited smoke. In his writings Plato's logic that *like seeks like* appears. He had some knowledge of metallurgy. To him Nature was the only real alchemist and he admitted that he had never known an alchemist who could accomplish a perfect transmutation. He termed alchemy a "pretended science," "a beggarly union of genius and fire," and stated that alchemical gold was turned to a powder after repeated trials by fire.

Roger Bacon (1214?–1294), called *Doctor Mirabilis* by his contemporaries, was a Franciscan monk and the leading English alchemist. He was an inventive genius much in advance of his time who added materially to knowledge by his mathematical studies and experiments. A great number of practical inventions are commonly ascribed to him, though in many cases the proofs are lacking. Among his writings are found a recipe for making gunpowder, directions for the construction of a telescope, and a study of the rainbow which is said to be extremely good.

He recognized the value of experimentation and mathematical deduction. He felt that the better one learns to base life and knowledge upon a mathematical basis, the better one learns to avoid error, uncertainty, doubt, and unnecessary work. He believed in divine inspiration and held all things to be possible. He practiced what he preached and wrote many books, although many forgeries exist.

Bacon was a profound believer in alchemy but wrote soberly and clearly. He summarized its theories but largely relied upon the works of a pseudo Avicenna. He studied at Oxford but probably did not really have the doctor's degree. Schoolmen, as a rule, frowned upon alchemy, and it was practiced at this time mostly by "adepts" whose writings between 1250 and 1500 are full of unintelligible and obscure jargon. The "alchemist" appears in the writings of Chaucer (A.D. 1400) and is criticized severely in Ben Jonson's play *The Alchemist* (1610). Bacon became interested in science as a result of contact in Paris with Peter of Maricourt who was the author of a book on *The Magnet*. Bacon had ideas which were far in advance of his time concerning, for example, flying machines and automotive transportation. He described scientific and chemical methods that are still used today. Long before the time of Paracelsus, he felt that medicine should make use of remedies provided by chemistry. He knew languages so well that he wrote scientific papers in Hebrew, Greek, Syriac, and Arabic, as well as in Latin. His open criticism of famous monks, such as Albertus Magnus and Thomas Aquinas, eventually brought disgrace to Bacon, and it is generally thought that he spent the last fifteen years of his life in prison. At one time he states that he spent more than 2,000 livres (about $50,000) on books, apparatus, assistants, and "forming friendships" during a period of ten years.

Ramon Lull (1235–ca. 1315), sometimes called *Doctor Illuminatus*, was a romantic Spanish nobleman. This man was a poet, philosopher, mystic, alchemist, artist, troubadour, and missionary who loved the mythical picture more than the reality. He prized alchemy as representing that part of natural philosophy which had to do with the perfecting and ennobling of things. To him the alchemistic art was grace, not to be learned and not to be taught. He regarded mercury and sulfur as the fundamental constituents of all matters. He prepared potash (potassium carbonate) from "wine stone" (cream of tartar) and nearly anhydrous alcohol by drying over potassium carbonate. He was familiar with the action of nitric acid on metals and described aqua regia. He lost his life on a missionary expedition, being stoned to death by the natives.

Arnold of Villanova (1240–1313) was a French or Spanish physician and the author of several medical treatises and alchemical books. He described the distillation of wine and used it in medicine. He is said to have made artificial gold for Pope Boniface VIII. He taught that "there abides in nature a certain pure matter which being discovered and brought by art to perfection converts to itself proportionately all imperfect bodies that it

BERNARD PALISSY
1510–1589

touches." This was the main source of inspiration to alchemists. He also wrote that "our medicine has power to heal."

Bernard Palissy[1] (about 1510–1589) was a leader of chemical and scientific thought in France, just as Bacon was in England. He emphasized the value of experimental results rather than belief in the speculation of philosophers. He invented enameled pottery, established a factory, and made beautiful pieces in which the forms of animals are produced in their natural colors. He had the first mineralogical and geological collection in Paris and lectured on chemistry, geology, mineralogy, and agriculture; and his numerous works are so well written that they have been studied as models by the school children of France. As an ardent Calvinist he was imprisoned several times and finally died in one of the dungeons of the Bastille.

Denis Zachaire (Dionysius Zacharius) was another French alchemist of repute. He wrote a book on alchemy which was published in Antwerp in 1567.

Bernard Trevisan (1406–1490) was an Italian gentleman who spent his life and his fortune in the vain search for the secret of transmutation. Gold, to him, was the most perfect of metals, and since Man is the most perfect creature, he felt that out of man must come the secret of gold. He, therefore, worked with the blood and urine of man.

One of the most remarkable of the alchemistic books was the *Triumphal Chariot of Antimony* which was supposedly written by a Benedictine monk named **Basilius Valentinus** near the end of the fifteenth century. Attempts to find out more about this person have all been in vain, and the general belief that now prevails is that no such person ever lived. He is not mentioned by his contemporaries, there is no record of his having been in any monastery, and his reputed writings contain references indicating that his works were written probably by several persons in the second half of the sixteenth century. These writings are clearer than those preceding them, so that many of the experiments can be repeated and verified. A real service was done by these writings in characterizing the metal antimony and many of its more important compounds.

[1] See Mary Louise Foster, "Bernard Palissy, Sixteenth Century Scientist," *J. Chem. Ed.*, **8**, 1045–1059 (1931).

During this period there lived in Italy the celebrated **Leonardo da Vinci** (1452–1519). He was not only a famous painter but was also gifted to a rare degree in science. He was brilliant in mathematics, astronomy, mechanics, hydraulics, geology, geography, and cosmogony. He discovered capillarity, and a hundred years before Francis Bacon he showed a greater grasp of the principles upon which experimental science is based. His ideas were far in advance of his time and were hidden in manuscript from which no one was able to extract their wisdom.

Decay of Alchemy.—After the fifteenth century, as chemistry became gradually more scientific, alchemy in the narrow sense tended to die out and acquired an ill repute through the character of its devotees. The more brilliant of these secured positions at the courts of petty princes where they made a precarious living by playing upon the avarice of their patrons, while the less fortunate ones practiced similar frauds in a humbler sphere. Finally conditions must have become extremely bad, for the story goes that Frederick of Würzburg maintained a special gallows which he employed solely for hanging alchemists. The careers of these men were sometimes extremely romantic, but with this the history of chemistry has, of course, nothing to do.

It must not be thought, however, that the idea of transmutation died out completely. It merely ceased being the dominating thought underlying the development of chemical theory. In France there still exists an alchemical society, and in Germany a certain Franz Tausend recently swindled many people, some very prominent, out of over one hundred thousand dollars by claiming to produce gold from base metals. In a public test he succeeded in apparently producing a grain of gold from very inexpensive materials. It was finally shown, however, that he had succeeded in introducing gold surreptitiously with the ashes of a cigaret. Many chemists even today believe in the possibility of transmutation, although perhaps none thinks that it will ever be the basis of a commercially profitable undertaking.

To the alchemist, all metals and, indeed, all matter are one in origin and are produced by an evolutionary process. The soul in them is one and the same; it is only the soul that is permanent; the body or outward form is transitory. Obviously this belief shows philosophical depth and insight. The alchemists grasped a fundamental truth but distorted it and made it appear grotesque in some of their writings.

Literature

In addition to Hoefer and Kopp the following books by Berthelot are of interest:

Les Origines de l'alchimie, 1883.

Collections des anciens alchimistes grecs, 1887–1888.

La Chimie au moyen âge, 1893.

A. E. Waite has also done a distinct service by translating into English and publishing a number of old alchemistic writings. Among these may be mentioned *The Triumphal Chariot of Antimony*, by Basilius Valentinus; *The New Pearl of Great Price*, by Bonus of Ferrara; and an extremely interesting old collection called *The Hermetic Museum*. These are all published by Elliott of London.

CHAPTER III

CHEMISTRY IN THE RENAISSANCE

Attention has already been called to the eclipse of free intellectual life which accompanied the downfall of the Roman Empire. During the Middle Ages there was little mental activity save that which was under the direct protection of the Church, and here everything naturally centered upon the exposition of the Scriptures and the writings of the Fathers; indeed scarcely any profane literature was looked upon with favor except the writings of Aristotle who, strangely enough, enjoyed an authority not inferior to that of the saints and martyrs.

The Revival of Learning.—In the fourteenth century there began a new intellectual movement which found expression everywhere as a reaction against authority and an assertion of the rights of the individual to think and act for himself. First, came a revival of interest on the part of Italian scholars in the secular literature of ancient Greece and Rome which brought a realization of the greater intellectual freedom of ancient times and an ardent desire to imitate it in letters and in art. Momentum was given to the movement by the fall of Constantinople in 1453 which scattered the scholars of the Eastern Empire throughout the West, while the invention of printing, which came at about the same time, made possible a hitherto undreamed-of multiplication of books and gave a new impulse to literary effort. This was also the age of great discoveries. The voyages of Columbus and Vasco da Gama opened new fields to exploration, and many thousands in the spirit of Cortez, Pizarro and Magellan sought fortune and adventure in the New World. At the same time a revolt against religious authority was going on in Germany. Luther posted his theses upon the church door at Wittenberg in 1517, and about the same time even the sciences showed some signs of an awakening. Of these, astronomy had fared best in ancient times because its study was so closely associated

31

PARACELSUS
1493–1541

with geometry, and it was therefore natural that this science should be the first to feel the impulse of new life. In the first years of the sixteenth century, Copernicus came to the conclusion that the sun, and not the earth, is the center of the solar system, and he gave a brief account of this epoch-making discovery to the world in 1530.

Chemistry was not so fortunate. It could free itself only with difficulty from the mysteries and superstitions of alchemy. But even here progress began, and this first appears as a reform in the practice of medicine attempted by Paracelsus.

Paracelsus.—Philippus Aureolus Paracelsus, whose real name was Theophrastus Bombastus von Hohenheim, Eremite of Hohenheim (the name is in a measure characteristic of the man) was born in Einsiedeln, Switzerland, about 1493. At the age of sixteen he was a student at Basel, and after this time he is said to have traveled extensively. In 1527 he was made a lecturer in the medical faculty at Basel, having received his appointment upon the recommendation of Erasmus. Paracelsus was already famous for his marvelous cures and now devoted this academic position to the establishment of his revolutionary theories and the denunciation of more conservative practitioners. His successes won him the malignant envy of some of his colleagues, while his methods and manners shocked and offended others. Within two years, a scandalous quarrel with a prominent canon over a professional fee made it necessary for Paracelsus to quit Basel in hot haste. From this time he led a wandering life with varying fortunes and finally died in reduced circumstances at Salzburg in 1541. Paracelsus was a most voluminous writer, no less than two hundred and thirty-four publications being ascribed to him. These dealt not only with alchemy and medicine, but also with astrology, magic, and theology. The following selections will show his clear and vigorous style and throw some light upon his character and point of view:

But to explain the method of teaching in a few words I must first speak of myself. I, being invited by an ample salary of the rulers of Basle, for two hours in each day, do publicly interpret the books both of practical and theoretical medicine, physics and surgery whereof I myself am author, with the greatest diligence, and to the great profit of my hearers. I have not patched up these books after the fashion of others, from Hippocrates, Galen, or any one else, but by experience, the great teacher, and by labor, have I composed them. Accordingly, if I wish to prove anything, experiment and reason for me take the place of authorities. Wherefore, most excellent readers, if any one is delighted with the mysteries of this Apollonian art, if any one lives and desires it, if any one longs in a brief space of time to acquire this whole branch of learning, let him forthwith betake himself unto us at Basle and he will obtain to far greater things than I can describe in a few words. The ancients gave wrong names to almost all the diseases; hence no doctors, or at least very few, at the present day, are fortunate enough to know exactly diseases, their causes, and critical days. Let these proofs be sufficient, notwithstanding their obscurity. I do not permit you to rashly judge them before you have heard Theophrastus. Farewell. Look favorably on this attempt at the restoration of medicine.

And again:

In the meantime, I extol and adorn, with the eulogium rightly due to them, the Spagyric physicians. These do not give themselves up to ease and idleness, strutting about with a haughty gait, dressed in silk, with rings ostentatiously displayed on their fingers, or silver poignards fixed on their loins, and sleek gloves on their hands. But they devote themselves diligently to their labors, sweating whole nights and days over fiery furnaces. These do not kill the time with empty talk, but find their delight in their laboratory. They are clad in leathern garments, and wear a girdle to wipe their hands upon. They put their fingers among the coals, the lute, and the dung, not into gold rings. Like blacksmiths and coal merchants, they are sooty and dirty, and do not look proudly with sleek countenance. In presence of the sick they do not chatter and vaunt their own medicines. They perceive that the work should glorify the workman, not the workman the work, and that fine words go a very little way toward curing sick folks. Passing by all these vanities, therefore, they rejoice to be occupied at the fire and to learn the steps of alchemical knowledge. Of this class are: Distillation, Resolution, Putrefaction, Extraction, Calcination, Reverberation, Sublimation, Fixation, Separation, Reduction, Coagulation, Tincture and the like.

The fundamental idea of Paracelsus seems to have been that life is essentially a chemical process. If, then, man is a chemical compound (as the theories of the day would seem to demand) of mercury, sulfur, and salt, then good health must be the sign that the elements are mingled in the correct proportions, but illness shows that one or more of these elements is deficient. The logical treatment, therefore, is to dose the patient with that which he lacks in some form suitable for assimilation. Such considerations induced Paracelsus to abandon the herbs and extracts chiefly used by the physicians of his time and to prescribe inorganic salts. Indeed, mercury and its compounds owe their present prominence in the pharmacopoeia originally to him.

In the mystical writings of Paracelsus the *heart* is the moon and the *liver* is Jupiter. Gastric digestion, he thought, was caused by a spirit called *Archeus,* and diseases, in many cases, the result of morbid deposits in the body which he compared to the deposition of argols (crude cream of tartar) from wine on standing. His elements, mercury, sulfur, and salt, stood for (1) inflammability, (2) fusibility and volatility, and (3) fixity and incombustibility. In the body he compared these with spirit, soul, and body. He appears to have been the first to call the spirit of wine *alcohol* and the first in Europe to mention zinc.

As we read of his theories, we must ask ourselves with some dismay what could have been the state of therapeutics in the fifteenth century if *this* was an improvement! As a matter of fact, the medical profession was long divided between the old doctrines and the new, the disciples of Paracelsus idolizing him and pointing with pride to his marvelous cures while his enemies denounced him as a quack. With these controversies and the other interesting physiological ideas of Paracelsus we are not concerned. His service to chemistry consisted essentially in this, that he induced the alchemists to give up the search for gold and to devote their chemical skill to the preparation of remedies, while at the same time he compelled the physicians to learn a little chemistry. This did good in both directions. The gain to chemistry was that the medical profession included then, as always, educated men, whose mental power far surpassed that of the alchemists of the day. We must not leave Paracelsus without recalling his magnificent motto, "Let him not belong to another who may be his own."

Agricola.—There could have been no greater contrast to Paracelsus than his contemporary George Bauer (1494–1555), a German who wrote under the Latinized form of his name, Agricola. He lived in Joachimsthal and Chemnitz and was versed in medi-

cine, chemistry, and metallurgy. Uninterested in the controversies of his time, he devoted himself to making valuable
observations in his chosen field and recording them with accuracy
and clearness. His real services are, therefore, greater than those
of Paracelsus, but just at this time a fiery controversialist like the
latter was needed to set men thinking. It is a splendid tribute to
Agricola that his great work *De Re Metallica* served as a valued
handbook in metallurgy until comparatively recent times. The
author's mental attitude, however, found little imitation in his
own day, and the controversy between the Paracelsian and Anti-
Paracelsian schools of medicine raged on, men like Torquet de
Mayerne and Adrian de Mynsicht supporting the views of Paracelsus, while Andreas Libavius was among the most prominent of
those who opposed the new doctrine. In this controversy argument and denunciation so far exceeded experiment that not so much
was won for the science as ought to have been the case. Indeed
the Paracelsians dared not submit some of their views to the test
of experiment because the fundamental doctrine of their master—
that man was composed of mercury, sulfur, and salt—could
not be verified by decomposing him again into these substances.

Valerius Cordus (1515–1544) wrote the first pharmocopoeia
and described the preparation of ether from alcohol and sulfuric
acid. The name *ether*, however, does not seem to have been
applied to this medicine until 1730 when Frobenius called it
spiritus aethereus or *vini vitriolatus*. Ether was probably known
at about the thirteenth century.

John Dee (1527–1608) was an English mathematician and
astrologer. After Queen Mary's death in 1558, he was accused
of using enchantment and causing her death and spent some time
in prison. He was later released and came into favor with Queen
Elizabeth, who got him to set an appropriate date for her coro-
nation, and in 1578 she sent him abroad to consult with German
physicians and astrologers concerning the cause of her illness.
In 1581 he collaborated with **Edward Kelley** who claimed to have
discovered the philosophers' stone and to be able to raise spirits
from the dead. Dee's speculum or mirror is a pink-tinted piece
of glass about the size of an orange which is preserved in the
British Museum.

Andreas Libavius (c. 1540–1616) was a German schoolmaster who wrote *Alchymia* in 1597.   This can be regarded as perhaps the first real textbook of chemistry.   In it a survey is made of the genuine chemical knowledge of the time.   Libavius describes a laboratory which had in conjunction with it a storage place for chemicals, a preparation room, a room for the laboratory assistants, a room for crystallizing and freezing, and a wine cellar. He wrote other books and described various analytical tests, particularly dry reactions.   Anhydrous stannic chloride has been called *Libavius's fuming liquor*, after him.   One of his contemporaries was **Raphael Eglin** (1559–1622) who was the first to use the word *phlogiston*, which later, under Stahl and his followers, played a very important part in the theory of oxidation and reduction.

Michael Maier (1568–1622) was a very remarkable German Lutheran physician who won fame as an alchemist, philosopher, mystic, classical scholar, and musician.   In alchemy he was a writer, rather than a laboratory worker.   He is said to have received the doctorate in medicine at Rostock in 1597 and probably had achieved considerable reputation when he left his home in Holstein in 1608 at the age of forty.   Soon after this he was appointed physician to Emperor Rudolph II at Prague who used Maier as private secretary and made him a count.   The emperor was an enthusiastic patron of "the divine art" and had an unrivaled library which Maier enjoyed, as he was an omnivorous reader.   After the death of the Emperor in 1612, Maier spent some time in England, probably to learn English in order to be able to translate Norton's *Ordinall* into Latin verse. **Thomas Norton** (1532–1584) was an English lawyer who wrote poetry and was active in politics.   From 1619 to 1622, Maier was physician to the Landgraf Moritz of Hesse and practiced medicine at Magdeburg from 1612 until his death in 1622.

Maier's voluminous writings started in 1614 and continued through the next six or seven years.   At that time it appears that the public was much interested in alchemy, as was apparent from the popularity of Ben Jonson's play *The Alchemist* (1610). The text of this play showed an unrivaled mastery of the vocabulary and imagery of alchemy.   At one place Jonson writes:

I'll show you a book where Moses and his sister
And Solomon have written of the art
* Aye, and a treatise penned by Adam
O' the philosophers' stone, and in high Dutch.

Maier's writings are very obscure in style and show a passion
for extensive titles. He had no critical faculty, and his credulity
was unbounded. His first book, *Arcana Arcanissima (The Most
Secret of Secrets)* consists of six parts devoted to an alchemical
interpretation of Egyptian and Greek mythology. In 1616 he
published *De Circulo Physico (Squaring the Circle of the Physicist)*,
and in 1617 appeared Latin texts of which the following are the
English translations: *Contributions of the Twelve Nations to the
Golden Table; A Jest in Earnest; A Swarm of Pseudo-chymical
Drones Exposed; Peace after Noise; Golden Themis.* In 1618, his
chief publications were *The Golden Tripod, Atalanta Fleeing,* and
The Traveller's Companion. There were other writings of similar
nature.

The most interesting of these works is *Atalanta Fugiens* which
contains fifty copper engravings of emblematic pictures designed
to illustrate the relationship between alchemistic doctrine and
classical mythology. Each engraving bears a cryptic title, a
discourse, and a Latin epigram, which is set to music, probably
of Maier's own composition; this was in agreement with the
belief that music entered into the mysteries of the hermetic art.
In this there are some fifty fugues for three voices and Maier
attributed some of the dissonances to errors made in copying the
music. Maier's works are full of what we would now regard to
be erudite nonsense, but they exerted considerable influence upon
chemical thought, and the eminent scientist Sir Isaac Newton
(1642–1727) is known to have read them with care.

Maier took an active part in the publishing of some of the
writings of the reputed **Basil Valentine** and refers to them
repeatedly. It is generally thought that Basil Valentine never
lived and that his famous works were probably written by the
publisher Thölde in 1604, although accredited to a Benedictine
monk of about 1470. In Maier's writings there is to be found
no clue as to the real identity of Basil Valentine. Maier has
much to say concerning the "Brethren of the Rosy Cross,"
which combined the alchemistic code with a peculiar system of

mystical philosophy, but Maier himself probably did not belong to this fraternity. Maier's *The Golden Tripod* forms a part of the *Musaeum Hermeticum,* first published by Lucas Jennis in Germany in 1625. An English version, called *The Hermetic Museum, Restored and Enlarged,* was published as late as 1893, which shows that interest still prevails concerning alchemistic writings.

There were a host of other alchemical adepts, who were contemporaries of Maier, but who accomplished very little toward increasing chemical knowledge. The Frenchman **Denis Zachaire,** or Dionysius Zacharias, was one of these. Some say he lived from 1510 to 1550, but others say 1519 to 1556. He claimed to have found the philosophers' stone and was on a journey with the intention of showing the stone to other adepts when he was assassinated by his traveling companion, who also ran off with Zachaire's wife. **Cornelis Drebbel** (1572–1633) accidentally discovered in 1630 a method of dyeing wool a brilliant scarlet with cochineal after mordanting the wool with stannic chloride. This became of considerable technical importance.

Van Helmont.—Considerable interest attaches to the work of the Belgian physician, Jan Baptista Van Helmont (1577–1644). Van Helmont must have possessed a peculiar personality, for with an innate taste for the mysterious and occult, he still combined the capacity for accurate observation and clear thinking. In consequence his writings contain strange contradictions. He not only believed in the transmutation of metals, but claimed that he himself had accomplished this, and his attitude toward several other alchemistic traditions is equally credulous. In contrast it is of interest to trace one of the experiments which led him to reject the elements of Paracelsus and adopt water as the primordial substance. Finding a small willow weighing only 5 pounds, he planted this in 200 pounds of earth and watered it regularly for 5 years. At the end of this time he removed the earth from the roots and found its weight unchanged, while the willow now weighed 169 pounds. From this he concluded that at least 164 pounds must represent water, since the earth had not changed in weight and the willow had received no other nourishment. We must consider this an exceptionally good scientific investigation for the times. We are tempted to smile

JAN BAPTISTA VAN HELMONT
1577–1644

at the conclusion, but the fact is that Van Helmont had no means of observing the assimilation of carbon dioxide by the plant. There is nearly twenty times as much argon in the atmosphere as carbon dioxide, and since the former gas remained undiscovered until the closing years of the nineteenth century, we must forgive Van Helmont for underestimating the importance of the latter.

It is interesting, however, that this oversight should have been made by the very man who discovered carbon dioxide, for it was Van Helmont who first recognized that a gas which did not support combustion was formed when wood is burned, and that the same substance is produced by the action of acids upon limestone and during the process of fermentation. Indeed, he is the first writer to use the word *gas*, and he distinguishes such substances from vapors as less easily converted to liquids. It is interesting to note that Van Helmont, as well as Sir Isaac Newton (1642–1727), denied the corporal existence of fire and regarded fire as merely the outward sign of an intensely heated gas. In medicine, Van Helmont considered most physiological processes as fermentations and dwelt less than his predecessors upon hypothetical elements and more upon substances actually found in the body. This led him to classify diseases as acid and alkaline and to treat them by neutralization. As successors of Van Helmont, Franciscus de le Boë Sylvius (1614–1672) and Otto Tacchenius, who died in 1675, may be mentioned. Their contributions to chemistry and medicine were along similar lines.

Glauber.—No account of this period would be complete without mention of Johann Rudolph Glauber[1] (1604–1670) who perhaps came nearer than any of his predecessors to being a chemical engineer. Glauber lived chiefly by the sale of secret medical preparations, and his writings, which are delightfully quaint, abound in all sorts of alchemistic superstitions. He was, nevertheless, a shrewd observer, and quite original in his thinking. He wrote a number of books, and one is noteworthy

---

[1] Glauber was born in Bavaria and died in Amsterdam. Kopp and most other authorities give 1668 as the date of Glauber's death, but Jorissen, *Chem. Weekbl.*, **11**, 1076 (1914); **15**, 268 (1918); *Chem. Ztg.*, **51**, 17 (1927), has looked up the data concerning the burial and states positively that Glauber was buried March 10, 1670.

because it is essentially a treatise upon political economy. It is entitled *Teutschlands Wohlfahrt* and points out how Germany may develop its own resources, especially along chemical lines, and so become independent of other countries. The author's name is perpetuated for us in Glauber salt, a designation still retained for crystalline sodium sulfate. It is described in his *Miraculum Mundi*, where he calls it *sal mirabile*, not only on account of its value as a remedy but, among other things, for its property of dissolving carbon. We now know of course that when carbon is fused with sodium sulfate no real solution takes place. The sulfate is reduced to sulfide while carbon dioxide escapes. To Glauber, however, the disappearance of the carbon was evidence that it had been dissolved. He showed how sodium, "spirit of salt," could be prepared by heating common salt with green vitriol and alum or clay (1646–1649) and in 1658 described the action of oil of vitriol on common salt. He recognized the fact that salts consisted of acid and base and mentions the "chemical garden" formed by adding salts of metals to sodium silicate solution. He realized that silica was present in the compounds formed. He interpreted correctly many cases of metathesis, a class of reactions which had not been well understood. Thus he explained the formation of antimony trichloride (butter of antimony) from antimony sulfide and corrosive sublimate. The effect of heating sal ammoniac with oxide of zinc was explained by saying that the zinc oxide combines with the acid of ammonium chloride because of the "greater affinity" of the zinc oxide; it was not generally recognized until toward the end of the nineteenth century that the volatility of the hydrogen chloride was the most important cause of the reaction. Glauber also described the preparation of acetic acid by the distillation of wood and other processes which have since been developed on a large scale. At the time of Glauber, progress was being made in many of the industries associated with chemistry. Palissy had made considerable improvements, not only in pottery, but also in rational agriculture, Venetian glassmakers were doing some of their most skillful work, Agricola had laid the foundations of metallurgy and made valuable beginnings in assaying. The art of dyeing was also becoming improved and more systematic, the first handbook devoted to this subject appearing about 1540.

Sylvius.—Franciscus de le Boë Sylvius (1614–1672) was a professor of medicine at Leiden and appears to have had the first university "laboratorium." He himself, however, was essentially a theorist and represents the end of the iatrochemical period, although some have called him the founder. He believed that the activity of the living organism was determined by chemical processes and thought that acid and alkali in the body fluids was of great importance. This Partington calls "a survivor of the old humoral pathology and precursor of the modern cult of p_H."

Literature

There is a life of Paracelsus in English by Hartman, London, 1887. See also Waite, *Hermetic and Alchemical Writings of Paracelsus*, 2 vols., London, 1894.

Original editions of Glauber's books in both Latin and German are still extant though rare.

Herbert Hoover has published an admirable English translation of Agricola's *De Re Metallica*. The numerous quaint and interesting illustrations of the original are faithfully reproduced.

CHAPTER IV

BOYLE AND HIS CONTEMPORARIES—THE PHLOGISTON THEORY

Chemistry made but slow progress even in the seventeenth century, but from this time on we shall meet with men who were willing to pursue the study in the same spirit in which Galileo, Huygens, and Kepler were devoting themselves to astronomy and physics.

Boyle.—First among these comes Robert Boyle (1627–1691) the most broad-minded and widely cultivated man who had yet interested himself in chemistry. Boyle was the seventh son and fourteenth child of the Earl of Cork who sent him to Eton at the age of eight. Three years later he went to the Continent for the completion of his studies and remained till 1644, when he returned to England and took up his residence at Stalbridge Manor in Dorset. Here Boyle became associated with a club of progressive men interested in science who, because they had no fixed place of meeting, called themselves "The Invisible College." In 1644 Boyle removed to Oxford and in 1680 to London. The organization was unpopular at first, as all associations are apt to be whose members "seek new things," but good fortune came from an unexpected quarter when Charles II saw fit to dabble in science. Experimentation grew fashionable at court, and The Invisible College, under the king's favor, became the Royal Society in 1662, an institution destined to be an important agency in the advancement of science from that day to this. Boyle was prominent in the councils of the society until his death.

Boyle never married but devoted his life to the study of science and religion. Largely because of his work on gases, he has been called the Father of Modern Chemistry. He also helped to lay the foundation of analytical chemistry. Up to this time, too, much attention had been paid to the writings of the ancients, but

JOHN MAYOW
1645–1679

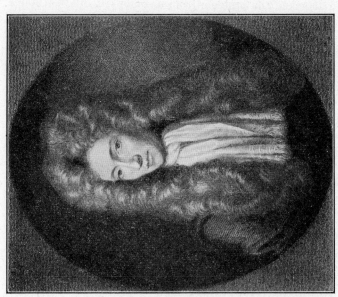

ROBERT BOYLE
1627–1691

45

Boyle taught the value of experimentation and showed a sceptical spirit and truly scientific attitude toward some of the myths that had been handed down concerning chemical phenomena.

Work in Pneumatics.—He is best remembered by his work in pneumatics.   To appreciate this we must recall that previous to his time little progress had been made toward explaining the action of so simple a mechanism as the suction pump.   It was commonly stated that Nature abhorred a vacuum, and accordingly when air was removed by the piston, water must go in to take its place.   Those who tried to raise water more than 34 feet by this means, however, soon found that under these circumstances the "abhorrence" was not sufficient to produce practical results.   At last it occurred to Torricelli that it was the pressure of the air upon the surface of the water which forced the latter into the tube.   If this were true it stood to reason that the atmosphere would balance a much shorter column of mercury than of water.   Torricelli tried this in 1643 and so invented the barometer.   A little later Pascal observed that when a barometer was carried to a height the mercury fell, another confirmation of Torricelli's views.

Boyle attacked the problem from a somewhat different angle. Otto von Guericke, the inventor of the air pump, had published an account of his discovery in 1654.   Reading this, Boyle decided to construct a new and superior pump which he completed in 1659.   With this instrument he tried many experiments.   Among others he placed a barometer under the receiver, and when the air was removed by the pump he had the pleasure of observing that the mercury continually fell, proving conclusively that it was the pressure of the air which supported the column.   In 1660 an account of these experiments was published in a treatise *On the Spring of the Air*.   The book was attacked by one Franciscus Linus who explained the barometer in his own fashion, maintaining that the mercury column was sustained by an invisible internal cord.   This explanation was characterized by Boyle as harder to understand than the facts were without it, which is in itself no mean test for a hypothesis.   In his reply to Linus, Boyle states his famous law that the volume of a gas varies inversely as the pressure, and he describes the experiment by which he established this, *i.e.*, air being confined in the closed arm of a U tube while it was subjected to varying pressures by pouring mercury into the other arm.

In addition to this important discovery Boyle did much valuable work in fields strictly chemical. He was the first to use the term "chemical analysis" in its modern significance. In fact, he did more to systematize the various qualitative tests then in use than any of his predecessors. His complete works are a formidable production for he was a voluminous and prolix writer, who delighted in the Platonic dialogue. One of his works, which did a real service, was *The Sceptical Chemist*, published in 1661. In this he attacked the "elements" of the alchemists and defined an *element* as something which has not been decomposed. This definition held until quite recently. We now believe that the atoms of all elements are composed of electrically charged particles and that the properties of the element depend on the number and distribution of these particles; an element is now defined as a substance in which all the atoms have the same atomic number.

Robert Hooke (1635–1703) worked with Boyle as his assistant in his experiments with the air pump. Hooke was perhaps the first to suggest a rational theory of combustion. He recognized the fact that there was something in the air that caused combustion and that much heat and what we call "fire" resulted from combustion. He described the burning of a candle and showed that the combustion took place where the vapor from the candle came in contact with air. Hooke was a brilliant scientist but was interested in so many things that he originated much but perfected little. His law governing the elasticity of solid bodies was discovered in 1660 and published in 1676 in the form of a Latin anagram. Hooke was miserly, cynical, irritable, and solitary. He spent much time criticizing his contemporaries, such as Isaac Newton, with claims that their ideas originated in Hooke's mind. His ideas on the undulatory nature of light and on gravitation, however, were sound and merely needed perfecting. He discovered with the microscope the cellular structure of living organisms.

Mayow and Hales.—Among Boyle's writings there is a paper upon the function of the air in combustion, but in this he was not so fortunate in his conclusions as his younger contemporary,

John Mayow (1645–1679), a graduate of Oxford and a medical practitioner, who recognized that the air contains a substance that unites with metals when they are calcined, that it changes venous to arterial blood, and that it occurs in saltpeter. For this reason he called it *spiritus nitro-aerius*. It seems possible that if Mayow had lived longer he might have discovered oxygen and so given the world a truer conception of the nature of combustion than it was destined to have for years to come. Somewhat later than Boyle and Mayow lived Stephen Hales (1677–1761), a clergyman who took interest in the study of gases and devised many clever means for their manipulation. Mayow and Hales may be regarded as the direct forerunners of Priestley.

Hale's work was quantitative, but his poor results were due to lack of pure starting materials. His work undoubtedly was the inspiration of later work by Black and Cavendish. He measured the "air" obtained by heating various substances in a gun barrel by collecting it over water. Among the materials used were coal, red lead, saltpeter, and iron filings with dilute acids. To him all gases were "air." In experiments on respiration he found he could breathe a definite quantity of air much longer if it were made to pass between exhalation and inhalation through rags which had been moistened with caustic potash solution. He stated that plants draw some part of their nourishment from the air through their leaves. He regarded air as an element.

Kunkel, Becher, and Lémery.—The mental attitude shown by Boyle and his associates in England represented, so far as chemistry was concerned, a more advanced position than had yet been attained upon the Continent. Here Boyle's most prominent contemporaries were Johann Kunkel (1630–1703) and Johann Joachim Becher (1635–1682). The former was a chemist at various courts and an expert in the manufacture of glass. His *Ars Vitraria* is a comprehensive treatise on this subject. After many vicissitudes Kunkel finally found favor and a title at the court of Charles XI of Sweden. Kunkel introduced the art of blowpipe analysis, showed the similarity of putrefaction and fermentation, and discovered phosphorus, quite independently of Boyle and of Brand, who also discovered it at about the same time. Becher was an uneasy spirit who divided his time

between teaching, chemical theorizing, and the promotion of
various socialistic and financial schemes which frequently
involved industrial applications of chemistry; thus he was the
first to take out a patent for distilling coal, suggesting that the
tar might serve for the preservation of cordage while the gases
would be suitable for smelting since they gave "a flame ten feet
long." The world, however, was not yet ready for a coal-tar
industry, so this venture and many others like it came to nothing.
Becher lost the friendship of those who had put money into his
schemes, and more than once he had to flee the country, though
no charges of personal dishonesty are recorded against him.
Becher's writings on chemistry had no little vogue. They were
for the most part visionary and alchemistic in spirit, but in one
point they were destined to have a great influence upon the
thought of the eighteenth century. Becher adopted as elements
three earths—the mercurial, the vitrifiable, and the combustible.
It was this last, the *terra pinguis*, which was destined to become,
in the hands of Stahl, the foundation of the great phlogiston
theory. In 1673, Becher tried to persuade Prince Herman of
Baden to furnish him considerable silver to use with good Dutch
sand for the purpose of making gold as a scientific experiment.
Nicolas Lémery (1645–1715) was the best known French contemporary. His *Cours de chymie* was translated into Latin,
English, Dutch, German, and Spanish and had a considerable
effect upon chemical thought of this period. Lémery was the
first to distinguish between vegetable and mineral chemistry or
organic and inorganic chemistry.

Stahl.—Georg Ernst Stahl (1660–1734) studied medicine at
Jena where he also lectured on chemistry. He received his
degree in 1683 and in 1687 became physician to the Duke of
Saxe-Weimar. In 1694 he was made professor of medicine at the
University of Halle and in 1716 became physician to the king of
Prussia. At Halle he taught medicine, physiology, pathology,
dietetics, pharmacology, and botany. He developed a quarrelsome disposition and became bitter and melancholy. His
writings appear deliberately obscure and difficult in many cases.
Some are printed in a mixture of Latin and German, interspersed
with alchemistic symbols provided with Latin case endings. In
his youth, Stahl believed in alchemy but later warned against its

frauds. As proof that metals do not ripen into gold, he stated that British tin was the same then as when exploited by the Phoenicians in ancient days. Without a knowledge of Stahl and his ideas, the eighteenth century would be hard to understand with respect to chemistry. He was a man of great ability and had a keener insight into chemistry than did Paracelsus. His studies on oxidation and reduction were of special importance and although his basic idea was fundamentally wrong, he had a great deal of positive knowledge, and his conceptions proved incentive to other work. He recognized the unity of oxidation and reduction processes, whether they were concerned with putrefaction, fermentation, respiration, or the production of metals from oxides. He saw that the reducing power was transferable. He clarified the conception of acid, base, and salt.

The Phlogiston Theory.—Stahl is best known as the founder of a system of chemical philosophy—the first of those comprehensive theories that have successively, since his day, dominated chemical thought. The subject is interesting, therefore, not only in its own account, but for what it can teach us concerning dominant theories in general.

The fundamental idea in the phlogiston theory was that all combustible substances possessed one component in common which escaped in the act of burning. For this Stahl expressed his indebtedness to Becher, but the idea itself was really much older since the alchemists used the term "sulfur" in much the same sense. The alchemists, however, were content to acknowledge this as a dogma and disregarded it at their pleasure, whereas Stahl treated his phlogiston as a definite chemical component and used it as a guide in everyday laboratory practice.

Reactions Explained by Phlogiston.—The theory was clearly based upon the common-sense observation of that kind of combustion with which everybody is most familiar. When a piece of wood burns, we seem to see flames issue from it at every pore and pass upward. The wood blackens, cracks open, and when the flames are gone, the fragments glow for a few moments and then crumble to ashes. What more natural conclusion than that a fire substance, *phlogiston*, has escaped while the ashes are left? It would follow from this that the wood is a compound of phlogiston and the ash. This is capable of wide expansion. If

GEORG ERNST STAHL
1660–1734

HERMAN BOERHAAVE
1668–1738

phosphorus be burned instead of wood, the "ash" is white and bulky, it attracts water and then gives an acid reaction, hence phosphorus is a compound of phlogiston and phosphoric acid. Sulfur burns completely, and we might conclude that sulfur was pure phlogiston were it not for the choking fumes that are evolved. When these are absorbed in water, acids of sulfur are formed which with phlogiston must have made up the original sulfur. When tin and lead are calcined in the air a voluminous ash is formed. The metals, therefore, consist of these calxes plus phlogiston. Iron in rusting undergoes a slow combustion and the metal consists of the rust and phlogiston. If the calxes of the metals are heated with carbon (which is rich in phlogiston), the carbon gives its phlogiston to the calx and the metal is obtained, a simple explanation of the smelting process. But we need not stop here. The theory may be equally well applied to reactions in the wet way. If iron be introduced into a solution of blue vitriol, it goes into solution while copper is precipitated. Obviously the iron gives up its phlogiston to produce the copper, and we can even draw some conclusions concerning the quantitative relationships involved, for the iron, which disappeared, and the copper, which is precipitated, must represent those quantities that contain the same amount of phlogiston. Some of the later believers in the theory took this step. They also recognized the resemblance of the vital processes to combustion and stated that, as our bodies are consumed, the lungs constantly exhale phlogiston!

Faults of the Theory.—These illustrations will at least serve to show that a theory is not necessarily true because it can explain a great number of facts. Here was a theory false to the verge of the ludicrous, which yet coordinated most facts familiar to the chemists of the day and enabled them to use their knowledge efficiently for the solution of new problems. The phlogiston theory was, therefore, well fitted for its position as a great working hypothesis, and this gave it universal credit in spite of faults so glaring that it is now hard to see why they were not patent to every thoughtful observer.

The faults are themselves instructive. In the first place, no one had ever seen any phlogiston or could mention a single one of its properties, save that it departed on combustion. It was, therefore, a hypothetical substance devised for a single purpose. This, however, troubled no one. It no more occurred to anyone to go out and look for phlogiston than it occurs to us to attempt the isolation of the "luminiferous ether."

Another difficulty was that air is required for combustion. Geber knew this, and it was stated in the book ascribed to Basilius Valentinus (see page 21) and must have been generally understood by anyone who could successfully build a fire. The difficulty was met by the statement that the phlogiston did not simply go away in combustion; it united with the air or some portion of it. If there was no air present the fire went out because the phlogiston had nothing with which to combine.

A more serious difficulty lay in the fact observed by at least Boyle, Mayow, and Rey[1] that when metals are burned, the calx weighs more than the metal, whereas if burning meant a loss of phlogiston it should weigh less. To us this seems insuperable, but at that time it received little attention. Few persons made quantitative experiments and those who did, seem to have seriously confused weight with specific gravity, tacitly assuming that a pound of lead must be heavier than a pound of feathers. Others more logical, to whom the fundamental facts were brought home, defended their beloved hypothesis with another still more daring. When fire leaves a substance its *upward* flight shows that it possesses the quality of *levity* or negative weight. Unlike all other substances, it is not attracted to the center of the earth but repelled from it. Hence the more phlogiston a substance contains the lighter it is! There is, of course, nothing inherently absurd in the idea of something not amendable to the attraction of gravitation, but that just this hypothetical substance should be the only one to show the property might have set men thinking. Unfortunately, there is much in a great hypothesis which tends to prevent thinking.

Hoffmann, Boerhaave, Marggraf.—A prominent contemporary of Stahl was Friedrich Hoffmann (1660–1742), who was for some

---

[1] Rey is sometimes spoken of as though he came near discovering the facts concerning combustion. His charmingly written and amusing paper on *The Increase in Weight of Tin and Lead on Calcination* (1630) has been reprinted by the Alembic Club, and everyone who wants to spend a pleasant half hour should read it. No one who does so, however, will be likely to believe the author capable of making any serious discovery.

years professor at Halle and a vigorous and voluminous writer. His experimental investigations were largely concerned with the examination of mineral waters, and in testing for their various constituents he did much toward perfecting the analytical methods of his time. He showed that sulfates are not the same as nitrates and that the base (or calx) from alum is different from that of chalk. Hitherto such calxes were considered identical. Another contemporary was Hermann Boerhaave (1668–1738), an eminent professor at the University of Leiden, who acquired fame as a teacher in both medicine and chemistry. His great work, entitled *Elementa Chemiæ*, was published in 1724 and long ranked as chief authority upon the subject. The book appeared in more than twenty-five editions in Latin, French, and German. It was the most learned and the clearest text on chemistry that had been written up to that time. It contained all the chemical facts and processes known, all stated simply and clearly. Chemistry was shown to be a science and an art of great importance, not only to medicine, but to mankind in general.

Boerhaave scarcely mentioned phlogiston but stated that sulfur was a compound of sulfuric acid and of a combustible oil *pabulum ignis*. He believed in alchemy, and his perseverance is illustrated by the fact that he kept mercury for fifteen years at an elevated temperature to see if it would undergo any change. He also distilled one sample of mercury over five hundred times to see if he could detect any change in volatility as a result of such treatment. The modern conception of chemical affinity is based on the ideas of Boerhaave.

Among the most prominent of the German phlogistonists was Andreas Sigismund Marggraf (1709–1782), who was for many years director of the laboratory of the Academy of Sciences in Berlin. Marggraf made some important discoveries, among which may be mentioned the distinction of magnesia from alumina, and the use of the flame coloration for distinguishing soda from potash. He recognized that gypsum, barytes, and potassium sulfate are all derivatives of sulfuric acid and observed that phosphorus gains in weight when burned. This, however, did not shake his allegiance to the phlogiston theory. Marggraf made considerable use of the microscope and by its means detected the presence of sugar in the beet, an observation destined to bear fruit industrially. He prepared potassium cyanide, noticed the solvent action of its aqueous solution on metal salts, and obtained Prussian blue.

Geoffroy and His Tables of Affinity.—Among the French chemists of this period, Étienne François Geoffroy (1672–1731) is particularly worthy of mention. To distinguish him from his younger brother, who was also interested in science, he is often called Geoffroy the Elder. He was a prominent lecturer at the Jardin du Roi and the Collège de France and did a signal service with his *Tables of Affinity* which were presented to the Academy of Science between 1718 and 1720. The fundamental idea underlying these tables was the following: If we consider a given base, say caustic potash, we recognize that it reacts vigorously with a variety of substances, especially with acids, and it is natural to inquire which of these has the greatest affinity for the base. Geoffroy tried to answer this question by the plausible assumption that when an acid has combined with a base and the product is brought into contact with a second acid, the latter, if it has a greater affinity for the base than the first, will expel it. For every base, therefore, it should be possible to prepare a list of acids in such order that any one substance will expel from combination all those that succeed it. This will constitute a table of affinity for the given base. A similar table might, of course, be constructed for an acid or indeed any other substance and would take a form like the following:

Fixed alkali	Vitriolic acid
Vitriolic acid	Fixed alkali
Acid of nitre	Volatile alkali
Marine acid	Absorbent earth
Acid of vinegar	Iron
Sulfur	Copper
	Silver

Geoffroy's assumption was an attractive one for it seems easy to believe that if, in the case of a given compound, we knew all the substances that had affinity for it, and the relative degree of that affinity, the chemistry of the substance would be thereby completely determined. Today, however, we know that tem-

ETIENNE FRANÇOIS GEOFFROY
1672–1731

perature, pressure, solubility, and the nature of the medium have
so much to do with the course of chemical reactions that such
tables could never do justice to more than a portion of the truth.
Nevertheless, they served their day as a convenient and compact
form for collating chemical facts.

Rouelle.—Another eminent French teacher of chemistry was
Guillaume François Rouelle (1703–1770), who should be mentioned here, were it only for the fact that he numbered Lavoisier
among his pupils. He was, however, himself a scientist of no
mean ability and fixed more clearly than any had done before
him the idea of a salt as an addition product of acid and base (not
acid and metal), and he distinguished between neutral, acid, and
basic salts, something which often mystifies beginners even in
our own times.

Mikhail Vasilevich Lomonosov (1711–1765).—One of the most
remarkable chemists of this period was Lomonosov. He was
born in a small Russian village and his father was a peasant
fisherman. Not being permitted to go to school, he learned to
read by studying church books, which were the only ones available. After the death of his mother, his stepmother took a
violent dislike to the lad and objected to his wasting so much
time over books and in December, 1730, he obtained a passport
that permitted him to leave his home for a year.

After several weeks tramping, he reached Moscow and in
January succeeded in entering the Academy of Divinity by pre-
tending to be the son of a nobleman. Here he was a big, husky
lad of twenty with a loud voice doing schoolwork with lads eight
or ten years younger. He got an allowance of 3 kopeks a day
(about 18 cents) for food and all other expenses. He passed
rapidly from class to class and became proficient in Latin but
was disappointed in not being able to study natural science,
which was not taught there. In 1734 he was obliged to admit
that he was a peasant but was allowed to remain in the school
because he was the best pupil. He could not, however, become
a priest because of his humble birth.

Peter the Great had founded the Russian Academy of Sciences
at St. Petersburg in 1720, and a University College was a part
of it. In 1735 there were so few students that the Senate
ordered the Moscow Divinity School to send to the University

Mikhail Vasilevich Lomonosov
1711–1765

twenty of their best boys. There were, however, only twelve suitable boys in the two upper classes, and Lomonosov was one of these. In 1736 an expedition was exploring Siberia, and they had need of an expert in chemistry, mining, and metallurgy. There was none available, so Lomonosov and two others were sent to Germany to study. There they worked at Marburg under the philosopher Christian von Wolff, who was also a member of the Russian Academy. The students were allowed 300 rubles a year (about $1,250), but the sudden transition from poverty and restraint to affluence and freedom was too much for them and at the end of three years their debts amounted to about $50,000 of modern money and Professor von Wolff had to help settle their debts. From Marburg the three Russians went to Freiburg to work under J. F. Henckel who also had charge of the money that was sent from Russia and over this Lomonosov and Henckel quarreled violently. In May, 1740, Lomonosov went to Leipzig to see the Russian ambassador but could not find him. He went back to Marburg and married the daughter of a church official. He started back home but was advised to wait for orders from Russia. On his way back to Marburg he was caught by a Prussian recruiting officer and placed in a fortress at Wesel. He escaped, but had several hair-breadth escapes later, until in May, 1741, he was called back to Russia and was appointed to the staff of the Academy at a salary of 360 rubles.

Lomonosov then began to compose odes on festive occasions which were more powerful and sonorous than any that had been written previously in the Russian tongue. His philological work on Russian grammar is recognized as valuable. After the death of Peter the Great the Academy became dominated by Germans, and Lomonosov became intemperate and quarrelsome so that he was placed in prison where he studied hard and wrote several papers. In 1745 he was made professor of chemistry at the Academy and had there the first chemical laboratory where students were taught to make scientific experiments. He learned to make mosaic pictures of colored glass and as a result of such work was granted an estate of 40,000 acres with three villages and 211 male serfs under his control.

During his life, Lomonosov tried to better the lot of the peasant. He really created the scientific language of Russia, and the foundation of the University of Moscow was due to his efforts. From 1755 to his death he was the head of this university and the gymnasium.

Lomonosov can be called the first real physical chemist because he looked at chemistry from the standpoint of physics and mathematics; his ideas were at least a hundred years in advance of his time. This is true particularly of his theory with respect to atoms and molecules. Matter he thought composed of extremely small particles of finite dimensions, which are imperceptible but are the cause of all properties. When matter is heated the oscillatory and gyratory motions of these particles become accelerated. When the rotary motion is great enough, the substance melts or volatilizes. These views are remarkable because it was then generally believed that heat (caloric) had substance, and it was not until the second half of the nineteenth century that the mechanical nature of heat was proved by the experiments of Mayer and others.

Lomonosov's theory of the gaseous state recognized the existence of tiny atoms moving with great rapidity and constantly colliding with one another. His ideas were almost identical with those of Waterstone (1845), Clausius, and Kronig (1856–1857), and his ideas on compressibility of gases anticipated those of Dupré (1864) and Van der Waals (1873). He also had a fairly clear conception of the absolute zero.

Lomonosov considered a difference in properties to be due sometimes to a difference in the arrangement of the atoms, which is what Berzelius had in mind in 1829. In studying solutions, he sought to determine how much would dissolve in a given volume, the density of the solution, the change in total volume, the lowering of temperature as a result of the dissolving, the expansion of the solution from the freezing to the boiling point, the freezing point and boiling point of the solution, the solubility of one salt in a saturated solution of another, the refractive index of the solution, the rise in a capillary tube, the appearance under the microscope, and the changes brought about by the electrical current. Lomonosov studied burning and calcining in 1742 and attributed the gain in weight to something taken from the air. He repeated Boyle's experiment of calcining in a closed vessel and found there was no gain in weight until more air was admitted. Lavoisier also proved, some 31 years later, that Boyle was wrong. Lomonosov believed in the conservation of matter and that when a body gained in weight some other body lost weight. He did not believe in phlogiston but sometimes mentioned it in his lectures.

Hellot, Macquer, and Baumé.—Between 1745 and 1756 beautiful porcelain was made at Vincennes, aided by the chemists Hellot and Macquer. At Vincennes, Hellot had charge of the technical production. In 1756 the factory moved to Sèvres. Pierre Joseph Macquer (1718–1784) was lecturer and professor of chemistry at the Medical School in Paris. In 1776–1777 he noticed that water was deposited on a cold piece of porcelain held over a flame of burning hydrogen. He believed that phlogiston was the *matter* of light. In 1746–1748, Macquer discovered the arsenates of sodium and potassium. He made important studies on dyeing and wrote a textbook and dictionary of chemistry. Antoine Baumé (1728–84) was another French chemist who, after serving as apprentice to C. J. Geoffroy, was made professor at the École de Pharmacie. His business interest in chemical products enabled him to retire in 1780 in order to devote his time to the study of applied chemistry, but he was ruined by the French Revolution and forced to go back into business. He devised improvements in bleaching silk, dyeing, gilding, and purifying saltpeter, but he is best known for his invention of the hydrometer which bears his name. He wrote numerous papers and books, prepared a few esters and stated that, if chemists were to have affinity tables, it would be necessary to have one for solutions at the ordinary temperatures and another for reactions of fusion.

Literature

Thomas Birch published the complete works of Boyle in six imposing volumes. The second edition appeared in 1772. There is an attractive account of his life and work in Thorpe's *Essays in Historical Chemistry*, 2d ed., London, 1902. *The Sceptical Chemist* has been reprinted in *Everyman's Library.*

Mayow's studies of the *Spiritus Nitro-Aerius* have been published by Ostwald in his *Klassiker der Exakten Wissenschaften*, No. 126, and in *Alembic Club Reprints*, No. 17.

See also the fascinating paper by Jean Rey, *Alembic Club Reprints*, No. 11.

The interesting story of Lomonasov has been told by B. N. Menschutkin, *Chem. News*, **115**, 73–75, 85–87 (1912); *J. Chem. Ed.*, **4**, 1079–1087 (1927).

CHAPTER V

THE LATER PHLOGISTONISTS—THE DISCOVERY OF OXYGEN

Black on Magnesia Alba.—With Joseph Black (1728–1799) we come to the eminent group of distinguished chemists whose work contributed so largely to the overthrow of the phlogiston theory, and it is especially interesting to see how they themselves almost without exception remained blind to this, its most important significance. Black was born in France of Scottish parentage. He had seven brothers and six sisters. He learned English from his mother and was sent to Belfast at the age of twelve. Later he studied medicine at the University of Glasgow and came under the influence of William Cullen (1712–1790), an excellent teacher of chemistry. Black himself became professor at Glasgow and made some important discoveries in physics, developing independently the idea of specific heat and of latent heat, though his work was not formally published. He is best remembered by chemists for his work on *magnesia alba* which he presented for the doctor's degree in 1754. In this investigation he took up the study of what we now call magnesium carbonate as a new substance which he desired to characterize, and he proceeded to try some experiments upon it from which he was able to draw important conclusions. In the interest of compactness we may sum up Black's results in a series of propositions:

1. *Magnesia alba* when strongly heated loses about half its weight and yields a new substance *magnesia usta* (magnesium oxide).

II. With vitriolic acid *magnesia alba* yields epsom salt (magnesium sulfate) with effervescence.

III. *Magnesia usta* when similarly treated yields epsom salt without effervescence.

IV. In a solution of epsom salt, mild alkali (potassium carbonate) precipitates *magnesia alba* and the solution on evaporation yields vitriolated tartar (potassium sulfate).

JOSEPH BLACK
1728–1799

HENRY CAVENDISH
1731-1810

V. Mild alkali effervesces with acids while caustic does not.

VI. Mild alkali is made caustic by addition of *magnesia usta*.

When arranged in this form it is particularly easy to see what a handicap upon the chemists of that time was the use of a nomenclature necessarily incapable of expressing chemical relationships, and how impossible it then was to know whether all substances in a reaction were accounted for or not. Nevertheless, Black interpreted his results with perfect accuracy. From II and III he concluded that the difference between *magnesia alba* and *magnesia usta* was the gas ("fixed air") liberated from the former by acids, and that it was the expulsion of the same gas which accounted for the loss of weight when *magnesia alba* was heated (I). II and IV showed that *magnesia alba* could be regenerated from *magnesia usta* by the aid of mild alkali, hence the latter must contain fixed air which it surrenders in the reaction. This is further confirmed by V which shows that mild alkali differs from caustic by its content of fixed air. Finally VI completes the caustifying of the alkali by the action of magnesia. Black saw at once that these reactions were analogous to those involved in the ancient method of preparing caustic alkali from quicklime. He accordingly repeated his experiments using limestone instead of *magnesia alba* and so reached the correct conclusion that the burning of lime consists essentially in the expulsion of fixed air.

Such a result was utterly opposed to the explanations hitherto current. According to the latter, when lime was heated in the kiln phlogiston entered into it making it fiery or caustic. Later when the quicklime was treated with mild alkali another transfer of phlogiston occurred and the latter became caustic in its turn.

It is what might have been expected from his clear habits of thought that in later years, when Lavoisier had once shown the way, Black was among the first to adopt the new views.

Cavendish.—England is conspicuous for the number of its men of wealth and family who have devoted their lives to science. Boyle was a prominent example and we find another in Henry Cavendish (1731–1810), a nephew of the third duke of Devonshire. Cavendish was of an eccentric turn, and countless stories are told of his strange habits, his shyness and his aversion to women. He lived as a recluse and devoted practically his entire time to research, and although in middle life he inherited a fortune which made him one of the richest men in England, this had no influence upon his regular and frugal habits. As might be expected in such a character his work was done with little thought of fame, and much of the best of it remained entirely unknown till long after his death. Cavendish was the first to make a thorough study of hydrogen and he gave it the name of "inflammable air" in a paper published in 1766. The evolution of a combustible gas when a metal is dissolved in acids was observed much earlier. We are reasonably sure that it was known to Paracelsus and Van Helmont, and we know that it was isolated by Boyle. Cavendish identified hydrogen with phlogiston, and this was entirely in the spirit of current views, for if a metal is a compound of a base with phlogiston then when the base unites with an acid to form a salt phlogiston must escape.

About 1783, after the discovery of oxygen, Cavendish combined this gas with hydrogen by means of the electric spark, and so established the composition of water. In 1785 while conducting experiments of this kind he noticed that oxygen and nitrogen when sparked in this way over water yielded nitric acid, and applied the idea to the complete absorption of atmospheric nitrogen. He always found, however, a small inert residue whose volume could not be further reduced and which he estimated at about $\frac{1}{120}$ of the whole. It is interesting to note that in spite of this valuable clue so faithfully recorded, argon and the other rare gases of the atmosphere remained undiscovered for more than a hundred years.

It is now hard to see how Cavendish could have accounted for his results in terms of the phlogiston theory, but he did so on the assumption of Priestley that oxygen was "dephlogisticated air," that portion of it, namely, which unites with phlogiston on combustion. He was not ignorant of the work of Lavoisier, and acknowledged frankly that the latter's views would explain the results of his experiments "nearly as well," but after weighing both opinions he clung to the old for what now seems a curious reason. He writes:

There is one circumstance also, which though it may appear to many not to have much force, I own has some weight with me; it is, that as plants seem to draw their nourishment almost entirely from water and fixed and phlogisticated air, and are restored back to those substances by burning, it seems reasonable to conclude, that notwithstanding their infinite variety they consist almost entirely of various combinations of water and fixed and phlogisticated air, united according to one of these opinions to phlogiston, and deprived according to the other of dephlogisticated air; so that, according to the latter opinion, the substance of a plant is less compounded than a mixture of those bodies into which it is resolved by burning; and it is more reasonable to look for great variety in the more compound than in the more simple substance.

The modern organic chemist certainly finds his compounds sufficiently complex without phlogiston.

Some of the best work of Cavendish was in the domain of physics, where in his later years he worked much upon latent and specific heats, and by an ingenious method he made a measurement of the density of the earth which was extremely accurate for the times. He also was interested in astronomy and in meteorology.

Torbern Olof Bergman (1735–1784) was a prominent Swedish contemporary of Black and of Cavendish. In 1767 he made strenuous application for the vacant chair in chemistry at the University of Upsala and obtained it although most of his previous work had been in botany, entomology, mathematics and physics. He improved the methods of analytical chemistry and laid special stress upon blowpipe analysis. Although some of his own chemical analyses of minerals were not very accurate his work was very popular and separations that we now use in analytical chemistry, such as the precipitation of calcium oxalate in the presence of magnesium, were known to him. He has been called the Father of Analytical Chemistry. His *Opuscula Physica et Chemica* in six volumes is a learned treatise. He prepared tables of affinity which were very similar to those of Geoffroy, published sixty years previously. He was regarded as an authority and manifested a truly scientific spirit although he could not be classed as a brilliant scientific discoverer.

Scheele.—Few investigators of any age have been gifted with such natural powers of observation and such experimental skill as Karl Wilhelm Scheele, who was born in Stralsund (then Swedish) on December 19, 1742. He was the seventh of eleven children and was of German descent. Scheele was apprenticed to an apothecary in Göteborg at the age of fourteen and he

TORBERN OLOF BERGMAN
1735–1784

KARL WILHELM SCHEELE
1742–1786

remained there for eight years, constantly devoting his spare
hours to the study of such chemical books as were available and
trying numerous experiments on his own account. In 1765 he
went to Malmö and thence he removed to Stockholm in 1768.
Between 1770 and 1775 he was at Upsala and in the latter year
he purchased a little apothecary shop in Köping where he continued to work until his early death in 1786. Life was a hard
struggle with ill health and poverty always, and in the earlier
years his great scientific attainments were also little appreciated,
so that his communications sent to learned societies too frequently remained pigeon-holed for long periods, neither published
nor returned.

There was a change for the better when, through his friend
Gahn, Scheele became acquainted with Torbern Bergman, then
professor at Upsala and Sweden's most prominent chemist. It
is said that in the beginning of the acquaintance Scheele was
able to explain something which had hitherto troubled Bergman.
The latter had observed that although saltpeter ordinarily
evolves no red fumes when treated with acetic acid, it does so after
being strongly heated. Scheele supplied the following explanation: When the nitre is heated, phlogiston enters into it from the
fire, and the residue (which we now call potassium nitrite) gives
off this phlogiston in red fumes when a weak acid is added.
Most of Scheele's explanations took a similar form, but we
must not lose sight of the essential point—the product of heating
does represent a lower state of oxidation (higher phlogistication
in Scheele's vocabulary) than the original substance. Here
Scheele was perfectly clear and correct.

Magnesia Nigra.—It is the same in his celebrated study of
magnesia nigra[1] in which he for the first time characterized the
elements barium and manganese, and discovered chlorine and
oxygen. He starts with manganese dioxide and from it prepares
many of the compounds of this element which are now most
familiar. In reading, one is constantly impressed by Scheele's
sureness of touch, how instinctively he sees the next experiment
to try, and how, though he works under the handicap of the

---

[1] *Magnesia nigra* was the name given to the mineral pyrolusite (MnO_2),
sometimes called black oxide of manganese. *Magnesia alba* referred to a
basic carbonate of magnesium, $Mg(OH)_2.3MgCO_3.3H_2O$.

phlogiston theory and makes scarce a quantitative measurement, he yet follows this chameleon-like element through all its changes of valence without serious mental confusion, and he is so clear concerning the essentials of every reaction that if we substitute reduction and oxidation for phlogistication and dephlogistication, the whole not only reads intelligibly but is practically accurate today.

Discoveries of Scheele.—Scheele's discovery of chlorine and oxygen has just been mentioned. We now know from the notebooks first published long after his death that he prepared the latter element in three or four different ways before the famous experiments of Priestley in 1774. To the latter of course still belongs the credit of independent work, prior publication, and consequent influence upon his contemporaries. Other elements whose compounds were first studied by Scheele were tungsten and molybdenum. The mineral in which he found the latter, *molybdaena nitens*,[1] had long been confused with graphite. Scheele distinguished the two and showed that graphite is a form of carbon. He was also the first to make a thorough study of hydrogen sulfide and in his work on the compounds of arsenic he discovered the pigment now known as "Scheele's green" (copper arsenite) as well as the deadly arsine gas, since so valuable for detecting small quantities of the element.

His organic researches were no less remarkable. He discovered glycerin and uric acid, and originated a method for purifying and isolating organic acids which is still in constant use. For this purpose he first prepared their calcium salts and then decomposed the latter with sulfuric acid. He applied this method widely, preparing oxalic, tartaric, malic, citric and gallic acids. He also obtained lactic acid from sour milk and, by the oxidation of milk sugar, discovered mucic acid. One of his most famous investigations is that upon Prussian blue which led among other things to the preparation of hydrocyanic acid. This he describes in detail—its odor, its peculiar taste and the warm sensation it gives in the mouth, but there is nothing in his paper to lead one to believe that he knew it to be poisonous. Surely this apothecary who without modern laboratory facilities could survive the discovery of arsine and prussic acid must have led a charmed life!

[1] Now known as molybdenite, MoS_2.

Air and Fire.—Scheele's one book was entitled *On Air and Fire* and was published in 1777. In it he gives a complete account of his views upon combustion and it seems worth while to attempt a brief outline of his reasoning, for it shows us the phlogiston theory just before its fall, as understood by the ablest of its devotees.

Scheele begins by a series of experiments which prove that the air is made up of two gases. One of these supports combustion and this he names "fire-air." The other he calls "spoiled-air." By burning substances in a measured volume of air and noting the decrease in volume he determines with adequate accuracy the relative proportions of the two gases, and he finds that he can absorb the fire-air not only by burning sulfur or phosphorus but by various reagents, especially "liver of sulfur" and freshly precipitated ferrous hydroxide.

He next attempts to explain the mechanism of combustion, and directs our attention to the burning of sulfur in a volume of air confined over water. What becomes of the fire-air? It is not in the water because on examination this proves to contain only acid of sulfur (known to be a component of sulfur!). Neither can it be in the air since this has decreased in volume. During the combustion, however, light and heat have left the vessel (Scheele is the first to distinguish radiant heat from that transmitted by convection) and he draws the bold conclusion that the fire-air has united with the phlogiston to form heat and light and that in this form the two substances have left the flask. That heat contained phlogiston would have been considered self-evident in those days, for proof was found in such experiments as that with saltpeter described on a previous page (70), so it only remained for Scheele to show the presence of fire-air and phlogiston in light. The former he does not attempt, but the latter he proves to his satisfaction in the following elegant and original way. He has a sure criterion for phlogiston in the evolution of red fumes with nitric acid; thus calx of copper (copper oxide) evolves no fumes when treated with the acid, but metallic copper (which contains phlogiston) does so copiously. Scheele accordingly exposes silver chloride to light and in that way obtains traces of metallic silver (he was the first to observe this reaction) and he proves its presence by the addition of nitric acid which now gives fumes, whereas the unilluminated silver salt did not. He reasons that the metal obtained its phlogiston from the light (!) since it was the latter which caused the change. Such was the phlogiston theory!

Priestley.—Joseph Priestley, whose discovery of oxygen is an important mile-stone in chemical history, was born March 13, 1733, in Fieldhead, Yorkshire. Priestley's health was delicate in his early years so that his education was obtained mostly by private instruction and suffered many interruptions. Nevertheless he was fond of books and gradually acquired a considerable knowledge of ancient, modern and even oriental languages. He also had some opportunity to study the natural philosophy of those days. He finally decided to enter the ministry and in 1755 began preaching to a small dissenting congregation at Needham Market. This was the first of a series of such pastorates, but Priestley was never a very successful preacher on account of an impediment in his speech, and he did some teaching as opportunity offered, interesting himself more and more in chemical experiments, especially upon gases, a study for which he was eminently fitted by unusual manipulative skill. This scientific work attracted attention and Priestley became a Fellow of the Royal Society in 1766 and a foreign associate of the French Academy of Sciences in 1772. In the latter year he also obtained a congenial position as librarian and literary companion to Lord Shelburne with whom he traveled on the Continent and thus gained opportunity for contact with the most eminent scientific men in France, including Lavoisier. In 1780 Priestley was pensioned by Lord Shelburne and again began preaching, this time in Birmingham. When the French Revolution broke out he warmly espoused its principles, and in 1791 his attendance at a dinner held to celebrate the anniversary of the fall of the Bastille so infuriated some of his fellow-citizens that they sacked his house and burned the chapel where he preached. Priestley took this as a hint to resign his pastorate, and though he later undertook another charge he found himself so unpopular that in 1794 he decided to abandon England for America. He settled in Northumberland, Pennsylvania, and died there February 6, 1804.

JOSEPH PRIESTLEY
1733–1804

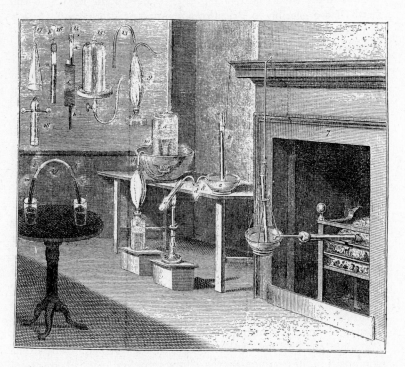

PRIESTLEY'S LABORATORY

75

Priestley wrote much on theology and other topics, but his best title to fame is the work recorded in his *Experiments and Observations on Different Kinds of Air*, published between 1774 and 1786. Priestley constantly ascribes his discoveries to chance, and some critics have taken him at his word and condemned his work as planless and haphazard. Impulsive bunglers, however, do not make such discoveries, and we shall come nearer to the truth if we ascribe to Priestley an innocent literary affectation of modesty akin to that found in Montaigne who, for that matter, might well have written the following:

I do not think it at all degrading to the business of experimental philosophy, to compare it, as I often do, to the diversion of *hunting*, where it sometimes happens that those who have beat the ground the most, and are consequently the best acquainted with it weary themselves without starting any game; when it may fall in the way of a mere passenger; so that there is but little reason for boasting in the most successful termination of the chase.

Priestley's most conspicuous improvement in the methods of gas-manipulation of his time was the use of mercury instead of water in the pneumatic trough. This enabled him to isolate numerous gases which had hitherto been missed on account of their solubility in water. Among these were sulfur dioxide, hydrochloric acid and ammonia. The last two he designated as "marine acid air" and "alkaline air" respectively. He mingled them in the hope of obtaining a "neutral air" and so synthesized ammonium chloride. This salt had, of course, been known for many centuries. He passed electric sparks through ammonia gas and noted that hydrogen was formed. The exact composition of ammonia was, however, first settled by Berthollet some time after. Priestley also heated fluorspar with sulfuric acid and obtained silicon fluoride. It is interesting that Scheele had also tried this experiment, but because he passed the gases into water he obtained hydrofluorsilicic acid.

Priestley recognized clearly the analogy between combustion and respiration, and, as early as 1772 before he discovered oxygen, he was able to demonstrate experimentally the most important reciprocal relation between animal and plant life, for he found that air in which a candle had been burned until it went out spontaneously, again became respirable and capable of supporting combustion after plants had grown in it for some time. Work of this kind involved experiments with animals, usually mice, and he writes like this concerning his methods of manipulation:

For the purpose of these experiments it is most convenient to catch the mice in small wire traps, out of which it is easy to take them, and holding them by the back of the neck, to pass them through the water into the vessel which contains the air. If I expect that the mouse will live a considerable time, I take care to put into the vessel something on which it may conveniently sit, out of reach of the water. If the air be good, the mouse will soon be perfectly at its ease, having suffered nothing by its passing through the water. If the air be supposed to be noxious, it will be proper (if the operator be desirous of preserving the mice for farther use) to keep hold of their tails, that they may be withdrawn as soon as they begin to show signs of uneasiness; but if the air be thoroughly noxious, and the mouse happens to get a full inspiration, it will be impossible to do this before it will be absolutely irrecoverable . . . Two or three of them will live very peaceably together in the same vessel; though I had one instance of a mouse tearing another almost in pieces, and when there was plenty of provisions for both of them.

The Discovery of Oxygen.—In 1774 Priestley was heating all the substances he could find by means of a large burning lens, and collecting any gases evolved over mercury in the hope of obtaining new gases and observing their properties. It was in this way that he came at last to prepare oxygen. He writes:

With this apparatus, after a variety of other experiments an account of which will be found in its proper place, on the 1st of August, 1774, I endeavored to extract air from *mercurius calcinatus per se* [mercuric oxide] and I presently found that, by means of this lens, air was expelled from it very readily. Having got about three or four times as much as the bulk of my materials, I admitted water to it, and found that it was not imbibed by it. But what surprised me more than I can well express was that a candle burned in this air with a remarkably vigorous flame, very much like that enlarged flame with which a candle burns in nitrous air, exposed to iron or liver of sulfur; but as I had got nothing like this remarkable appearance from any kind of air besides this particular modification of nitrous air, and I knew no nitrous acid was used in the preparation of *mercurius calcinatus*, I was utterly at a loss how to account for it.

It was some time before Priestley realized that the gas which he had thus isolated was the very component of the atmosphere which supports life and combustion; but Mayow had observed long before that the latter gave red fumes with "nitrous air" (nitric oxide), and Priestley made use of the fact that these fumes (nitrogen peroxide) are soluble in water to make a rough analysis of the air. The new gas, of course, showed the reaction strongly. Concerning its physiological action he writes as follows:

From the greater strength and vivacity of the flame of a candle, in this pure air, it may be conjectured that it might be peculiarly salutary to the lungs in certain morbid cases, when the common air would not be sufficient to carry off the phlogistic putrid effluvium fast enough (see page 53). But, perhaps, we may also infer from these experiments, that though pure dephlogisticated air might be very useful as a *medicine*, it might not be so proper for us in the usual healthy state of the body: for as a candle burns out much faster in dephlogisticated than in common air, so we might, as may be said, *live out too fast*, and the animal powers be too soon exhausted in this pure kind of air. A moralist, at least, may say that the air which nature has provided for us is as good as we deserve.

My reader will not wonder that, after having ascertained the superior goodness of dephlogisticated air by mice living in it, and the other tests above mentioned, I should have the curiosity to taste it myself. I have gratified that curiosity by breathing it, drawing it through a glass siphon, and, by this means, I reduced a large jar full of it to the standard of common air. The feeling of it to my lungs was not sensibly different from that of common air; but I fancied that my breath felt peculiarly light and easy for some time afterward. Who can tell but that, in time, this pure air may become a fashionable article in luxury? Hitherto only two mice and myself have had the privilege of breathing it.

We have seen that Priestley called the gas he had discovered dephlogisticated air, his idea being that this was the component of the atmosphere with which the phlogiston united when it emerged from a burning substance. He called nitrogen "phlogisticated air," and this nomenclature would seem to imply that he considered it a product of such union. If so nitrogen should sometimes appear as a product of combustion, but this contradiction was overlooked, like every fact which told against the phlogiston theory. Like Scheele, Priestley missed entirely the real significance of his discovery. Both were so sure that something was always *given off* in combustion that they had lost the power to believe that the burning body *united with* one of the gases of the atmosphere even when they saw the latter disappear before their eyes. Such blindness was really less pardonable in Priestley than in any of the others, for he not only could not draw the correct conclusion from his own experiments, but all the brilliant work of Lavoisier a little later failed utterly to convince him, and he defended the theory of phlogiston to the last. As late as 1800, he wrote to a friend:

I have well considered all that my opponents have advanced, and feel perfectly confident of the ground I stand upon . . . Though nearly alone I am under no apprehension of defeat.

The phlogiston theory, in spite of what now appears to be its obvious faults, was a scientific theory and did much to coordinate the prevailing knowledge of chemistry. It marks a stage in the development of the theory of oxidation and reduction. The loss of phlogiston corresponds to an oxidation, or, as we sometimes say, to a loss of electrons by atoms present in the substance oxidized. A gain of phlogiston corresponds similarly to a gain of electrons by atoms present in the oxidizer or substance reduced. One cannot, however, always substitute the word *electron* for phlogiston. Thus "phlogisticated air" by no means indicates "electronized air."

The epoch following that in which the phlogiston theory flourished is a rigorously quantitative one, making chemistry more a science and less an art. Wurtz, therefore, in his dictionary of chemistry called chemistry a "French science founded by Lavoisier." We shall see, however, that the ideas concerning phlogiston were not suddenly abandoned by all reputable chemists.

Early American Chemists.—When Priestley in 1794 left England and settled in Pennsylvania, chemistry had already made a start in the United States. In 1789 there appeared in the first volume of the *Transactions of the American Philosophical Society* a paper by Dr. John de Normandie, *An Analysis of the Chalybeate Waters of Bristol in Pennsylvania.* The paper shows a scientific spirit of inquiry, and it is interesting to note that the analysis was made with the aid of chemical balance and the steps of the analytical procedure are clearly indicated.

The first chemist appears to have been **John Winthrop, Jr.** (1606–1676), the first governor of Connecticut and son of the famous Puritan governor of the Massachusetts colony. He practiced medicine, prepared many of his own remedies for which he imported laboratory equipment and chemicals from England, and established in New England foundries, glass works, besides some chemical industries. Winthrop's friend Stirk or Starkey (1622–1665) was graduated from Harvard in 1646 and practiced medicine in Cambridge and Boston until 1650, when he went to England. He wrote on alchemy under the name of *Eirenaeus Philalethes* and claimed to have discovered the secret of transmutation in 1645.

In 1647, Jonathan Brewster, the son of Elder Brewster of Plymouth, was seeking the grand elixir, as was William Avery in Boston in 1684. Aaron Dexter (1750–1829) began to teach chemistry at the Harvard Medical School in 1782, and Lyman Spalding (1775–1881) taught chemistry in the medical school of Dartmouth College, which was founded in 1798. At Harvard John Gorham (1783–1829) taught chemistry for nearly twenty years and wrote a treatise called *The Elements of Chemical Science.*

The arrival of Priestley in America and his frequent presence among men interested in science acted as a stimulus upon chemical thought here. An attempt was made to get Priestley to settle in Philadelphia and he was offered, through Dr. Rush, a chair in chemistry at the University of Pennsylvania in 1794. The offer was declined. The position was accepted by James Woodhouse. Priestly worked on carbon dioxide in America but this gas had been prepared by Lassone in France in 1776.

Benjamin Rush (1745–1813) was a remarkable man as a chemist, physicist, teacher, author, and statesman. He was probably the first professor of chemistry in a reputable institution of the United States of America, the Philadelphia Medical School. He published in 1770 the first book on chemistry by an American teacher. He was a signer of the Declaration of Independence, a member of Congress, treasurer of the United States mint, and a cultured scientist, as well as statesman.

BENJAMIN RUSH
1745–1813

81

Edgar F. Smith called him the founder of chemical education in America. His son Richard Rush (1780–1859) was an eminent statesman and diplomat.

Woodhouse.—James Woodhouse (1770–1809) was graduated from the University of Pennsylvania and taught there. He published the *Young Chemist's Pocket Companion* which was probably the first experimental guide written for students in chemistry. He was called to the chair of chemistry at the University of Pennsylvania after Priestley had declined the honor in 1794. Silliman, the elder, attended Woodhouse's lectures in 1802–1804.

Woodhouse wrote extensively, was deeply interested in the overthrow of the phlogiston theory, and argued strongly against some of the views of Priestly toward whom, however, he showed no personal hostility.

In 1792, James Woodhouse formed the Chemical Society of Philadelphia, which was perhaps the first chemical society in the world and lasted for seventeen years. The minutes of the meetings appear to have been lost, but there are still in existence several addresses made to the society. Thus Thomas P. Smith delivered an oration in 1798 on *A Sketch of Revolutions in Chemistry* in which he traced the course of chemistry from the earliest times down to Lavoisier.

Cooper.—Thomas Cooper (1759–1841) was born in London and was a graduate of University College, Oxford, England, where he studied law. He was a materialist in philosophy and a freethinker in religion. Because of his antimonarchic beliefs, he was elected a member of the National Assembly of France during the Reign of Terror, but he did not serve long. At one of the meetings he resented remarks made by Robespierre and challenged him to fight a duel. Robespierre refused but planned to have him either assassinated or guillotined. Cooper, learning this, escaped to England, but, like his friend Priestley, found it necessary to migrate to the United States. He became interested in politics and was appointed a judge of a Pennsylvania court, but was impeached after a little while. His standing in society remained good, however, and he was made professor of chemistry at Dickinson College, Pennsylvania. After three years there, he came to Philadelphia and was professor of chemistry and mineralogy at the University of Pennsylvania, where Robert Hare was teaching chemistry in the Medical School. Later he was called to Columbia College in South Carolina and was soon made its president.

Cooper was the editor of Thomas Thomson's *System of Chemistry*, and in 1816 he delivered a lecture on the *Importance of Chemistry to the Medical Man* and showed that all the secretions of the body had to do with chemical reactions. He was remarkable for the extent of his knowledge and a voluminous writer on law, science, medicine, and political economy. The friendship between Cooper and Priestley was a strong one, and this is remarkable because, although each was talented, they were quite unlike in temperament. Cooper's brain was keener, more penetrating and searching, but Priestley was more liberal. Priestley possessed more knowledge, but Cooper made greater use of what he knew and was more original and more philosophical. Priestley was calm, placid, and candid in debate, but Cooper was vehement, fiery, and likely to set traps to confuse, perplex, and entrap his antagonist.

John Maclean was born in Scotland but was appointed professor of chemistry at Princeton in 1795, a position which he held until 1812, being the first professor of chemistry there. Silliman states that he was a brilliant man with all the acumen of his native Scotland. It was Maclean who influenced Silliman to become a chemist. His published papers dealt with the phenomenon of combustion and the erroneous teaching of the doctrine of phlogiston. He died in 1814.

Priestley, Cooper, and Maclean were three of our early chemists who were born and trained abroad but spent much of their lives in the United States. At the close of the eighteenth century, Dr. Maclean of Princeton was regarded as one of the best-known chemists in the United States.

Count Rumford.—Another interesting man of the same era was born in Massachusetts, spent much of his life abroad, but in founding an important chair in chemistry at Harvard College did much for chemistry here. Benjamin Thompson was born in Woburn, Massachusetts, in 1753 and died at Auteuil, France, in 1814. He attended lectures at Harvard. When nineteen he married a widow with considerable property which was the

BENJAMIN THOMPSON, COUNT RUMFORD
1753–1814

foundation of his success. Although a major in the militia, his neighbors distrusted him, so on the evacuation of Boston in 1776 by the British troops, he accepted the commission from Governor Wentworth to carry dispatches to England. He was appointed an undersecretary of state in England, but his political duties did not interfere with some scientific studies. After the war, he started to join the Austrian army to fight the Turks, but at Strasbourg he met Prince Maximilian who invited him to enter the civil and military service of Bavaria. Thompson accepted the invitation and accomplished a great deal, being meanwhile knighted by George III. In 1791 he was made a count of the Holy Roman Empire and chose the title name Rumford, the town where his wife's people lived in America, now Concord, New Hampshire. He returned to England and lived a private life for several years.

His studies on the transformation of mechanical energy into heat laid the foundation for the law of the conservation of energy. He combated the view that heat was a material body but regarded it as a result of motion. In 1799, together with Sir Joseph Banks, he founded the Royal Institution, the later home of Sir Humphry Davy and of Faraday. At Harvard he founded the Rumford chair of chemistry, made famous by Eben Horsford and Wolcott Gibbs. After the death of his first wife, he married the widow of Lavoisier. She loved society while he cared more for flowers and Nature, so that their married life was not a happy one and they finally separated.

Silliman.—There were two men by the name of Benjamin Silliman, father and son, who developed chemistry at Yale University. The father, or Silliman the elder, as he is called, was born in 1779 in Connecticut and died in New Haven, Connecticut, in 1864. He was graduated from Yale in 1796 and was appointed professor of chemistry and mineralogy in 1802, retiring in 1853. He was the first professor of chemistry at Yale and is best known as founder, in 1818, of the *American Journal of Science and Art*, the first truly scientific journal in the United States. He wrote several books besides editing his journal. He was the first to make hydrofluoric acid in America and discovered bromine in American brines. He was a great teacher and much sought after as a public lecturer, being able to hold the attention

BENJAMIN SILLIMAN
1779–1864

ROBERT HARE
1781–1858

of any audience with a scientific lecture, and the experiments he performed during these lectures were very impressive.

His son was born in 1816 at New Haven and died in 1885. He was graduated from Yale in 1837 and after serving his father as assistant, was made professor in 1847 in the school of applied chemistry which formed the nucleus of the Sheffield Scientific School of Yale. He was professor of medical chemistry and toxicology at Louisville, Kentucky, from 1849 to 1854, when he succeeded his father at Yale. He helped edit his father's journal. His lectures on agricultural chemistry at New Orleans in 1845–1846 were probably the first of the kind ever given in the United States. He wrote several books, published a number of scientific papers, and did considerable work as a chemical expert.

Robert Hare (1781–1858) was the father of electrochemistry in America. He operated the first electric furnace for the preparation of calcium carbide, graphite, and phosphorus and prepared metallic calcium by electrolyzing its chloride. He discovered the oxyhydrogen blowpipe and used platinized asbestos as a catalytic agent in the synthesis of ammonia. He spent all his life in Philadelphia, was a prominent educator and taught at the University of Pennsylvania. He was the inventor of the first electric furnace, the mercury cathode, and the electrical method of igniting blasting charges.

Literature

Black's *Experiments upon Magnesia, Quicklime, and Some Other Alkaline Substances* has been reprinted by the Alembic Club. His lectures were published with a biographical preface by John Robison in 1803. Sir William Ramsay devotes a chapter to Black in his *Essays Biographical and Chemical*, London, 1908.

A *Life of Cavendish*, by George Wilson, was published by the Cavendish Society, London, in 1851. See also Thorpe's *Essays*. His experiments on air may be found in the *Alembic Club Reprints* No. 3.

An English edition of Scheele's *Chemical Essays* was issued by Thomas Beddoes in 1786, and one of his *Air and Fire* by J. R. Foster in 1785. The latter is also reprinted in Ostwald's *Klassiker*, No. 58. Scheele's account of his experiments bearing on the discovery of oxygen are to be found in *Alembic Club Reprints*, No. 8. His laboratory notebooks and other memoranda were collected by Nordenskiöld in 1892 and published under the title *Nachgelassene Briefe und Aufzeichnungen von Karl Wilhelm Scheele*.

Priestley's *Experiments and Observations on Different Kinds of Air* is still to be found in some libraries and is most interesting reading. The portion of it bearing directly on the discovery of oxygen can be found in *Alembic Club Reprints*, No. 7. There is an attractive life of Priestley by Thorpe, London, 1906, who also devotes a chapter to him in his *Essays*.

Priestley in America, 1794–1804, by Edgar F. Smith, Philadelphia, 1920, 174 pages. This little book is a charmingly written description of the last ten years of Priestley's life and constitutes a beautiful appreciation of his character and personality.

The story of chemistry in the American colonies and in the early days of the United States of America can be found in *Notable New England Chemists*, by Lyman C. Newell and Tenney L. Davis, in *Chemistry in America*, by Edgar F. Smith, and in *Eminent American Chemists*, by D. H. Killifer.

CHAPTER VI

LAVOISIER

Antoine Laurent Lavoisier was born in Paris, August 26, 1743, and began his studies at the *Collège Mazarin* where he came in contact with some distinguished teachers, notably Rouelle in chemistry.   As early as 1766 a gold medal was awarded him by the Academy of Sciences in recognition of a paper dealing with the problem of lighting a large town.   In 1768 he was made an *adjoint chimiste* to the Academy and began to present frequent reports upon the greatest variety of topics.   In 1769 he became associated in a subordinate capacity with the Farmers General of the revenue and soon after was made a member of the board.   In 1775 he was appointed *régisseur des poudres* and made valuable suggestions for the improvement of the product.   The foregoing, however, represent only a portion of his public activities.   We find him serving with tireless energy on all sorts of boards and commissions both national and municipal, solving with equal skill troublesome problems of administration like taxation, banking, coinage, public charity and scientific agriculture. With the outbreak of the Revolution these activities at first increased, but the board of Farmers General gradually became objects of suspicion and rumors of peculation were circulated concerning them.   In 1791 the board was suppressed and Lavoisier's administration of the *régie des poudres* was attacked by Marat to whom Lavoisier had been so unfortunate as to give personal offence.   In November, 1793, the Farmers General were put under arrest, and in May of the following year they were sent for trial before the Revolutionary Tribunal, one of the principal charges against Lavoisier being that he had put water in the soldiers' tobacco.   The result of the trial was the usual foregone conclusion and Lavoisier was condemned to death by the guillotine within twenty-four hours, the judge cynically remarking: *"La République n'a pas besoin des savants."*   The

ANTOINE LAURENT LAVOISIER
1743–1794

Some of Lavoisier's Apparatus

sentence was carried out on May 8, 1794, and the feeling of pos-
terity concerning the wrong thus done the world found fit expression at the time in the bitter words of Lagrange: "It took them
but a moment to cut off that head, though a hundred years,
perhaps, will be required to produce another like it."

Temperament and Method of Investigation.—Lavoisier
brought to the study of chemistry the equipment most needed
at this time—the habits and mental attitude of the trained
physicist. We shall often have occasion to see that chemistry
has gained enormously by the influence of those whose point of
view has been preeminently physical, men who do not care to
prepare new compounds or discover new reactions, but who
prefer to weigh and measure, and in this way gain insight into
the mechanism of chemical changes already familiar on the
qualitative side. Lavoisier is one of the most conspicuous examples of this type of mind while Scheele admirably represents
the opposite extreme, and this makes it especially interesting
to see how the two men once solved the same problem, each in a
manner characteristically his own.

The alchemists had observed that when water is boiled for
some time in a glass or earthen vessel it can no longer be distilled
without leaving a solid residue, and if the boiling be really long-
continued a sediment appears. They interpreted this as a
transformation of *water* into *earth* under the influence of *fire*.
The fundamental fact had been confirmed by Boyle, Boerhaave,
and many others, but the explanation seemed essentially improbable to Lavoisier and about 1770 he demonstrated its falsity
by the following experiment. He boiled a *weighed* quantity of
water in a *weighed* pelican for a hundred days. The pelican
was a closed vessel having a long neck bent back upon itself
which served the same purpose as the modern reflux condenser.
At the end of the long boiling the total weight of the flask and
its contents had not changed, showing that nothing had been
lost or received from the fire. The weight of the flask, however,
had diminished, while the sum of the weights of water and
sediment was greater than that of the original water by a practically equivalent amount, showing that the solid material had
come from the glass and not from the water. Scheele proceeded
differently. He also boiled water a long time in glass, but he

weighed nothing.   Instead he tested the sediment qualitatively, and finding that it contained potash, silica and lime, which he knew to be constituents of glass, he came to the same conclusion as Lavoisier.   Who can say that one method was superior to the other?   At the present time, of course, we use one method to supplement the other as occasion demands, but when it comes to original work it still holds true that the great advances in one line are rarely made by the same men who make great advances in the other.   The two types of investigators remain distinct.

Work on Combustion.—Lavoisier's work upon the nature of combustion followed naturally from that just described.   Here also he burns weighed quantities of material and carefully weighs the products, and from his results he is able to draw far-reaching conclusions.   On November 1, 1772, he handed to the secretary of the Academy a sealed note which read as follows:

About eight days ago I discovered that sulfur in burning, far from losing weight, rather gains it; that is to say that from a pound of sulfur may be obtained more than a pound of vitriolic acid, allowance being made for the moisture of the air.   It is the same in the case of phosphorus.   The gain in weight comes from the prodigious quantity of air which is fixed during the combustion and combines with the vapors.

This discovery, which I have established by experiments which I consider decisive, has made me believe that what is observed in the combustion of sulfur and phosphorus may equally well take place in the case of all those bodies which gain weight on combustion or calcination.   I am persuaded that the gain in weight of the metallic calces is due to the same causes.   Experiment has completely confirmed my conjectures.   I have reduced litharge in closed vessels, employing the apparatus of Hales, and I observed that a considerable quantity of air is evolved just at the moment when the litharge changes to metal, and that this air occupies a volume a thousand times greater than the quantity of litharge employed.

Since this discovery seemed to be one of the most interesting which has been made since the time of Stahl I have felt it my duty to place this communication in the hands of the secretary of the Academy, to remain a secret until I can publish my experiments.

Theory of Combustion.—It is clear from the above that Lavoisier now fully realized the important consequences which must follow if combustion really proved to be a union of the burning substance with the air or some part thereof. One experiment now follows another rapidly and in the fall of 1774 Lavoisier publishes his work on the calcination of tin. He takes a weighed portion of the metal, seals it in a weighed flask large enough to contain considerable air and heats the whole until the metal appears well calcined. When cold he finds that the system has neither gained nor lost in weight, and he then breaks the seal. A partial vacuum is revealed by air rushing in, and he now finds the weight of the flask increased by exactly the same amount as the tin itself has gained, showing that the calcination consisted in a transfer of gas from the air to the tin. He further finds that when sufficient tin is used an air is left which will calcine no more tin, and from this he concludes that only a part of the air reacts in combustion. Still later in the same year, after the first experiments of Priestley, he heats mercury in a limited volume of air until a considerable quantity of the red oxide has been formed, and notes the decrease in the volume of air, which finally reaches a maximum. He next, like Priestley, heats the mercuric oxide alone and fixes with precision the properties of the gas evolved and the vigor with which it supports combustion.

In 1777 he sums up his theory of combustion in the following four propositions:

1. In every combustion heat and light are evolved.

2. Bodies burn only in *air éminemment pur* (this was Lavoisier's first name for oxygen).

3. The latter is used up by the combustion, and the gain in weight of the substance burned is equal to the loss of weight shown by the air.

4. By the process of combustion the combustible substance is usually changed to an acid; the metals, however, are calcined.

The Chemical Revolution.—In spite of the clearness of Lavoisier's presentation, and the skillful experiments by which his conclusions were supported, his views at first made little impression until another series of experiments carried on in 1782 and 1783 led to a conclusion of a similar kind. Lavoisier turned his attention to the composition of water, and though his experiments followed those of Cavendish, yet he was able to interpret them as Cavendish could not. Original was his quantitative decomposition of steam by passing it over hot iron. He also burned oxygen and hydrogen, forming water synthetically and measuring all quantities involved. Still later he experimented in the same way with carbonic acid, found that it was formed by the union of carbon and oxygen and fixed its composition by weight. He also confirmed what Black had done on the causticization of lime. The cumulative effect of these researches led to the sudden conversion of most French chemists at about 1785, and the new ideas were firmly fixed by the publication of Lavoisier's great textbook *La Traité Élémentaire de la Chimie* in 1789. The change was well called the Chemical Revolution, for it inverted completely the chemical point of view. The mysterious hypothetical substance, phlogiston, which did not obey the law of gravitation, and changed its properties arbitrarily as theoretical considerations dictated, was banished from the science and the law of conservation of mass vindicated once for all. This made possible quantitative analysis and the chemical equation. The latter is a convenience in form of expression which we owe to Lavoisier, and of whose assistance in stating and solving chemical problems he made immediate use.   He writes:[1]

If I distil an unknown salt with vitriolic acid and find nitric acid in the receiver and vitriolated tartar in the residue, I conclude that the original salt was nitre, and I reach this conclusion by mentally writing the following equation based upon the supposition that the total weight is the same before and after the operation.

If x is the acid of the unknown salt, and y is the unknown base I write:

$x + y$ + vitriolic acid = nitric acid + vitriolated tartar = nitric acid + vitriolic acid + fixed alkali.

Hence I conclude: x = nitric acid, y = fixed alkali, and the original salt was nitre.

Nothing like this had ever appeared before in chemical literature and what a fog of mystery and superstition it removed!

Lavoisier was a pioneer in the analysis of organic substances, which he burned in air or oxygen and determined the weight of carbonic acid formed. He had some trouble with his absorption apparatus which was rather crude but many of his analyses were surprisingly good. He also, like Priestley, appreciated the

[1] This is a much abridged paraphrase of the original statements in French.

analogy between respiration and combustion and made quantitative experiments to determine the rate of the oxidation in the animal body. This he assumed to take place in the lungs. We may consider this work as the beginning of physiological chemistry.

The New Nomenclature.—In 1782, Guyton de Morveau (1737–1816) published in the *Journal de Physique* a paper suggesting reforms in chemical nomenclature. The work of Lavoisier had made the time ripe for such a movement and a commission in which Guyton de Morveau was associated with Lavoisier, Antoine François de Fourcroy (1755–1809) and Berthollet was appointed to consider the whole matter. In 1787 the results of their deliberations were published under the title, *Méthode d'une Nomenclature Chimique*. This work did away with many of the fanciful and arbitrary names previously in use, and substituted such as were based on chemical composition. Speaking broadly it is hardly too much to say that it laid the foundation upon which our modern international nomenclature now stands.

Chemical Knowledge before the Revolution.—Books written from the phlogistic point of view are now so difficult to read that we are inclined to underestimate the chemical knowledge of that period, so that a glance at the tables of Lavoisier's *Traité Élémentaire* which contrast the old names with the new may furnish a wholesome corrective. It is true, of course, that up to this time the subject of chemical composition had been in the utmost confusion, for if a metal was to be considered as a compound of its calx with phlogiston, and the compound weighed less than the sum of its component parts, then such words as element and compound had no significance, and as a matter of fact the terms do not seem to have been much contrasted. Nevertheless, certain things were clear. The differences which distinguish acids, bases and salts could not be overlooked. Salts were regarded as addition products of acid and base, and some of the newest and less familiar were already named as such. Acid and basic salts were already distinguished from neutral ones by the excess of one component, and emphasis had been laid upon the fact that it was the base and not the metal which formed the salt by direct addition. When a metal did dissolve in acid to form a salt it must first give up phlogiston (evolve hydrogen) as zinc did in muriatic acid, or else the acid must itself be phlogisticated (reduced) as when copper reacts with sulfuric or nitric acids. What we should now call differences in state of oxidation were also recognized, and nitrates distinguished from nitrites, manganates from manganous salts and the like.

Among organic compounds no rational system was yet possible. Well-known substances like sugar and alcohol had of course their present names, but these were then devoid of general chemical significance; the majority of such compounds had names suggestive of the source from which they had been derived like "oil of turpentine" or "sweet spirits of nitre." How far this went is illustrated by the old tradition (which the author has never been able to verify) that in one book of this period cow's butter is found classified with "butter of antimony," $SbCl_3$. Nevertheless a good many substances had received extensive qualitative study and the field had recently been much enriched by the work of Scheele upon the vegetable acids.

Lavoisier's Table of Elements.—Lavoisier's *Traité Élémentaire* was originally begun in order to expound and promulgate the new nomenclature, and one of the most interesting things in the book is the table of the elements, for it admirably reveals the author's point of view. Following Boyle, he defines these as substances which cannot be further decomposed, and divides them into four groups. The first comprises the elementary gases, oxygen, hydrogen and nitrogen along with heat and light. The second contains those elements like sulfur and phosphorus which on oxidation yield acids—elements which we now classify as metalloids. In the third group are the metals, while the fourth is made up of the "earths": lime, magnesia, baryta, alumina and silica. These of course could not be classified otherwise since they had not as yet been decomposed. The same might have been said of the alkalies, soda and potash, but Lavoisier is so certain that these are oxides of "radicals" soon to be discovered that he explicitly refuses to include them.

The modern reader is apt to feel surprise in finding heat and light in the list. We have to remember, however, that our modern conception of energy and its transformations was then unknown, and that men like Scheele were still explaining phenomena by considering heat and light as corporeal substances.

	Noms nouveaux.	Noms anciens correspondans.
Substances simples qui appartiennent aux trois règnes, & qu'on peut regarder comme les élémens des corps.	Lumière	Lumière.
	Calorique.........	Chaleur.
		Principe de la chaleur.
		Fluide igné.
		Feu.
		Matière du feu & de la chaleur.
	Oxygène	Air déphlogistiqué.
		Air empiréal.
		Air vital.
		Base de l'air vital.
	Azote	Gaz phlogistiqué.
		Mofète.
		Base de la mofète.
	Hydrogène........	Gaz inflammable.
		Base du gaz inflammable.
Substances simples non métalliques oxidables & acidifiables.	Soufre	Soufre.
	Phosphore	Phosphore.
	Carbone	Charbon pur.
	Radical muriatique .	Inconnu.
	Radical fluorique...	Inconnu.
	Radical boracique. .	Inconnu.
Substances simples métalliques oxidables & acidifiables.	Antimoine	Antimoine.
	Argent	Argent.
	Arsenic	Arsenic.
	Bismuth	Bismuth.
	Cobalt	Cobalt.
	Cuivre..........	Cuivre.
	Etain	Etain.
	Fer.............	Fer.
	Manganèse.......	Manganèse.
	Mercure	Mercure.
	Molybdène	Molybdène.
	Nickel..........	Nickel.
	Or.............	Or.
	Platine	Platine.
	Plomb	Plomb.
	Tungstène	Tungstène.
	Zinc	Zinc.
Substances simples salifiables terreuses.	Chaux..........	Terre calcaire, chaux.
	Magnésie	Magnésie , base du sel d'epsom.
	Baryte	Barote , terre pesante.
	Alumine	Argile, terre de l'alun, base de l'alun.
	Silice	Terre siliceuse, terre vitrifiable.

LAVOISIER'S TABLE OF THE ELEMENTS

Lavoisier did not do this. He recognized that they did not possess weight, but he also realized how constantly their appearance is associated with chemical change, and he regarded heat as a kind of atmosphere which surrounds the ultimate particles of all bodies causing repulsion and hence expansion. He was also familiar with the disappearance of heat when a substance passes from the solid to the liquid, or from the liquid to the gaseous condition, and he was inclined to interpret this chemically as a combination of heat with the substance. Similarly in regard to light, we find the statement that silver salts probably absorb it, and that light also combines with growing plants, since they die or change their properties when deprived of it.

We have already seen how the old system had magnified the importance of phlogiston and made it the center of all chemical explanations. When Lavoisier substituted reduction for phlogistication and oxidation for dephlogistication it was only natural that the newly discovered element oxygen should usurp the position of exaggerated importance from which phlogiston had just been displaced. This is exactly what happened. Every element found its position in the system of Lavoisier according to its relation toward oxygen. Metals had hitherto been compounds of bases with phlogiston. They now became the elements which united with oxygen to form bases. The metalloids on the other hand became the elements which united with oxygen to form acids, indeed the very name *oxygen* or "acid former" was intended to express this fact.

The Oxygen Theory of Acids.—It seemed to follow naturally that all acids must contain oxygen, and Lavoisier did not hesitate to draw this conclusion. Boric acid was therefore to him the oxide of a "radical" as yet unknown, and for this radical he finds a place in the table of the elements. In so doing he was justified by subsequent events, but the fact that he made the same assumption in the case of hydrochloric and hydrofluoric acids was destined later to prove most unfortunate. One minor difficulty arose at the start. If there is no phlogiston, and oxygen is the essential component of acids, why do they evolve *hydrogen* with metals? An "explanation" was soon found, however, to this effect: Water is simultaneously decomposed; the hydrogen is evolved as such, while the oxygen unites with the metal to form

Berthollet Visits Lavoisier at the Laboratory
of the Sorbonne

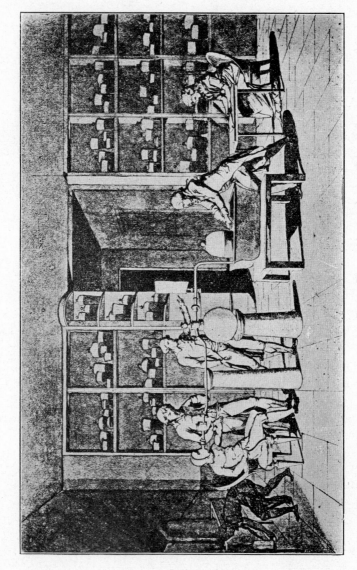

SOME OF LAVOISIER'S EXPERIMENTS ON RESPIRATION

From a Drawing by Madame Lavoisier

a base, which now can add an acid to form a salt. What a debt all chemical theorists owe to water!

Lavoisier could not, of course, reduce organic chemistry to a system, but he did apply the same principle of classification to the organic acids. He knew how frequently these could be prepared by processes of oxidation, as acetic acid for example is prepared from alcohol, or oxalic from cane sugar. He therefore regarded these acids also as oxygen compounds of *"compound radicals"* which latter he thought of as usually being composed of carbon and hydrogen, but which might sometimes contain also phosphorus, nitrogen or sulfur. He even suspected the presence of nitrogen in some acids like acetic and tartaric which we now know do not contain it. It will repay us to note carefully the sense in which Lavoisier uses the word *radical*. To him it signifies the element or group of elements which enters into combination with oxygen. It is a word which has changed its meaning frequently since his day。

One of the first to adopt Lavoisier's view concerning combustion was Joseph Black who taught it in Scotland before 1784. C. L. Berthollet accepted the theory in 1785, as did Guyton de Morveau in 1786 and Fourcroy in 1786–1787. Chemists outside France soon followed suit, and only a few of the older ones, like Priestley and Cavendish in England, Macquer in France, and Wiegleb in Germany, refused to do so.

Literature

Grimaux, *Lavoisier*, 1743–1794, *d'après sa Correspondance ses Manuscrits*, etc., Paris, 1888, is the principal biography, but contains comparatively little on the chemical side. Lavoisier's complete works were published under the auspices of the Minister of Public Instruction in six volumes between 1864 and 1893. There are numerous appreciations. See particularly Berthelot, *La Révolution Chimique*, 1890, and the *Essay* by Thorpe which presents a less flattering view.

CHAPTER VII

THE LAW OF DEFINITE PROPORTIONS

The work of Lavoisier had supplied a theoretical basis for quantitative analysis, and he himself did some pioneer work in this branch of the science.

Improvements in the technique of quantitative analysis were soon after introduced by such men as Vauquelin (1763–1829) in France and Klaproth (1743–1817) in Germany. Louis Nicholas Vauquelin, a professor in Paris, discovered chromium (1798), beryllium oxide, and other beryllium compounds (1798), besides isolating asparagine, camphoric, quinic, and cyanic acids from natural products. At that time, it was generally assumed that the percentage composition of a chemical compound is always the same, regardless of its source. We now call this generalization the *law of definite proportions* and recognize it as a corner stone of the science. At the end of the eighteenth century, however, it was not adequately supported by experiment, and good was done through the attack upon it made by Berthollet.

Berthollet.—Claude Louis Berthollet was born in Talloire, Savoy, in 1748. He came to Paris at the age of twenty-four and began the practice of medicine, in which he was very successful. In 1780 he was made a member of the Academy, and about the same time gave up his practice in order to devote himself to work for the government. We have already seen how he cooperated with Lavoisier in the reform of chemical nomenclature. Later he was a professor at the École Normale. Berthollet became associated with Napoleon at the time that works of art were being removed from Italy to France; he gave him instruction in chemistry, and later accompanied him to Egypt. Berthollet received many honors during the Consulate and Empire, and was made a peer by the Bourbons after the restoration. He died at Arceuil in 1822. His chief service to industry was

CLAUDE LOUIS BERTHOLLET
1748–1822

the introduction of chlorine as a bleaching agent—a discovery which he declined to patent.

Statique Chimique.—It was while in Egypt in 1799 that he presented to the Institute in Cairo an article upon *The Laws of Chemical Affinity*. This set forth the fundamental ideas which he later included in his famous book, *Essai de statique chimique*. Berthollet began with an attack upon the tables of affinity (page 56). We have already seen how these were originated by Geoffroy, and some consideration has been given to their fundamental faults. In spite of these faults the tables had remained in use as a convenient form for registering chemical information. Lavoisier employed them freely in his *Traité élémentaire*, and Bergman in Sweden had enlarged them so that they would be applicable within a wider range of experimental conditions. Berthollet condemned them as wrong in principle. If there were any truth in them, then affinity should be something absolute, and one acid should expel another completely from its salts. Berthollet could show that this was rarely the case. Instead, the *quantities* involved play an extremely important role, and by adding a sufficient quantity of one reagent, the apparent course of a reaction can frequently be reversed. The familiar decomposition of steam by iron and the reduction of iron oxide by hydrogen is a case in point, but Berthollet could cite many other examples. He pointed out that when two salts are mixed, the acid and basic components are in an equilibrium in the solution, and the reaction which may take place depends in part upon the affinities, in part upon the masses present, and in part upon other secondary considerations which are nevertheless decisive in certain cases, *viz.*, solubility or volatility of one of the reacting combinations. Thus if sulfuric acid expels carbonic from its salts, it is not because of its greater affinity for the base, but because the carbonic acid is volatile and cannot remain to compete. If sulfuric acid decomposes barium chloride, it is again not so much a matter of affinity as of the insolubility of barium sulfate. We see how close these ideas come to our modern notions of equilibrium and reversible reaction. Indeed, if Berthollet had been a little clearer as to the importance of concentration as distinguished from mere quantity, he would have come very close to the law of mass action. Unfortunately for the success of his own contentions, but doubtless fortunately for the progress of the science, he felt that his observations led him to certain other conclusions not so well justified by the facts. It seemed natural for him to conclude that within certain limits, elements ought to unite in all proportions, and he published analyses which went to show that they did so. From this point of view it seemed natural to expect that copper and sulfur, for example, would combine in varying proportions according to which element was present in excess. He recognized, it is true, that some well-characterized compounds seemed to show constant composition, but he attributed this to the insolubility of certain combinations or to their peculiar capacity for crystallization. Finally, he pointed out that no sharp line can be drawn between what we call chemical union and solution, especially as the latter is illustrated in alloys and glasses. If Berthollet had kept his attention focused upon these latter forms of combination, it seems not unlikely that he might have maintained his views longer than he did. As a matter of fact, he chose to meet the issue frankly upon the composition of salts and oxides, where he was open to attack.

Controversy with Proust.—The attack came from Joseph Louis Proust (1754–1826), a talented Frenchman then professor in Madrid. There resulted a controversy in the journals which lasted nearly eight years and was carried on by both sides with the greatest brilliancy and most unfailing courtesy. At the end, Proust was left in possession of the field, for wherever Berthollet supposed that he had prepared a series representing all degrees of composition, Proust was able to show that there were really always involved mixtures of *two* substances, each of which when pure had different properties and showed *constant* chemical composition. Proust is therefore to be regarded as the discoverer of the law of definite proportions.[1]

The Duke of Wellington is credited with saying, "There is nothing worse than a great victory except a great defeat," and

[1] How near he came to discovering the law of multiple proportions is shown by the fact that he went so far as to calculate the different amounts of oxygen which unite with 100 parts of copper in the two oxides. The correct figures are 12.6 and 25.2 which would have revealed the law, but owing to faulty analyses Proust obtained 18 and 25.

this is often true of scientific controversies. The defeat of Berthollet meant that the good in his contentions was discredited along with the bad, and in consequence little attention was paid to chemical equilibrium and mass action for more than fifty years, although Carl Friedrich Wenzel (1740–1793) studied the rate of solution of metals in acids and found in 1777 that the rate is proportional to the concentration of the acid which is an early recognition of the mass action law. At the end of the eighteenth century, however, the law of definite proportions was something the world needed at the moment, and if it had been discredited in 1799 the progress of the science would have been seriously retarded.

Neutralization Phenomena.—Before the controversy between Proust and Berthollet began, an interesting study which approached the subject of chemical composition from another point of view was being made in Germany. We have seen what a discouragement the phlogiston theory had been to all quantitative thinking. Nevertheless even the earliest chemists had made some quantitative observations. From the time of Geber, it had been recognized, for example, that a certain *quantity* of acid was necessary in order to neutralize a given amount of base, and in 1699 Homberg had attempted to determine the quantities of several different acids which neutralized an ounce of potash. Glauber is credited with the important statement that when two neutral salts are mixed, the solution remains neutral whether any chemical reaction is observable or not. About 1775 both Bergman and Kirwan tried to determine the amounts of different acids that neutralize a given quantity of the same base, and the reverse, but owing to crude experimental methods could deduce no generalization. Bergman, however, noticed that when copper is immersed in a neutral silver nitrate solution, silver is deposited and copper dissolves, while the solution remains neutral. He concluded that the weights of dissolved copper and precipitated silver are the quantities of those metals which contain the same amount of phlogiston (see page 53). Lavoisier reversed this, stating that the weights of two metals that dissolve in a given quantity of the same acid are the weights which unite with the same quantity of oxygen.

Richter.—The credit for combining these observations into a system was reserved to Jeremias Benjamin Richter (1762–1807) who at the time this work was done was "arkanist" at the royal porcelain factory in Berlin. He published two books, dealing with this subject; one, *Anfangsgründe der Stöchiometrie*, appeared serially between 1792 and 1794, the other, *Ueber die neueren Gegenstände in der Chemie*, between 1792 and 1802. Richter was particularly impressed by the fact that two neutral salts can react without loss of neutrality. He saw that if sulfate of potash, for example, reacts with nitrate of lime to form nitrate of potash and sulfate of lime, then the preservation of the neutral reaction requires that the *amount* of lime which passes from the nitric to the sulfuric acid must be chemically equivalent to the *amount* of potash which passes from the sulfuric to the nitric acid. If we then determine the quantities of lime and potash respectively which unite with a given weight of sulfuric acid we know that some other definite weight of nitric (or any other) acid will neutralize just these same quantities of both bases, so that when this quantity of acid has been determined experimentally for one base, it will hold good for the other also. Richter then prepared a large number of tables showing the quantities of different bases which would neutralize 1,000 parts of a given acid, and parts of different acids which would neutralize 1,000 of a given base, and was able to show that in the tables for different acids the bases all came in the same order and that the numbers involved were proportional. The same held true of the acids in the tables for bases.

G. E. Fischer.—In his books Richter confused these valuable ideas with fanciful speculations of no importance; his language was archaic, and his style such as might have been expected from a man who would invent the word *stoichiometry*. For these reasons his work made little impression at the time, and might have been forgotten altogether, had not G. E. Fischer, who translated into German the works of Berthollet, introduced into the *Statique chimique* a note summing up Richter's conclusions. Fischer was not only fortunate in his mode of expression, but he much improved the usefulness of Richter's tables by condensing them all into one. If to the table containing the quantities of bases which neutralize 1,000 parts of sulfuric acid we add the quantities of acids having the same neutralizing power as 1,000 parts of sulfuric acid, then the resulting table is a complete list of the weights of all acids and bases which are chemically equivalent. Fischer's table comprised twenty-one acids and bases. Some figures selected from it appear here, Fischer's original figures being compared with what would now be considered the correct ones. In calculating the latter, the reader will bear in mind that the bases are computed as oxides and the acids as anhydrides, according to the theory then current which regarded salts as addition products.

Bases		True value	Acids		True value
Alumina	525	425	Sulfuric	1,000	1,000
Magnesia	615	503	Carbonic	577	550
Lime	793	700	Oxalic	755	900
Potash	1,605	1,180	Phosphoric	979	888
Soda	859	775	Nitric	1,405	1,350

Equivalency.—Neither Richter nor Fischer used the word, but we realize clearly that, so far as it goes, this is a true *table of chemical equivalents* or proportions by weight in which substances combine. It was the first of its kind. We can see readily enough that the idea might have been carried much farther without introducing any new principle. Richter recognized clearly that when a metal precipitates another, the quantities involved are chemically equivalent, so that through a single quantitative relationship between one of the acids and one of the metals, all of the latter might have been brought into the table. Indeed it could have been enlarged in this way until it included every element. We should then have a complete table of combining weights in which the numbers involved would, it is true, bear no superficial resemblance to our modern atomic weights; nevertheless, multiplication by a single factor would transform this table into one in which every number stood in a simple relation to those weights. Such a table would suffice for every stoichiometrical calculation.

Most of us have arrived at our conception of combining weights through the atomic theory and the gas laws. It is therefore interesting to see that these relationships not only can be, but, as a matter of historical fact, actually were derived from a study of neutralization phenomena, without any use of the atomic conception and without any hypothesis concerning the ultimate constitution of matter.

Literature

Berthollet's *Essai de statique chimique* was published in 1803. The author's earlier paper delivered at Cairo is to be found in Ostwald's *Klassiker*, No. 74.

A comprehensive treatment of the development of the science from the time of Lavoisier down to the date of its publication is to be found in Kopp's *Die Entwickelung der Chemie in der neueren Zeit*, Munich, 1873.

An excellent presentation of the same period is given in Ladenburg's *Vorträge über die Entwickelungsgeschichte der Chemie*. An English translation of one of the earlier editions by Dobbin has been published by the Alembic Club.

CHAPTER VIII

DALTON AND THE ATOMIC THEORY

The Atomic Conception.—The tendency to refer all physical phenomena to the mechanical motions of corpuscles, atoms, or ultimate particles is a very old one which helps us to visualize processes whose details it is difficult to keep before the mind without it.

The atomic theory was taught at an early date in India, but it is not certain whether the idea was developed independently there or was borrowed from the Greeks. Strabo, in his *Geography*, stated that a Phoenician, Mochos, was the originator of the "ancient opinion about atoms," but nothing more is known of him, and it is generally agreed that speculations about atoms began with the early Greeks. Anaxagoras (498–428 B.C.) taught that bodies are divisible without limit. "Gold is composed of little seeds of gold, flesh of little fleshes." These seeds were not atoms as we understand them. Aristotle states that Leucippos (about 500 B.C.) was the real originator of the atomic theory. The theory was adopted and extended by Democritus (460–370 B.C.) who taught that atoms are hard, have form, size, and possibly weight. They are so small that they cannot be seen and are in constant motion. All the physical sciences have used the conception freely at one time or another, and it took very definite form in the mind of Newton who expressed himself on the subject as follows:

It seems probable to me that God in the beginning formed matter in solid, massy, hard, impenetrable, movable particles, of such sizes and figures, and with such other properties, and in such proportion, as most conduced to the end for which He formed them; and that these primitive particles, being solids, are incomparably harder than any porous bodies compounded of them; even so very hard as never to wear or break in pieces, no ordinary power being able to divide what God Himself made one in the first creation. While the particles continue entire they may compose bodies of one and the same nature and texture

112

in all ages; but should they wear away, or break in pieces, the nature of things depending on them would be changed.

The above is an admirable restatement of the ideas of Democritus as applied to physics, and in a vague philosophical way to chemistry, but no one before 1800 had realized that these same ideas might be so developed that they could give quantitative account of the composition of all substances, and of their reactions upon each other. This is what chemists understand by the *atomic theory*, and its discoverer was John Dalton.

Dalton.—Dalton once had occasion to write a brief account of his own life, and since it is short and characteristic, it may be given entire:

The writer of this was born at the Village of Eaglefield about 2 miles west of Cockermouth, Cumberland. Attended the village school there & in the neighborhood till 11 years of age, at which period he had gone through a course of Mensuration, Surveying, Navigation, &c, began about 12 to teach the Village School & continued 2 years afterwards; was occasionally employed in husbandry for a year or more; removed to Kendal at 15 years of age as assistant in a boarding School, remained in that capacity for 3 or 4 years, then undertook the same School as a principal & continued it for 8 years, & while at Kendal employed his leisure in studying Latin, Greek, French & the Mathematics with Natural Philosophy, removed thence to Manchester in 1793, as Tutor in Mathematics & Natural Philosophy in the New College, was 6 years in that Engagement, & afterwards was employed as private & sometimes public Instructor in various branches of Mathematics, Natural Philosophy & Chemistry chiefly in Manchester, but occasionally by invitation in other places, namely London, Edinburgh, Glasgow, Birmingham & Leeds.

There need only be added that Dalton was born about September 6, 1766, and that he died in Manchester, July 27, 1844. He was the son of a poor Quaker weaver, and as the little autobiography shows, he was from his earliest youth thrown upon his own resources. Yet with endless perseverance he always devoted every free hour to intellectual pursuits. He was a reserved, silent man, frugal of words as of money (though kindly and generous in the essentials), and so regular in his habits that his neighbors could set their clocks by his movements—a man distrustful of the results of others, who had to work everything

JOHN DALTON
1766–1844

out in his own original way. He was by no means gifted as an experimenter, and for financial reasons it was long necessary for him to work with the crudest apparatus, often of his own construction; yet all these handicaps could not prevent him from discovering several of the laws which rest at the very foundation of the science.

Color Blindness.—It is interesting to see that he accomplished all this by taking up the work which lay nearest, beginning with studies of his own color blindness and the weather. Dalton was almost the first to make a systematic study of color blindness, and though his investigation yielded no important results it showed all his characteristic diligence. Dalton's own case must have been an extreme one, for in describing one of his lectures at the Royal Institution, he wrote to a friend: "In lecturing on optics I got six ribands—blue, pink, lilac, and red, green and brown—which matched very well, and told the curious audience so."

Studies in Meteorology.—No subject seems to have interested Dalton so much as meteorology. He faithfully kept a daily record of the weather and allied phenomena from 1787 till the very day before his death, and it contains no less than 200,000 separate observations. The brief vacations which he allowed himself were spent mostly in the Lake District where it was his favorite occupation to climb mountains with such instruments as he could carry, in order to compare atmospheric conditions at different altitudes. All this led naturally to an interest in gases and a study of their properties in the laboratory. In the first year of the nineteenth century we find him reading a paper before the Manchester Literary and Philosophical Society in which he announces the discovery of some of the most important laws concerning gases. Among these were the law that gases expand equally for a given rise of temperature, that the vapor pressures of liquids are the same at equal intervals of temperature above and below their boiling points, that at constant volume each gas in a mixture exerts the same pressure as if the other gases were absent, and consequently, that the solubilities of mixed gases are proportional to their partial pressures. Dalton had also observed that the composition of the atmosphere was independent of the altitude, and he had shown that this was not due simply to mechanical agitation, by experiments in which heavy gases diffused upward into lighter ones, while the latter diffused downward, even through very narrow tubes.

The Atomic Theory.—The atomic theory grew more naturally out of studies of this kind than had been realized until comparatively recently. It was not published by Dalton till his *New System of Chemical Philosophy* appeared in 1808, but he communicated informally some years earlier the fundamental ideas involved, the first occasion being a table of atomic weights which is appended practically without comment to a paper delivered in 1803 on the subject of the solubility of mixed gases. The late Sir Henry Roscoe did a valuable service by unearthing from the archives of the Manchester Literary and Philosophical Society, Dalton's laboratory notebooks and other manuscripts which now make it clear just how the conception grew up in his mind. One of the most important of these documents is the syllabus of a lecture delivered in 1810, which reads in part as follows:

Having been long accustomed to make meteorological observations, and to speculate upon the nature and constitution of the atmosphere, it often struck me with wonder how a *compound* atmosphere, or a mixture of two or more elastic fluids, should constitute apparently a homogeneous mass, or one in all mechanical relations agreeing with a simple atmosphere.

Newton had demonstrated clearly in the 23d Prop. of Book 11 of the *Principia* that an elastic fluid is constituted of small particles or atoms of matter which repeal each other by a force increasing in proportion as their distance diminishes. But modern discoveries having ascertained that the atmosphere contains three or more elastic fluids of different specific gravities, it did not appear to me how this proposition of Newton's would apply to a case of which he, of course, could have no idea. The same difficulty occurred to Dr. Priestley, who discovered this compound nature of the atmosphere. He could not conceive why the oxygen gas, being specifically heaviest, should not form a distinct *stratum* of air at the bottom of the atmosphere, and the azotic gas[1] one at the top of the atmosphere. Some chemists upon the Continent— I believe the French—found a solution of the difficulty (as they apprehended). It was *chemical affinity*. One species of gas was held in solution by the other; and this compound in its turn dissolved water—

---

[1] Nitrogen.

hence *evaporation*, rain, etc. This opinion of air dissolving water had long been the prevailing one, and naturally paved the way for the reception of that which followed—of one kind of air dissolving another. It was objected that there were no decisive *marks* of chemical union when one kind of air was mixed with another. The answer was, that the affinity was of a very slight kind, not of that energetic cast that is observable in most other cases. I may add, by-the-bye, that this is now, or has been till lately, I believe, the prevailing doctrine in most of the chemical schools in Europe. In order to reconcile—or, rather, adapt—this chemical theory of the atmosphere to the Newtonian doctrine of repulsive atoms or particles, I set to work to combine my atoms upon paper. I took an atom of water, another of oxygen, and another of azote, brought them together and threw around them an atmosphere of heat as per diagram.[1] I repeated the operation, but soon found that the watery particles were exhausted (for they make but a small part of the atmosphere). I next combined my atoms of oxygen and azote one to one; but I found in time my oxygen failed. I then threw all the remaining particles of azote into the mixture, and began to consider how the general equilibrium was to be obtained. My triple compounds of *water, oxygen,* and *azote* were wonderfully inclined by their superior gravity, to descend and take the lowest place. The double compounds of *oxygen* and *azote* affected to take a middle station; and the azote was inclined to swim at the top. I remedied this defect by lengthening the wings of my heavy particles—that is, by throwing more heat around them, by means of which I could make them float in any part of the vessel. But this change unfortunately made the whole mixture of the same specific gravity as azotic gas. This circumstance would not for a moment be tolerated. In short, I was obliged to abandon the hypothesis of the chemical constitution of the atmosphere altogether as irreconcilable to the phenomena. There was but one alternative left—namely, to surround every individual particle of *water*, of *oxygen*, and of *azote* with heat, and to make them respectively centres of repulsion, the same in a *mixed* state as in a *simple* state. This hypothesis was equally pressed with difficulties, for still my oxygen would take the lowest place, my azote the next, and my steam would swim upon the top. In 1801 I hit upon an hypothesis which completely obviated these difficulties. According to this, we were to suppose that atoms of one kind did *not* repel the atoms of another kind, but only those of their own kind. This hypothesis most effectually provided for the diffusion of any one gas through another, whatever might be their specific gravities, and perfectly reconciled any mixture of gas to the

---

[1] The diagrams referred to in this quotation are no longer accessible.

Newtonian theorem. Every atom of both or all the gases in the mixture was the centre of repulsion to the proximate particles of its own kind, disregarding those of the other kind. All the gases united their efforts in counteracting the pressure of the atmosphere, or any other pressure that might be exposed to them.

This hypothesis, however beautiful might be its application, had some improbable features. We were to suppose as many distinct *kinds* of repulsive powers as of gases; and, moreover, to suppose that *heat* was not the repulsive power in any one case—positions certainly not very probable. Besides, I found from a train of expts. which have been published in the "Manchester Memoirs" that the diffusion of gases through each other was a *slow* process, and appeared to be a work of considerable effort.

Upon considering this subject, it occurred to me that I had never contemplated the effect of *difference of size* in the particles of elastic fluids. By *size* I mean the hard particle at the centre and the atmosphere of heat taken together. If, for instance, there be not exactly the same *number* of atoms of oxygen in a given volume of air as of azote in the same volume, then the *sizes* of the particles of oxygen must be different from those of the azote. And if the *sizes* be different, then—on the supposition that the repulsive power is heat—no equilibrium can be established by particles of unequal sizes pressing against each other.

This idea occurred to me in 1805.[1] I soon found that the *sizes* of the particles of elastic fluids *must* be different. For a measure of azotic gas and one of oxygen if chemically united, would make nearly *two* measures of nitrous gas, and these *two* could not have *more* atoms of nitrous gas than the *one* measure had of azotic or oxygen. (*See* diagram.) Hence the suggestion that all gases of different kinds have a difference in the *size* of their atoms; and thus we arrive at the reason for that diffusion of every gas through every other gas, without calling in any other repulsive force than the well-known one of heat. This, then, is the present view which I have of the constitution of a mixture of elastic fluids.

*   *   *   *   *   *   *   *   *   *   *   *

The different *sizes* of the particles of elastic fluids under like circumstances of temperature and pressure being once established, it became an object to determine the relative *sizes* and *weights*, together with the relative *number*, of atoms in a given volume. This led the

[1] Roscoe points out that Dalton must have mistaken the date here, for he had given a table of atomic weights in 1803.

way to the combination of gases, and to the number of atoms entering into such combinations the particulars of which will be detailed more at large in the sequel. Other bodies besides elastic fluids—namely, liquids and solids—were subject to investigation, in consequence of their combining with elastic fluids. Thus a train of investigation was laid for determining the *number* and *weight* of all chemical elementary principles which enter into any sort of combination one with another.

Dalton's Reasoning.—Nothing could show more clearly than the above the mechanical trend of Dalton's mind and the pictorial methods by which he reached his conclusions. It was not chemical analysis, as with Richter, that led him through the law of multiple proportions to the conception of atoms. On the contrary, the atomic hypothesis was always a part of the working machinery of his mind. He solved his problems by putting the individual particles down on paper and patching them together. The diagrams in his *New System* brought this out most strongly. Dalton depicted his hard particle in the center of a square and filled in the intervening space with rays emanating from the atom. These constituted his "atmosphere of heat," and the whole looked much like a spider. Finally he ranged his atoms of one gas over those of another, and seeing that squares of equal size would fit over each other perfectly, each ray meeting a corresponding ray from another atom, he took this as conclusive evidence that gases whose atoms were of the same size could not diffuse through each other. If, however, they were of different sizes, then the rays would meet unevenly, motion would be set up, and the gases would interpenetrate. Knowing the density of the different gases, Dalton now saw that he could calculate the relative diameters of his atoms if he knew their relative weights, so he proceeded to study the best available analyses and to make others of his own in order to determine the proportion by weight in which the elements combine.

The Law of Multiple Proportions.—As he anticipated, this revealed the law of multiple proportions, *viz.*, that the weights of an element which unites in more than one proportion with another element stand to each other in a simple ratio. This he took as a confirmation of his original hypothesis, and, adopting hydrogen as a standard of reference, he proceeded to calculate

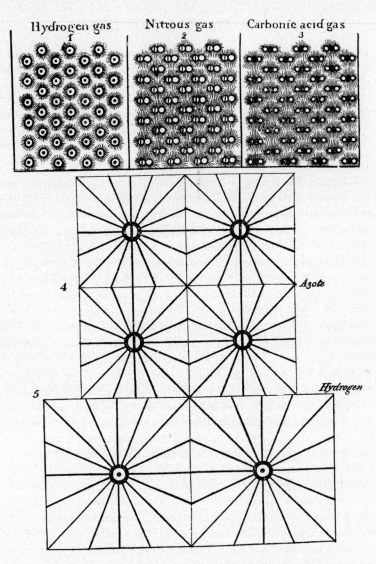

SOME OF DALTON'S PICTURES OF ATOMS

(Note the *different volumes* occupied by atoms of hydrogen and nitrogen.)

Reproduced from Roscoe and Harden's *A New View of Dalton's Atomic Theory*, by the kind permission of Macmillan and Co.

his atomic weights. Here, however, he encountered difficulties, the seriousness of which he seemed at first to have hardly realized.

Dalton's Atomic Weights.—In Dalton's time water was the only known compound of oxygen and hydrogen. The analysis tells us that in this substance the weight of oxygen is eight times that of hydrogen. The atomic weight which we select for oxygen, however, will vary according to the number of atoms which we accept as entering into combination in this substance. If the formula is HO_8, then the atoms of oxygen have the same weight as those of hydrogen; if it is HO_{16}, then they are only half as heavy and so on. Dalton had no data by which he could decide such a problem, yet realizing the immense practical utility of his discovery, he felt that it justified some assumption, and he selected the simplest. Where the elements united in but one proportion, he assumed that but one atom of each was concerned. When they united in more than one proportion the compound which was best known received the simplest formula, this of course being modified by such considerations as made the atomic weight consistent when derived from two or more compounds of the same element. Dalton accordingly adopted the formula HO for water, which gave oxygen an atomic weight of 8. Similarly, since ammonia was then the only known compound of hydrogen and nitrogen, he gave it the formula NH, from which we should now calculate the atomic weight of nitrogen as 4.5. Similarly carbon would be 6 if ethylene were CH and marsh-gas CH_2. Dalton's own figures differed widely from these, but the discrepancy is due to the imperfections of quantitative analysis at that time. His symbols were original with him, and he never gave them up, indeed he characterized our modern alphabetical ones as "unscientific!"

Objections to the Theory.—Richter's work had not been widely read, and the ideas of Dalton so simplified chemical thinking and calculation that they were hailed with great enthusiasm. The more clear-sighted, however, soon realized that his assumption which assigned the simplest formula to the best known compound had no rational foundation. They pointed out that there was no known criterion by which the number of atoms taking part in a given combination could be determined, and while they acknowledged the value of the law of multiple proportions, they felt that, stripped of its speculative superstructure, Dalton's discovery amounted to simply this: that the elements always combine in proportions by weight that are multiples of a certain unit. These men recognized, of course, that this law could not be visualized except on the assumption that combination took place by atoms, and that the relative weights of such atoms must be simple multiples or submultiples of the combining weights obtained by Dalton or Richter. What they denied was that there was any way of determining *which* multiples ought to be selected. Others had more faith. They saw that the atomic hypothesis, if true, gave a deeper insight into the constitution of matter than could be obtained without it, and although they realized that many of Dalton's numerical values must be wrong, they trusted to the future for the discovery of data which should justify his fundamental idea.

Gay-Lussac.—In 1808, the same year in which Dalton published the first portion of his *New System,* important data bearing directly upon the subject of the atomic weights were furnished by Joseph Louis Gay-Lussac. This brilliant scientist was born at St. Leonard in 1778. He had received an excellent education in Paris and had become an assistant of Berthollet who admitted him to his celebrated *Société d'Arcueil.* He was destined to high distinction; he became professor at the Sorbonne and later at the Jardin des Plantes, and in 1839 he was made a peer. At the time we are discussing he was at the outset of his scientific career, which had opened in 1802 with a paper on the effect of temperature upon the volumes of gases. In this he enunciated the famous law, now often referred to by his name, to the effect that for every degree of temperature all gases expand $\frac{1}{273}$ of their volume at 0°. He ascribed the priority, however, to Charles.[1] Gay-Lussac's methods of standardizing acids and titrating silver solutions are still considered accurate and are much used today.

Louis Jacques Thénard (1775–1857) did some work with Gay-Lussac. His experiments with hydrogen peroxide and its salts, on

---

[1] G. Amontons in 1702 had an idea concerning this law, and Volta described it in 1793. Dalton's statement concerning the expansion caused by heating gases was not quite accurate and the experiments made by Charles in 1787 were rather crude.

JOSEPH LOUIS GAY-LUSSAC
1778–1850

12

ozone, and on detection of aluminum, as well as studies on fermentation, diabetes, and the manufacture of Dutch white lead, are worthy of mention. He published a treatise on chemistry which was translated into German.

Chemical Combination by Volume.—In 1805 Gay-Lussac and Alexander von Humboldt had collaborated in an investigation intended to determine the exact proportions by volume in which oxygen and hydrogen combine under the influence of the electric spark. They found that no matter which gas was in excess, 100 measures of oxygen always reacted with just 200 measures of hydrogen within the limits of experimental error. Struck with the simplicity of this relation, Gay-Lussac continued the investigation to see whether similar relations obtained in the case of other gases. He found this to be the case, and in 1808 he was able to show, among other things, that 100 measures of ammonia gas unite with just 100 of hydrochloric acid; that 100 measures of nitrogen unite with 50 of oxygen to form nitrous oxide, with 100 to form nitric oxide, and with 200 to form nitrogen peroxide; that ammonia is formed by the union of 1 volume of nitrogen with 3 of hydrogen, and that the volumes of oxygen in the two oxides of sulfur stand in the ratio of 2:3. Gay-Lussac expressed his conclusions in the modest form that chemical reactions between gases take place in simple volume ratios and that when contraction occurs in such reactions, the diminution in volume stands in a simple ratio to the volumes of the original gases.

Bearing upon the Atomic Weights.—Since chemical reactions take place between simple multiples of the combining weights, and since the volumes of combining gases also stand in a simple ratio, it follows that the weights of equal volumes must stand in a simple ratio to the combining weights. In gases the space between the atoms must be large in proportion to that occupied by the atoms themselves, so it did not seem unreasonable to suppose that the volume (sphere of influence) occupied by an atom might be the same for all gases, and this would lead to the conclusion that the weights of equal volumes are strictly proportional to the atomic weights. Gay-Lussac makes no attempt to revise Dalton's atomic weights on this basis, but he does say that he considers his own work a valuable confirmation of Dalton's fundamental idea, and that it offers a basis for the selection of multiples less arbitrary than Dalton's original assumptions. This view appealed to many others and was urged upon Dalton by his friend Professor Thomson of Glasgow and by Berzelius.

Dalton's Attitude.—Dalton, however, declined to make any use of the idea, partly, no doubt, because, as we have seen, the atomic theory had originally been suggested to his mind by the belief that the particles of gases are *not* of the same size. In 1812 he writes to Berzelius:

> The French doctrine of *equal measures* of gases combining, etc., is what I do not admit, understanding it in the mathematical sense. At the same time I acknowledge there is something wonderful in the frequency of the approximation.

And in his manuscript notes for a lecture delivered in 1807 appears the following:

> *Query*, are there the same *number* of particles of any elastic fluid in a given volume and under a given pressure? No; azotic and oxygen gases mixed equal measures give half the number of particles of nitrous gas, nearly in the same volume.

Dalton's "mathematical" objection arose from the fact that he quite erroneously supposed Gay-Lussac's experimental results to be less trustworthy than some of his own and of his friend Henry, which gave less simple ratios. The second argument discloses a real difficulty which remained insuperable to many minds at that time. Nitric oxide *does* occupy the same volume as the constituent quantities of nitrogen and oxygen which compose it, and yet it is clear that the number of "atoms" of nitric oxide must be one-half that of the oxygen and nitrogen combined; or, as we should say today, there are but half as many *molecules* of nitric oxide as there are *atoms* of nitrogen and oxygen which combine to form it. As we know, many other gas reactions present the same difficulty.

Avogadro's Hypothesis.—A solution was found by Amadeo Avogadro (1776–1856), long professor of physics at Turin. In 1811 he published in the *Journal de physique* an article setting forth the hypothesis which we now connect so prominently with his name. In it he shows that such discrepancies as that just mentioned can be harmonized if we assume that the smallest

AMADEO AVOGADRO
1776–1856

particles of the elementary gases thought of by Dalton are themselves compound, just as in the so-called *compound gases*. He draws a distinction, therefore, between *molecules intégrantes* (the *physical* units of gases which determine their volume, etc. and for which we still retain the name *molecule*), and *molecules élémentaires* (the *chemical* units for which we now use the word *atom*). Of only the former is it true that equal volumes contain an equal number. He points out that any convenient number of atoms may be assumed in the molecule of an elementary gas, though for the common ones, two is the maximum hitherto found necessary, and he shows that reactions formerly interpreted as cases of simple addition must now be considered as involving decomposition followed by addition or metathesis; so that in the special case just mentioned, we can write as we do today:

$$N_2 + O_2 = 2NO$$

In 1814, the eminent physicist Ampère advanced similar ideas, though he did not put the case quite so clearly as Avogadro had done, for he assumed four instead of two atoms in the molecules of the elementary gases, and he confused the issue by a fruitless attempt to connect the atomic constitution of solids with their crystalline form.

Reception of the Theory.—These ideas of Avogadro and Ampère play so important a part in modern chemical theory that it is difficult to realize that, when first published, they made no impression whatever. It was not until 1860, when Cannizzaro read his brilliant paper on a *Course in Chemical Philosophy* at a congress of chemists meeting at Karlsruhe, that chemists began to realize the importance of the ideas taught by Cannizzaro's former teacher, Avogadro.

In the sequel we shall often feel that much unfortunate confusion might have been avoided if Dalton and Gay-Lussac could have adopted the suggestion of Avogadro and made common cause to present these views to the world. There is a chance that, in such a case, the atomic and molecular hypotheses might have taken, far earlier than they did, the place in chemical thinking which they hold today. What might have been is, however, as fruitless a topic in history as in the more familiar relations of common life, and we can only ask why the ideas of Avogadro received so little attention from his contemporaries.

It has been suggested that this was because Avogadro was visionary and accompanied his theoretical speculations by no experimental work. We also know that some chemists of eminence impatiently denounced his views on the ground that they involved fractions of atoms, whereas the word atom *means* something which cannot be divided (*Greek* α-privative and τέμνω to cut). We cannot seriously believe, however, that even in the earlier days of the nineteenth century, scientific men would reject a really useful hypothesis purely on grounds of etymology. The real reason lies deeper. The scientific world judges hypotheses by certain hard standards which are, on the whole, just and sound. These demand that a hypothesis shall not only explain the given series of facts for which it was originally designed, but that it shall also give account of others more remote and shall lead to the discovery of new facts and relationships; in short, that it shall enable us to make predictions. At this time Avogadro's hypothesis was not in a position to do these things, and therefore, it was justly (even if unfortunately) disregarded. As a result, the atomic theory failed to come fully to its own for fifty years.

Wollaston's Equivalents.—In England especially, a powerful skeptical school soon sprang up, of which the most important representative was William Hyde Wollaston (1766–1828). Wollaston made some analyses of neutral and acid salts which brilliantly confirmed the law of multiple proportions, but he nevertheless refused to accept the atomic theory, essentially for the reasons already stated on page 122. He fully recognized, however, the practical value of the combining weights, and in 1814, we find him busy determining what he calls *equivalents*. Wollaston was the first to use this word in a chemical sense, and this deserves more than passing notice because its meaning has undergone important changes in the course of the many controversies in which it has figured since his day. Now, of course, it has a rather restricted meaning and refers to such weights of reagents as balance or neutralize each other, as in the case of acids and bases or of metals which precipitate each other. The relative weights determined by Richter were, therefore, true equivalents in the modern sense. Wollaston's equivalents, however, were only multiples or submultiples of the combining weights, selected solely on the basis of maximum simplicity and consistency. They were, therefore, in principle, nothing else than Dalton's atomic weights without their speculative significance.

Prout's Hypothesis.—If the atomic theory had opponents, it also found some friends whose enthusiasm was not always tempered by discretion. Among these was William Prout (1785–1850), an English physician much interested in physiological chemistry who, in 1815, published an anonymous paper in which he called attention to the closeness with which the atomic weights of the elements so far as then determined approximated whole numbers. He did not stop there but expressed the opinion that hydrogen was therefore, the universal substance, and that the atoms of other elements were really aggregates of hydrogen atoms. Prout soon made eminent converts, including Dalton's friend, Thomson, and this doubtless because he gave expression to the repugnance which we all feel toward believing in seventy or more different kinds of matter. In its original form, the hypothesis was easy to disprove as soon as the atomic weight of chlorine, for example, was fixed at approximately 35.5, but its more ardent supporters, of course, immediately proceeded to reduce their hypothetical unit first to the half, and then to the *tenth* of an atom of hydrogen; always keeping a little within the decreasing experimental error. We are, of course, not concerned with discussions of this kind. What interests us historically is the fact that the fundamental idea underlying Prout's hypothesis, from the *materia prima* of the alchemists to the electrons of the present day, is something which will not down, and which has had much influence upon the work and thinking of many master minds.

Henry and Thomson.—Two other Englishmen deserve mention here. William Henry (1775–1836) originally intended to be a physician, but after finishing his studies and obtaining his degree, ill health prevented him from practicing medicine. He devoted himself to research, chiefly on gases, and in 1803 published the law now bearing his name which states that the solubility of gases in water is proportional to the pressure when no chemical reaction takes place. Thomas Thomson (1773–1852) also studied medicine and, after obtaining the M.D. degree in 1779, taught chemistry for twelve years. He was a subeditor of the *Encyclopaedia Britannica* and of the journal called *Annals of Philosophy* which was merged with the *Philosophical Magazine* in 1827. He was connected with the University of Glasgow from 1817 until his death, establishing the first chemical laboratory for students in Great Britain. In 1825, Liebig at Giessen and Amos Eaton at Troy, New York, also established laboratories for students, but the first such laboratory was established by Lomonosov, in Russia, in 1748. Thomson was one of the chief exponents of the doctrine of Dalton, was inclined to accept Prout's hypothesis, and published numerous texts, including a history of chemistry.

Humboldt.—Friedrich Heinrich Alexander, Baron von Humboldt (1769–1859) was educated for a political career in Germany. In 1789 he wrote a treatise on the geology of the Rhine Valley. As assessor of mines in Berlin he found time to travel extensively in Europe and South America from 1792 to 1804 and made Paris his headquarters from 1808 to 1827. During this time he was much lionized as a scientific explorer. He may be regarded as the founder of physical geography and meteorology in their larger aspects.

Gmelin.—Leopold Gmelin (1788–1853) began teaching in 1813 at Heidelberg where he remained till his death. He discovered potassium ferricyanide in 1827, and the first edition of his standard *Handbuch* appeared in 1817–1819. In its revised form, it remains today one of the most authoritative reference books on inorganic chemistry.

Klaproth.—Martin Heinrich Klaproth (1743–1817) was sixty-seven years old when he was appointed professor of chemistry at the University of Berlin when it was founded in 1810. He started, like Liebig and Scheele, as an apothecary's assistant. Originally a believer in the phlogiston theory of Stahl, he was one of the first in Germany to reject it. He improved the methods of analytical chemistry, and much of the present laboratory technique originated with him. He made countless mineral analyses, discovered uranium in pitchblende, and did important work in connection with the chemistry of zirconium, cerium, titanium, strontium, yttrium, and tellurium. He discovered that ferric chloride dissolves readily in ether which is made the basis of the well-known Rothe separation. He wrote a six-volume book on the chemistry of minerals. He was modest, unassuming, and very gentle in correcting the mistakes of others.

Literature

Dalton's *New System of Chemical Philosophy* was published in 1808. There is an excellent life of Dalton by his friend Henry, published by the Cavendish Society in 1854. There is a more recent one by Sir Henry Roscoe, entitled *John Dalton and the Rise of Modern Chemistry*, 1895. A book which deserves special attention is Roscoe and Harden's *A New View of the Origin of Dalton's Atomic Theory*, 1896.

Contributions of Dalton, Gay-Lussac, Avogadro, and Wollaston to the atomic and molecular theories are to be found in the *Alembic Club Reprints* Nos. 2 and 4. See also Ostwald's *Klassiker* No. 3 for the work of Dalton and Wollaston, and No. 8 for that of Avogadro and Ampère.

CHAPTER IX

THE EARLY HISTORY OF GALVANIC ELECTRICITY

While men like Richter and Dalton were making their great contributions to pure chemistry, Italian scientists were studying the manifestations of a new form of energy. This was galvanic electricity—something hitherto entirely overlooked—but destined henceforward to exert the greatest influence not only upon chemistry but in almost every department of life.

Galvani's Discovery.—A paper published in 1791 by Luigi Galvani, a distinguished physician of Bologna, describes the accident which first drew his attention to the subject. He relates how he was one day in his laboratory where some partially dissected frogs were lying on a table near a static electrical machine. It then so happened that one of his assistants touched the bare crural nerve of one of the frogs with a scalpel just at the moment when a spark was drawn from the machine, and was surprised to notice a sharp twitching of the frog's leg. Galvani's attention was called to the occurrence and a series of systematic experiments was immediately begun. These showed that the effect could be produced at will so long as the nerve was touched with any metal, and that the twitching was more violent if at the same time the frog's leg was also connected with the ground. Since the twitching was induced by the electric spark and did not take place when the nerve was touched with a non-conductor, Galvani concluded that the phenomenon was electrical and tried numerous experiments to see if it could be induced by atmospheric electricity in thunderstorms. In the course of these experiments, another accident due to arranging the frogs upon hooks showed that neither the spark of the electric machine nor lightning in the vicinity was necessary to produce the effect. It was sufficient to put the crural nerve and the extremity of the leg in metallic contact, and the action was much stronger if the circuit connecting them consisted of two different metals. Fur-

132

LUIGI GALVANI
1737–1798

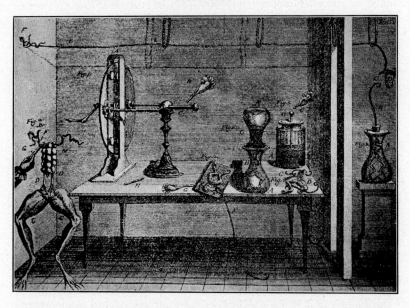

SOME OF GALVANI'S EXPERIMENTS WITH FROGS' LEGS AS DEPICTED
IN HIS ORIGINAL COMMUNICATION

133

thermore, the nature of the two metals made a perceptible difference in the violence of the muscular contraction. In his interpretation Galvani does not seem to have laid as much weight on this fact as he should have done. The relationship between the nerve and muscle suggested to him an analogy with the Leyden jar, and he confirmed this to his satisfaction by coating both nerve and muscle with tinfoil and thereby accentuating the effect. This led Galvani to name the new force animal electricity and to believe that it had its source in the organs of animals, where it might play an important role in physiological processes.

Volta's Explanation.—Galvani's paper produced a great impression and numerous scientists repeated the experiments. Among these was Alessandro Volta (1745-1827), professor of physics in Pavia, whose conclusions, however, differed radically from those of Galvani. In the first place, he laid weight upon the essential condition that the ends of the metallic circuit must be different in order to produce the twitching. They may indeed be of the same metal, but in this case there must be at least some difference in the surfaces, or the effect will not be shown. Further, he produced the same effect by connecting two points on the nerve by a metallic circuit in which the muscle was not included, and in this way showed that the muscle was not essential to the phenomenon; it therefore formed no part of a Leyden jar, and its contraction was simply a secondary effect due to the irritation of the nerve. Considering then the nerve and the two metals, it seemed reasonable to suppose that the former might be replaced by any moist conductor, and it was soon found that this was the case. As early as 1760 J. G. Sulzer had called attention to the fact that when the moist tongue is thrust between two plates of different metals which remain in contact at their edges a peculiar taste is observed, and it is clear that this sensation, like the twitching of the frog's leg, is merely an extremely sensitive electroscope which permits the detection of currents far weaker than any which had hitherto been studied by such apparatus as was then in use—all of which had been designed for dealing with the high potentials of static electricity. Volta conducted many series of experiments in which the metals and moist conductors were all varied and made every

ALESSANDRO VOLTA
1745-1827

effort in his power to characterize the new phenomena as truly electrical. At last, by means of a condenser of his own design he succeeded in multiplying the charge until it would show the familiar effect upon an electroscope, and rightly concluded that the essential difference from static electricity was greater quantity at a lower potential. As a result of these studies Volta utterly rejected the animal origin which Galvani had ascribed to the phenomena he had observed and sought the cause rather in the mere contact of the two metals. Volta next tried to determine what electrical relation dry metals had to each other. He brought them in contact, then separated them, and by tests with an electrometer satisfied himself that whenever two metals come into proximity one exhibits a positive and the other a negative charge. Even as early as 1792 Volta published a list of substances in such an order that each is positive toward all which follow it and negative to all which precede. This was the first *potential series*. By its aid one should always be able to predict the direction of the current when any two metals in contact are also separated by a moist conductor.

The Contact Theory.—Volta's theoretical conception of the matter was extremely simple. Every solid contains the "electric fluid" under a state of tension characteristic for that solid. If now two solids are brought into contact the fluid passes from the region of the higher to that of the lower tension. If in addition there is a moist conductor in the circuit this acts—"in a manner not yet thoroughly understood"—as a kind of "semipermeable wall" through which the fluid may pass back to its original source. This was Volta's celebrated contact theory of electricity. Its author fully realized that it involved perpetual motion, but our modern ideas concerning the conservation of energy had little place in the scientific thinking of the day, and Volta was rather proud than otherwise of this aspect of the case. He had some right to be proud of his theory, for in spite of this fundamental fault, it was so simple and self-consistent that it held the field for several decades as the most practicable working hypothesis.

The Chemical Theory.—This contact theory of Volta had hardly been formally stated before another theory essentially chemical was set up in opposition by J. W. Ritter (1776–1810).

Ritter called attention to the fact that when two metals in moist condition are left in contact, corrosion of one of them proceeds far more rapidly than when they are isolated. He rightly interpreted this as an electrical phenomenon and ascribed the current to the oxidation of one of the metals. He contended that without the oxidation there is no current, and found a convincing argument in the fact that Volta's potential series might

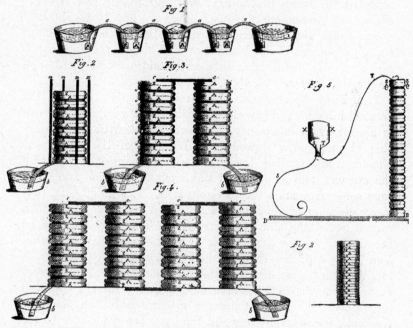

VOLTA'S PILE

serve equally well as a list representing the order of the relative affinities of the substances concerned for oxygen.

Volta's Pile.—Volta meanwhile was busy with attempts to obtain stronger currents[1] and attained this object by a logical application of his contact theory. He reasoned essentially as follows: The electric fluid passes from silver to zinc and if a

[1] In 1792 Valli ingeniously attempted to accomplish a similar result by connecting the nerves and legs of fourteen frogs in series. The results were ambiguous.

moist conductor is present it can pass through this to silver again. Hence if we add a second pair of plates in the same order the second silver passes the fluid on to the second zinc with its own intensity augmented by that of the current which it has received from the moist conductor. Volta accordingly laid upon a plate of silver one of zinc, and upon this a layer of cloth or pasteboard dipped in water or a salt solution, and then repeated the series indefinitely, getting stronger and stronger currents as the number of plates increased. Finally, he obtained not only direct effects upon the electroscope, but also the familiar static phenomena of shock and spark. This was the famous *pile* of Volta. He described it in a letter addressed to Sir Joseph Banks, dated March 20, 1800.

The First Electrolysis.—The communication excited the greatest interest, and experiments with the new apparatus began in almost every laboratory. All were struck with the remarkable chemical effects produced. In May of the same year Nicholson and Carlisle described the decomposition of water by the current, and solutions of numerous salts, acids and bases were soon after subjected to electrolysis. It is interesting that many phenomena which now seem to us a matter of course then caused something akin to amazement. That water should be decomposed by the current was by no means unexpected, since Van Troostwijk and Deimann had already achieved that result in 1789 with the aid of a powerful static machine. What caused surprise was the fact that the oxygen and hydrogen appeared separately. Where was the water decomposed? If at the positive pole, for example, how did the hydrogen get across to the negative pole unobserved? Similar difficulties arose in the case of salt solutions. If potassium sulfate be electrolyzed, acid appears at one pole and alkali at the other. Even if the solution is strongly alkaline the liquid in the vicinity of the positive pole soon becomes acid. Experiments like the following were tried: The negative pole of a battery was surrounded by a potassium sulfate solution and the positive by water. Between the two and in communication with both was a vessel containing strong alkali. Sulfuric acid soon appeared at the positive pole. How did it get through all the alkali without being neutralized on the way?

Grotthuss's[1] Theory of Electrolysis.—Such puzzles proved very troublesome until Ch. J. D. von Grotthuss in 1805 explained the phenomena by a successive decomposition and recombination among the molecules of the electrolyte. In the case of water, for example, the negative pole attracts an atom of hydrogen from an adjacent water molecule. This is evolved as gas; and the oxygen left over robs another molecule of its hydrogen to take the place of the first. This goes on all the way to the other electrode where the last oxygen is attracted to the positive pole and is evolved in its turn. This explanation proved adequate for a long time.

The Contact and Chemical Theories in Opposition.—These discoveries strengthened the faith of those who believed in the

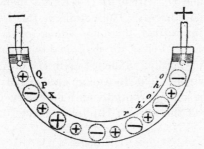

The Mechanism of Electrolysis According to Grotthuss

chemical origin of the current, but Volta himself remained blind to this aspect of the question. In his first communication he had mentioned none of the chemical effects of his battery in spite of the frequent opportunities he must have had to observe them. He described, for example, putting both terminals into the same vessel of water but he said no word of gas evolution. Later, when such effects were called to his attention he expressed a good deal of surprise and interest, saying in substance that his battery was so wonderful a thing that remarkable effects both physical and chemical might well be expected of it, but he regarded the latter as secondary and accidental. So the two schools stood opposed to each other as they were destined to do for years to

---

[1] The name appears in this form in the journals where most of his work is published. At least three other spellings are to be found in well-known modern books.

come.   The "chemists," as they came to be called, could always
maintain that contact offers no explanation for the work done,
that a current never passes through a solution without chemical
oxidation and reduction, and that when the chemical action
ceases the current stops.   The "physicists," on the other hand,
found their chief argument in the potential existing between dry
metals, but they could also hold up to their opponents that the
strength of the current stands in no definite relation to the
chemical reaction going on in the electrolytic cell, that very
vigorous chemical reactions often proceed without producing
any electrical phenomena whatever, and finally that when such
chemical action does take place, it is often demonstrable that it
begins only when the circuit is closed and therefore cannot be
the cause of the current.   The details of this long controversy
are extremely interesting, but they belong to the special history
of electrochemistry.   Here we shall deal with that subject only
where it exerts a marked influence upon the development of the
science as a whole.   The foregoing account of its beginnings,
however, seems an appropriate and necessary introduction to
any discussion of the work of Humphry Davy.

Literature

To the student of electrochemistry Ostwald's *Elektrochemie, ihre Geschichte
und Lehre* cannot be too highly recommended.   With admirable clearness
the author traces the whole development of the subject from the earliest
observations of Galvani down to about 1895.   The text consists largely of
extensive quotations from the work of the original investigators, unified and
illuminated by clear and helpful running commentary.   In spite of its
formidable size the book is a model of what an intensive historical study
should be.

Galvani's original pamphlet is reprinted in Ostwald's *Klassiker* No. 52,
as are also the earlier papers by Volta, Nos. 114 and 118, and those by
Grotthuss, No. 152.

CHAPTER X

HUMPHRY DAVY

Humphry Davy was born at or near Penzance in Cornwall, England, on December 17, 1778. His father, Robert Davy, was proficient in wood-carving but after his marriage in 1776 was occupied chiefly with farming. The eldest son of eight children, Humphry as a lad was precocious but did badly at school because of his bouyant disposition and love of sport. Many years later in a letter to his mother he remarked: "After all, the way in which we are taught Latin and Greek does not much influence the important structure of our minds . . . What I am, I have made myself." Two of his early interests remained with him through life—his passion for fishing and for writing verse— indeed in later years some of his poetry earned a good deal of praise. On the death of his father, in 1794, Davy entered the office of a local physician whom he assisted in the preparation of remedies; but he soon developed such a taste for startling experiments and explosions that his employer saw him go without regret. One of his friends, however, who had heard of his interest in chemistry gave Davy an introduction to Dr. Thomas Beddoes which was destined to be a turning-point in his life. The discovery of new substances of striking properties always inspires physicians to try these upon their patients, and the recent investigations of Priestley and others had led Dr. Beddoes to found in Bristol what he called a "pneumatic institute." Here he intended to prepare the new gases and experiment upon their physiological action. Davy was put in charge of this laboratory in 1798, and immediately began preparing and inhaling gases. Some of these experiments nearly cost him his life, but his perseverance was soon rewarded by the discovery of the remarkable physiological action of nitrous oxide, now familiarly spoken of as laughing gas. This discovery made a popular appeal, and the inhalation of nitrous oxide became a fad, with the result that

HUMPHRY DAVY
1778–1829

A Séance at the Royal Institution in Davy's Time. (*From a Contemporary Cartoon.*)

Reproduced from Thorpe's *Humphry Davy—Poet and Philosopher*, by the kind permission of Cassel and Co.

143

Davy soon acquired a popularity which doubtless won him the professorship at the Royal Institution in 1801.

The Royal Institution.—Not long before this time, Count Rumford, who was then very influential in the scientific circles of London, had persuaded some friends of kindred tastes to unite with him in establishing this institution. It exists for the purpose of securing for those interested in such topics courses of lectures dealing with the latest discoveries in science and the arts. The professor in charge has a completely equipped laboratory at his disposal, primarily for the requirements of the lectures, but also for the prosecution of his own researches. The standard of appointments has always been kept high, so that from that day to this the professors have been scientists of great eminence, and the Institution has remained an important center in English scientific life.

Davy was only twenty-two when he received the appointment, but his lectures at once aroused enthusiasm on account of the brilliancy of his delivery and his skill in experimentation. At the same time his personal magnetism made him immensely popular, so that fashionable society, which had smiled upon him in Bristol, fêted and lionized him in London. Davy was knighted in 1812 and made a baronet in 1818. The combined burdens of vigorous scientific and active social life, however, seriously impaired his health, and he broke down altogether in 1826. Repeated journeys to the Continent brought little relief, and he died in Geneva, May 29, 1829.

Scientific Work.—The historical significance of Davy's scientific work lies chiefly in what he did to determine which substances ought to be considered as elements. Lavoisier had taken the most important step toward an answer to this question but he had left it in a rather unsatisfactory state. His list of elements (see page 61) was partly incomplete and partly dependent upon certain assumptions which we now recognize as inspirations of genius but which nevertheless still lacked experimental foundation. For example, he included lime and alumina among his elements because, while probably oxides, they had not yet been decomposed, and he was so certain that the alkalies were oxides that he dropped them from the list. Silica he classified as an earth, and the acids of salt, borax and fluorspar he also considered oxides, and put in the list the *radicals* of those acids. It was the great service of Davy, partly by his own work and partly by that of others whom his researches inspired, that most of the questions involved here were definitely settled.

Studies in Electricity.—In 1801 the scientific world was full of interest in voltaic electricity, and Davy, now that he was in charge of a well-equipped laboratory, threw himself with energy into the study of these phenomena. His early experiments were on electrolysis, and especially in the study of the various combinations of substances which would yield currents. One of the most important results was the discovery that active cells could be constructed which contained only one metal and two liquids. This work, however, was soon overshadowed by that of which he began to give an account in the Bakerian lecture of 1806. This investigation began with the consideration of a comparatively unimportant problem which, however, gained dignity by the scrupulous care and experimental skill which Davy employed in its solution.

Isolation of the Alkali Metals.—Nicholson and Carlisle, as well as others who had studied the electrolysis of water, had noticed the formation of acid and alkali at the poles, and concluded that the decomposition was by no means so simple a phenomenon as it seemed. Davy, however, showed that pure water is a much less common substance than is commonly supposed, and that samples previously electrolyzed had contained impurities derived either from the containing vessel or from the atmosphere. He then showed that pure water electrolyzed in vessels of gold yields only oxygen and hydrogen in chemically equivalent quantities. Davy had already obtained acids and bases by the electrolysis of salts, and he now tried the new force upon substances not hitherto decomposed. He caused to be constructed the most powerful battery then in existence, and with it attempted to decompose the alkalies. He first used strong solutions of potash, and then fusions of the dry alkali without results, but the following extract from the Bakerian lecture of 1807 describes his final success:

A small piece of pure potash, which had been exposed for a few seconds to the atmosphere, so as to give conducting power to the surface, was placed upon an insulated disc of platina, connected with the negative side of the battery of the power of 250 of 6 and 4,[1] in a state of intense activity; and a platina wire, communicating with the positive side, was brought in contact with the upper surface of the alkali. The whole apparatus was in the open atmosphere.

Under these circumstances a vivid action was soon observed to take place. The potash began to fuse at both its points of electrization. There was a violent effervescence at the upper surface; at the lower or negative surface, there was no liberation of elastic fluid; but small globules having a high metallic lustre, and being exactly similar in visible characters to quicksilver, appeared, some of which burnt with explosion and bright flame, as soon as they were formed, and others remained, and were merely tarnished, and finally covered by a white film which formed on their surfaces.

The isolation of potassium above described was soon followed by that of sodium, and Davy made an extensive study of the properties and chemical relations of each. The importance of the discovery and the surprising properties of the new metals aroused the greatest interest and Davy found himself world-famous almost in a day. What he had done also encouraged others to work along similar lines. Gay-Lussac and Thénard soon found that they could obtain sodium and potassium in still better yield by reduction with metallic iron, and here-after a healthy rivalry sprang up between Davy and the French chemists which, on the whole, was for the benefit of all concerned.

Davy, like Lavoisier, regarded the caustic alkalies as oxides and the similarity of these substances to ammonia led him to attempt the decomposition of the latter. Here an unfortunate blunder made him state that the dry gas contained 7 or 8 per cent of oxygen. This statement stood among others of the highest accuracy and had some unfortunate theoretical conse-quences, for many chemists were misled, and Davy's results for a time displaced those of Berthollet who had correctly deter-mined the composition of the gas some years before. Davy also made a study of ammonium amalgam, and finding that it decomposed readily into ammonia and hydrogen he raised the question whether free sodium and potassium might not also contain hydrogen, a conclusion for which their combustibility

---

[1] This means a voltaic battery of 250 pairs of plates each 6 by 4 inches in size.

seemed to speak. Not only Davy but also Gay-Lussac and
Thénard considered this question seriously, but the latter
chemists finally furnished the most definite proof that it could
not be true. They burned potassium in dry oxygen, and found
that no water was formed in the process. If the potassium contained any hydrogen it must therefore still be present in the
peroxide. The latter, however, is readily decomposed by carbon dioxide into oxygen and potassium carbonate, in neither of
which can any hydrogen be found.

Davy next accomplished the decomposition of the alkaline
earths but this proved more difficult. Acting upon a suggestion
of Berzelius, he mixed the earths with mercuric oxide and subjected the mixtures to the action of his battery. This yielded
amalgams from which the metals could be prepared with some
difficulty. Barium, strontium, calcium and magnesium were
thus added to the list of elements known in the free state.

Davy now tested the effects of the current upon boric acid and
silica, but without success. Nevertheless the former was soon
decomposed by Gay-Lussac and Thénard who fused it with
metallic potassium, and silicon was isolated by Berzelius who
heated silica with iron and carbon. Alumina was not decomposed until 1827, but no one any longer doubted that it was an
oxide. This left of the *radicals* of Lavoisier's list only those of
muriatic and hydrofluoric acids. These, however, we must not
confuse with the elements chlorine and fluorine. Instead they
were hypothetical entities which had been introduced into
chemical theory by Lavoisier's erroneous conception concerning
the nature of acids. Since this conception was long dominant
and destined to have unfortunate consequences for many years
to come, we must divest ourselves of some modern ideas which
now seem axiomatic and learn to think in its terms.

Lavoisier's Theory of Acids.—Rouelle had fixed the idea of a
salt as an *addition product* of acid and base (page 58) and Lavoisier had incorporated this idea in his system. The term "acid"
was at this time universally applied to the substance which we
call the anhydride, while what we call the acid was considered as
the acid plus a certain quantity of more or less adventitious
water—akin to water of crystallization. If Lavoisier had used
our symbols he would therefore have formulated sulfuric acid as

SO_3 and the reagent which we now call by that name SO_3,HO (Dalton's atomic weights). When this reacts with lime, calcium sulfate and water are produced, the latter coming entirely from the acid in the sense of the following equation:

$$CaO + SO_3,HO = CaO,SO_3 + HO$$

Here both acid and base are oxides, and Lavoisier doubtless believed that this was always the case, but while several of the bases had not been decomposed, there was no question that carbonic, sulfuric and phosphoric acids were oxides. He therefore believed that oxygen was the essential constituent in every acid, and gave the element its name on that account. It now remains for us to inquire how muriatic acid, for example, could be fitted into such a system. This was done rather ingeniously as follows:

The Muriaticum Theory.—Since all acids contain oxygen, muriatic can be no exception, and since the dry gas acts upon dry oxides like lime to form water it must also contain that compound, just as sulfuric acid does. The real anhydrous acid must therefore be the oxide of a radical as yet unknown but commonly called *murium* or *muriaticum*. If we designate this by X, then anhydrous muriatic acid will be XO, and the well-known gas HO,XO. What then is chlorine? Scheele had discovered this substance by treating muriatic acid with the black oxide of manganese and had naturally given to the product the name of "dephlogisticated marine acid." After the discovery of oxygen Berthollet changed this to "oxidized muriatic acid" or "oxymuriatic acid" which it had since retained. Everyone believed that it contained oxygen and this was supported by the oxidizing action of bleaching powder, the evolution of oxygen gas from chlorine water, and a number of other reactions which really had not been carefully studied. It will perhaps help us to acquire the point of view of the times if we formulate some of the familiar reactions of chlorine and muriatic acid both in the terms of the *muriaticum* theory and also in our modern formulas:

(1) $NaO + HO,XO =$ $Na_2O + 2HCl =$
            $HO + NaO,XO;$ $2NaCl + H_2O.$

(2) $HO,XO + O = HO + XO_2;$ $2HCl + O = H_2O + Cl_2.$

(3) $H + XO_2 = HO,XO;$ $H_2 + Cl_2 = 2HCl.$

(4) $Na + XO_2 = NaO,XO;$ $2Na + Cl_2 = 2NaCl.$

It will be seen that the *muriaticum* theory explained these reactions satisfactorily from the quantitative as well as the qualitative side, and in the Bakerian lecture of 1808 we find Davy entirely in accord with this view, though evidently rather disappointed that his attempts to prepare the anhydrous acid had been so unsuccessful. When the ordinary acid was treated with a dry base it lost its water readily enough:

$$NaO + HO,XO = HO + NaO,XO$$

but no water could be extracted from the gas by dehydrating agents, so he next attempted to obtain the anhydrous acid by decomposing a dry chloride with another acid (YO), in the sense of the equation:

$$NaO,XO + YO = NaO,YO + XO$$

Under no circumstances, however, could this reaction be made to take the indicated course. He heated numerous muriates with anhydrous boric acid and with dry silica but could get no trace of decomposition till moisture was admitted to the vessel. Then indeed muriatic acid was evolved but it was the familiar gas which he believed to contain water.

The Elementary Nature of Chlorine.—If muriatic acid contains oxygen then oxymuriatic acid (chlorine) must contain still more, but all Davy's attempts to obtain oxygen from it were equally fruitless. It might be supposed that if oxymuriatic acid contained oxygen phosphorus would remove it. Davy writes on this point as follows:

I have described, on a former occasion, the nature of the operation of phosphorus on oxymuriatic acid, and I have stated that two compounds, one fluid, and the other solid, are formed in the process of combustion, of which the first, on the generally received theory of the nature of oxymuriatic acid, must be considered as a compound of muriatic acid and phosphorous acid, and the other of muriatic acid and phosphoric acid.[1] It occurred to me that if the acids of phosphorus really existed in these combinations, it would not be difficult to obtain them and thus to gain proofs of the existence of oxygen in oxymuriatic acid.

[1] $P_2 + 3XO_2 = P_2O_3, 3XO$
$P_2 + 5XO_2 = P_2O_5, 5XO$

I made a considerable quantity of the solid compound of oxymuriatic acid and phosphorus by combustion, and saturated it with ammonia, by heating it in a proper receiver filled with ammoniacal gas, on which it acted with great energy, producing much heat; and they formed a white opaque powder. Supposing that this substance was composed of the dry muriates and phosphates of ammonia; as muriate of ammonia is very volatile, and as ammonia is driven off from phosphoric acid, by a heat below redness, I conceived that by igniting the product obtained, I should procure phosphoric acid; I therefore introduced some of the powder into a tube of green glass, and heated it to redness, out of contact of air by a spirit lamp; but found, to my great surprise, that it was not at all volatile nor decomposable at this degree of heat, and it gave off no gaseous matter. * * * I contented myself by ascertaining that no substance known to contain oxygen could be procured from oxymuriatic acid, in this mode of operation.

The above experiment represents only one of many convincing ones, which showed that no oxygen could ever be obtained from chlorine or dry muriatic acid, and that when it appeared in reactions involving one of these substances its presence could always be accounted for in some other way. Davy accordingly held that it was simpler to assume that "oxymuriatic acid" is an element to which he now gave the name *chlorine* on account of its color. It is worth while to emphasize the fact that Davy did not prove that chlorine was not a compound, nor is such proof possible. Chlorine may still contain oxygen (or titanium for that matter) but so long as no other element can be obtained from it, its compound nature is a gratuitous assumption. Numerous chemists who admired Lavoisier, and valued a logical system more than experimental evidence, preferred for some time longer to make this assumption, and Gay-Lussac and Thénard were particularly hard to convince. Indeed they supported the *muriaticum* theory with some very ingenious experiments. As fate would have it, however, they themselves soon furnished the most satisfactory evidence against the theory. In 1813 Gay-Lussac published a famous paper upon iodine, then recently discovered by Courtois, and in the following year another paper on cyanogen which is equally noteworthy. These investigations involved a study of hydriodic and hydrocyanic acids; and the important analogies which connect these with hydrochloric, together with the certainty that there is no oxygen in hydrocyanic acid, soon satisfied all that there was no oxygen in any of them.

The Hydrogen Theory of Acids.—Davy drew the logical conclusion from these results, and was inclined to proclaim hydrogen and not oxygen as the essential component of acids. Unfortunately the influence of Lavoisier's name and the force of tradition prevented the general adoption of this idea. Instead scientists accepted the compromise suggested by Gay-Lussac which involved the creation of a new class of compounds called *hydracides* to include those acids which contain no oxygen. Hydrochloric, hydriodic and hydrocyanic acids obtained their present names at that time.

The above constitute Davy's most important investigations from the historical point of view. On the practical side, he invented the safety lamp for miners in 1817, and in 1825 he suggested that the copper with which the bottoms of ships were then universally sheathed might be protected from corrosion by the addition of comparatively small pieces of zinc. The corrosion was diminished, but the accumulation of marine growths upon the plates was so much accelerated that the idea proved impracticable.

Theory of Chemical Affinity.—Toward Dalton's atomic theory Davy maintained a sceptical attitude akin to that of Wollaston. His experiments with electricity, however, led him to a theory of chemical affinity which has interest as a sign of the times. Davy had at first been a supporter of the "chemical" view, but the repetition of some of Volta's experiments with the electrometer not only converted him to the contact theory, but led him to develop it into a general theory of chemical combination. He found, for example, that copper is always positive toward sulfur, and that this difference in polarity becomes accentuated with rise of temperature. Finally, the elements unite to form copper sulfide with an evolution of heat which Davy ascribed to the neutralization of the electric charges. Till this time chemists had compared chemical affinity to gravitation, and some had gone so far as to suggest the identity of the two forces. Now, however, it was natural that Davy and his contemporaries should identify chemical affinity with electricity. Davy held that when the atoms of two substances are brought into proximity they assume opposite electrical charges and finally unite as the charges are neutralized.   This gives a consistent explanation of electrolytic decompositions by the current.   The constituent elements receive from the poles of the battery the electric charges which they possessed before combination, and they can henceforward again exist in the free state.   This idea was never developed into a complete system by Davy, but the same general idea lay at the foundation of the theories advanced later by Berzelius.

Davy and Faraday.—It has often been said that Davy's greatest discovery was Michael Faraday. Faraday, who was born in Newington, Surrey, in 1791, was of very humble parentage and began life as a bookbinder's apprentice in 1804. He not only became an expert in this handicraft but by reading the books as well as binding them[1] he gradually acquired a considerable knowledge of many subjects which interested him, particularly things which had to do with natural science.   The story of his meeting with Davy is told in the following letter.

To J. A. Paris, M. D.
Royal Institution, December 23, 1829.

My dear Sir:—You asked me to give you an account of my first introduction to Sir H. Davy, which I am very happy to do, as I think the circumstances will bear testimony to the goodness of his heart.

When I was a bookseller's apprentice I was very fond of experiment and very averse to trade.   It happened that a gentleman, a member of the Royal Institution, took me to hear some of Sir H. Davy's last lectures in Albemarle Street.   I took notes, and afterwards wrote them out more fairly in a quarto volume.

My desire to escape from trade, which I thought vicious and selfish, and to enter into the service of Science, which I imagined made its pursuers amiable and liberal, induced me at last to take the bold and simple step of writing to Sir H. Davy, expressing my wishes, and a hope that if an opportunity came in his way he would favor my views; at the same time I sent the notes I had taken of his lectures.

The answer, which makes all the point of my communication, I send you in the original, requesting you to take great care of it, and to let me have it back, for you may imagine how much I value it.

You will observe that this took place at the end of the year 1812, and early in 1813 he requested to see me, and told me of the situation of assistant in the laboratory of the Royal Institution, then just vacant.

[1] The phrase is Ostwald's.

At the same time he thus gratified my desires as to scientific employment, he still advised me not to give up the prospects I had before me, telling me that Science was a hard mistress, and in a pecuniary point of view but poorly rewarding those who devoted themselves to her service. He smiled at my notion of the superior moral feelings of scientific men, and said he would leave me to the experience of a few years to set me right on that matter.

Finally, through his good efforts, I went to the Royal Institution early in March of 1813, as assistant in the laboratory; and in October of the same year went with him abroad, as his assistant in experiments and in writing. I returned with him in April, 1815, resumed my station in the Royal Institution, and have, as you know, ever since remained there.

I am, dear Sir, ever truly yours,

M. Faraday.

When Faraday accepted this position it commanded a salary of 25 shillings a week and the use of two small rooms in the upper story. The incumbent could hardly be said to have deserved more, for he had never enjoyed anything but the most elementary schooling, and had had no regular training in science. It is splendid evidence of his genius that within two or three years he was making discoveries in both chemistry and physics which rivalled in quality those of his master. As we all know, his later studies on the relations of electricity and magnetism stand at the foundation of modern electrical engineering.

Most of the terms now used in connection with the electrochemistry of solutions are due to Faraday.[1] In place of the word pole, he used that neutral term, *electrode*. He applied the term *electrolyte* to every substance that can be decomposed by the action of the current and the decomposing process he called *electrolysis*. The positive electrode he called the *anode* and the negative electrode the *cathode*. He called the components of salts *ions* and named them *anions* and *cations* according to whether they migrated to the anode or to the cathode during electrolysis. The electromagnetic unit, the *farad*, and the quan-

---

[1] It is true that in inventing these new terms, which Faraday published in 1834, he had received considerable assistance from the eminent scholar, Rev. William Whewell, D.D. (1794–1866), whose aid Faraday had solicited in 1833. The idea of the new nomenclature appears to be due to Faraday but the actual terms were suggested by Whewell.

tity of electricity corresponding to a unit charge on the gram-atom, the *Faraday*, are named after him. He did pioneer work in the liquefaction of gases, and among his other discoveries which interest chemists are that of magnetic optical rotation, the isolation of benzene and of the two sulfonic acids of naphthalene. It may be appropriate to add that to Faraday's friends his scientific attainments were surpassed by the peculiar charm of his personality. We shall have occasion to discuss some of his further contributions to chemistry later on. He succeeded Davy at the Royal Institution in 1825 and spent the remainder of his active life there. He died in 1867.

Faraday was interested in religion. During the eighteenth century several congregations were formed in different parts of England by Robert Sandeman, the son-in-law of a Presbyterian minister, John Glas. They were called Sandemanians or Glasites. Each church was governed by elders who were like the elders of the early Christian church. Faraday was brought up under the influence of this sect and married the daughter of one of the elders. In 1840, Faraday himself was elected an elder and preached on alternate Sundays during three and a half years.

Literature

The Works of Humphry Davy (in nine volumes) were published by his brother John Davy in 1834. The first volume is biographical. T. E. Thorpe has also published a life entitled *Humphry Davy, Poet and Philosopher*, London, 1896. Selections from Davy's work on chlorine have been reprinted by the Alembic Club, No. 10. The latter paper should also be read in connection with No. 13 of the same series, which gives an idea of the earlier views as to the nature of chlorine, as expressed by Scheele, Berthollet, Guyton de Morveau, Gay-Lussac, and Thénard. Davy's work leading to the discovery of the alkali metals may be found in *Alembic Club Reprint* No. 6.

Among the better books on Faraday may be mentioned the *Life and Letters* by Bence Jones, London, 1870, and *Faraday as a Discoverer* by John Tyndall, London, 1870.

Ostwald devotes a chapter each to Davy and Faraday in his *Grosse Männer*, Leipzig, 1909, and Thorpe's *Essays* contain a chapter on Faraday. A good account can also be found in Bugge's *Das Buch der grossen Chemiker*.

CHAPTER XI

BERZELIUS, THE ORGANIZER OF THE SCIENCE

Jöns Jakob Berzelius was born in Väfersunda, Sweden, August 20, 1779. His father, who was a teacher in Linköping, died in 1783, and the mother's second marriage, soon followed by her early death, left the young Berzelius to grow up in the home of relatives where his slender means made him a not altogether welcome guest. These experiences did much to embitter his early years, and matters were hardly improved at the *gymnasium* where he distinguished himself, indeed, by love of natural history but took little interest in the classics, and was unwilling to make any attempt to win the favor of those whose specialties he disliked. On his departure the authorities handed him a certificate stating that he "justified only doubtful hopes"—an amusing commentary on the perspicacity of teachers.

Berzelius next studied medicine at Upsala but found the sciences rather poorly represented there, and the same fatality which had pursued him at the *gymnasium* involved him in unfortunate misunderstandings with the professors. These had mostly to do with formalities but they prevented cordial relations. It may encourage those dissatisfied with academic standards to know that when Berzelius came to be examined in chemistry the professor in charge stated that he deserved to fail, but expressed willingness to overlook the candidate's shortcomings if he could give a better account of himself in physics —which he fortunately did.

Berzelius meantime went on with chemical investigations carried out partly in the laboratory and partly in his own rooms. In 1802, all examinations being over, he went to Stockholm and took up hospital work, devoting his spare hours to chemistry. The work done soon attracted the attention of men connected with the college of medicine, and Berzelius was gradually drawn into closer touch with that institution, first as "adjunct" and

JÖNS JAKOB BERZELIUS
1779–1848

finally as professor. As he grew famous, honors, medals, titles and emoluments were showered upon him in a profusion which must have made some amends for the hardships of his early life. He died August 7, 1848.

Work on the Combining Weights.—Among the earliest investigations of Berzelius were some upon electricity which we shall take up later, but about 1810 there began to appear from his pen a series of articles entitled: *An Attempt to Determine the Definite and Simple Proportions in which the Constituents of the Inorganic World are Combined with Each Other.* These articles continued till about 1818 and represented work begun as early as 1807. In one sense it was a topic with which Berzelius was actively concerned until his death. He had been much impressed with the ideas of Dalton and Richter, but he had seen more clearly, perhaps, than anyone else, that they could never become the basis of a system until they were supported by an experimental foundation unattainable by men so inferior in analytical skill. Berzelius therefore set himself no less a task than to determine with the utmost possible accuracy the combining weights of the elements; and, within a little more than ten years, he accomplished this for forty-three of them by the preparation, purification and analysis of no less than two thousand of their compounds with his own hands. This was done at a time when quantitative analysis as we now understand the term hardly existed, and Berzelius was obliged in the majority of cases laboriously to work out his methods as he went along. We have also to remember that in his time the reagents themselves had for the most part to be prepared or extensively purified, and that the laboratory facilities of Berzelius boasted little beyond those afforded by an ordinary kitchen. The results speak for themselves. Below stands a selected list in which some of the atomic

	Berzelius, 1826	International commission, 1931
Lead	207.12	207.22
Chlorine	35.41	35.457
Potassium	39.19	39.10
Sulfur	32.18	32.06
Silver	108.12	107.88
Nitrogen	14.05	14.008

weights published by Berzelius in 1826 are compared[1] with those of the international commission for 1931. When we have admitted that in the case of many of the less common elements the divergence was much larger, and that the surprising agreement was sometimes due to a fortunate balancing of errors not appreciated by Berzelius, the achievement still stands as a remarkable monument to his genius. Henceforward quantitative analysis was destined to stand essentially upon its modern footing and no theory unable to square with its standards could any longer receive consideration.

Literary Activity.—Nor was this by any means the only occupation of Berzelius during these years. In addition to his activity as teacher he published no less than thirty papers dealing with other chemical problems and he developed a complete system of chemical philosophy which, in logical unity and comprehensiveness of scope, surpassed anything hitherto known. This he communicated to the world partly through the pages of his famous *Jahresbericht* which he founded in 1810, and continued to edit until his death, and partly by the great textbook which he began in 1808 and which passed through five editions and was translated into several languages. The minute first-hand knowledge of his facts which rings through every line of these writings, the hitherto unequalled accuracy of his results, and his unquestioned integrity gave to Berzelius a position altogether unique, so that in 1820 he ranked as a kind of lawgiver whose mere opinions often counted more in the public mind than facts and figures carefully ascertained by others. Such a position of acknowledged superiority doubtless contributed to make him autocratic and intolerant in his later years, but for us the important consequence is that his views had the utmost influence in every department of the science. We must therefore consider them in detail.

Chemical Problems at the Beginning of the Nineteenth Century.—The moot points in chemical theory in the beginning of the nineteenth century we already know. They can be stated in

---

[1] Berzelius's standard of reference was $O = 100$. The results in this table are calculated to $O = 16$ and made comparable with our own by the use of modern formula-weights which sometimes differ from those of Berzelius for reasons which we shall appreciate more clearly later on.

questions as follows: How are chemical compounds to be formulated? Can atomic weights (as distinguished from combining weights) be determined? What is the essential constituent of acids? What is the source of the galvanic current, and what is the mechanism of its action in electrolysis? What is chemical affinity and is any quantitative measure thereof possible? On all of these subjects Berzelius had decided views supported by an immense amount of experimental data.

He did much to facilitate all chemical discussion and calculation by inventing our modern alphabetical chemical symbols which were entirely original with him, and by developing a system of chemical nomenclature which was essentially an adaptation of that of Lavoisier to the Germanic languages. Indeed, we shall best understand the spirit which animated the work of Berzelius if we consider him as an admirer and disciple of Lavoisier; he consciously made it his life-work to extend and complete the chemical system which the great Frenchman had left unfinished.

The Atomic Weights.—This manifested itself everywhere, even in the question of the atomic weights. Here Berzelius saw at once the hopelessness of Dalton's assumption that the best-known compound must have the simplest formula, and he looked about for other criteria. He was satisfied that he had found one in Gay-Lussac's law of combining gas volumes and he adopted as his principal standard the assumption that the atomic weights of *elementary* gases are proportional to the weights of equal volumes. This, however, at that time could not carry him far. Dalton had already pointed out that equal volumes of *compound* gases could not contain equal atoms, and while the discrepancy involved here might have been obviated by an intelligent application of Avogadro's hypothesis, Berzelius was by temperament opposed to such a notion, and declined to consider an explanation which involved a contradiction in terms so flagrant as fractions of atoms. He was therefore limited to the elementary gases and these were so few in number that they might have appeared as likely to represent the exception as the rule. For the majority of the elements some other auxiliary standard was necessary and Berzelius found this in the varying quantities of oxygen with which the various elements could combine. This was partly because oxygen combines so freely with almost all other elements, but quite as truly because of the exaggerated opinion of the importance of oxygen which he had inherited from Lavoisier (see page 100).   Berzelius once wrote, "Oxygen is the center about which all chemistry revolves," and similar expressions are common in his writings.   His work upon the combining weights and the analysis of salts had led him to formulate the rule that when an acid unites with a base the ratio of the oxygen in the acid to that in the base is a simple whole number.

The method by which Berzelius worked this out in a specific case may be of interest.   He prepared lead sulfate by oxidation of the sulfide with nitric acid, and showed qualitatively that no lead or sulfuric acid was left in excess in the supernatant liquid.   It followed that the ratio of lead to sulfur must be the same in the sulfate as in the sulfide.   Lead sulfate, however, was regarded as a binary compound of lead oxide and sulfuric acid (what we now term the anhydride).   Since now the amount of oxygen combined with a given amount of lead in the oxide is already known, the balance of it—or three times that quantity—must in the sulfate be combined with the sulfur, and the number of atoms of oxygen in sulfuric acid must be three or some multiple of three.   In the absence of any evidence requiring a larger number, Berzelius's assumption would be that it was exactly three, and we could now employ these data to determine the atomic weight of sulfur, for since the atomic weight of oxygen is fixed by its density at 16, the formula SO_3 for sulfuric acid fixes the atomic weight of sulfur at 32.   Turning now to the basic component in lead sulfate we might further argue that *if* the atomic weight of lead is that quantity which unites with 16 units of oxygen then the same is likely to hold true for metals like barium and calcium.   The validity of the fundamental assumption as well as that of the suggested analogy would, however, in this case have to be supported by other evidence of a similar kind.   It is easy to see that the reasoning of Berzelius is superior to that of Dalton, but it is also clear that he really makes use of the latter's principle of maximum simplicity, and that arbitrary assumptions have by no means been excluded.   When, in such a case, the sum total of assumptions leads to a system free from contradictions we can attach a high degree of probability to the results. The system of Berzelius never quite reached that stage, and he himself was so conscious of its imperfections that we find him modifying his figures repeatedly as long as he lived.

Law of Dulong and Petit.—In 1819 two papers appeared which threw fresh light upon the subject because they suggested new criteria. The first of these was by Dulong and Petit,[1] and called attention to the remarkable relationship which exists between the atomic weights and the specific heats. The authors had been determining the latter constant for a large number of substances, and were impressed with the fact that in the case of most of the solid elements, when the specific heats were multiplied by the atomic weights then current, the result was a constant. They also expressed the results in the form that "the atoms of all the elements have the same heat capacity," that is to say if a certain quantity of heat will warm 63 grams of copper one degree it will do the same for 56 grams of iron. Where the constant product above referred to was not obtained, it could be reached in most cases by multiplying or dividing the atomic weight employed by a simple factor. Dulong and Petit made bold to take this step, feeling that they had here a new standard resting upon a measurable physical constant, and free from the assumptions involved in the reasoning of Berzelius and Dalton.

We now know that the law is not sufficiently infallible to justify such disregard of all other considerations. Some of the determinations of Dulong and Petit were inaccurate, in other cases the specific heat varies widely with the temperature, involving an embarrassment in the selection of comparable conditions, and finally, for reasons which are even now not completely understood, the law seems unreliable in the case of the elements of lowest atomic weight. Berzelius's own attitude in the matter was cautious and conservative. He threw some doubt upon the accuracy of the determinations, but later was persuaded

[1] Pierre Louis Dulong (1785–1838) began as a physician in the poorer districts of Paris. He became an assistant to Berthollet, taught chemistry at the normal schools of Alfont, was made professor of physics at the École Polytechnique in 1820 and director in 1830. In 1815 he discovered nitrogen chloride and lost an eye in the investigation.

Alexis Thérèse Petit (1791–1820) was professor of physics at the École Polytechnique.

to divide by two the atomic weight of silver which he had previously adopted. He declined, however, to modify the atomic weight of carbon as the theory of Dulong and Petit seemed to demand, because that would have made the oxides CO_2 and CO_4 respectively, which chemical reasons did not permit him to accept. Time has amply justified his decision.

	Potassium	Difference between K and Rb (Zn and Mg, Cu and Zn)	Rubidium	Differences between Rb and Cs (Zn and Mg, Cu and Zn)	Caesium	Diffs btw. Zn and Mg, Cu and Zn
Magnesium	$K_2Mg(SO_4)_2.6H_2O$		$Rb_2Mg(SO_4)_2.6H_2O$		$Cs_2Mg(SO_4)_2.6H_2O$	
	No. of measurements / Limits / Mean		No. of measurements / Limits / Mean		No. of measurements / Limits / Mean	
$p:p$ $p:c$ β	20 / 71°6'—71°29' / 71°18' ; 44 / 77°50'—78°14' / 78°1' , 78°12'	27' 59' 1°11'	20 / 70°46'—70°57' / 70°51' ; 40 / 76°58'—77°8' / 77°2' , 74°1'	1°11' 1° 1°7'	20 / 69°22'—69°50' / 69°40' ; 34 / 75°50'—76°14' / 76°2' , 72°54'	
Zinc	$K_2Zn(SO_4)_2.6H_2O$		$Rb_2Zn(SO_4)_2.6H_2O$		$Cs_2Zn(SO_4)_2.6H_2O$	
	No. of measurements / Limits / Mean		No. of measurements / Limits / Mean		No. of measurements / Limits / Mean	
$p:p$ $p:c$ β	24 / 71°8'—71°26' / 71°14' ; 42 / 77°55'—78°9' / 78°1' , 75°12'	30' 55' 1°5'	20 / 70°41'—70°49' / 70°44' ; 40 / 77°0'—77°13' / 77°6' , 74°7'	1°1' 1° 1°8'	24 / 69°36'—69°58' / 69°43' ; 40 / 75°49'—76°25' / 76°6' , 72°59'	
Copper	$K_2Cu(SO_4)_2.6H_2O$		$Rb_2Cu(SO_4)_2.6H_2O$		$Cs_2Cu(SO_4)_2.6H_2O$	
	No. of measurements / Limits / Mean		No. of measurements / Limits / Mean		No. of measurements / Limits / Mean	
$p:p$ $p:c$ β	23 / 71°54'—72°3' / 71°58' ; 27 / 78°13'—78°27' / 78°20' , 75°32'	14' 41' 50'	18 / 71°37'—71°55' / 71°44' ; 36 / 77°35'—77°44' / 77°39' , 74°42'	44' 45' 52'	25 / 70°48'—71°14' / 71°0' ; 27 / 76°47'—76°59' / 76°54' , 73°50'	

A TYPICAL GROUP OF ISOMORPHIC SUBSTANCES

Reproduced from Freund's *The Study of Chemical Composition*, by the kind permission of the author and the Cambridge University Press.

Isomorphism.—The other paper referred to was by Eilhard Mitscherlich (1794–1863), soon after a student of Berzelius and later professor in Berlin, where he succeeded Klaproth. He made some valuable studies of vapor densities and the simpler compounds of benzene, then a rare substance. His principal work, however, was in those departments of chemistry most

EILHARDT MITSCHERLICH
1794–1863

allied to mineralogy and crystallography, of which the present work on isomorphism was a most auspicious beginning. Earlier investigators had sometimes noted marked similarity of crystalline form among different substances as well as the formation of certain mixed crystals. Mitscherlich, however, was at this time entirely ignorant of these observations, and in fact was just beginning his studies in crystallography. He also carried his observations much farther than others had done and referred back the now familiar phenomena of isomorphism to similarity of chemical composition. Working at first with the phosphates and arsenates he found that whatever metal was taken as a base there was always to be found the most perfect similarity in the properties of all the salts, not only in crystalline form but also in solubility and other properties, the similarity extending to the quantity of water of crystallization to be found in each. Examination of other series such as the alums and vitriols soon showed that this was no isolated case and Mitscherlich came to the conclusion that

The same number of atoms combined in the same manner produce the same crystalline form. This form is independent of the nature of the atoms and is fixed only by their number and mode of combination.

It will be seen that so far as the choice of atomic weight is concerned isomorphism does not offer an entirely independent criterion like that of the specific heats, but rather an aid in reasoning by analogy which may be employed as follows: If we formulate ordinary alum as $KAl(SO_4)_2.12H_2O$ and the atomic weights of potassium and aluminum are considered as known quantities, then the atomic weights of sodium and iron are the parts by weight of those elements which unite with sixty-four parts of sulfur in ferric sodium alum, $FeNa(SO_4)_2,12H_2O$.

Berzelius gave rather more weight to such considerations than to those suggested by Dulong and Petit and he was induced thereby to modify his views concerning the atomic weight of chromium and some other elements. His reasons are best stated in his own words because they throw light upon his whole method of reasoning with regard to atomic weights.[1]

[1] The quotation follows the translation of the passage by Ida Freund in her admirable book, *The Study of Chemical Composition*.

It is known that the oxide of chromium contains three atoms of oxygen. Chromic acid for the same number of chromium atoms contains twice as much oxygen, which would be six atoms; but in its neutral salts chromic acid neutralizes an amount of base containing one-third as much oxygen as it contains itself, a relation found to hold in the case of all acids with three atoms of oxygen (*e.g.*, sulfuric acid and sulfates). In order to harmonize the multiple relation between the amount of oxygen in the oxide and in the acid, it is most probable that the acid contains three atoms of oxygen to one atom of chromium, and the oxide three atoms of oxygen to two of chromium. Isomorphous with the oxide of chromium are those of manganese, iron and aluminium; these also we know to contain three atoms of oxygen, and consequently must represent them as containing two atoms of the radical. But if the ferric oxide consists of $2Fe + 3O$, the ferrous oxide is $Fe + O$, and the whole series of oxides isomorphous with it contains one atom of the radical and one atom of oxygen. * * * Unfortunately in these matters the certainty of our knowledge is as yet at so low a level that all we can do is to follow along the lines of greatest probability.

The Dualistic System.—It is in his views on chemical composition and the nature of acids that Berzelius reveals most strongly the influence of Lavoisier. It is estimated that in his *Traité Élémentaire* Lavoisier included approximately nine hundred substances, and of all this number there were only about thirty, aside from the elements, which could not be classified as acids, bases or salts. It is therefore entirely natural that Lavoisier should regard all chemical union as allied to salt formation. His views on the latter subject we understand already. Salts were binary addition products of acid and base, and these in their turn were binary addition products of metal and oxygen and of non-metal and oxygen respectively. Union occurred in pairs, and the system was distinctly dualistic.

Lavoisier regarded oxygen as the acid-forming element and yet made it just as necessary a component of bases. There is only an apparent contradiction here because the general tendency of oxygen was regarded as acidic though the other element might overcome this tendency; thus chromium with a certain amount of oxygen forms a base but with more oxygen an acid. Lavoisier too was prevented from carrying his generalizations to their logical conclusion by the fact that in his day many of the bases had not yet been proved to be oxides. Davy's discovery of the

alkali metals removed this difficulty and left Lavoisier's system
of chemical composition essentially complete, save for the
troublesome case of hydrochloric acid among the acids and
ammonia among the bases. We have already seen in the previous chapter the difficulty which Davy had encountered in convincing his contemporaries that chlorine did not contain oxygen.

Berzelius and the Chlorine Theory.—Berzelius was among
those who fought most stubbornly in the defense of the older
view. Even as late as 1815 he writes an article a hundred pages
long in which he uses every argument to show that the old theory
was still capable of explaining the facts, and urging all chemists
to retain it in the interest of the unity of the science. He closes
with the words:

I demand of every chemical principle that it agree with the sum
total of chemical theory and be capable of incorporation therewith.
Otherwise I must reject it until such time as incontestable evidence in
its favor makes it necessary to recast the entire system.

It is as necessary in science as in politics that there should be a
conservative party, and it is always well that someone should
speak in such terms as those just quoted, but the immense
authority of Berzelius and the increasing obstinacy which characterized him in his later years did much to retard the acceptance
of many new and helpful ideas. This intolerance of Berzelius
has become so associated with most that is written about him
that there is a real danger that those who know him only through
tradition or his polemical writings will not appreciate the genial,
tolerant and open-minded side of his character. As late as 1836
when the hydrogen theory of acids was again under discussion
from another point of view we find him writing to Heinrich Rose:

The experiments with anhydrous sulfuric acid and chlorides interest
me greatly. They appear to lead to the long-expected conclusion that
strong sulfuric acid is not SO_3 or even $SO_3 + H_2O$ but $SO_4 + H_2$, and
that the same theory holds good for the haloid salts as for those of the
oxygen acids.

and again two years later to Liebig on the same subject:

I shall be entirely satisfied to place the new view beside the old
as another means of explanation, and after all what are any of our
views but means of explanation?

It is but fair to say, however, that this apparent conversion to the hydrogen theory was only temporary and that he published nothing in its favor. So far as the earlier controversy was concerned, the work of Gay-Lussac upon the cyanides and iodides showed Berzelius that the old view was untenable, and by 1820 he gave up the contest and accepted the compromise suggested by Gay-Lussac and by Dulong according to which there could be two kinds of acids, the oxygen acids which formed salts directly by the addition of metallic oxides, and the halogen acids (or hydro-acids) which formed salts by substitution of that hydrogen by a metal. Berzelius was loath to draw this distinction between substances so similar in all other properties, but he could in this way save his dualistic system, oxygen salts being still binary compounds of acid and base, while haloid salts were binary compounds of metal and halogen.

Supposed Oxygen Content of Ammonia.—The case of ammonia deserves a word of comment. Though markedly basic it differed from all other bases in that it contained no oxygen. When therefore in 1808 Davy thought he had discovered evidence that it did contain this element, Berzelius grasped at the idea and supported it for many years. Even the discovery by Henry and the younger Berthollet that ammonia could be decomposed quantitatively into nitrogen and hydrogen did not suffice to drive the idea from his mind. He next assumed that nitrogen was itself an oxide, and the atomic weight of *nitricum*, its hypothetical radical, appeared for a long time in his tables of atomic weights. The arguments of Berzelius were ingenious but we need not enumerate them here as they have no historical significance. He had surrendered the point completely by 1822, and was doubtless assisted to the change of view by a suggestion of Ampère to the effect that when ammonia formed salts it first added water yielding ammonium oxide, which could then form addition products with acids in a manner entirely orthodox.

Despite these minor concessions the dualistic system still remained a consistent whole. Inorganic substances could still be classified as elements, binary compounds of elements (like chlorides, sulfides and oxides), and finally as salts, which were either binary compounds of the elements or of the oxides (acids and bases). Salts could further combine with acids to form still other binary compounds which we call acid salts, with bases to form basic salts, or with other salts to form double salts.

During the life of Lavoisier this dualism which seemed to run through all inorganic nature lacked any adequate theoretical explanation. There seemed to be no good reason why other forms of combination should not occur, and various ternary compounds were recognized and classified as such. With the beginning of the nineteenth century, however, a new force had come upon the scene, and nearly all chemists now regarded electricity as either identical with chemical affinity or closely connected with it.

Electrical Explanation of Chemical Action.—Soon after leaving the university Berzelius, in collaboration with his friend Hisinger, had carried on a series of experiments upon the electrolysis of salt solutions with as large a battery as their means permitted them to construct, and had observed the separation of salts into acid and base, which is now so familiar a phenomenon. These experiments made a great impression upon Berzelius and led him to set electricity as well as oxygen at the foundation of his chemical system. This was based on ideas not dissimilar to those of Davy, but with characteristic energy and passion for detail he developed them much further and won them a wider recognition. Davy had assumed that when the atoms of different elements approach each other they assume opposite electrical charges of greater or lesser intensity according to the nature of the substances concerned. Berzelius was even more mechanical in his conceptions, and assigned to every atom two poles like those of a magnet, upon one of which was concentrated positive and upon the other negative electricity. For the same atom, however, the quantity or intensity of the charge (Berzelius was not clear on this point) was by no means equal. Chlorine, for example, possessed an excess of negative, the alkalies of positive electricity. Oxygen was to Berzelius the "absolutely negative" element, and he placed this at one end of a series, in which potassium occupied the other extreme. Between stood the other elements, positive or negative according to their relative positions, hydrogen being at or near the neutral point. This was of course merely another form of the potential series, derived in this case from chemical considerations.

Electrical Explanation of Dualism.—The above was in beautiful harmony with the dualistic system already outlined and furnished a complete explanation for it. Sulfur was positive toward oxygen and therefore could unite with it to form sulfuric acid, which in its turn was by no means neutral, but rather, on account of its large oxygen content, decidedly negative. In the same way positive calcium united with the negative oxygen to form lime, in which the electrical character of the metal predominated, so that it was distinctly electropositive. Finally sulfuric acid and lime could themselves unite to form a salt, calcium sulfate CaO,SO_3, much more nearly neutral but not necessarily absolutely so, for a difference in charge had to be assumed for salts in order to account for the formation of double salts like alum.

One limitation the theory brought with it. Ternary compounds were no longer possible. Substances united with each other because they were positive or negative, hence union could take place only in pairs, and substances apparently ternary like potassium cyanide must be regarded as compounds of an element with a binary compound.

Berzelius sums the matter up in the following frequently quoted passage:

If these electrochemical views are correct, it follows that every chemical compound depends entirely and alone upon the two opposite forces of positive and negative electricity; and therefore every compound substance consists of two parts united by the action of their electrochemical character since no third force exists. Hence it follows that every compound substance, whatever the number of its components, can be divided into two parts of which one is positively and the other negatively electric; for example sulfate of soda is not composed of sulfur, sodium and oxygen, but of sulfuric acid and soda, and these in their turn, can be separated into positive and negative components. In the same way alum cannot be considered as a compound directly of its elements, but is to be looked upon as the product of the reaction between sulfate of alumina as the negative element and sulfate of potash as the positive element.

The formula here suggested for alum, $K_2O,SO_3 + Al_2O_3,3SO_3 + 24H_2O$, is interesting to the modern reader as an extreme case of dualistic formulation. It will be observed that in all these cases the theory tacitly involves the continued independent existence of the oxide within the salt. In lead sulfate, for example, one-fourth of the oxygen is still thought of as combined with the lead and the rest with the sulfur.

Berzelius's Explanation of Electrolysis.—It will be seen that the theory of chemical composition just outlined is admirably adapted to explain all the facts then known concerning electrolysis. The current, according to this theory, merely separates the salt into the positive and negative components of which it is composed and these appear primarily at the poles. The effect can, of course, be obscured in individual cases by secondary reactions. An acid according to Berzelius is not decomposed by the current. It simply increases the conductance of the water, which alone is decomposed into oxygen and hydrogen. A salt like potassium sulfate, on the other hand, decomposes into potassium oxide and sulfuric acid, both of which are hydrated by the water. The evolution of oxygen and hydrogen at the poles is, however, due solely to the simultaneous decomposition of the water. When a metallic salt like zinc sulfate is electrolyzed neither the acid nor the water is decomposed, but only the base, metallic zinc appearing at one pole and the oxygen at the other. Some contemporaries of Berzelius thought that zinc sulfate behaved primarily like potassium sulfate—the hydrogen formed by the decomposition of the water then reducing the zinc oxide originally formed at the negative pole. He himself, however, rejected this notion, because under ordinary conditions zinc slowly decomposes water with evolution of hydrogen. With reference to the origin of the current Berzelius like Davy at first supported the "chemical" theory, and like him went over later to the other side. A brief account of his reasons can best be given when we come to consider his attitude toward Faraday's law.

The foregoing may serve as a rather inadequate outline of the dualistic electrochemical system of Berzelius as it stood practically complete in the years which immediately followed 1820. It was almost universally accepted, for, in spite of doubtful points here and there, it furnished a consistent, reasonably satisfactory explanation of practically every known reaction in the inorganic field. Though it was before long to meet vigorous attacks under which it ultimately succumbed, yet it constituted the most important single factor in chemical theory for many years, and fragments of it remain incorporated in our phraseology to this day. Even today some of the older chemists still cling to the theory in balancing chemical equations of oxidation and reduction and most of us report analytical results in terms of the dualistic theory when analyzing minerals or inorganic salts. If Berzelius did not originate all its fundamental ideas, nevertheless it was he who practically single-handed gave it unity and vitality, and as we have seen he enjoyed a corresponding prestige.

Wöhler's Reminiscence.—We have a pleasant personal reminiscence of Berzelius and his surroundings at just this time when he was at the height of his fame, from the pen of Friedrich Wöhler. For some years it had been the habit of Berzelius to invite to his house by ones and twos certain young chemists of thorough training and great promise, and permit them to spend a year or more in his laboratory. This was, of course, a wonderful educational opportunity and of those who had the advantage of it few failed to achieve marked distinction in later years. Wöhler was in Stockholm during the winter of 1823–24 and he has given an account of his experiences in an article entitled *Jugenderinnerungen eines Chemikers.*[1] It should be quoted entire, but we have room for only the following fragments:

With beating heart I stood at Berzelius's door and rang the bell. A neatly dressed, stately man of fresh appearance opened. It was Berzelius himself. He welcomed me in a most friendly way, said that he had been expecting me for a long time, and talked about my journey, of course all in the German language, in which he was as proficient as in French and English. When he took me into his laboratory I was as if in a dream, doubting if it was a reality to see myself in these classic rooms, and so at the goal of my wishes.

On the following morning I began work. I obtained for my special use a platinum crucible, a balance with weights, a wash-bottle, and above all a blowpipe upon the use of which Berzelius laid great stress. At my own expense I had also to provide alcohol for the lamps and oil for the blast lamp; the ordinary reagents and utensils were had in common; but ferrocyanide of potassium, for example, was not to be had in Stockholm so I had to order it from Lübec. I was at that time the

[1] *Berichte der Deutschen Chemischen Gesellschaft*, vol. 8, p. 838 (1875).

FRIEDRICH WÖHLER
1800–1882

only one in the laboratory; before me Mitscherlich and H. and G. Rose had been there, and after me came Magnus.   The laboratory consisted of two ordinary rooms with the very simplest arrangements: there were neither furnaces nor hoods, neither water system nor gas.   In one of the rooms there were two ordinary long work-tables of pine wood, at one of them Berzelius had his place, at the other I had mine.   Against the walls stood some closets with the reagents, in the middle the mercury trough and the blast-lamp table, the latter under a flue leading into the chimney of the stove.   Beside these was the sink, consisting of a stone water-holder with a stop cock and a pot standing under it where each day the severe Anna the cook had to wash the dishes.   In the other room were the balances and some presses with instruments and utensils; nearby still another little workshop with a lathe.   In the kitchen close by, in which Anna prepared the food, stood a small heating furnace seldom used and the constantly heated sand-bath.

* * * * * * * *

In the investigation of cyanic acid which I took up again Berzelius interested himself very much.   To his great satisfaction he showed me what he had said in his *Jahresbericht* about my earlier experiments with this acid, and expressed the opinion that the existence of the same had contributed much to the greater probability of the chlorine theory. I was much surprised to hear him now speaking of chlorine instead of oxidized muriatic acid as, up to this time, he had been a firm defender of the old opinion.   Once when Anna was cleaning a dish, she remarked that it smelled strongly of oxidized muriatic acid.   Berzelius said, "Listen, Anna, you must not say oxidized muriatic acid any more.   Say chlorine, it is better."

* * * * * * * *

By repeated operations we had such quantities of potassium as had never before been produced.   For the analyses at that time, we prepared pure caustic potash by burning potassium on water.   Berzelius was as a rule cheerful, and during the work he used to relate all sorts of fun, and could laugh right heartily over a good story.   If he was in bad humor and had red eyes, one knew that he had an attack of his periodic nervous headache; he would then shut himself up for days together, ate nothing and saw no one.   A new observation always gave him great pleasure and with beaming eyes he would then call to me, "Well, Doctor, I have found something interesting."

Sometimes Berzelius kept me with him in the evening, when the talk was on his journeys in France and England, on Gay-Lussac, Thénard, Dulong, Wollaston, H. Davy and other distinguished men of science of that period, upon whose shoulders we of a later generation

now stand, all of whom he knew personally and whose individuality
he well understood how to characterize. Chief in his esteem and
veneration were Gay-Lussac and Humphry Davy; of the latter he
always spoke with the greatest admiration of his genius. He corresponded with them all and preserved their letters. With pleasure I
took advantage of his permission to read them, and later too he gave
me his interesting journals of his travels to read, which contained a
full account of his visits to Paris and London.

The article closes with an interesting glimpse of Davy who just
then happened to be enjoying a vacation trip in Sweden.

Literature

A German translation of Berzelius's *Selbstbiographische Aufzeichnungen*
appears as No. 7 in Kahlbaum's attractive series entitled *Monographien
aus der Geschichte der Chemie*, Leipzig, 1903. An account of Berzelius's
life down to 1821 by Söderbaum constitutes No. 3 of the same series.

The reminiscences by Wöhler are in the *Berichte der Deutschen Chemischen
Gesellschaft*, vol. 8, p. 838 (1875). Berzelius's early work on atomic weights
down to 1812 is in No. 35 of the *Klassiker*.

From this point on the thorough student of chemical history must depend
more and more upon the journals, of which the most important during the
first part of the nineteenth century were Berzelius's *Jahresbericht*, the
Annales de la Chimie et de la Physique which contain most of the work of
French chemists, and Liebig's *Annalen der Chemie und Pharmacie* containing
most of that published by Germans.

Since, between 1820 and 1860, the most important advances in chemistry
were made in the organic field, attention should be called to two excellent
histories of organic chemistry.

Geschichte der organischen Chemie von ältester Zeit bis zur Gegenwart by
Edv. Hjelt, Brunswick, 1916, 537 pages.

Geschichte der organischen Chemie by Carl Graebe, Berlin, 1920, Vol. I,
403 pages. This first volume covers the period from about 1770 to 1880.

Still more recent books are: Sir William Tilden's *Famous Chemists* (1921),
which sketches the lives of some of the most prominent chemists of the
past. B. Jaffe's *Crucibles*, New York, (1930), an extremely interesting,
popular account of typical careers from the different ages, written in the
imaginative style of the novelist. G. Bugge's *Das Buch der grossen Chemiker*
(1930), a very comprehensive book in two volumes, written with characteristic German thoroughness in essay form by twenty-seven scholarly chemists
of Germany, Russia, Sweden, Switzerland and Italy. At the end of the
book there is a bibliography of fifty-three pages telling where information
can be obtained concerning chemists of all times.

CHAPTER XII

THE BEGINNING OF ORGANIC CHEMISTRY

In spite of the remarkable work of Scheele, who perhaps made more important chemical discoveries than anyone else, knowledge of the carbon compounds at the beginning of the nineteenth century was less developed than that of the elements commonly occurring in minerals. Organic chemistry was divided into vegetable chemistry and animal chemistry, and in the textbooks of Thomson and of Berzelius we find descriptions of sugar, organic acids, gum, indigo, bitter principle, tannin, camphor, and india rubber, as well as of gelatin, albumin, fibrin, urea, blood, saliva, and urine, mostly from the standpoint of the physician and with little attention paid to their chemical relations. It was recognized that these substances contain carbon, hydrogen, and often oxygen, nitrogen, and sulfur, but comparatively little attention was paid to the isolation of pure chemical compounds from the products of plant and animal life. It was generally believed that a special *vital force* was necessary to produce these organic compounds. Wöhler in 1835 wrote to Berzelius that "organic chemistry appears to me like a primeval forest of the tropics, full of the most remarkable things." Today, about a hundred years later, we find organic chemistry the most systematically developed branch of chemistry.

To be sure, a number of carbon compounds had been subjected to careful study. Alcohol is described in a manuscript of the twelfth century, and ether is described in a work of Valerius Cordus who died in 1544. Boyle, in 1661, described an "adiaphorus spirit" obtained by the dry distillation of boxwood, which undoubtedly was a mixture of methyl alcohol and acetone. In 1608, benzoic acid was described by Blaise de Vigenère (1522–1596), and Scheele described the preparation of many organic acids, glycerol, hydrocyanic acid, and a number of esters. He "saponified" esters by boiling them with caustic alkali.

Lavoisier regarded organic substances as formed along the same lines as mineral substances and when oxygen was present imagined this united to a *radical,* a name introduced in the modern sense by Guyton de Morveau in 1787. This radical contained merely carbon and hydrogen in the case of the simpler compounds. Sugar was the lower, and oxalic acid the higher, oxide of a hydrocarbon radical. In 1817, Berzelius extended his dualistic theory to organic compounds and said, "All organic substances are oxides of compound radicals. The radicals of vegetable substances consist usually of carbon and hydrogen and those of animal substances contain carbon, hydrogen and nitrogen."

The methods of analyzing organic compounds had been well developed as a result of the work of Lavoisier, Stahl, Gay-Lussac, Thénard, and Berzelius. The alkaloid bases were studied by Sertürner (morphine in 1805) and strychnine, brucine, quinine, and cinchonine were isolated by Pelletier and Caventou (1820).

Dalton, in 1803, gave the formulas of some simple organic compounds, which, when changed to our modern notation, gave to ethylene the formula CH; ether was C_2O, alcohol was CH_2O, and sugar was CHO_2. Berzelius established formulas for citric acid, tartaric acid, oxalic acid, succinic acid, and starch. His "acids" were, as a rule, what we now call *anhydrides,* just as CO_2 is often called *carbonic acid.* Berzelius's formulas were remarkably good, although the values for hydrogen were often a little high. Berzelius's analyses showed that the laws of chemical combination applied to organic, as well as to inorganic, compounds. The theory that a mysterious *vital force* was necessary received a death blow when Wöhler in 1828 synthesized urea by heating together an alkali cyanate and an ammonium salt. This was not, however, the first synthesis of an organic compound, for Scheele had synthesized oxalic acid in the latter part of the eighteenth century. Important work in organic chemistry was accomplished by the French chemist Chevreul.

Michel Eugène Chevreul was born at Angers in 1786 and died in Paris in 1889, probably living longer than any scientist of the Christian era. In 1804 he entered the laboratory of Vauquelin as assistant and was also assistant in the natural history museum of the Jardin des Plantes. In 1813 he was made professor at the Lycée Charlemagne and later became director of the Gobelins Tapestry Works where he carried out researches on color contrasts (1839). In 1830 he succeeded Vauquelin as professor at the museum and in 1863 became its director. He resigned the latter office in 1863, retaining the professorship. His one-hundredth birthday was made the occasion of a great celebration. His best known work, upon which his fame rests to a great measure. was published in 1823, *Recherche chimique sur les corps gras d'origine animale.* Up to that time chemists regarded soaps as a compound of fat and alkali, although Scheele had studied glycerol in 1783, and Geoffroy had noticed that the fatty acids liberated on treating a soap with acid were different from the original fats. Chevreul prepared stearin and olein and isolated two acids which he called stearic and oleic acids. In his paper is to be found the first, accurate, scientific theory of the saponification process and his explanation of the chemistry of fats and oils was remarkably clear. As a result of these studies, Chevreul placed stearin candles on the market, replacing the objectionable tallow dips.

Before considering the fate of Berzelius's dualistic system after the attempt was made to apply its principles to organic chemistry, it will be necessary to introduce three younger chemists destined to take an active part in dealing with the problems which now pressed for solution. These were Wöhler, Liebig, and Dumas.

Wöhler.—Friedrich Wöhler was born in Eschersheim near Frankfurt in 1800. He studied medicine at Marburg and Heidelberg where he came under the influence of Leopold Gmelin (1788–1853) who aroused his interest in chemistry and sent him with warm recommendations to Berzelius. Gmelin told him it would be a waste of time to listen to lectures, and he probably never heard a lecture on chemistry. Of his life at Stockholm we have had some account in the last chapter. As a result of his experiences in Sweden, he became a skillful analyst. At a later period he translated Berzelius's textbook into German. He returned to Germany in 1824 as teacher in the *Gewerbeschule* at Berlin where he remained until 1831. In that year he became professor in a similar institution recently founded at Cassel. In 1836 he accepted the professorship of chemistry at Göttingen where he remained till his death in 1882.

Wöhler's scientific work covered a wide field, and we shall have frequent occasion to refer to it. Among those investigations which have less historical significance may be mentioned his discovery of aluminum in 1827 and his work upon boron, silicon, and titanium. In the organic field he added much to our knowledge of the cyanates and other substances of this class, and he practically laid the foundation for all subsequent work in the study of uric acid. He was highly distinguished as a teacher and drew to Göttingen many students from other countries, especially from America. His method of preparing phosphorus is practically the same as that used today. The variety of Wöhler's work is astonishing; he worked with nearly every known element. His *Lehrbuch der Chemie* in 1875 had been published in fifteen editions.

Liebig.—Justus Liebig was born in Darmstadt in 1803. His father did a small business in oils, colors, and the more common chemicals, many of which he prepared himself. In such a laboratory and the workshops of artisans in the vicinity, Liebig first acquired his interest in chemical phenomena and what he afterward referred to as his "visual memory." While borrowing chemical books for his father, he also obtained access to the court library and devoured all the books bearing on chemistry which he could find there, taking them, as he afterward related, in the order they happened to stand upon the shelves. At the age of sixteen Liebig was apprenticed to an apothecary, and while he soon mastered the chemical side of the business he suffered a misfortune like that which Davy underwent in a similar position. As a boy he had learned from watching the traveling showmen how to prepare silver fulminate, a substance which long had a peculiar fascination for him. Experimenting with it in his new quarters he brought on an explosion which is said to have removed a portion of the roof, and is known to have removed Liebig from the business. He next besought his father to send him to the university. Means were found for this and accordingly in 1820 he matriculated at Bonn, but a year later followed his teacher Kastner (whom after all he did not find very satisfactory) to Erlangen. Here he joined one of the student societies which came under the ban of the government on account of its political tendencies, and in consequence he found it prudent to abandon

JUSTUS LIEBIG
1803–1873

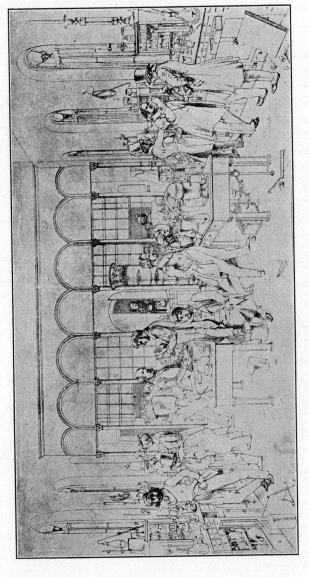

INTERIOR OF LIEBIG'S LABORATORY AT GIESSEN

From the Drawing by Trautschold, 1842

4–Keller; 5–Dr. Will; 6–Strecker; 7–Aubel (famulus); 9–Warrentrapp; 10–Scherer; 13–A. W. Hofmann

the university. By this time also he was convinced that he could not get such instruction in chemistry as he wanted in Germany, and he applied for a traveling scholarship from the Hessian government in order to continue his studies in Paris. After some difficulties this was granted in 1822, largely through Kastner's help. In Paris his abilities, combined with some good fortune, brought Liebig into pleasant relations with Alexander von Humboldt who then spent most of his time in Paris and especially devoted himself to promoting the interests of young men of great promise. By Humboldt he was introduced to Gay-Lussac who admitted him to his laboratory, where he carried out an investigation upon fulminic acid which still commands interest. Meantime the University of Erlangen had conferred the doctor's degree upon Liebig and in 1824 he returned to Germany as professor in the small university of Giessen. The death of the only other professor in the department, Wilhelm Ludwig Zimmermann (1780–1825), soon left him in full charge, but the salary was small and all chemical facilities of the worst.

The Laboratory at Giessen.—Finally a deserted barracks was secured and in this was organized a laboratory for general instruction in chemistry. A course of study was adopted which has in a measure served as a model for all laboratories of instruction ever since. The student was thoroughly drilled in qualitative and quantitative analysis, prepared some organic compounds, and then carried out an investigation suggested by the professor in charge. Despite its limitations, the laboratory soon became famous on account of the brilliant researches which proceeded from it and the inspiration of Liebig's teaching, so that students flocked to it from all over the world. Liebig's own work covered an astonishing range of topics and was at first devoted almost entirely to pure organic chemistry, though later his interest turned with especial favor to agricultural, physiological, and food problems. Hence his association with the famous "beef extract" by which he is still probably best known to the non-chemical public. Liebig's health was much affected by the strenuous efforts of his early career, and laboratory instruction became such a burden to him that in 1852, when called to the professorship at Munich, he accepted only on the condition that he should be entirely relieved of work of this character—a peculiar attitude for the man who had introduced laboratory instruction into Germany. Liebig died at Munich in 1873.

Liebig's laboratory at Giessen was by no means the first in which instruction was given to beginners in chemistry. As early as 1748, Lomonosov established a similar laboratory at St. Petersburg. Thomas Thomson had a small teaching laboratory in Glasgow in 1817, and Amos Eaton started a laboratory for beginners at Troy, New York, in the same year that Liebig started his laboratory (1825). F. C. Accum (1769–1839) also opened a laboratory at London about 1800 for teaching and research. Several well-known Americans studied there.

Organic Analysis.—One of his earlier chemical investigations had to do with perfecting the methods of organic analysis. We have already seen that Lavoisier had made important beginnings along this line, and Berzelius and Gay-Lussac had also added improvements, but Liebig gave to the organic combustion practically its present form and is said to have boasted with characteristic hyperbole that he had so simplified the process that any intelligent monkey should now be able to conduct it successfully. Most students, however, are of the opinion that, if he spoke truly, there is something wrong with the Darwinian theory. The personality of Liebig is an extremely interesting one. He represents what the Germans call a *Feuergeist*, eager, enthusiastic, combative, willing to sacrifice himself (and everyone else) in the pursuit of truth, and inspiring all who surrounded him with the same zeal. He demanded the uttermost of his students and assistants (something for which they thanked him in later years), and he had little patience with anyone who would not stand up for his opinions with an energy akin to his own. It is related that having listened to the praise of someone whom he disliked, he finally interjected: "He may be a good man for all I know, but he gives me only a cotton-wool resistance."

Friendship of Liebig and Wöhler.—Such a temperament makes all the more interesting Liebig's remarkable friendship for Wöhler whose nature was the antithesis of all this. Their acquaintance began with a controversy. About 1823 Liebig, who had just analyzed silver fulminate, found that it had the same composition that Wöhler had assigned to the cyanate. That two different substances should have the same composition was then something unheard of, and Liebig, with characteristic self-confidence, declared Wöhler's analyses incorrect. A personal interview not long after led to the repetition of the analyses and Wöhler's vindication, for Liebig seldom allowed his prejudices to blind him to an experimental fact, and here a discovery of the first magnitude was involved, for this was the first case of *isomerism*. The word, however, was not used till 1830 when Berzelius applied it to the relation between tartaric and racemic acids, a case of finer isomerism than he himself realized. Soon after clearing up this point, Liebig and Wöhler undertook in collaboration some important investigations in organic chemistry and this gradually brought about the warmest personal attachment. They exchanged frequent letters as long as they lived, and it is fortunate that these have been preserved and published. They are interesting on the scientific side because they show us in an entirely informal way how certain problems came to be studied and the manner in which they were attacked. On the human side also they illuminate for us two interesting personalities, both men so thorough, so conscientious, unselfishly devoted to the cause of science and to the truth, but in all else so different—Liebig running over with enthusiasm, irritable, keen for conflict, finding no language quite strong enough to express his feelings, while Wöhler is all gentleness and peace, cautiously avoiding the mildest overstatement, yet gifted with keen insight and full of sly humor which he artfully employs to moderate the turbulence of his friend.

From 1831 Liebig was the most influential editor of the *Annalen der Chemie und Pharmacie*, which acquired its great prestige under his leadership, and he considered it one of the chief duties of the editorial office to defend the truth by pointing out to all poor workers and slovenly thinkers the error of their ways. This course earned him as much gratitude as a similar attitude toward his contemporaries did for Socrates. He made hosts of enemies and became involved in bitter controversies. These too often led him to passionate outbursts which all Wöhler's gentle counsel was unable to restrain, even when expressed as beautifully as in the following passage:

To make war upon Marchand (or anyone else for that matter) is of no use. You merely consume yourself, get angry, and ruin your liver and your nerves—finally with Morrison's Pills. Imagine yourself in the year 1900, when we shall both have been decomposed again into carbonic acid, water and ammonia, and the lime of our bones belongs perhaps to the very dog who then dishonors our grave. Who then will care whether we lived at peace or in strife? Who then will know anything about your scientific controversies—of your sacrifices of health and peace for science? No one: but your good ideas, the new facts you have discovered, these, purified from all that is unessential, will be known and recognized in the remotest time. But how do I come to counsel the lion to eat sugar!

It was indeed a hopeless task, as we may see from Liebig's reply to a similar appeal to spare Mitscherlich.

Poggendorff is a fool, *mon cher*, and even you are half a one with all your representations, which I nevertheless take in good part because I know they are well meant. ———— now knows what he had need to be told—and trembles. That is enough. All the bile which had been long concentrating in me on his account I have now poured out upon him, and I feel relieved to know that the miserable half-way relationship has become clear upon enmity. No one is more willing than I to acknowledge a goat when I happen to have shot one, but on the other hand I am bound to defend my convictions to the very death. That and no more have I done.

Dumas.—Jean Baptiste André Dumas was born in Alais in 1800. He attended a school where emphasis was placed on the study of the classics, and he showed marked ability. He became interested in natural science but was advised that he needed a knowledge of mathematics, rather than Greek or Latin. This knowledge Dumas attempted to obtain by studying books in the library. He had a desire to go to sea in order to observe the world, but his more practical father preferred to apprentice him to an apothecary of Alais in 1815. A year later he went to another apothecary in Geneva. Here he had the benefit of associating with the scientific men of the city, including Pictet, de la Rive, de Candolle, and de Saussure. He early interested himself in physiological problems and even at this time did some work upon iodine as a cure for goiter, the physiological effects of digitalis, the analysis of body fluids, and the part played by the red corpuscles of the blood. These biochemical studies called forth highly favorable comment from Berzelius. It also attracted the attention of Alexander von Humboldt who, having occasion to pass through Geneva, took pains to look up Dumas.

JEAN BAPTISTE ANDRÉ DUMAS
1800–1884

and, being impressed with his talents, urged him to come to Paris, assuring him that he would find a better scientific atmosphere. Dumas took his advice in 1823 and so began his career in the metropolis at the same time as Liebig and under very similar auspices. Dumas's success in Paris was immediate and complete, and we soon find him installed as a teacher at the Athenaeum and later at the Sorbonne, as well as giving instruction in other institutions. Dumas was a superior experimenter and clear thinker with an unusual gift of exposition and an imagination which led him to bold and original generalizations. These qualities not infrequently made him a thorn in the side of men like Liebig and Berzelius, who doubtless excelled him in thoroughness but were not quite his equals in brilliancy. As a result he almost always emerged without serious harm from the not infrequent controversies in which they tried to overwhelm him by force of accumulated facts. His *Traité de chimie* was published in eight volumes in 1828–1848 and was translated into German.

We now associate Dumas's name with our usual method for the determination of nitrogen in organic compounds, with a method for ascertaining vapor densities, and with an experimental determination of the oxygen-hydrogen ratio which was a model of accuracy for its time. He also carried on numerous studies in organic chemistry especially such as had to do with the phenomena of substitution and to these we shall have occasion to refer later on. After 1848 Dumas's teaching and experimental work was much interfered with by his devotion to questions of public service such as education, public health, and the like. At one time he was a member of the cabinet, and he served on numerous commissions. He died at Cannes in 1884.

Organic Chemistry in 1825.—It would be difficult to describe the state of organic chemistry in 1825 from any entirely consistent point of view. Certainly no such point of view then existed. Many important facts were known, but all generalizations were extremely vague and unsatisfactory. Lavoisier, indeed, had extended his theory of acids to those of the organic field. He considered these acids to be oxides of *compound* radicals as distinguished from the simple radicals (elements) of the inorganic world. No generalizations were made concerning these radicals though it was assumed that they contained carbon and hydrogen. Other elements, however, were by no means excluded, and when Gay-Lussac studied the cyanogen compounds in 1815, he applied the term to the CN group. Ammonium, too, had been known as a *radical* since Davy's time. By 1825, also, the general chemical character of alcohols, ethers, and esters (or compound ethers as they were then called) was fairly well understood, but with all compounds received formulas which now seem confusing on account of certain theoretical considerations to which we must next devote our attention.

According to the dualistic system, the formula of an "anhydrous acid" was best fixed by deducting from the formula of a salt that of the base; thus in calcium sulphate, CaO,SO_3, the acid is SO_3. It followed that in calcium acetate, $C_4H_6O_4Ca$, the acid was to be considered as that which combined with the lime, *viz.*, $C_4H_6O_3$. The fact that glacial acetic acid contains a molecule more water than this was disregarded, and it became the habit when an acid was analyzed to throw away enough oxygen and hydrogen from the formula to account for whatever water was "lost" in salt formation. If this water could be easily expelled from the free acid by heat, it was called water of crystallization, if not, the name applied was "water of composition," or some other term of as little significance. The vapor density was allowed to have no influence in the determination of the formula because, since the rejection of Avogadro's ideas by Dalton and Berzelius, most chemists had adopted an attitude of reserve as to the significance of this property. If we accept the above formula for acetic acid, then ethyl alcohol (from which it is formed on oxidation) naturally becomes $C_4H_{12}O_2$, and ether, which can be formed by dehydrating alcohol, appears as $C_4H_{10}O$. Similarly marsh gas was usually written C_2H_8, and ethylene C_2H_4. The foregoing still fails to give a complete idea of the existing confusion, for many chemists whose theories followed those of Wollaston (page 128) were using the equivalents $C = 6$ and $O = 8$. Still others, more eclectic in taste, preferred $C = 6$ and $O = 16$ and wrote their organic formulas on this basis. We may concede at the outset that in 1825 it would have been utterly impracticable to determine the constitution of an organic compound in the sense in which we now employ that expression.

The false view of the nature of acids, however, which has just been described, and which was imposed upon organic chemistry from without, solely in the interest of a consistent system, blinded chemists to obvious and simple relationships and prevented them from doing even what they might toward a natural systematization of the facts. We shall see that this unfortunate tendency was destined to do still further harm in the future, and there is no more instructive example than this of what a pernicious theory can sometimes do toward obstructing the healthy progress of science.

Original Attitude of Berzelius.—Although the ideas outlined above were essentially dualistic, Berzelius did not at first make any serious attempt to emphasize this, or to apply his system at all generally in the organic field. A wise caution led him to point out that the organic compounds were all products of the animal or plant organism. He therefore ascribed their existence, as well as their original formation, to the *vital force* and freed them for the present from the tyranny of his electrochemical rules. In 1828, however, Wöhler made a discovery which cut off hope that the issue could much longer be avoided in this way. He treated potassium cyanate with ammonium sulfate in the hope of obtaining ammonium cyanate, but the solution on evaporation yielded instead urea! The cyanates were at that time classed as inorganic compounds, and not long after they were prepared from the elements, so that the complete synthesis of one well-known organic product of the animal organism was an accomplished fact. Other syntheses followed, and it soon became evident that the assumption of a "vital force" was an untenable hypothesis. Organic compounds, like inorganic, must owe their existence to chemical affinity, but concerning the nature of chemical affinity Berzelius was already committed. It was a manifestation of "the two opposing forces of positive and negative electricity* * *since there is no third force" (see page 169). To apply such a theory to organic compounds, it was necessary to think of these as composed like salts of a positive and a negative component, and since in the majority of cases organic compounds are not electrolytes, the nature and composition of the components could only be ascertained by bold assumptions based on other facts of chemical experience.

The Etherin Theory.—Berzelius was as yet by no means ready to indulge in such speculations when in 1828, the same year as Wöhler's discovery, Dumas made the suggestion that a considerably better insight into the chemistry of many substances associated with ordinary alcohol might be attained if they were all considered as addition products of ethylene. We shall employ modern atomic weights in illustrating his views, for Dumas was now using the atomic weights C = 6 and O = 16, hence his formulas appear needlessly confusing to the modern eye.

Dumas pointed out that the substances we now term ethyl halides might be advantageously formulated as addition products of ethylene and halogen acids; alcohol, of ethylene and water; while ether was a compound of ethylene with less water; ethyl acetate, of ethylene, water, and acetic acid; and ethyl sulfuric acid was an addition product of ethylene, sulfuric acid, and water, as indicated in the following table:

	Modern formula	Dumas's formula
Ethyl chloride	C_2H_5Cl	$C_2H_4 + HCl$
Alcohol	C_2H_5OH	$C_2H_4 + H_2O$
Ether	$(C_2H_5)_2O$	$2C_2H_4 + H_2O$
Ethyl acetate	$CH_3COOC_2H_5$	$2C_2H_4 + C_4H_6O_3 + H_2O$
Ethyl sulfuric acid	$C_2H_5SO_4H$	$C_2H_4 + SO_3 + H_2O$

To us, these formulas appear somewhat unnatural, but it was possible to support them by a good deal of experimental evidence. They explained fairly well the formation of ethylene and ether by the action of dehydrating agents upon alcohol; the formation of ethyl acetate by the action of the acid upon alcohol, and of ethyl sulfuric acid by the action of sulfuric acid upon alcohol or upon ethylene.

The theory had another advantage which appealed strongly to Dumas. It represented ethylene as analogous to ammonia. We have already seen how the marked difference between the latter substance and other bases had induced Davy to seek for oxygen in its composition (page 146) and had led Berzelius to doubt even the elementary nature of nitrogen (page 167). According to Dumas, however, ammonia now found its natural place among the organic radicals. Ammonium chloride, $NH_3 + HCl$, was comparable with ethyl chloride, ammonium acetate, $2NH_3 + C_4H_6O_3 + H_2O$, with ethyl acetate and so on. Dumas became so enamoured with this feature of his theory that he declared ethylene a true base which *would* turn litmus blue *if* it were only soluble in water!

Benzoyl.—Berzelius received the new ideas with cautious reserve. They were essentially dualistic in spirit, but they failed to emphasize that importance of oxygen which was the vital point in his system. He commented, therefore, to the effect that Dumas had found an interesting and suggestive way of symbolizing the relationship of the compounds mentioned, but he expressed no faith that the latter were really so constituted. The theory was, however, soon to receive support from another quarter. In 1832 Liebig and Wöhler published their justly famous paper upon the oil of bitter almonds. As we know, this material consists essentially of benzaldehyde, the first substance of this important class to receive thorough study. Liebig and Wöhler observed its oxidation to benzoic acid, its transformation to benzoin; and by the action of chlorine they obtained benzoyl chloride, and from this, by double decomposition, the bromide, iodide, and cyanide, as well as benzamide and ethyl benzoate. The theoretical results of the investigation may be summed up in the statement that in all these compounds they found evidence for the presence of a common radical, $C_{14}H_{10}O_2$, which they named *benzoyl*. It was, as we see, our modern benzoyl whose formula, however, had been doubled from theoretical considerations like those already discussed. To Liebig and Wöhler benzaldehyde was an addition product of this radical with hydrogen, $C_{14}H_{10}O_2 + H_2$; benzoic acid with oxygen, $C_{14}H_{10}O_2 + O$; benzoyl chloride with chlorine, $C_{14}H_{10}O_2 + Cl_2$, and so on. The close relationship of all the compounds with each other was indisputable, and Berzelius was so carried away by the brilliant achievement that he wrote to Liebig and Wöhler a most enthusiastic letter in which he suggested the use of the name *Orthroin* for the new radical, to show that its discovery meant the dawn of a new day for the science, and at the same time he confessed his own belief that ethylene was the true radical in the alcohol group, and suggested that it henceforth be called *Etherin*. For this reason Dumas's original suggestion is known as the *etherin theory* to this day.

Berzelius and the Ethyl Theory.—The enthusiasm of Berzelius was short-lived. The etherin theory did not bring out the importance of oxygen in the way that his system demanded. Lavoisier had defined a compound radical as a group of elements which behaves like a single one, and unites with oxygen to form an acid. To Lavoisier these expressions meant essentially the same thing, for to him the chief function of any element was to unite with oxygen. Of late years, however, that part of the definition was being lost sight of. In cyanogen, in ammonium, and now in etherin, what was being emphasized was the permanence of the group, not its union with oxygen. As early as 1833, Berzelius resolved to maintain this latter point at all costs. A radical was to him that which unites with oxygen. It therefore could not contain oxygen. This decided him to break with the theory of etherin and benzoyl and set up other radicals which would fit better into his system. He sought an occasion for this in a question of little intrinsic importance. The etherin theory formulated the barium salt of isethionic acid as $2C_2H_4 + 2SO_3 + BaO + H_2O$, and that of ethyl sulfuric acid as $2C_2H_4 + 2SO_3 + BaO + H_2O$. Inasmuch, however, as one salt did not go over into the other by boiling with water it could not, he explained, contain water ready formed. He therefore assumed a new radical *ethyl*, C_4H_{10}. The oxide of ethyl was ether, $C_4H_{10}O$, and ether might be considered as uniting with anhydrous acids to form esters just as metallic oxides united with them to form salts. Ethyl acetate was a binary addition product of ether and acetic acid, $C_4H_{10}O + C_4H_6O_3$, entirely analogous to calcium acetate, $CaO + C_4H_6O_3$. Benzoyl, also, he discarded as a radical. He now regarded it as the oxide of a true radical, $C_{14}H_{10}$, of which benzoic acid is a still higher oxide. Ammonia also found a place in the system, for in accordance with the line of argument developed on page 116 its analogy with other bases can be preserved by assuming that in salt formation ammonia takes up the superfluous water of the acid to form ammonium oxide, which then adds directly to the acid. On this basis ammonium sulfate is to be written $N_2H_8O + SO_3$, ammonium nitrate, $N_2H_8O + N_2O_5$, and ammonium acetate, $N_2H_8O + C_4H_6O_3$.

The fundamental idea will perhaps appear more plainly if some of the characteristic formulas are tabulated:

Ethyl, C_4H_{10}	Calcium acetate, $CaO,C_4H_6O_3$
Ether, $C_4H_{10}O$	Ethyl acetate, $C_4H_{10}O,C_4H_6O_3$
Alcohol, $C_4H_{10}O,H_2O$	Ammonium oxide,[1] $(NH_4)_2O$
Acetic acid,[1] $C_4H_6O_3$	Ammonium sulfate, N_2H_8O,SO_3
Glacial acetic acid, $C_4H_6O_3,H_2O$	Ammonium acetate, $N_2H_8O,C_4H_6O_3$

Liebig adopted these views, pointing out that alcohol could be considered as a compound of ether and water, $C_4H_{10}O + H_2O$. There resulted a long controversy between Liebig and Dumas into the details of which we have no occasion to enter. Dumas, however, acknowledged his conversion in 1837, and the two chemists agreed to collaborate henceforward in their studies in organic chemistry.

This "era of good feeling" proved to be only the moment of calm before the storm, but the situation has interest because it represents the last great triumph of Berzelius. For the moment, a dualistic system essentially electrical, based upon the combination of positive and negative elements or radicals with oxygen, held practically undisputed sway in both organic and inorganic chemistry. Such a condition, however, could not last.

Liebig's Acetyl Theory.—By 1839 Liebig had again begun to modify his views. Some time before, Regnault had treated ethylene chloride with alkali and obtained chloroethylene which he formulated, $C_4H_6Cl_2$. This contains too little hydrogen to be an etherin compound, and it naturally suggested the adoption of C_4H_6 as a radical. Liebig accepted it as such and named it *acetyl* because acetic acid, $C_4H_6O_3$, could be considered as its oxide. By its use, also, acetic acid and ordinary alcohol could be formulated from a common point of view, for etherin itself could now be regarded as a compound of acetyl with hydrogen, while ethyl was a compound either of etherin with hydrogen or of acetyl with more hydrogen. Liebig pointed out with great satisfaction that this latest of his theories was one upon which the adherents of both etherin and ethyl could now compromise in

[1] Hypothetical.

harmony. He seems hardly to have realized that to attain this formal harmony he had sacrificed almost all the principles involved in the idea of radicals.

Review.—The theoretical conceptions which have just been outlined are commonly grouped together under the name of the first radical theory. This had begun with etherin and one of its most fundamental ideas was the reality of the radicals. They were supposed to preexist in the compound and in a measure determine its chemical properties by their own independent behavior. This made it at first a fundamental tenet of the creed that the radicals should be capable of existence in the free state. This was true of ethylene and the existence of free cyanogen and free cacodyl was considered important evidence that these complexes were true radicals. When etherin was exchanged for ethyl it was for the sake of consistency, to make the theories of organic and inorganic combination similar in form but, as Dumas pointed out, it involved the sacrifice of a real compound for a hypothetical group. Finally, when ethyl gave place to acetyl, it was merely in the interest of harmony and convenience. The radical had now become something artificial, and the word was beginning to acquire its modern meaning, *viz.*, a number of elements grouped together for convenience in tracing genetic relationships. As much as this would probably not have been admitted by its adherents at this time, but the theory had nevertheless purchased flexibility at the cost of significance, and no one except Berzelius any longer preserved enough faith in the reality of its fundamental principles to defend it efficiently from the vigorous attack which was about to be launched against it by Dumas.

Before discussing the reaction that eventually set in against the views of Berzelius as related to organic chemistry, the lives of three other chemists of the period deserve mention.

Samuel Guthrie, Jr. (1782–1848), of New York discovered chloroform independently of Soubeiran, Liebig, and Dumas. Souberein and Liebig both prepared chloroform in 1831, and Dumas in 1834 established its true formula. Guthrie described his method of preparing it in January, 1832, without knowledge of the work of either Soubeiran or Liebig. Guthrie called the compound *chloric ether*, a name which is not at all appropriate and, moreover, had been used by Thomson in 1820 to describe the "oil of the Dutch chemists" ($C_2H_4Cl_2$). He also called the solution of chloroform in alcohol

CHRISTIAN FRIEDRICH SCHÖNBEIN
1799–1868

sweet whiskey. Guthrie had studied at the University of Pennsylvania and was a surgeon in the war of 1812.

In 1831, the second volume of Silliman's *Elements of Chemistry* appeared and in it the physiological relations of the Dutch liquid were touched upon and the statement made that "Its medical powers have not been ascertained, but from its constitution and properties it is highly probable that it would be an active diffusive stimulant." This attracted the attention of Guthrie, who had an active and original mind, and he conceived the idea of making it by distilling alcohol in the presence of chloride of lime. He obtained a good yield of what was really a solution of chloroform in alcohol. Even although Soubeiran and Liebig probably made chloroform before Guthrie did, it is fairly certain that its therapeutic effects were discovered in America. Dr. Eli Ives of New Haven, Connecticut, used chloroform in 1832 to relieve the paroxysm of an aged person suffering from asthma, and Guthrie's own daughter was probably the first person to be anesthetized by tasting it.

Guthrie also experimented boldly with fulminating compounds and manufactured large quantities, for commercial purposes, of original and varied composition. He also invented a process for the rapid conversion of potato starch into sugar.

Amos Eaton (1776–1856) was a lawyer, as were Avogadro and Benjamin Silliman. He was interested in botany, biology, mineralogy, geology, chemistry, and physics. He was born in Chatham, New York, and was graduated from Williams College in 1799. While practising law he became acquainted with professors of Columbia University. In 1810 he started a popular course on botany and wrote a text on the subject. In 1815 he became disgusted with the law and listened to Silliman's lectures at Yale. In 1820 he published a *Chemistry Notebook for the Country Classroom.* This was privately printed at Troy, New York, and after five editions was followed in 1822 by the *Chemical Instructor.* He had a hand in starting the Rensselaer Polytechnic Institute at Troy and started a chemical laboratory there for students of chemistry in 1824, almost a year before Liebig opened his laboratory at Giessen. He introduced the Rensselaerian plan of teaching and made the students prepare lectures and perform experiments. He was an able and versatile man.

Christian Frederich Schönbein (1799–1868) was born at Metzingen, Swabia, and after studying at Tübingen, Erlangen, and Paris, was professor of chemistry at Basel from 1829 until his death. He was an original and talented investigator who discovered ozone and worked on hydrogen peroxide, auto-oxidation, passivity of iron, hyposulfites, catalytic action, poisoning of catalysts, hydrocyanic acid, and nitrocellulose. He published more than 360 papers on chemical subjects.

Literature

The personal elements in the discussion of this period are best brought out in the letters of the participants. The most interesting collections are the following: Mitscherlich, *Gesammelte Schriften*, Berlin, 1896, which contains some interesting letters by Berzelius; *Briefwechsel zwischen Berzelius und Wöhler*, edited by Wallach, Leipzig, 1901; and *Briefwechsel zwischen Liebig und Wöhler*, edited by Hofmann, Leipzig, 1888. An interesting collection of youthful letters by Wöhler has also been published by Kahlbaum under the title *Friedrich Wöhler, ein Jugendsbildniss in Briefen*, Leipzig, 1900.

Liebig's character attracted many biographers. The authoritative life is that by Volhard, Leipzig, 1904. A much shorter one was published in English by Shenstone, New York, 1895. Liebig's character and temperament are also thoughtfully discussed in Ostwald's *Grosse Männer*. Hofmann's lecture before the Chemical Society of London in 1875 was separately published in the following year under the title *The Life and Work of Liebig*. Hofmann included a German version of the same address in his *Zur Erinnerung an Vorangegangene Freunde* (3 vols.), Braunschweig, 1888. This collection also contains commemorative addresses on Wöhler and Dumas. The two latter are discussed in Thorpe's *Essays*.

As pointed out in the last chapter the scientific work of the period is best studied in the journals. For those to whom these are not accessible a comprehensive discussion can be found in the pages of Kopp and Ladenburg already alluded to. See also Ostwald's *Klassiker*, No. 22 for the paper of Liebig and Wohler on the radical of benzoic acid.

The work of Samuel Guthrie, Jr., is discussed in Edgar F. Smith's *Chemistry in America*, and by Tenney L. Davis in *Archeion*, **13**, No. 1 (1931); the life of Amos Eaton is outlined by H. S. Van Klooster, *J. Chem. Ed.*, **15**, 453–460 (1938), and that of Schönbein by R. E. Oesper, *J. Chem. Ed.*, **6**, 432–40, 677–685 (1929).

CHAPTER XIII

THE REACTION AGAINST BERZELIUS

Substitution in Organic Chemistry.—Hofmann vouches for the tradition that Dumas's interest in substitution began when a great social function at the Tuileries was spoiled by the choking fumes emitted from the candles. These were turned over to Dumas for investigation, who found that they had all the superficial appearance of ordinary candles but emitted clouds of hydrochloric acid when lighted. It proved that the wax from which they had been made had been bleached by chlorine and this evidently had entered into its chemical composition. Dumas soon after proceeded to treat many other organic compounds with chlorine and bromine, and he found a common if not universal result, that in such cases more or less hydrogen was substituted by an equivalent quantity of halogen. It also frequently happened that this exchange caused surprisingly little change in properties.

The Nucleus Theory.—About 1836 Dumas's countryman Laurent took up the idea and developed it into a flexible and comprehensive system which came to be called the Nucleus Theory. It was essentially a radical theory in which, however, new radicals could be formed by substitution whenever this was convenient, so that it could readily be made to cover almost any possible cases. As a system of classification this had many merits, and it was adopted for this purpose in Gmelin's great *Handbuch*. We have, however, no occasion to discuss its details, for it was frankly artificial and never received any recognition by the great chemical authorities. Liebig attacked it vigorously on the experimental side, Berzelius denounced it even more bitterly as a theory, and Dumas largely ignored it because he was himself about to take up a somewhat similar position.

First Type Theory.—In 1839 he treated acetic acid with chlorine and obtained trichloroacetic acid. In spite of the great

197

difference in composition the new acid resembled acetic in a striking degree. It had the same basicity, and when distilled with alkali one yielded chloroform while the other yielded marsh-gas, showing that these two substances also stood to each other in the same relation as the two acids. Upon these reactions Dumas based what later became known as the first Type Theory. In this he distinguished on the one hand *chemical* types to which belonged substances closely resembling each other like chloroform and bromoform, and on the other, *mechanical* types where the similarity was more formal but the relationship was still one of substitution. The following list illustrates the latter class.

Marsh-gas.. $C_2H_2H_6$
Formic acid....................................... $C_2H_2O_3$
Chloroform.. $C_2H_2Cl_6$
Carbon chloride................................... $C_2Cl_2Cl_6$

It will be seen that by force of habit the formulas are still written in a dualistic manner, but the dualistic spirit is entirely absent. Dumas compares the relation of atoms in a compound to that of the planets in the solar system. Compounds according to his view are built upon a chemical type, and their properties depend upon the number of the atoms making up the type together with their relative position. The nature of the atoms themselves is of far less consequence. Dumas points out with much feeling that in all the radical theories it had hitherto been an unprofitable necessity to divide every compound into two parts whether anything in its chemical behavior called for such a division or not. To him henceforward every compound is one unit, and while electrical forces may be involved in its formation, there is no strict dualism, and no fixed charges of electricity belonging to particular atoms are involved.

The instances of substitution continued to multiply and the new theory became popular. Dumas, however, in his enthusiasm applied it with a freedom which alarmed the more thoughtful. He was anxious to see substitution in every reaction, he recognized not only substitution of hydrogen in the types, but also of halogen, oxygen and even of carbon—all without changing the type. The substituent also might be not only an element but a group, so that in the eyes of Dumas compounds became associated where no one else could see a relationship. These excesses came near bringing the whole idea into ridicule, and in 1840 an article was published in the *Annalen* ostensibly from the pen of a certain S. C. H. Windler[1] in which the author describes the remarkable results which he has obtained by treating manganese acetate with chlorine. In this way he substituted first the hydrogen, then the oxygen, then the carbon, and finally the manganese, and so obtained a product similar to the original acetate but which consisted entirely of chlorine and water. He then goes on to recommend for use as nightcaps certain fabrics, which he says may be had in Paris, which have all the properties of cotton, though they consist entirely of chlorine!

Despite such good-natured attempts at satire most of the leading chemists of the time were seriously convinced that there was much which was sound and profitable in the new views, although, as might have been expected, the attitude of Berzelius was irreconcilably hostile and bitter.

Attitude of Berzelius.—When Laurent originated the nucleus theory, Berzelius had condemned it without mercy because it involved the substitution of hydrogen by chlorine in the radicals. For him the halogens and sulfur were *negative* elements, and, while they might sometimes replace oxygen in the electro-negative portion of a complex, just as one metal replaces another in a series of salts, yet that halogen should replace hydrogen in a positive radical without changing the chemical nature of the latter was unthinkable. It goes without saying that Dumas's views, which rejected dualism altogether, were to Berzelius nothing less than unspeakable heresy. So far as trichloroacetic acid was concerned, he denied everything which could be denied, maintaining as long as possible that this acid had no similarity to acetic acid. When, however, in 1842 Melsens succeeded in reversing the substitution and passing back from the chlorinated compound to acetic acid the analogy could no longer be disputed. Berzelius then took refuge in a new formula for acetic acid. It was no longer a simple oxide of C_4H_6 but a "conjugate" compound of oxalic acid C_2O_3 combined with a group C_2H_6. This latter was called the *copula*, and in this copula substitution in the sense of Dumas and Laurent might take place—apparently

[1] It was written by Wöhler.

because it really was not the seat of the acid properties of the compound:

Acetic acid.................................... C_2O_3, C_2H_6
Trichloroacetic acid.......................... C_2O_3, C_2Cl_6

This curious attempt, to keep half a molecule dualistic by sacrificing the other half, contained an idea of which Kolbe was able to make valuable use later. At the time, however, it was generally regarded as only a makeshift designed to save acknowledgment of defeat.

In 1837 Liebig and Dumas dealt a blow to another favored theory of Berzelius. This time the attack was upon the oxygen theory of acids, and the occasion was furnished by certain researches of Graham published about four years earlier.

Graham.—Thomas Graham was born in Glasgow in 1805 and graduated from the university there in 1824. After two years spent in the laboratory of J. C. Hope in Edinburgh, he returned to his native city and began teaching mathematics and chemistry, at first privately and then in the Mechanics Institute and the Andersonian Institution. In 1837 he was called to University College in London, and in 1841 published his *Elements of Chemistry* which Sir William Ramsay in 1908 characterized as one of the best books ever written of its kind. It was translated into German by Otto, and served as the foundation for the well-known Graham-Otto text.

In 1836 Graham became a member of the Royal Society of London, and in 1841 became the first president of the Chemical Society of London, after which A. W. Hofmann patterned *Die Deutsche Chemische Gesellschaft* in 1862.

In 1854 he succeeded Sir John Herschel as master of the mint, a position which he retained till his death in 1869. As early as 1829 he had already begun the study of diffusion in gases which led to the discovery of his famous law, that the rate of diffusion is inversely proportional to the square root of the density. He next proceeded to study the diffusion of liquids and here his researches laid the foundations of our knowledge of osmosis and drew the distinction which we still make between crystalloid and colloid solutions. Indeed he is justly regarded as the founder of colloidal chemistry. The work upon phosphoric acid with which

THOMAS GRAHAM
1805–1869

ALEXANDER
WILLIAM WILLIAMSON
1824–1904

Reproduced from Thorpe's
History of Chemistry, by
the kind permission of G. P.
Putnam and Sons.

we are immediately concerned was published in 1833. His scientific publications were collected by Young and Smith in 1876 and when printed together filled 660 large octavo pages. Sir William Ramsay likens him to Boyle and contrasts him with Cavendish and Davy.

The Polybasic Acids.—To the chemist of the twentieth century there are few things harder to realize than that in 1833 all acids were considered as monobasic, even sulfuric, oxalic and carbonic. That these acids are dibasic seems well-nigh self-evident to us, chiefly because we think of the existence of acid salts, but we have to remember in the first place that monobasic acids, notably hydrofluoric, frequently form acid salts, and furthermore that the dualistic system formulated these compounds in a manner entirely out of harmony with the modern point of view. The neutral and acid sulfates of potassium, for example, were written K_2O,SO_3 and $K_2O,2SO_3$ respectively, and the latter substance was called the *bisulfate* because it represents the union of the base with twice as much acid as in the neutral salt. It is true that this disregarded the additional water for which our modern formula $KHSO_4$ accounts, but in accordance with a point of view with which we are already familiar this was regarded as something akin to water of crystallization. In the same way there were bicarbonates $K_2O,2CO_2$, bichromates $K_2O,2CrO_3$, and so forth, whose names still persist colloquially, though this last example, where there is no water. well shows how the dualistic theory also concealed the difference between acid and pyro-salts.

Another difficulty lay in the fact that many chemists at this time doubled the atomic weights of the alkali metals, writing KO,SO_3, NaO,SO_3, as well as CaO,SO_3. This confused utterly the distinction between the univalent and bivalent metals, though any allusion to valence is really misleading in this connection, for the conception simply did not exist, and there were then no data on which it could have been built up. Chemists were by no means agreed as to whether water should be written HO or H_2O and in such a state of things to speak even of the valence of oxygen is an absurdity.

When Graham took up the study of phosphoric acid two phosphates of soda were recognized. One was the salt we now

call the pyrophosphate, $Na_4P_2O_7$, and the other the ordinary
disodium phosphate Na_2HPO_4. It is well to remember that
the latter is neutral to phenolphthalein and some other indicators.
Their distinct individuality was shown by the fact that in solution one gave a white precipitate with silver nitrate and the other
a yellow, and Berthollet had observed that, in the latter case, the
solution became acid after precipitation, an apparent exception
to Richter's rule (page 109). In spite of this difference in properties, both salts, if we disregard the water, seemed equally
entitled to the formula $2Na_2O,P_2O_5$ and the relationship was
considered a case of isomerism. Graham's fundamental experimental discovery was that when the ordinary phosphate is heated
it loses water, and the residue goes over to the pyrophosphate
which now of course gives the characteristic white precipitate
with silver nitrate. The difference between the two salts was
therefore the molecule of water lost in heating, and this could
hardly be water of crystallization, else solutions of the two salts
would be identical. Graham went on to prepare the meta-
phosphate and showed that its relation to the acid phosphate
NaH_2PO_4 is analogous to that between the pyrophosphate and
the (so-called) neutral one. Furthermore it was found possible
to prepare double salts of phosphoric acid which differed in
their properties from the phosphates of either metal considered
separately, and this also led to the conclusion that here two or
more bases are combined in the same molecule, and Graham
was able to show that all which he had discovered concerning
phosphoric acid held equally true of arsenic acid. Graham
concluded that in such acids the essential thing is the water
content. To him, therefore, an acid was no longer what it
was in the eyes of Lavoisier and Berzelius, the oxide of a non-
metal, but rather the compound of such an oxide with a certain
quantity of water which he called "basic water." Salt formation
consequently consisted in substitution of this basic water by a
metallic oxide. These ideas may be made clearer by the following table which shows the composition of a number of common
phosphates both in accordance with Graham's view and as we
should now formulate them.

	According to Graham	Modern formula
Phosphoric acid	$P_2O_5,3H_2O$	H_3PO_4
Tertiary phosphate of soda	$P_2O_5,3Na_2O$	Na_3PO_4
Ordinary phosphate of soda	$P_2O_5,2Na_2O,H_2O$	Na_2HPO_4
Pyrophosphate of soda	$P_2O_5,2Na_2O$	$Na_4P_2O_7$
Pyrophosphoric acid	$P_2O_5,2H_2O$	$H_4P_2O_7$
Acid phosphate of soda	$P_2O_5,Na_2O,2H_2O$	NaH_2PO_4
Metaphosphate of soda	P_2O_5,Na_2O	$NaPO_3$
Metaphosphoric acid	P_2O_5,H_2O	HPO_3
Microcosmic salt	$P_2O_5,Na_2O,(NH_4)_2O,H_2O$	$Na(NH_4)HPO_4$

It will be recognized from the above that Graham's conclusions involve no break in the traditional theory of acids. The only novelty is that in the free acids and acid salts "basic water" now plays the role of positive component.

Liebig on the Polybasic Organic Acids.—In 1837 Liebig and Dumas undertook an extension of the work of Graham by studying the polybasic organic acids. It will be recalled that they had just concluded an armistice with the declaration that they would henceforward study organic chemistry in collaboration. One brief paper on this subject was the only one so published before relations again became strained, but in the following year Liebig went on with the work alone, and after studying the salts of such acids as citric, tartaric, cyanuric and muconic, came to the conclusion that these were true polybasic acids. The criterion by which Liebig decided whether or not he had to do with a polybasic acid was the formation of salts containing two or more bases; thus if tartaric acid is neutralized with a mixture of soda and ammonia a double salt is formed unlike either sodium or ammonium tartrate. Liebig considered this evidence that tartaric acid must neutralize two atoms of base. His conclusion was of course correct but his method was in a measure faulty for it misled him in the case of sulfuric acid. When this acid is neutralized with an equivalent mixture of potash and soda a mixture of the two sulfates is obtained. Liebig therefore continued to consider sulfuric acid monobasic. There were other minor errors of the same kind in the work, but these sink into insignificance in comparison with the far-reaching general conclusions which Liebig was able to draw from it. In the first place he abandoned the theory of composition which Graham had so ingeniously applied to phosphoric and arsenic acids. In these special cases it was possible to obtain the salt of one acid from that of another by merely driving off water. In the organic field we can see how difficult it would be to apply the same reasoning, if we think of the complex reactions which take place when tartaric or citric acids are distilled. When the water of crystallization has been removed from an organic acid there is no way in which any special form of water it may contain can be distinguished from any other atoms of oxygen and hydrogen in its composition, nor is there any reason to assume that it contains any, except for the sake of theoretical uniformity. In fact, Liebig was fast becoming weary of all these different hypothetical forms of water with which the dualistic theory had loaded organic compounds, and he decided that it was far simpler and more satisfactory to discard the oxygen theory of acids, and define these substances as compounds containing *hydrogen* which can be replaced by a metal. It will be recalled that Davy had made a move in the same direction long before, but the opposition of Berzelius had limited the application of the idea to those acids known to contain no oxygen, and Berzelius had denied the elementary nature of chlorine to the last possible moment in order to maintain uniformity in the theory of acids. He argued with much force that if the existence of hydrogen acids is admitted, then the action of sulfuric acid upon magnesia for example:

$$SO_3,H_2O + MgO = SO_3,MgO + H_2O$$

becomes entirely different from that of hydrochloric acid upon the same base:

$$2HCl + MgO = MgCl_2 + H_2O$$

but he finally accepted the contradiction rather than secure uniformity in the only logical way, by surrendering the oxygen theory of Lavoisier. Liebig, however, now took this step and expressed himself in words of characteristic energy:

In order to explain one and the same phenomenon we use two sets of forms; we are forced to assign to water the most manifold properties; we have basic water, halhydrate water,[1] water of crystallization; we

---

[1] Liebig applies this term to the "basic water" of acid salts such as $P_2O_5,2Na_2O,H_2O$.

see it enter compounds where it ceases to exercise any of these functions, and all this for no other reason than that we have drawn a distinction between haloid salts and oxygen salts, a distinction which we do not observe in the compounds themselves. They have similar properties in all their relationships.

As might have been expected Berzelius protested with great vigor, but Liebig's opinions carried the day, and though chemists long continued in their writings to formulate the salts of oxygen acids in the old way, they did so henceforward more from force of habit than conviction. The old point of view had become intrenched in the nomenclature, and occasionally crops up even in the literature of the present day.

It should be emphasized that Liebig's discoveries were not entirely incompatible with a dualistic conception of acids and salts. The former might still be written as compounds of hydrogen with a radical like SO_4, but to attempt this involved so complete a break with the historical associations of the idea as to surrender it altogether, and the tendencies of the time all led in the latter direction. Unitary conceptions were fast replacing the old dualistic ones. We have seen how Dumas was already evolving the idea that organic compounds are built upon unitary types and are related to each other by *substitution*. This word became the shibboleth of the day and salts began to be defined as acids in which hydrogen is *substituted* by a metal.

Vapor Density as a Measure of Molecular Weight.—These attacks were by no means the first to which the system of Berzelius had been subjected. It will be recalled that the fundamental criterion which had guided him in the selection of atomic weights had been the law of combining gas volumes originally suggested by Gay-Lussac, and which Berzelius had adopted in the form that equal volumes of the *elementary* gases contain the same number of atoms. About 1826 Dumas became interested in a line of reasoning similar to that of Avogadro, and in order to test this experimentally he devised the method of determining vapor densities which we still associate with his name. The results were a disappointment. He had expected to find strict proportionality between the vapor density and combining weight, but when he came to vaporize mercury and sulfur he obtained values incompatible with so simple a hypothesis.

He might of course have assumed as we do today that the number of atoms in the molecule of an elementary gas is a constant which is characteristic for the element concerned, but at this time such an assumption seemed justified by no other independent evidence and Dumas drew instead the alternative conclusion that vapor densities were an unreliable guide in the determination of molecular weights. Berzelius, too, felt constrained to agree with him in so far as to limit the application of Gay-Lussac's hypothesis to those elements which are gaseous under ordinary conditions. In this form, of course, the generalization had become so limited in its application as to be well-nigh worthless.

Polymorphism.—It was hardly better with the other criteria, the laws of isomorphism and of atomic heats. As specific heats were determined with greater accuracy it became increasingly evident that the law of Dulong and Petit was inapplicable to the elements of low atomic weight, at least within the ordinary range of temperature. Furthermore the discovery of polymorphism by Mitscherlich did much to weaken the theoretical conclusions which had been drawn from his earlier discovery of isomorphism. If one and the same substance can crystallize in two or more totally different forms, of what value are speculations based upon the fact (perhaps only a coincidence) that different compounds sometimes crystallize in forms essentially the same?

Faraday's Law.—Still another difficulty for Berzelius was found in Faraday's law. In 1834 Faraday, while seeking additional evidence for the identity of static and galvanic electricity, hit upon a standard of comparison in the decomposition of potassium iodide. When a battery of Leyden jars is discharged through a piece of filter-paper wet with a solution of potassium iodide and starch, a blue stain is produced at the point where the positive pole touches the paper. It occurred to Faraday to measure the time required by a weak galvanic battery of known strength to produce a stain of the same intensity. He then reasoned that the quantities of electricity which had passed must be the same in the two cases. He followed up these observations with a long series of remarkable experiments in which a great variety of substances were decomposed by the current, and the quantities of material formed at the electrodes compared with the amount of hydrogen liberated from a solution of dilute

MICHAEL FARADAY
1791–1867

sulfuric acid which was connected in series. In all cases he found that these quantities were proportional to the combining weights of the substances concerned.

These results convinced Faraday that chemical affinity is identical with electricity and gave him, as he believed, the best criterion hitherto attained for the determination of atomic weights, for at this time he thought that only such salts are decomposed by the current as consist of one positive and one negative atom. The figures obtained on this supposition could not, however, be harmonized with the atomic weights of Berzelius. In the case of the elementary gases the latter had followed Gay-Lussac in the belief that equal volumes contained an equal number of atoms. With hydrogen as unity this would give oxygen the atomic weight of 16 and water the formula H_2O. The current, however, liberates from water eight grams of oxygen for one of hydrogen and in consequence, for Faraday, the formula of water was HO and the atomic weight of oxygen 8. Similar reasoning led to atomic weights for carbon, calcium and some other elements half as great as those of Berzelius, while those of the halogens remained the same. It will be recalled that these figures are essentially the same as the so-called "equivalents" advocated by Wollaston in 1813. They had found little acceptance on the continent on account of the dominating influence of Berzelius but they had always been popular in England and, from this time on, were destined to come into still more general use, rather to the detriment of the science.

Faraday's Researches in Electricity.—The portion of Faraday's famous *Experimental Researches in Electricity* which we have just briefly sketched was a contribution of the utmost importance to the special field of electrochemistry and smoothed the way for the great advances which were later to be made there. It was at this time, for example, that Faraday introduced the words *anode, cathode, ion,* etc., terms now so important in the theory of electrolytic dissociation. Faraday of course did not grasp the fact that electrolytes become dissociated by the simple fact of solution, nor were his ions quite identical in individual cases with those which we now assume. Nevertheless he did recognize the ion as that portion of a dissolved substance which carries the current in

electrolysis.   All this served to make the conception helpfully
familiar later on.

That which was immediately important was the clearness with
which Faraday showed that a certain definite *quantity* of electricity is involved whenever a chemical equivalent is transformed
by the current.   This threw a new light upon the old controversy
concerning the origin of the current itself (page 136) and made it
clearer than ever to Faraday that this could be accounted for
only as the result of the chemical action in the battery.   Such
reasoning, however, failed utterly to convince Berzelius, who had
some time before gone over to the contact theory, being converted
thereto by an experiment which he ever afterward quoted as

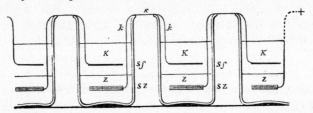

EXPERIMENT ILLUSTRATING THE ARGUMENT OF BERZELIUS FOR
THE CONTACT THEORY OF THE ORIGIN OF THE GALVANIC
CURRENT

absolutely conclusive.   The reasoning involved is something like
this: In a simple cell containing copper, zinc and sulfuric acid,
those who believe in the chemical origin of the current must
attribute it to the action of the acid upon the zinc.   If, now, a
cell could be constructed in which the copper was acted upon and
the zinc not, then the current should flow in the opposite direction.   To test this Berzelius immersed zinc in a solution of zinc
sulfate and then, without mixing, carefully introduced above
the zinc sulfate a solution of nitric acid in which was finally
immersed a plate of copper.   At first, of course the copper was
attacked, but as soon as the metallic plates had been connected
by a wire the current passed *in the customary direction* and the
zinc began to go into solution.   To the mind of Berzelius this
was conclusive evidence that the current is the *cause* and not the
effect of the chemical action in the battery, and can sometimes
even reverse the natural course of such action.

Faraday's law also touched Berzelius in a point where he was still more sensitive, for by implication it seemed to threaten the whole theory of chemical action which he had built up upon the assumption that different electrical charges are carried by the various elements. Faraday, it is true, had clearly pointed out that while the *quantity* of electricity was proportional to the quantity of change, it was the *intensity* of the current required to effect a given decomposition which was the measure of the affinities concerned. Nevertheless, few scientists had hitherto clearly differentiated the two conceptions and Berzelius was certainly now too old to learn. In his textbook he complains that according to Faraday's view

. . . the same electric current which separates an atom of silver from an atom of oxygen also separates an atom of potassium from an atom of oxygen, whereas the first is one of the loosest and the last one of the firmest combinations which we know.

Berzelius, of course, could have no sympathy with such a view and he attacked it bitterly though to little purpose. The experiments of Faraday were too convincing.

The Combination of Influences against Berzelius.—Bitterness, unfortunately, was destined to be the portion of Berzelius's later years. He had spent his life in a single-hearted devotion to the science which has never been excelled, and had devoted his great talents and tireless energy to organizing and establishing it upon foundations which he believed to be impregnable; yet now at the close of his life he had to see practically every generalization upon which he had set his heart undermined and discredited, while the world was filled with new doctrines which he believed could lead only back to chaos.

In a sense he was right. The newer discoveries had clouded the simplicity and order promised by the older generalizations. The law of isomorphism, for example, had been weakened by the discovery of polymorphism. The law of Dulong and Petit had shown a painful number of exceptions. Vapor densities had proved an unreliable measure of molecular magnitude chiefly on account of dissociation—a phenomenon not understood. The discoveries of Faraday threw into still further doubt all the criteria for the determination of atomic weights, and struck directly at the cherished electrical theory of chemical affinity. The work of Liebig on the polybasic acids displaced oxygen from the sacred place at the center of the chemical system where Lavoisier and Berzelius had done so much to maintain it, and finally—worst and most crushing of all—the theory of electric dualism had broken down utterly in the organic field, and the arch-heretic Dumas was even now setting up in its place a unitary system destined to convince chemists that electricity played no fundamental part in chemical reactions. With a different temperament Berzelius might have possessed his soul in patience resting on the record of his magnificent experimental work, but he valued his theoretical system above everything, and in its defence spent too much of his last years in violent personal attacks upon its enemies. As a matter of fact the collapse of the great system did lead to a period of general scepticism toward the very possibility of far-reaching generalizations, but out of this confusion there gradually rose another system better than the old, in which each important principle championed by Berzelius was destined to find its appropriate place.

Marc Antoine Augustus Gaudin (1804–1880) was a Frenchman of this period who had a very clear idea of atoms and molecules. He was certain that the molecules of oxygen and hydrogen had at least two atoms and, largely from the experiments of Dumas and of Berzelius, published in 1833 a table of atomic weights of twenty elements. He called the atomic weight of oxygen 1 but if his values are recalculated to $O = 16$ they agree very well, in most cases, with our present values. He is to be regarded as one of the founders of our present atomic theory.

Literature

There is a life of Graham by Robert Angus Smith, Glasgow, 1884. Thorpe devotes a chapter to him in his *Essays*. There is also an appreciation in Hofmann's *Zur Erinnerung*. His work on the phosphoric acids is in *Alembic Club Reprint* No. 10, while Liebig's paper on the polybasic organic acids is to be found in Ostwald's *Klassiker* No. 26.

Faraday's *Experimental Researches in Electricity* was published in book form between 1844 and 1847, and there is a modern reprint in *Everyman's Library*. Most of the work has also been reprinted in the *Klassiker*, Nos. 86, 87, 134, and 136. Their bearing upon chemistry in general and their influence upon contemporary thought are fully discussed in Ostwald's *Elektrochemie*.

CHAPTER XIV

GERHARDT AND THE CHEMICAL REFORMATION— WILLIAMSON

During the period of confusion and scepticism ushered in by the collapse of dualism, it was for a time impracticable for any comprehensive theoretical system to gain a hearing. Attempts to found such systems were, of course, soon begun, and while none of these at first gained any general acceptance, one or two contained elements of truth which later proved of value. The most important of these movements was that inaugurated by Laurent and Gerhardt. These two friends represented the revolutionary spirit of their time. They were enthusiastic over new methods, recognized no authority of the past and threw themselves heart and soul into the battle which eventually resulted in a distinct separation of the fields of organic and inorganic chemistry.

Laurent.—Auguste Laurent was born at La Folie near Langres, France, in 1807 and began his scientific studies in the École des Mines at Paris. Having distinguished himself in chemistry, he obtained in 1831 a subordinate position at the École Centrale des Arts et Manufactures, where he continued his studies under Dumas and received the doctorate in 1837, meanwhile spending some time in industrial work, largely as a result of a quarrel with Dumas. In the following year he became professor at Bordeaux and remained there till 1848 when his appointment as assayer of the mint enabled him to return to Paris. He died in 1853.

Gerhardt.—Charles Frédéric Gerhardt was born in Strasbourg in 1816. His first chemical studies were undertaken in Karlsruhe from 1831 to 1833 and during the following year at Leipzig. Even at this early age he showed the natural bent of his genius by attempting a classification and revision of the formulas of the natural silicates which won commendation from Berzelius. His father now looked for the son's assistance in the manufacture

213

CHARLES GERHARDT
1816–1856

of white lead, but young Gerhardt had no patience with the industrial side, and after a brief experience of army life which he liked no better, he spent a year with Liebig at Giessen where his talents and enthusiasm won him the admiration of his teacher. After one more attempt to adapt himself to the white lead industry he quarreled definitely with his father and set out for Paris almost penniless. Here his abilities gained him the notice of Dumas and other scientists, but his radical theories and uncompromising way of stating them made him a thorn in the side of the more conservative. In 1841 Gerhardt obtained a professorship at Montpellier which he left in 1848 in order to work with Laurent at Paris, where they founded a school of chemistry which was destined to prove a disappointment. In 1855 Gerhardt became professor in Strasbourg and died there in the following year, when fortune was just beginning to smile upon him.

There is a story to the effect that when a fellow-student at Giessen once asked Gerhardt about a big manuscript he was carrying, the latter replied that it was "The Chemistry of the Future." The story might equally well have fitted Laurent. Both were radical reformers by nature, and both had to suffer as such reformers must in the appreciation of their scientific contemporaries as well as in their personal ambitions. This drew them together, and after 1843 they did practically all their work in collaboration, hence it is practically impossible to assign to each his share in their mutual services to science. They both possessed in an unusual degree the power of discovering important relationships underlying masses of apparently unrelated facts, and as their facilities for experimentation were meagre they not infrequently placed emphasis upon experimental data which later proved to be untrustworthy. This too often permitted their opponents to discredit their conclusions without answering their arguments.

Laurent had been interested in substitution ever since the earliest work of Dumas on that subject, and had gone even farther than the latter in applying the principle (page 197). As early as 1836 he attempted a classification of organic compounds in which he considered them as substitution products of certain fundamental complexes which he called "radicals," somewhat as we now derive the aliphatic compounds from the hydrocarbons of the methane series. This system came to be spoken of as the Nucleus Theory. It had many good points, but it was crushed by the denunciations of Liebig and Berzelius and so never came into general use.

Chemical Notation in 1840.—In 1840 system was sadly lacking in organic chemistry. Compounds were still classified in the textbooks according to their natural sources, and nomenclature and notation were in the worst confusion. We have seen how the dualistic theory had given to acetic acid the formula which we now assign to the anhydride, $C_4H_6O_3$, and how alcohol and ether had thus naturally become $C_4H_{10}O,H_2O$ and $C_4H_{10}O$, respectively. Liebig also had doubled the formula of tartaric acid in order to account for its basicity, and in this way most of the organic compounds had come to be formulated on what was known as a four-volume basis. This meant that one formula weight occupied in the gaseous condition the same volume as four units of hydrogen. Thanks to Dumas the vapor densities of most common volatile compounds were now well known, but on account of such anomalous cases as ammonium chloride, phosphorus pentachloride, mercury and sulfur, no authoritative significance was attached to them, and no one was disturbed by the prevalent inconsistency which wrote alcohol and acetic acid on the four-volume basis while ether, hydrogen sulfide, water, and carbon dioxide received two-volume formulas. Most chemists, however, followed Berzelius in writing hydrochloric acid H_2Cl_2. For him the molecular magnitude of an acid was the amount which unites with one molecule of potassium oxide or of silver oxide and he had decided to write these KO and AgO respectively. This had the further disadvantage that it concealed the dibasic character of sulfuric acid.

The foregoing, however, accounts for only a part of the prevalent confusion. Alongside of the atomic weights of Berzelius, Wollaston's equivalents had maintained their ground and as the former declined in authority the latter came more and more into use. Maximum simplicity of formulation was, however, the only criterion for the selection of equivalents, and hence each individual felt free to choose as he pleased. Most followed

Wollaston in writing $C = 6$, $O = 8$, but many made other combinations and the journal literature of the time is extremely difficult reading in consequence. Berzelius made matters worse by an ill-judged compromise. He wrote what were called barred formulæ, a line drawn through a symbol standing for a double atom. $\overline{H}O$ for example could be interpreted according to the reader's predilections to mean either that *one equivalent* of oxygen united with one of hydrogen to form water, or that *one volume* of oxygen united with *two volumes* of hydrogen.

Gerhardt's Atomic Weights.—Gerhardt attempted a reform by reducing all formulas to a common volume basis. Up to 1842 he made four volumes the standard and incidentally framed an ingenious argument against the dualistic theory as applied to acids. The substance we know as acetic acid was then written $C_4H_6O_3,H_2O$ as a compound of the true hypothetical acetic acid with water. On a four-volume basis, however, water is H_4O_2 and in consequence acetic acid even as written above cannot contain water apart from the radical, and the dualistic formulation is inadmissible. A little later Laurent and Gerhardt after collating the formulas of all organic compounds whose composition could be considered well established, found that these were all divisible by two, and they then adopted the two-volume standard. This led to a series of atomic weights essentially in accordance with Avogadro's hypothesis. About the same time Regnault was obtaining valuable results in a study of specific heats which might have been utilized to support these views, but Gerhardt was fundamentally an organic chemist and physical constants really interested him little. What he desired was a standard of chemical comparison and he sought this in a comprehensive study of a multitude of chemical reactions. How far he really was from our modern point of view is shown by the concluding words of his famous paper of 1842, "Atoms, volumes and equivalents are synonymous terms." Even here, however, he was as well off as any of his contemporaries.

Atoms and Equivalents.—The word *equivalent* had been a stumbling-block for a generation. We have seen how profitably Richter had used the idea quite in the modern sense as the weight of one element which may replace or represent another in a given chemical reaction. Wollaston, however, had introduced the *word,* and had used it to denote a fixed quantity which we might define as the "simplest practicable combining weight." The two ideas have so much in common that the word was constantly used in both senses and there arose a confused idea that atoms must be equivalent, and that an atom of base must just neutralize one of acid. This doubtless fostered the prejudice which considered all acids monobasic until the work of Graham and Liebig. Even this, however, had not been pushed to its logical conclusion and the first clear distinction between atom and equivalent was drawn by Laurent in a memorable paper published in 1846. Here he pointed out that equivalency is a relationship depending upon the nature of the reaction concerned, while the standard of molecular magnitude must be sought in the vapor density. This carried with it the conclusion that the molecules of gases like hydrogen, oxygen and nitrogen must contain two atoms. He called such gases dyadides. However simple and logical this seems to us, it made no impression at all upon his contemporaries. The times were in a state of strange confusion which Ladenburg, in commenting upon Gerhardt's original suggestions, has characterized so well that the paragraph is worth quoting entire.

It must appear strange to any unprejudiced person that the "equivalents" which Gerhardt proposes for the elements are the same, with a few exceptions, as the atomic weights suggested by Berzelius in 1826. It is also noteworthy that Gerhardt does not mention Berzelius or even appear to know that he is adopting the latter's figures, while Berzelius on his side evidently does not notice the agreement for he attacks Gerhardt's paper violently. What I find most remarkable of all, however, is the fact that when Gerhardt made his proposal many eminent chemists (I mention only Liebig and his pupils) were already using the very ratios of atomic weights (at least for the most important elements) which Gerhardt now recommended as new, while a few years later Gmelin's equivalents, against which Gerhardt's attack was directed, had come into general use.

To Gerhardt the idea of diatomic gases was welcome, for it enabled him to treat the substitution of hydrogen by chlorine gas, for example, as a metathesis and thus bring it into line with other organic reactions. In fact he developed this idea into a comprehensive theory of chemical combination. When two substances react, according to Gerhardt, the essential thing is the formation of some simple inorganic compound while the remaining atomic groups combine with each other as they may:

$$C_6H_6 + HONO_2 = H_2O + C_6H_5NO_2$$

The Theory of Residues.—This is the basis of Gerhardt's Theory of Residues, sometimes spoken of as the Second Radical Theory because the residues as in the above instance frequently happened to have the same formulas as the radicals of the dualists. Gerhardt, however, stoutly denied their identity. To his mind they differed from the old radicals fundamentally in that no electrical character was assigned to them nor any separate existence in the molecule, and no pretence was made that they could ever be isolated. In spite of the fact that Gerhardt's work was destined to lead directly to our modern structural formulas, it was an article of faith with him that true structure could never be determined. He intended his formulas to suggest reactions of formation or decomposition and held that one and the same substance might properly be assigned different formulas according to the relationship which it was desired to emphasize; barium sulfate, for example, according to three independent methods of formation, might with equal propriety be written BaO,SO_3; BaS,O_4 or BaO_2,SO_2, and it had been a fundamental fault of the Berzelian system that it exalted the first at the expense of the others.

The Basicity of Acids.—Gerhardt gave a special name to products of metathesis like nitrobenzene. He called them "conjugate compounds" (a word which Berzelius had already employed in another sense) and noted that when one of the reacting substances is acidic its basicity is diminished by one in consequence of the operation. He applied this rule to the formation of ethyl sulfuric acid from alcohol and sulfuric acid and used it as an argument to establish the dibasic character of the latter. He also recognized that the formation of acid salts could not be considered conclusive evidence that an acid was polybasic because the salt might add a molecule of the free acid. He attached more weight to the fact that such acids can form esters, amides and so forth which are still acidic, and he contributed new facts in support of this view.

System of Classification.—No object was dearer to Gerhardt than the attainment of a consistent rational classification for organic compounds, and he attempted this by arrangements in series, distinguishing these as *homologous, isologous* and *heterologous*. The idea of homology had been introduced by Schiel and used by Dumas. By isologous compounds Gerhardt understood substances of analogous function like acetic and benzoic acids whose formulas showed some other difference than CH_2. Finally by heterologous compounds he meant substances of different function but connected by genetic relationships such as alcohol and acetic acid. These frequently though not always contained the same number of carbon atoms. According to Gerhardt every organic compound should find a place in at least two of these series, and he held that when its position in these series is fixed its whole chemical character is thereby determined; exactly as, to use his own illustration, the value of a playing card is determined by its suit and spot number.

The Amines.—The foregoing sets forth in outline what had been accomplished up to the year 1848 (the year of Berzelius's death) when support came to the new movement from unexpected quarters. In that year Wurtz discovered the primary aliphatic amines and called attention to their remarkable resemblance to ammonia. Opinion was at first divided as to their constitution, but in the following year Hofmann prepared not only primary, but also secondary and tertiary bases by the action of ammonia upon the alkyl halides. This convinced practically everyone that the new compounds were substitution products of ammonia, or according to the expression which now became common, that they belonged to the *ammonia type*.

Williamson's Work on Ethers.—In 1850 Williamson began his work upon the ethers which was destined to furnish Gerhardt with the *terme de comparaison* he had so long been seeking. Williamson was attempting to prepare new compounds. As Hofmann by treating ammonia with alkyl halides had obtained substituted ammonias, Williamson hoped to prepare a substituted alcohol by treating potassium alcoholate with ethyl iodide. Instead he obtained ordinary ether which at first surprised him, but he was quick to see that the experiment had furnished the key to many a puzzling problem in chemistry. At this time most chemists were writing alcohol C_4H_5O,HO, the ethylate $C_4H_5O,-KO$, and ether C_4H_5O. ($C=6$, $O=8$.) Laurent and Gerhardt, however, guided by the vapor densities, were already writing them as substitution products of water:

$$\left.\begin{array}{c} C_2H_5 \\ \\ H \end{array}\right\}O, \qquad \left.\begin{array}{c} C_2H_5 \\ \\ K \end{array}\right\}O, \qquad \left.\begin{array}{c} C_2H_5 \\ \\ C_2H_5 \end{array}\right\}O$$

Williamson saw at once that this latter view harmonized especially well with the results of his experiment, which he now formulated:

$$\left.\begin{array}{c} C_2H_5 \\ \\ K \end{array}\right\}O + C_2H_5I = KI + \left.\begin{array}{c} C_2H_5 \\ \\ C_2H_5 \end{array}\right\}O$$

It was still possible, however, to interpret the reaction on the old basis if one assumed that the ethylate first split into potassium oxide and ether, while the oxide then reacted with the iodide to form a second molecule of ether:

$$\begin{aligned} \text{I. } & C_4H_5O,KO \quad = KO + C_4H_5O \\ \text{II. } & C_4H_5I + KO = KI \ + C_4H_5O \end{aligned}$$

Williamson disposed of this possibility in an extremely elegant and simple way by treating potassium ethylate with *methyl* iodide. If the above interpretation were correct the reaction should produce equivalent amounts of ethyl and methyl ether:

$$\begin{aligned} \text{I. } & C_4H_5O,KO \quad = KO + C_4H_5O \\ \text{II. } & C_2H_3I + KO = KI \ + C_2H_3O \end{aligned}$$

If, on the other hand, Laurent and Gerhardt's view of the constitution of ether was correct then a new compound, methyl ethyl ether, should be the sole organic product of the reaction:

$$\left.\begin{array}{c} C_2H_5 \\ \\ K \end{array}\right\}O + \left.\begin{array}{c} CH_3 \\ \\ I \end{array}\right\} = KI + \left.\begin{array}{c} C_2H_5 \\ \\ CH_3 \end{array}\right\}O$$

The experiment decided in the latter sense, and the first acceptable *proof* for the new view was thereby furnished. Laurent and Gerhardt had studied hundreds of reactions and shown that their system was rational and self-consistent, but all this had carried little conviction because some other explanation was always possible. Williamson, however, had now shown by incontestable chemical evidence that, in one case at least, the formula must correspond to the vapor density. This gave the new doctrine an experimental foundation and it now began to make converts.

The Water Type.—Williamson himself followed up these experiments first by the study of other ethers, and then by showing that not only ethers but also alcohols, esters and acids belong to the *water type*. He also expanded this idea to include polybasic acids which he considered as derived from two or more molecules of water, writing sulfuric and phosphoric acids, for example, as

$$\left.\begin{array}{c} SO_2 \\ H_2 \end{array}\right\} O_2 \ \text{and} \ \left.\begin{array}{c} PO \\ H_3 \end{array}\right\} O_3$$

This idea was still further developed when Berthelot in 1854 showed that glycerol stood in the same relation to alcohol as phosphoric acid to nitric. This led Wurtz to the discovery of glycol, the simplest diatomic alcohol, and he formulated the two compounds:

$$\left.\begin{array}{c} C_6H_5 \\ H_3 \end{array}\right\} O_6 \ \text{and} \ \left.\begin{array}{c} C_4H_4 \\ H_2 \end{array}\right\} O_4 \ (C = 6, \ O = 8)$$

The Type Theory.—Williamson's discoveries gave fresh inspiration to Gerhardt, who soon followed his example by treating salts with acyl chlorides and so obtained the anhydrides of the monobasic acids.

$$\left.\begin{array}{c} C_2H_3O \\ K \end{array}\right\} O + C_2H_3OCl = \left.\begin{array}{c} C_2H_3O \\ C_2H_3O \end{array}\right\} O + KCl$$

This was perhaps his most appreciated experimental work. As we have seen, however, his chief talent was the organization of systems, and to the two types of water and ammonia he now added hydrogen HH, and hydrochloric acid HCl, deriving from the former the hydrocarbons and metal alkyls and from the latter the alkyl and acyl halides and the salts of the organic bases.

$$\left\{ \begin{array}{l} HC_2H_4 \\ \\ HC_2H_4 \end{array} \right. \qquad \left\{ \begin{array}{l} C_2H_5 \\ \\ Cl \end{array} \right. \qquad \left\{ \begin{array}{l} C_2H_3O \\ \\ Cl \end{array} \right.$$

Butane   Ethyl chloride   Acetyl chloride

Thus originated the second Type Theory, a system far more definite and comprehensive than that of Dumas, for Gerhardt forced into it all organic compounds.   It won friends also among the conservatives, for the groups which these found substituted in the types were the old radicals, and Liebig who had been a violent opponent of many of Gerhardt's views had some good words for this feature of his system.   Gerhardt, however, now as always, denied the radicals any objective reality, and considered the types themselves only as empty forms suitable for interpreting reactions and for classification.   He used them for this purpose in his *Traité de chimie organique*, the work by which he is still best known.   There is something pathetic in the fact that throughout the descriptive portion of this work he felt obliged to use the old formulas and atomic weights which he had spent his life in combating,[1] so little confidence did he feel that his own arguments had made enough impression to be understood.   The book itself, however, enjoyed the fullest recognition and converted many though by no means all to the new views. Unfortunately Gerhardt died just as it was completed and so missed even this partial triumph.

Williamson.—As we have seen, it was the work of Williamson, Wurtz and Hofmann which most effectually seconded the efforts of Gerhardt in establishing the Type Theory.   Of these Alexander William Williamson was born in London in 1824.   He studied first with Leopold Gmelin and then with Liebig at Giessen. Finally he devoted three years to the study of mathematics with Comte in Paris.   In 1849 he became professor at the University College in London and remained connected with that institution throughout his active life.   His important researches were carried out between 1850 and 1860 and for the most part were connected with the classic work upon ether which we have already considered.   He died in 1904.

[1] A friend who asked him why he had not clung to his own formulas, which were so much clearer, received the laughing reply: "Then no one would have bought my book!"

CHARLES ADOLPHE WURTZ
1817–1894

Wurtz.—Charles Adolphe Wurtz was born in Strasbourg in 1817 although his father was then a preacher in the neighboring village, Wolfisheim, and was not called to Strasbourg until 1826. Adolphe was, for a time, a schoolmate of Gerhardt. Like him he studied with Liebig and later became an assistant of Dumas. Being more fortunate in his friendships, however, he achieved a higher material success, succeeding Dumas at the *École de Médecine* in 1853 and in 1875 becoming professor at the *Sorbonne*. In addition to the work on amines and glycols already alluded to may be mentioned the well-known synthesis of hydrocarbons still associated with his name, and valuable contributions to the chemistry of the metallic hydrides, of the organic compounds of phosphorus, and of the hydroxy acids. Wurtz also contributed helpfully to the view that abnormally low vapor densities are due to dissociation. Wurtz, as a loyal Alsatian, was heart and soul with France in the Franco-Prussian war, which took place soon after his return from an interesting Egyptian trip which he took in company with Berthelot, Thénard and other prominent Frenchmen. During the war, when the supply of fats ran low, Wurtz succeeded in making colza oil palatable. He served France in connection with its food supply and with the conduct of hospitals. He was an efficient worker and during the examination periods he was accustomed to write letters and correct proofs, instead of merely paying attention to the examination. His literary activities were extensive, and among his works is an *Histoire des doctrines chimiques* whose opening sentences—"Chemistry is a French science. It was founded by Lavoisier of immortal memory"—have proved a veritable apple of discord among chemists of extreme national susceptibility. One of his earlier literary efforts was the translation into German of Gerhardt's *Précis de chimie organique*. His imposing *Dictionnaire de chimie pure et appliqué* is well known, and his *Traité de chimie biologique* well represents the knowledge of physiological chemistry of the period (1880–1885). Wurtz died in 1884.

Hofmann.—August Wilhelm Hofmann was born in Giessen in 1818. He entered the university there in 1836 with the intention of studying law. Later he came under Liebig's influence and decided to devote himself to chemistry which was destined to offer him an unusually brilliant and successful career.

AUGUST WILHELM HOFMANN
1818–1892

Reproduced from the *Chemical Society Memorial Lectures*, by the kind permission of the Council of the Society.

Having obtained the doctorate in 1841, he continued his studies with Liebig and became his assistant in 1843. In 1845 Hofmann accepted the position of docent at Bonn, and in the same year he was called to a professorship in the newly founded Royal College of Chemistry in London. Liebig's work on agricultural chemistry had aroused great interest in England, and the founders of the new institution desired to secure as its head some one who had been closely associated with Liebig. The latter suggested Hofmann, and the Prince Consort himself took an active interest in the appointment. Hofmann proved a tireless investigator and an unusually efficient and inspiring teacher. While in England he numbered among his pupils such men as Crookes, Abel, and Perkin. Hofmann's own studies had begun with aniline, and throughout his life most of his investigations bore some relation to compounds of that class. It was in his laboratory in 1856 that Perkin prepared the first aniline dye, *mauve*, and one of his assistants, Peter Griess, made the fundamental studies upon diazo compounds which later proved of so much importance in color chemistry. In general it may be said of Hofmann's work that, while seldom engaged directly with industrial problems, it dealt continually with those fundamental principles of organic chemistry which form the basis of the coal-tar industry. For this reason Germans are accustomed to date the beginning of their preeminence in this particular field from Hofmann's return to his native country. This took place in 1864, a call to Bonn being rapidly followed by one to Berlin where he continued his work with undiminished vigor till his death in 1892.

Hofmann was exceptionally happy as a writer and speaker. As president of the German Chemical Society, it frequently fell to his lot to deliver memorial addresses or write obituary notices which he wrought into works of real biographical value. Most of these have been published under the title *Zur Erinnerung an Vorangegangene Freunde* and constitute a veritable treasury of chemical remininiscence and appreciation.

Paul Schutzenberger (1829–1897) was born at Strasbourg and originally intended to adopt a medical career, but he became more interested in physical and chemical science. After obtaining the M.D. degree he taught chemistry in different French institutions for over forty years. He was a

Paul Schutzenberger
1829–1897

prolific experimenter and writer and was interested in industrial chemistry, particularly with respect to dye stuffs, but did a great deal of work on biochemistry. He is known for a long series of researches on the constitution of alkaloids and of proteins, for the preparation of several new series of platinum compounds, as well as for the discovery of hyposulfurous acid, $H_2S_2O_4$. He delighted in studies that took him away from the beaten track and pointed out fallacies or insufficiencies in existing theory. Toward the end of his life he became convinced that the elements were all formed by some process of condensation from one primordial substance of very small atomic weight and he also held that the atomic weight of a given element could vary within narrow limits and be modified according to the conditions under which a compound was formed. Our present belief that the atoms of all elements are composed of electrons and protons and concerning the existence of isotopes can be regarded as a development of these ideas.

Literature

Charles Gerhardt, sa vie, son oeuvre, sa correspondance, by his son Charles Gerhardt and E. Grimaux, Paris, 1900, is the authoritative biography. It makes, however, a painful impression by constantly holding up Gerhardt as a martyr at the hands of his contemporaries. There is also an interesting study of Gerhardt in Ostwald's *Grosse Männer*. It depends, however, upon the previously mentioned biography for its facts. *Le Centenaire de Charles Gerhardt*, published by the Société Chimique de France in 1916, contains a sympathetic account of his work by Marc Tiffenau. Gerhardt's own *Traité de chimie organique* is still interesting reading.

Williamson's work on ether was reprinted in *Alembic Club Reprints*, No. 16. That of Wurtz on ethylene glycol is to be found in the *Klassiker*, No. 170. There is an especially interesting memorial to Wurtz in Hofmann's *Zur Erinnerung;* also another, by Friedel, in the *Bulletin de la société chimique* for 1888.

The *Chemical Society Memorial Lectures*, London, 1901, contain appreciations of Hofmann by Playfair, Abel, Perkin, and Armstrong. The German Chemical Society also published a memorial volume in 1900, entitled *August Wilhelm von Hofmann, ein Lebensbild*. The biographical portion is written by Jacob Volhard, the chemical by Emil Fischer.

For a brief account of the life and work of Schutzenberger, see Tenney L. Davis, *J. Chem. Ed.*, **6**, 1403–1414 (1929).

CHAPTER XV

THE TRANSITION FROM THE TYPE THEORY TO THE VALENCE THEORY

While Laurent and Gerhardt were laying the foundations of the Type Theory, two other chemists, Kolbe and Frankland, were following an entirely different line of thought.

Kolbe.—Adolph Wilhelm Hermann Kolbe was born at Elliehausen near Göttingen in 1818, and at the age of twenty began the study of chemistry with Wöhler. In 1842 he became an assistant of Bunsen at Marburg, and three years later went to London where he worked under Playfair.

From 1847 till 1851 he devoted himself to literary work in connection with various chemical publications. In the latter year he succeeded Bunsen at Marburg, and in 1865 became professor at Leipzig where he remained till his death in 1884. After Erdmann's death in 1869, he was editor of the *Journal für praktische Chemie*. Kolbe was eminent as a teacher and a highly original thinker, distinguished alike for the brilliancy of his ideas and the caustic virulence of his polemical writings. Like Liebig, he emphasized the importance of laboratory work in chemical instruction.

Frankland.—Edward Frankland was born at Churchtown near Lancaster in 1825. After six years as an apothecary's assistant he began the systematic study of chemistry under Playfair in London. Here he met Kolbe and then like him worked for a time with Bunsen. Returning to England in 1847 he at first accepted a position in a school till in 1851 he obtained a professorship in Owens College, Manchester. Six years afterward he became lecturer at St. Bartholomew's Hospital and in 1863 professor at the Royal Institution. Two years later he succeeded Hofmann at the School of Mines with which the Royal College of Chemistry had just been merged. Frankland died on a visit to Norway in 1899. In addition to the work which we are about to consider he made many noteworthy contributions to organic chemistry and did practical work of much value in connection with the London water supply. In 1868 while engaged in a study of the solar spectrum in collaboration with Sir Norman Lockyer they observed certain lines which could not be attributed to any element then known to exist on the earth, and to this unknown substance they gave the name *helium*.

Frankland as well as Kolbe found the views of Gerhardt unsympathetic, and his types too artificial to be accepted as the foundation of a true chemical system. They therefore endeavored to construct something better by turning to account what was good in the old radical theory.

Conjugate Compounds.—It will be recalled (page 198) that this theory had been shipwrecked by Dumas's discovery of trichloroacetic acid and its close chemical resemblance to the parent substance. Berzelius was then writing "anhydrous" acetic acid $C_4H_3O_3$ ($C = 6$, $O = 8$) as a compound of negative oxygen with the positive radical C_4H_3. He could not, however, accept for the chlorine compound the corresponding formula $C_4Cl_3O_3$ because this would involve the incorporation of a negative element in the radical. The best he could do was to modify the formula of acetic acid and write it C_2H_3,C_2O_3 as a "conjugate" compound (addition product—see also page 219) of "anhydrous" oxalic acid and "methyl" which he called the *copula*. On chlorination, the oxalic acid, a true electrochemical compound, remained unchanged, while the copula (which had really been invented for this purpose) became substituted. This was generally regarded as a makeshift which really conceded all that it had been invented to avoid. Berzelius, however, never admitted this, and Kolbe and Frankland felt that if they could show that acetic acid really contained methyl and oxalic acid the theory would appear in a better light.

The Kolbe Synthesis.—Kolbe believed he had done this when he carried out the electrolysis of acetic acid. This reaction, which has since become an important synthesis, we now interpret as follows: Acetic acid, CH_3CO_2H, dissociates into the ions H^+ and $CH_3CO_2^-$. On electrolysis the hydrogen appears at the cathode, while at the anode the other ion $CH_3CO_2^-$ breaks up, forming carbon dioxide and ethane, the latter being produced by the combination of two methyl groups which the evolution of carbon dioxide has set free:

$$\begin{matrix} CH_3CO_2H \\ \\ CH_3CO_2H \end{matrix} = H_2 + 2\ CO_2 + \begin{matrix} CH_3 \\ | \\ CH_3 \end{matrix}$$

Kolbe's explanation seemed more simple. For him acetic acid is methyl plus oxalic acid, and on electrolysis the latter is oxidized to carbonic acid while the methyl is set free:

$$C_2H_3,C_2O_3 + O = C_2H_3 + 2CO_2$$

We now know of course that what Kolbe really obtained was not methyl but ethane. The proof of this, however, could not be furnished until some years later, so that Kolbe's conclusion seemed exceedingly plausible.

Other reactions were also observed which it was found possible to interpret in the same sense. Frankland and Kolbe were the first to carry out the hydrolysis of acetonitrile which we now formulate:

$$CH_3.CN + 2H_2O = CH_3.COOH + NH_3.$$

Like us they regarded the nitrile as a compound of methyl with cyanogen, C_2H_3,C_2N, and since the latter is known to yield oxalic acid on hydrolysis, they regarded the formation of acetic acid as a confirmation of their view:

$$C_2H_3,C_2N + 3HO = C_2H_3,C_2O_3 + NH_3.$$

The Metal Alkyls.—Finally in 1849, Frankland, by treating ethyl iodide with zinc, obtained a substance which we now know to be butane but which he considered as free ethyl:

$$C_4H_5I + Zn = ZnI + C_4H_5$$

just as Kolbe had considered the product of his electrolysis to be free methyl. Since this passed undisputed at the time, Frankland considered it as the fullest justification of his views, for to the believers in the old radical theory the best evidence for the existence of a radical was its isolation.

As by-products in the last reaction Frankland observed the formation of the zinc alkyls:

$$C_4H_5I + 2Zn = ZnI + ZnC_4H_5$$

substances which aroused great interest on account of their unexpected composition, their remarkable physical properties, and the synthetic reactions which could be accomplished by their use. It is perhaps upon this discovery that the fame of Frankland chiefly rests. The further study of these compounds, however, caused him to abandon his electrochemical views. In accordance with the latter the copula should have practically no influence upon the combining capacity of the other constituents of a compound, and zinc methyl, for example, ought when oxidized to yield zinc oxide methyl:

$$ZnC_2H_3 + O = ZnO, C_2H_3$$

No such reaction could, however, be carried out, and Frankland found it perfectly general that the power of a metal to unite with oxygen was diminished by one[1] for every alkyl group with

which it was combined. Thus cacodyl oxide $As \begin{cases} C_2H_3 \\ C_2H_3 \\ O \end{cases}$ could

only be oxidized to $As \begin{cases} C_2H_3 \\ C_2H_3 \\ O \\ O \\ O \end{cases}$, and stibethine $Sb \begin{cases} C_4H_5 \\ C_4H_5 \\ C_4H_5 \end{cases}$

to $Sb \begin{cases} C_4H_5 \\ C_4H_5 \\ C_4H_5 \\ O \\ O \end{cases}$. In short, cacodyl oxide and stibethine are

arsenious oxide and antimony oxide respectively in which more or less oxygen has been replaced by radicals. This is, however, just the point of view of the type theory, and though the types are not exactly those of Laurent and Gerhardt, Frankland now agrees essentially with them in regarding organic compounds as inorganic ones in which some element has been *substituted* by a radical. In the course of his general discussion Frankland writes as follows:

[1] *One*, that is, on the basis of the atomic weights which he was using. $C = 6$, $O = 8$, etc.

Frankland on Valence.—When the formulæ of inorganic chemical compounds are considered, even a superficial observer is struck with the general symmetry of their constitution; the compounds of nitrogen, phosphorus, antimony and arsenic especially exhibit the tendency of these elements to form compounds containing 3 or 5 equivalents of other elements, and it is in these proportions that their affinities are best satisfied; thus in the ternal group we have NO_3, NH_3, NI_3, NS_3, PO_3, PH_3, PCl_3, SbO_3, SbH_3, $SbCl_3$, AsO_3, AsH_3, $AsCl_3$, etc., and in the five atom group NO_5, NH_4O, NH_4I, PO_5, PH_4I, etc. Without offering any hypothesis regarding the cause of this symmetrical grouping of atoms, it is sufficiently evident from the examples just given, that such a tendency or law prevails, and that, no matter what the character of the uniting atoms may be, the combining power of the attracting element, if I may be allowed the term, is always satisfied by the same number of these atoms.

This passage, which was written in 1852, is often spoken of as the first statement of the valence theory, and in a sense this is true, at least so far as the principle is concerned. The *idea* of valence, however, could be of little value until the principles were established by which the actual valence of a given element could be determined, and here there was as yet no uniformity of opinion. Indeed the most superficial examination of the above list of formulas shows how little prepared Frankland himself was at this time to determine the actual valence even of oxygen. It is therefore quite natural that the idea bore no fruit until some years later.

Kolbe's Notation.—Kolbe was more conservative than Frankland and therefore slower to surrender his electrochemical ideas. Finally, however, he came to adopt the view that organic compounds are best considered as substitution products of inorganic ones, and he worked out a complex and highly original system in which he formulated practically all organic compounds as substitution products of carbonic acid. There is no occasion to discuss the details of this system, for it was hardly employed save by Kolbe and those under his immediate influence, but by its aid he was able to give account of many reactions more clearly than Wurtz and Gerhardt, and sometimes to predict compounds and reactions as yet unknown. The case most often quoted is that of the secondary and tertiary alcohols of which he not only predicted the discovery but also the behavior on oxidation. This was rightly hailed as a great triumph, and might have brought his system into general recognition had not the valence theory soon after supervened.

In general it may be said that the chief service of Frankland and Kolbe to chemical theory was the emphasis they placed upon the reality of the radicals. This compelled the disciples of Gerhardt to regard their own types as an expression of chemical constitution, and deterred them in some measure from classifying unlike things together on the sole basis of some purely formal analogy in their composition.

We have next to trace the steps by which the type theory grew into the valence theory. One of the greatest leaders in this movement was Friedrich August Kekulé.

Kekulé.—Kekulé was born in Darmstadt in 1829. He showed early talent in drawing and entered the University of Giessen with the intention of studying architecture. Here, however, Liebig's influence decided him for chemistry. After a year Liebig told him that he would probably ruin his health if he tried to become a good chemist and, as a matter of fact, Kekulé for many years allowed only three or four hours each day for sleep. He spent a year in Paris, where he came in contact with Gerhardt and other celebrated French scientists. Kekulé returned to Germany and was assistant to v. Planta at Schloss Reichenau.

The next year he spent in London as assistant to Stenhouse, where he became acquainted with Williamson, Frankland and Odling. Kekulé's first independent publication was printed in English and had to do with valence in organic compounds. In 1856 he became a docent at Heidelberg. Here he did some of his most important work, and in 1858 he was called to a professorship at Ghent. Ten years later he was made professor at Bonn, where he remained till his death in 1896. Kekulé always distinguished himself as a brilliant and daring thinker especially devoted to organic chemistry, a branch of the science which is indebted to his inspiration for many of its fundamental assumptions.

Multiple Types.—The first step toward a logical expansion of the type theory had been taken by Williamson when he introduced the so-called "multiple types." We have seen an example

FRIEDRICH AUGUST KEKULÉ
1829–1896

Reproduced from the *Chemical Society Memorial
Lectures*, by the kind permission of the Council of
the Society.

of these in the derivation of sulfuric acid from two molecules of water (page 222). Written out in full this took the form:

$$\left.\begin{array}{c} H \\ SO_2 \\ H \end{array}\right\} \begin{array}{c} O \\[2em] O \end{array}$$

and Williamson pointed out that the diatomic group SO_2 really took the place of one hydrogen in each of two molecules of water, thus holding them together:

$$\left.\begin{array}{c} H \\ H \end{array}\right\} O \\ \left.\begin{array}{c} H \\ H \end{array}\right\} O$$

A similar notation was quite extensively employed by others, and Kekulé in 1854 applied the idea in a somewhat unusual way to the action of phosphorus pentasulfide upon acetic acid forming thioacetic acid. He showed that this is really parallel to that of phosphorus pentachloride, oxygen in one case being replaced by sulfur and in the other by chlorine. In the latter case, however, "the product decomposes into acetyl chloride and hydrochloric acid, whereas when the sulfur compound of phosphorus is employed the groups remain together *because the quantity of sulfur which is equivalent to two atoms of chlorine is not divisible.*" He writes:

$$5 \left.\begin{array}{c} C_2H_3O \\ H \end{array}\right\} O + P_2S_5 = 5 \left.\begin{array}{c} C_2H_3O \\ H \end{array}\right\} S + P_2O_5$$

$$5 \left.\begin{array}{c} C_2H_3O \\ H \end{array}\right\} O + 2PCl_5 = \frac{5C_2H_3O.Cl}{5HCl} + P_2O_5$$

and cites as another example the action of the same reagents upon alcohol:

$$\left.\begin{array}{c} C_2H_5 \\ H \end{array}\right\} O \xrightarrow{P_2S_5} \left.\begin{array}{c} C_2H_5 \\ H \end{array}\right\} S \text{ but } \left.\begin{array}{c} C_2H_5 \\ H \end{array}\right\} O \xrightarrow{PCl_5} \begin{array}{c} C_2H_5.Cl \\ \hline HCl \end{array}$$

This of course only emphasizes in another way what Williamson had shown when he established the fact that oxygen can unite with two dissimilar radicals. Kekulé goes on to say:

It is not only a difference in formulation but an actual fact, that one atom of water contains two atoms of hydrogen and one atom of oxygen, and that the quantity of chlorine equivalent to one indivisible atom of oxygen is itself divisible by two, whereas sulfur like oxygen is dibasic so that one atom of sulfur is equivalent to two of chlorine.

Mixed Types.—A further advance was made in 1857 when Kekulé revived the marsh-gas type of Dumas and added it to hydrogen, water and ammonia. About the same time he introduced the idea of "mixed types." These resembled the multiple types but included the simultaneous use of molecules of different types. In this way it was possible to derive, for example,

$$\left.\begin{array}{c} H \\ C_2H_4 \\ SO_2 \\ H \end{array}\right\} \begin{array}{c} \\ O \\ O \end{array} \text{ from } \left.\begin{array}{c} H \\ \left\{\begin{array}{c} H \\ H \end{array}\right. \\ \left\{\begin{array}{c} H \\ H \end{array}\right\} O \\ H \end{array}\right\} O \text{ and } \left.\begin{array}{c} H \\ H \\ SO_2 \\ H \end{array}\right\} \begin{array}{c} N \\ \\ O \end{array} \text{ from } \left.\begin{array}{c} H \\ H \\ \left\{\begin{array}{c} H \\ H \end{array}\right. \\ H \end{array}\right\} \begin{array}{c} N \\ \\ O \end{array}$$

Ethyl sulfu-
ric acid   Sulfamic
acid

the left-hand brackets in the type formula designating in each case the hydrogen atoms which are replaced by a polyatomic radical. It is interesting in this connection to see how Kekulé defines a radical:

According to our view the radicals are nothing but the residues left unattacked by a given decomposition. In one and the same substance, therefore, according as a greater or smaller part of the atomic grouping is attacked, we may assume a greater or smaller radical.

For example, when we consider the salt formation of sulfuric acid we are led to the conclusion that it contains the radical SO_4. It appears then as water in which oxygen is replaced by the radical SO_4 and is comparable with hydrogen sulfide.

$$\left.\begin{array}{c}H\\H\end{array}\right\}O \qquad \left.\begin{array}{c}H\\H\end{array}\right\}S \qquad \left.\begin{array}{c}H\\H\end{array}\right\}SO_4$$

If, however, we consider the action of phosphorus pentachloride we find that the group SO_4 contains two atoms of oxygen which are replaceable by chlorine; we have

$$SO_2\left\{\begin{array}{c}H\Big|O\\[1em]O\Big|H\end{array}\right. \longrightarrow \begin{array}{c}HO\\SO_2Cl\\HCl\end{array} \longrightarrow \begin{array}{c}HCl\\\overline{SO_2.Cl_2}\\HCl\end{array}$$

and we must therefore assume that the radical SO_2 is present in sulfuric acid. A more penetrating decomposition shows us therefore that the group which in other decompositions remains unchanged (appears as a radical) is really only a compound of another radical (constitution of the radicals).

This last phrase, the constitution of the radicals, plainly shows the half-conscious tendency of the times toward explaining the transformations of the radicals by the arrangement of their component atoms. Kekulé himself did not go so far as this for some time, but he shows how interesting relationships can be emphasized by writing compounds as derivatives of different types, dinitrobenzene, for example, and phenylene diamine can have either of the following formulas:

$$\left\{\begin{array}{c}H\\C_6H_3(NO_2)_2\end{array}\right. \text{ or } \left\{\begin{array}{c}C_6H_4\\(NO_2)_2\end{array}\right. \qquad \left\{\begin{array}{c}H\\C_6H_3(NH_2)_2\end{array}\right. \text{ or } N\left\{\begin{array}{c}H\\H\\C_6H_4.NH_2\end{array}\right.$$

It may be remarked in passing that the theory of mixed types led to some formulas well-nigh grotesque in their complexity, and that Kolbe held the whole idea up to ridicule on this ground. The criticism would, however, have probably made a deeper impression had it come from some one other than Kolbe, whose own formulas were not always of the simplest. The following, for example, shows the way in which he wrote sulfo-acetic acid:

$$2HO \left\{ C_2 \left\{ \begin{matrix} H \\ SO_2 \\ SO_3 \end{matrix} \right\} \frown C_2,O_3 \right\}$$

In 1858 Kekulé published a celebrated paper in which he further emphasized the importance of the methane type and showed that whenever a hydrogen in methane is replaced, the carbon and the remaining hydrogen constitute a radical whose valence is increased by one:

$$CH_4 \longrightarrow CH_3Cl \longrightarrow CH_2Cl_2 \longrightarrow CHCl_3 \longrightarrow CCl_4$$

methyl being monatomic, methylene diatomic, and so on. He then took up the numerical ratio of hydrogen to carbon in the radicals, C_nH_{2n+1}, and the hydrocarbons, and came to the conclusion that when several carbon atoms occur together in a compound radical *they are connected with each other*. This idea, which now seems axiomatic, was highly original. It was scarcely implied in the older theories and was indeed rather foreign to their point of view. Once grasped, however, it gave the key to the constitution of all organic compounds. Kekulé himself, nevertheless, did not at once begin to write graphic formulas but rather expressed himself with great conservatism in words which might have been written by Gerhardt:

Rational formulæ are transformation formulæ (*Umsetzungsformeln*) and in the present state of the science they can be nothing else. By showing on the one hand the atomic groups which remain unaffected by certain reactions (the radicals), and on the other those which play a role in frequently recurring metamorphoses (the types), such formulæ give a picture of the chemical nature of the substance. Every formula which shows some reactions of a compound is *rational*. Of the different rational formulæ that which at the same time expresses the greatest number of metamorphoses is the *most rational*.

First Graphic Formulas.—The complete analysis of organic radicals down to the arrangement of their component atoms was first attempted by a Scotsman, Archibald Scott Couper in 1858 and independently by Kekulé in the same year. Couper wrote graphic formulas in the modern sense. He used, to be sure, eight as the atomic weight of oxygen, but since he assumed that two atoms of this element always occurred together in any organic compound his formulas are essentially like our own. The following examples will suffice:

$$
\begin{array}{ccc}
\mathrm{CH_3} & \mathrm{CH_3} & \mathrm{CH_3} \quad \mathrm{CH_3} \\
| & | & | \qquad | \\
\mathrm{CH_2} & \mathrm{CO_2} & \mathrm{CH_2} \quad \mathrm{CH_2} \\
| & | & \diagdown \quad \diagup \\
\mathrm{O-OH} & \mathrm{O-OH} & \mathrm{O-O} \\
\text{Alcohol} & \text{Acetic acid} & \text{Ether}
\end{array}
$$

In 1861 appeared the first portion of Kekulé's great textbook which emphasized and illustrated the new views with hundreds of examples. The foundations of modern organic chemistry were therein laid and, what is more important for us here, the date marks the time when the great contribution of organic chemistry to the historical development of the science as a whole was fully rendered. The theory of electrochemical dualism had broken down because it had failed to explain the reactions of organic chemistry. Slowly and laboriously through the stages of the type theory there had grown up in organic chemistry the unitary theory of structure which was now destined to become dominant in its turn.

The Vindication of Avogadro's Hypothesis.—The real service of organic chemistry had, however, been greater. It completed the atomic theory. Dalton had no sooner put forward the fundamental idea than he was confronted with the question; what are the atomic weights? This was seen to depend upon the composition of simple compounds. What is the formula for water? for ammonia? for methane? Dalton could not answer these questions, nor could any chemist answer them satisfactorily for fifty years. Avogadro's hypothesis seemed to offer hope of a solution, but it had been disregarded because for a long time it seemed only applicable to the few cases it had been designed to explain. The laws of Mitscherlich and of Dulong and Petit had promised much, and yet had proved in practice equally inconclusive. It was reserved for the typists to find more convincing arguments. Williamson's preparation of methyl ethyl ether first proved by chemical means that water could not have a simpler formula than H_2O, the work of Hofmann and Wurtz on the amines showed that the formula of ammonia could not be simpler than NH_3, and that of Kekulé and others on many organic substances fixed that of methane as CH_4. When now the vapor densities of all these compounds were studied, they proved throughout to have two volume formulas, and Avogadro's hypothesis was thereby rehabilitated.

Removal of the Difficulties.—Of course there still remained many contradictions and apparent inconsistencies to clear up. The chief difficulties which had always stood in the way of a general acceptance of the hypothesis had been, first, the anomalous vapor densities of certain inorganic compounds like ammonium chloride and phosphorus pentachloride; second, the vapor densities of elements like mercury and sulfur which seemed inharmonious with those of oxygen and hydrogen; and finally the disinclination which many felt toward believing that the smallest (physical) particles of the elements were themselves complex. General experience seems to show that chemical affinity is strongest between unlike elements, and that compounds are most stable when the components are dissimilar. How then could a molecule of hydrogen gas, for example, be made up of two atoms exactly alike? Such an idea was especially distasteful to the disciples of Berzelius, because his theory ascribed all chemical affinity to electric charges, and how could two atoms having exactly the same charge unite?

With the progress of time, however, experimental facts had accumulated in support of the discredited idea. Fabre and Silbermann in 1846 found that carbon gave off more heat when burned in nitric oxide than in pure oxygen. This could hardly be explained in any other way than by saying that what produced heat in both cases was the union of carbon and oxygen. The only thing which could absorb it, however must be the energy required to separate the oxygen from the nitrogen in the first case, and the oxygen *from itself* in the second. In other words the oxygen molecule must be compound.

The vapor density of sulfur also diminishes with rise of temperature far more rapidly than the law of Gay-Lussac requires, and this pointed to the compound nature of at least the denser form. Finally the enhanced reactivity of elements at the moment of liberation, the so-called nascent state, was hard to explain save by assuming the transitory existence of single atoms.

The abnormal vapor densities of compounds could also now be explained. It was due to *dissociation*. Ammonium chloride when sublimed decomposes into ammonia and hydrochloric acid which under ordinary circumstances recombine on cooling. If, however, the sublimation takes place in a vessel with a porous wall the lighter ammonia diffuses through this more rapidly than the hydrochloric acid, showing that at this temperature the gases are uncombined. Similarly in the case of phosphorus pentachloride, dissociation into the trichloride and chlorine could be proved experimentally.

The hypothesis of Avogadro had explained the reactions of oxygen, hydrogen, chlorine and nitrogen by the assumption that the molecule of each gas contained two atoms. To many it apparently seemed a necessary consequence that the same must hold true of every elementary gas. Avogadro himself certainly never drew any such conclusion, but the fact that the vapor density of mercury indicated a smaller number and that of sulfur a greater seemed generally to be taken as an argument against the theory. Once the other difficulties were disposed of, however, it was not difficult to show that there need be no uniformity among the elements in this respect.

The Service of Cannizzaro.—The foregoing facts were all known or at least available in 1858, but no one had summed them up or wrought them into a conclusive argument in support of the hypothesis, and the sad confusion of atomic weights and of chemical notation which had been growing worse since 1840 showed little sign of improvement. In 1860 at the instance of Weltzien, Wurtz and Kekulé a convention was called in the hope of bringing about some general understanding or at least some formal compromise. The meeting took place at Karlsruhe in September of that year. Dumas presided, and the other great lights of the science were well represented. Among those present was Stanislao Cannizzaro (1826–1910) then professor in Genoa but later in Palermo and at Rome.[1] Two years before, he had

[1] Stanislao Cannizzaro was an ardent follower of Garibaldi and constantly mixed up with political struggles when he was not busy with chemistry. He brought to the congress the message of his old teacher, Avogadro,

STANISLAO CANNIZZARO
1826–1910

written a little pamphlet entitled *Sunto di un Corso di Filosofia Chimica* describing the plan of instruction by which he was accustomed to introduce his own students to the subject of theoretical chemistry. He made Avogadro's hypothesis the foundation of his system, and showed with exemplary clearness and abundance of illustrative detail how this theory accounts for all forms of chemical combination and how the apparent contradictions were to be explained.

The convention proceeded as such assemblies commonly do. Many brilliant speeches were made but no general agreement was reached. Just at the close, however, the little booklet of Cannizzaro was distributed and seems to have made a wonderful impression upon all who read it. Lothar Meyer thus describes the effect upon himself:

I also received a copy which I put in my pocket to read on the way home. Once arrived there I read it again repeatedly and was astonished at the clearness with which the little book illuminated the most important points of controversy. The scales seemed to fall from my eyes. Doubts disappeared and a feeling of quiet certainty took their place. If some years later I was myself able to contribute something toward clearing the situation and calming heated spirits no small part of the credit is due to this pamphlet of Cannizzaro. Like me it must have affected many others who attended the convention. The big waves of controversy began to subside, and more and more the old atomic weights of Berzelius came to their own. As soon as the apparent discrepancies between Avogadro's rule and that of Dulong and Petit had been removed by Cannizzaro both were found capable of practically universal application, and so the foundation was laid for determining the valence of the elements, without which the theory of atomic linking could certainly never have been developed.

Once Avogadro's hypothesis had been definitely accepted the world possessed a reliable standard of atomic and molecular magnitude, and the investigator was able for the first time to feel sure when he was dealing with comparable quantities in

---

who was then dead and forgotten. His paper on *A Course in Chemical Philosophy* was so brilliant and interesting that it attracted more attention to the hypothesis of Avogadro than it had ever received during the lifetime of the author.

the case of elements as well as of compounds.   It is hardly too much to say that modern chemistry began in 1860.

Literature

The work of Kolbe upon the electrolysis of organic acids may be found in *Alembic Club Reprint* No. 15, and his system for the formulation of all organic compounds as derivatives of carbonic acid in the *Klassiker* No. 92.

A memorial lecture on Frankland was delivered by Armstrong before the Chemical Society of London in 1901, and printed in brief abstract in the *Proceedings* for that year, page 193.

A German translation of the pamphlet by Cannizzaro, *Sunto di un Corso di filosofia chimica*, is printed entire in Ostwald's *Klassiker* No. 30.   A brief account of Cannizaro's life and work is given by Lyman C. Newell, *J. Chem. Ed.*, **3**, 1361–1367 (1926).

Thorpe's collection contains essays on Cannizzaro and Kekulé.

Kopp's *Theoretische Chemie* is an extremely interesting book for the student of this period.   It is no easy task for the chemist of the twentieth century to "think himself back" into the point of view of the type theory, and to the one who desires to accomplish this Kopp's book can render valuable assistance.   Though published in 1863 it contains no mention of the valence theory and discusses the relative merits of the views of Williamson and Kolbe with great clearness from a contemporary standpoint.

CHAPTER XVI

THE PERIODIC LAW

Until Williamson and his co-workers had fixed the formula of water there was no agreement as to whether the atomic weight of oxygen was eight or sixteen, and a similar uncertainty was the rule with reference to the other atomic weights. In such circumstances it was really idle to discuss numerical relationships which might exist between them. By 1860, however, data had become available for fixing these numbers, and their mutual relationships attracted more and more attention.

The Atomic Weights.—If we may define an atom as the smallest quantity of an element known to exist in any of its compounds, and an atomic weight as the relative weight of such an atom, then the determination of this value involves two distinct problems. The first is exclusively analytical and is directed toward fixing the proportion by weight in which a given element unites with others. The second is concerned with determining what multiple or submultiple of the combining weight fulfills the other condition. We have seen how Berzelius had made it the chief object of his life to answer the first of these questions, and he performed his work with such thoroughness as to earn from Dumas the splendid tribute: "Whoever works under the same conditions as Berzelius obtains the same results as Berzelius. Otherwise he has not worked correctly." New times, however, bring new conditions and with improvement in technique all scientific measurements require revision. Dumas himself did valuable work of this kind, his determination of the oxygen hydrogen ratio in water being long considered a masterpiece.

Stas.—All previous work upon atomic weights, however, was surpassed by that of the Belgian chemist, Jean Servais Stas. Stas was born in Louvain in 1813. He originally took a degree in medicine and it was his interest in substances of physiological importance which first led him to enter Dumas's laboratory. Here in addition to his organic work he cooperated with Dumas in a determination of the atomic weight of carbon. In 1840 he began to teach in the military school at Brussels where he remained nearly twenty-five years, but at last became incapacitated for teaching on account of an ailment which affected his speech. He next accepted a position in the Mint which he resigned in 1872, living in retirement at Brussels till his death in 1891. Stas had early become interested in Prout's hypothesis, and resolved to devote his life to testing it by the most accurate possible determination of the combining weights. He refined the processes of quantitative transformation to a degree never before equaled, working with highly purified materials, employing exceptional weights of substance, making his weighings upon balances of hitherto unequaled precision, and exercising extraordinary care in his manipulations. Some of his precautions were, as a matter of fact, illusory, so far as their bearing upon the accuracy of the final results is concerned, as has been shown by the still more accurate figures, which have been obtained in recent years by Theodore William Richards and his co-workers in the Harvard laboratory, but none the less, the work of Stas still represents the maximum of human patience applied to quantitative analysis. His results convinced Stas that there was nothing in Prout's hypothesis unless one were willing to assume that the atomic weight of the primal substance was smaller than the experimental error in his determinations, which of course begs the entire question.

The second question: what multiple or submultiple of the combining weight is the atomic weight, was now at last in some position to be answered. It has been settled for most cases by the acceptance of Avogadro's hypothesis, since this fixed the molecular magnitude of compounds as the weight occupying in the gaseous state the same volume as two equivalents of hydrogen. Where this failed, as in the case of elements which form no volatile compounds, an intelligent application of the laws of atomic heats or of isomorphism could be depended upon to fix the true value with a higher degree of certainty. Numerical relationships between the atomic weights taken as a whole could therefore now be profitably considered.

Döbereiner's Triads.—The subject had indeed aroused interest long before. Certain groups of elements like the halogens and the alkali metals show a resemblance in physical and chemical properties which is so striking as to impress the most casual observer. The first recognition that such similarity might have anything to do with atomic weight was recognized by Prout who in the first paper setting forth his famous hypothesis (page 129) ascribes the chemical resemblance of iron, cobalt, and nickel to the fact that they all have the same combining weight (28). A more comprehensive generalization was made by Döbereiner in 1839.[1] He called attention to the fact that similar elements usually existed in groups of three which he called *triads*, and he showed that their combining weights possessed the numerical peculiarity that one was the mean of the other two. This applied to chlorine, bromine and iodine; to calcium, strontium and barium; to lithium, sodium and potassium; and to sulfur, selenium and tellurium, with an accuracy closer than a single unit. Platinum, iridium and osmium formed another triad, and also silver, lead and mercury (108; 104; 100). The reader will note how the true atomic weights of lead and mercury would spoil this relationship. When such classification failed, Döbereiner adopted incomplete triads. Phosphorus and arsenic, for example, represented such a group, as did also boron and silicon. Still other elements had to be classed in larger groups.

Pettenkofer and Dumas.—In 1850 Pettenkofer[2] called attention to the fact that the currently accepted combining weights of similar elements frequently differed from each other by some multiple of eight, thus in the alkalies we have lithium 7, sodium 23 (7 + 16), potassium 39 (23 + 16); and among the alkaline

---

[1] Johann Wolfgang Döbereiner was born near Hof in Bavaria in 1780 and died in 1849 at Jena where he had been professor of chemistry, pharmacy and technology since 1810. His experiments on catalysis led to the Schutzenbach Quick Vinegar Process (1822) and in 1823 he used spongy platinum in a device for igniting gas. He published over 170 papers and wrote books on pneumatic chemistry and on fermentation.

[2] Max Joseph von Pettenkofer was born in 1818 at Lichtenheim near Neuburg in Germany. He received the M.D. degree at Munich in 1843, worked under Liebig at Giessen and was placed on the faculty at Giessen in 1847. His work on the bile acids and his method of determining carbon dioxide in gas mixtures are well known. He was particularly interested in practical hygiene and was the apostle of good water, fresh air and proper sewage disposal. He died in 1901.

earths, magnesium 12, calcium 20 (12 + 8), strontium 44 (20 + 24), barium 68 (44 + 24).

Dumas aroused unusual interest by a paper in defense of Prout's hypothesis, which he delivered before the British Association in 1852. He conceded that in the triads the actual value of the middle term usually differed from the calculated one by a quantity well outside the experimental error of the determination, but he held that the elements are related by some law akin to that of homologous series in organic chemistry, wherein a simple formula of two or three terms accounts for the composition of any member of the series. In a series of similar elements, he argued that the general chemical character of the series is fixed by the equivalent weight of the lowest member, while the properties of the higher elements are determined by certain orderly increments in the combining weight. Thus in the nitrogen group, for example, we have

a	14	nitrogen	14
a + d	14 + 17	phosphorus	31
a + d + d'	14 + 17 + 44	arsenic	75
a + d + 2d'	14 + 17 + 88	antimony	119
a + d + 4d'	14 + 17 + 176	bismuth	207

He also pointed out certain relationships between dissimilar groups, showing that the difference of five between phosphorus and chlorine is repeated between arsenic and bromine and between antimony and iodine. These ideas were of course much elaborated with other examples in the original paper.

Gladstone, Cooke and Odling.—In 1853 J. H. Gladstone[1] stated that the atomic weights of similar elements might be related in three ways: They might be nearly the same, as in the cases of cobalt and nickel, or in that of palladium, rhodium and ruthenium; they might be in multiple proportion, as in the cases of the palladium group (53) the platinum group (99) and gold (197);

[1] John Hall Gladstone was born in London in 1827, studied under Graham in London and under Liebig in Giessen where he received the Ph.D. degree in 1847. In 1850 he became lecturer in chemistry at St. Thomas's hospital and was afterward prominent among English scientists, receiving the Davy medal from the Royal Society in 1897 after fifty years of researches which were numerous and of a wide range. He died in 1902.

or finally they might differ by a common increment as in the case of several instances previously cited.

In the next year Josiah P. Cooke[1] of Harvard College made a classification more elaborate and complete than any which had preceded it, and embracing many interesting details which cannot be discussed here. He divided the elements into six series each characterized by a special numerical relationship and published a series of tables bringing out these relationships as well as various other analogies among the different groups, laying special stress upon crystalline form. Like Dumas he considered that the fundamental cause of the relationships observed must be something akin to homology.

Odling[2] in 1857 published a classification into thirteen groups which were essentially triads, though elements were included which belonged to no triad. Later, in 1864 he pointed out that there is a marked continuity when the atomic weights are written in numerical order, and he noted that similar elements are frequently separated by 48, while intervals of 16, 40 and 44 are also commonly observed. This led him to believe that 4 might represent the unit of common difference, a surmise which has gained significance in our modern theories of atomic structure.

The Helix of de Chancourtois.—In 1863, A. E. Béguyer de Chancourtois, professor of geology at the *École des Mines* in Paris, published the first of a series of papers in which he brought out more clearly than had hitherto been done the fact that there is a regular recurrence of elements with similar properties when these are arranged in the order of their atomic weights. He chose a graphic method of representation. The convex surface of a vertical cylinder was ruled with 16 equidistant lines parallel to the axis, the number 16 having been chosen because it represented the atomic weight of oxygen. A helix

[1] Josiah Parsons Cooke was born in Boston in 1827 and died at Newport in 1894. He was professor of chemistry at Harvard from 1850. He published *Elements of Chemical Physics* (1860), *First Principles of Philosophy* (1868), *The New Chemistry* (1872, 1884), besides making numerous contributions to scientific journals.

[2] William Odling (1829–1921) was professor of chemistry at Oxford. It was he who instituted the practice of representing the valence of elements by lines above the symbol of an element.

was then drawn starting at the base and ascending the cylinder at an angle of 45°. In this way each intersection of the helix with one of the vertical lines could represent a unit of atomic weight, and the atomic weight of every element would be represented by a point on the helix. As a matter of fact, when the arrangement is complete the resemblance of elements which stand vertically above each other upon the cylinder is very marked. We are, however, not limited to vertical relationships. Any two points upon the curve can be connected by a line and when this is produced it must generate another or secondary helix, and de Chancourtois believed that all the elements whose atomic weights fell in such a line could be shown to stand to each other in some orderly chemical relationship. These ideas were interesting, but they seem to have made little impression upon contemporaries. De Chancourtois stated that the properties of elements were the properties of numbers. According to him the atomic weight was equal to $n + 16n'$ and in his system n was frequently equal to 7 or 16. He used whole numbers for his atomic weight, thus following Prout's hypothesis. The gaps in his system he did not regard as indicating missing elements but rather different varieties of known elements. Thus he believed that there was a kind of carbon with atomic weight 44 as well as one with atomic weight 12.

Newlands's Law of Octaves.—At about the same time Newlands[1] in England was publishing a series of papers dealing with atomic classification, in the first of which he made no great advance upon his predecessors. By 1865, however, the old equivalents which had served earlier investigators as a basis of comparison had given place to the atomic weights, and Newlands found that the simplest arrangement of these was also the most striking. He wrote the elements in the order of their atomic weights, and for convenience numbered them just as they occurred on this list. He then compared these numbers instead of the atomic weights

---

[1] John Alexander Reina Newlands was born in 1838 and died in 1898. He was an English chemist of Italian descent on his mother's side. He fought as a volunteer under Garibaldi in 1860. His various papers were collected and published in London in 1884 under the title *Discovery of the Periodic Law*. The Law of Octaves when first enunciated was ignored or ridiculed.

JULIUS LOTHAR MEYER
1830–1895

Reproduced from the *Chemical Society Memorial Lectures*, by the kind permission of the Council of the Society.

themselves, finding that "the numbers of analogous elements, when not consecutive, differ by 7 or a multiple of 7." Thus the ninth and sixteenth closely resemble the second (Li,Na,K). Newlands found it necessary to transpose a few elements in his list in order to make the above relationship hold, but it did not seem unreasonable that more accurate determinations of some atomic weights might justify the transpositions. He called his generalization the Law of Octaves and the story is told that when he first gave an account of it to the Chemical Society in London one prominent member asked "whether he had ever examined the elements according to the order of their initial letters," a remark which showed the amount of contemporary interest in such speculations. Nevertheless Newlands had pointed out more clearly than any previous chemist the periodic recurrence of similar properties among the elements. His system, however, showed no gaps and therefore left no room for new elements unless some entire octave should be discovered. This judicious sense of where the gaps must be, characterizes the more complete systems of Lothar Meyer and Mendelejeff.

Lothar Meyer.—Julius Lothar Meyer was born in Varel, Oldenburg, in 1830. He began the study of medicine at Zurich and Würzburg, and went to Heidelberg in 1854 where the influence of Bunsen and Kirchhoff drew him so far to the other extreme that we find him not long after at Königsberg engaged in the study of mathematical physics. Finally he received his degree at Breslau in 1858 and at once became a docent in the university there. After further teaching experience in a school of forestry in Neue Eberswalde, and at the *Polytechnicum* in Karlsruhe, he obtained in 1876 the professorship at Tübingen which he held till his death in 1895. Lothar Meyer was justly celebrated as a teacher, and his best-known book *Die modernen Theorien der Chemie*, first published in 1864, remained the standard work upon chemical generalizations till the rise of physical chemistry in the early nineties. His paper on *The Nature of Chemical Elements as Function of their Atomic Weights* was published in Liebig's *Annalen* in 1869.

Mendelejeff.—Dmitrij Ivanovitch Mendelejeff was born at Tobolsk, Siberia, in 1834 as the fourteenth and last child of his parents. He was not, as a boy, very studious and had little interest in the study of the classics. To the day of his death, he did all he could to do away with the compulsory study of Latin in schools. He entered the Pedagogical Institute at Petrograd in 1850 after considerable sacrifice on the part of his mother who died soon afterward. He was given a scholarship by the Institute and, although he spent a considerable part of the time in the hospital, being subject to hemoptysis so badly that at one time it seemed doubtful if he would survive, was graduated with honors after presenting a comprehensive and masterly dissertation on isomorphism in 1855. Because of

```
                        Ti= 50    Zr =  90      ? =180
                         V= 51    Nb =  94     Ta =182
                        Cr= 52    Mo =  96      W =186
                        Mn= 55    Rh =104,4    Pt =197,4
                        Fe= 56    Ru =104,4    Ir =198
                 Ni = Co= 59      Pd =106,6    Os =199
H=1                     Cu= 63,4  Ag =108      Hg =200
       Be = 9,4 Mg=24   Zn= 65,2  Cd =112
       B =11  Al=27,4    ?= 68    Ur =116      Au =197?
       C =12  Si=28      ?= 70    Sn =118
       N =14  P =31     As= 75    Sb =122      Bi =210
       O =16  S =32     Se= 79,4  Te =128?
       F =19  Cl=35,5   Br= 80     J =127
Li=7 Na=23    K =39     Rb= 85,4  Cs =133      Tl =204
              Ca=40     Sr= 87,6  Ba =137      Pb =207
               ?=45     Ce= 92
             ? Er=56    La= 94
             ? Yt=60    Di= 95
             ? In=75,6  Th=118?
```

MENDELEJEFF'S FIRST TABLE

the scholarship aid he had received, he was obligated to spend eight years in teaching and, although delegated to the Odessa *Gymnasium*, he was allowed to withdraw in the winter of 1855 because it appeared that he had only eight or nine months more to live. He then wrote another dissertation of 224 printed pages on specific volumes and was allowed to take an examination at the university at Petrograd in 1856. He was docent at the university, lecturing on theoretical and organic chemistry until 1859, meanwhile publishing several very commendable papers. He was then granted a traveling fellowship for two years' foreign study. He had originally intended to go to Paris and work under Regnault but went to Heidelberg instead to work under Bunsen and Kirchhoff. His neighbor in the laboratory was

DMITRIJ IVANOVITCH MENDELEJEFF
1834–1907

working with mercaptans and Mendelejeff did not like the smell so that he did all of his work at Heidelberg (1860–1861) in his own private laboratory, and the results were published in several physiochemical papers. In 1863 he obtained a professorship in the technical school at Petrograd, which he exchanged three years later for one at the university, where he remained till 1890. In 1893 he was made director of the Bureau of Weights and Measures. He died in 1907.

Mendelejeff was of a highly original turn of mind, and his great book, *The Principles of Chemistry*, has furnished investigators with a veritable mine of suggestive ideas for a generation, the author always having opinions of his own concerning even those points usually considered the most fixed and stereotyped. Among other things, he was an irreconcilable opponent of the theory of electrolytic dissociation and hardly less heterodox in many of his other views.

There was for a time a good deal of feeling between the friends of Lothar Meyer and those of Mendelejeff upon the question of priority in the discovery of the periodic law. Such questions however, need not detain us here. The fundamental idea, *viz.*, that the properties of the elements are a periodic function of their atomic weights, had been a slow growth, to which these two men independently gave the permanent form of expression. In 1882 the Royal Society conferred the Davy medal upon both in recognition of this fact, and we can well follow the spirit of their compromise. There is documentary evidence that Lothar Meyer had put in writing an arrangement of the elements as early as 1868. His first printed communication on the subject, however, was published in 1870 and contains a reference to the first paper by Mendelejeff.

This had appeared late in 1869, and a somewhat later one, printed in August, 1871, contained a long and complete exposition of his system. In it he pointed out in great detail how the position of an element in the table furnishes a guide for predicting the physical and chemical properties, not only of the element itself, but also of its compounds, and that this can sometimes be done with quantitative accuracy.

The modern student is so familiar with the periodic table that it is quite superfluous to point out the fundamental details upon which Mendelejeff here laid great emphasis, such as the significance of the various series and groups, the progressive changes in electrochemical character and in valence as we pass from one group to the next, the difference between the odd and even series, the peculiarities of the eighth group, and other special features. What impresses the reader of the present day is the thoroughness with which the author supports his view that practically everything about an element is in some way dependent upon its position in the system. It seems difficult to give an idea of this quality without a quotation from the original, and the following discussion concerning the position of indium will serve the purpose. Reference to the table on page 260 will assist in following the reasoning.

Since the atom analogs of indium, Cd and Sn, are easily reducible (even from their solutions by zinc) it must also be possible to obtain indium in this way. Since Ag (series 6, group I) is more difficultly fusible than Cd, and the same holds true of Sb as compared with Sn, it follows from the atom analogy Ag, Cd, In, Sn, Sb that indium must be more fusible than Cd. It melts at 176°. Ag, Cd and Sn are white (of a grayish white color). These properties also belong to indium. Cd is specifically lighter than Sn, consequently indium must have a lower specific gravity than the mean between Cd and Sn. In reality this is so. Cd = 8.6, Sn = 7.2, consequently the specific gravity of In must be less than 7.9. The observed value is 7.42. Since Cd and Sn oxidize at red heat but do not rust in the air, these properties must also belong to In although in a less degree than to Cd and Sn, because Ag and Sb oxidize with still greater difficulty. Everything above mentioned agrees with the experiment. The same conclusions are reached by comparing In with Al and Tl. The specific gravity of Al is 2.67 and of Tl 11.8. The mean is 7.2.

We may now pass to the properties of the oxides and the reactions of the salts. Indium and its atom analogs belong to the *odd* series, therefore the higher oxides cannot be strong bases. The basic character must be weaker in In_2O_3 than in CdO and Tl_2O_3 but stronger than in Al_2O_3 and in SnO_2. These conclusions are confirmed by the following facts. These oxides of Al and Sn dissolve in alkali to form definite compounds whereas the oxides of Cd and Tl are insoluble in alkali. Hence In_2O_3 dissolves in alkali without forming a definite compound. The oxides of Cd, Sn, Al, and Tl are difficultly fusible powders just like In_2O_3. The hydrate of In_2O_3, as might be expected, forms a colorless jelly. The oxides Al_2O_3 and SnO_2 are readily precipitated from their solutions by barium carbonate. So also In_2O_3. Hydrogen sulfide precipitates Cd and Sn from acid solutions, consequently indium is also precipitated. All these reactions have been confirmed by experiment.

Mendelejeff's Predictions.—Minute classification of this kind, however, was not enough for Mendelejeff, and he ventured boldly into prophecy. His table contained several vacant spaces, and from the position of these he made bold to predict not only the atomic weights of new elements which might be expected to occupy them, but also their physical properties and those of their compounds. These predictions found striking confirmation in the discovery of scandium, which showed the properties of his hypothetical "ekaboron," gallium with those of his "ekaluminum," and germanium with those of his "ekasilicon." In the last case, the predictions were verified with an accuracy almost startling, as shown in the following table:

	Properties predicted for "ekasilicon"	Properties observed in germanium
Atomic weight	72.0	72.3
Specific gravity	5.5	5.469
Atomic volume	13.0	13.2
Specific gravity of oxide	4.7	4.703
Boiling point of chloride	100°	86°
Specific gravity of chloride	1.9	1.887
Boiling point of ethyl compound	160°	160°
Specific gravity of ethyl compound	0.96	1.0

Agreement of just this marvelous kind was scarcely observed in other cases and must here be ascribed in some measure to chance, but it made a striking appeal to popular attention and doubtless did much to hasten the adoption of the periodic law as one of the fundamental chemical generalizations.

Meyer's Atomic Volume Curve.—We are indebted to Lothar Meyer for a particularly happy graphic representation of the law which he first developed in his famous atomic volume curve. The principle is the familiar one of plotting, by means of rectangular coordinates, the atomic volumes of the elements against their atomic weights. The resulting curve shows numerous points of interest. It takes the form of a series

Groups		0	I	II	III	IV	V	VI	VII	VIII
Hydrides			RH	RH_2	RH_3	RH_4	RH_3	RH_2	RH	
Oxides				R_2O 1.008	RO	R_2O_3	RO_2	R_2O_5	RO_3	R_2O_7	
Period	Series									
I	1	2 He 4.00	1 H 1.008							
II	2	10 Ne 20.18	3 Li 6.94	4 Be 9.02	5 B 10.82	6 C 12.01	7 N 14.01	8 O 16.00	9 F 19.00	
III	3	18 A 39.94	11 Na 23.00	12 Mg 24.32	13 Al 26.97	14 Si 28.06	15 P 31.02	16 S 32.06	17 Cl 35.46	
IV	4		19 K 39.10	20 Ca 40.08	21 Sc 45.10	22 Ti 47.90	23 V 50.95	24 Cr 52.01	25 Mn 54.93	26 Fe 55.84 · 27 Co 58.94 · 28 Ni 58.69
	5	36 Kr 83.7	29 Cu 63.57	30 Zn 65.38	31 Ga 69.72	32 Ge 72.60	33 As 74.91	34 Se 78.96	35 Br 79.92	
V	6		37 Rb 85.48	38 Sr 87.63	39 Y 88.92	40 Zr 91.22	41 Cb 92.91	42 Mo 96.0	43 Ma?	44 Ru 101.7 · 45 Rh 102.9 · 46 Pd 106.7
	7	54 Xe 131.3	47 Ag 107.88	48 Cd 112.41	49 In 114.8	50 Sn 118.7	51 Sb 121.76	52 Te 127.6	53 I 126.92	
VI	8		55 Cs 132.91; 67 Ho 163.5; 68 Er 167.6	56 Ba 137.36; 69 Tm 169.4; 70 Yb 173.0	57 La 138.92; 71 Lu 175.0	58 Ce 140.13; 72 Hf 178.61	59 Pr 140.9; 60 Nd 144.27; 61 Il 146–148; 73 Ta 180.88	62 Sm 150.4; 63 Eu 152.0; 74 W 184.0	75 Re 186.3	64 Gd 156.9 · 65 Tb 159.2 · 66 Dy 162.5; 76 Os 191.5 · 77 Ir 193.1 · 78 Pt 195.2
	9	86 Rn 222	79 Au 197.2	80 Hg 200.61	81 Tl 204.4	82 Pb 207.2	83 Bi 209.0	84 Po (210.0)	85 Alabamine 221.0	
	10		87 Vi	88 Ra 226.0	89 Ac (226)	90 Th 232.1	91 Pa (231)	92 U 238.07		

A MODERN TABLE OF THE PERIODIC SYSTEM

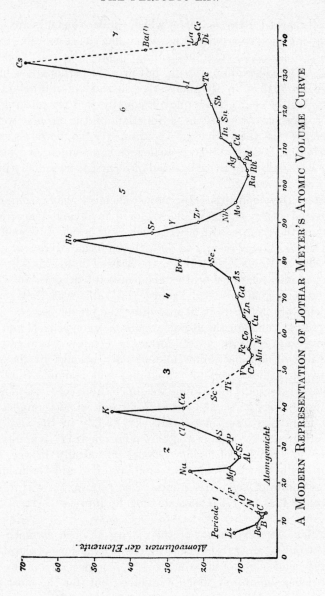

A MODERN REPRESENTATION OF LOTHAR MEYER'S ATOMIC VOLUME CURVE

of well-marked "waves," upon which similar elements are found occupying analogous positions. Ascending slopes contain electronegative elements, and descending slopes, the electropositive ones. The chief interest here, however, is perhaps less in the curve itself than in the suggestive method of representation, which can of course be employed equally well for plotting any other physical property as a function of the atomic weight. When we do this, whether the property be hardness, compressibility, boiling points of analogous compounds, or what we will, we usually find the same kind of recurrent periodicity in the properties concerned.

Later Developments.—Ingenious chemists have frequently suggested other representations, some involving a rearrangement of the groups, and others, such as those of Antropoff and of Harkins, having merely to do with the form. It is essentially the table of Mendelejeff which is the basis of discussion whenever the periodic relations of the elements are in question. One objection originally raised against this table was that certain elements did not seem to fit into quite the proper places. Thus the present value for the atomic weight of argon is 39.94 and that of potassium is 39.10, yet the former is certainly a rare gas with no valence, and potassium undoubtedly belongs to the same family as lithium, sodium, rubidium, and cesium. Similarly, in the eighth group, the atomic weights of iron, cobalt, and nickel are respectively 55.84, 58.94, and 58.69, but cobalt is unquestionably more like iron than is nickel. Finally in the sixth and seventh groups the atomic weight of tellurium is 127.5, and that of iodine is 126.93, yet iodine belongs chemically in the same group with fluorine, chlorine, and bromine, and tellurium is like selenium of the sixth group. The rare earths with atomic weights 140.2 to 175.0 also do not fit into the system very well.

Enthusiastic exponents of the theory at once assumed that these troubles arose from inaccurate determinations of the atomic weights, and scores of investigations were undertaken in the hope of revising the atomic weights involved but, for the most part, the most careful analytical work merely served to accentuate the difficulties. It was not until Moseley published his work on atomic numbers in 1913 and 1914 that any really satisfactory explanation of these apparent contradictions was given. This will be discussed later.

On the other hand, the law has been splendidly vindicated by some particularly severe tests, besides serving to indicate the probable existence of a number of unknown elements. The properties of such elements were predicted, with the aid of the law, before they were discovered. When Rayleigh and Ramsay discovered a whole family of new elements in the rare gases of the atmosphere, the question at once became rife as to where places for so many elements could be found in the periodic classification. It soon proved, however, that these gases formed a new group of their own with valence 0, whose existence could hardly have been predicted, but which, when once realized, harmonized entirely with the spirit of the law. So too, when radium was discovered, great interest was aroused as to where an element of such marvelous properties would find a place, but as soon as a determination of the atomic weight became possible, this element found the natural position below barium to which its chemical properties entitled it.

It is natural to ask what bearing, if any, this generalization has upon the question of the nature of the elements and other speculations in the spirit of Prout's hypothesis. Mendelejeff himself, with surprising conservatism and in spite of all the remarkable relationships he had discovered, declined to draw any conclusions and did not believe that his law necessarily threw any more light upon this perplexing question than such a generalization, for example, as that of Boyle. We shall soon see that the modern electron theory illuminates the periodic system from another point of view, but this must be postponed for consideration in its proper place.

Literature

Stas published *Recherches sur les rapports réciproques des poids atomiques*, Brussels, 1860, and *Nouvelles recherches sur les lois des proportions chimiques, sur les poids atomiques et leurs rapports mutuels*, 1865.

The papers of Lothar Meyer and Mendelejeff are reprinted in No. 68 of the *Klassiker*, while No. 66 gives the early work of Döbereiner and Pettenkofer. See also Garrett, *The Periodic Law*, London, 1909, and Venable, *Development of the Periodic Law*, Easton Publishing Company, 1896. One of the Chemical Society Memorial Lectures is devoted to Lothar Meyer, and one of Thorpe's *Essays* to Mendelejeff.

CHAPTER XVII

BUNSEN, BERTHELOT, PASTEUR, AND CONTEMPORARIES

Having traced the development of the science down to 1870, when the more fundamental of our modern views may be considered as definitely established, it seems appropriate to turn back and give an account of the work of other chemists to whom little, if any, allusion has been made. They may all be considered as younger contemporaries of Liebig and Wöhler, but they entered far less than these men into the theoretical controversies of their time.

The history of a nation should be a record of the development of the national character, but it is most easily written as a chronology of sieges and battles. So, too, the history of a science should record the progress of the race toward knowledge in some special field, but it easily becomes an account of dominant theories as they have superseded and conflicted with each other. Here and there, however, there arise great men whose lives are not spent in the service of any theory, but who rather provide science with those facts to which all theories must conform.

Bunsen, Berthelot and Pasteur exemplify this. In spite of wide differences in temperament and in their fields of activity, they resembled each other in their aversion to all unessential hypothesis, in the fundamental value of their work to humanity, and in the energy and devotion which they gave to that service.

Bunsen.—Robert Wilhelm Bunsen was born in Göttingen, May 31, 1811, his father Christian Bunsen being the librarian and professor of philology at the university. After attending the *Gymnasium* at Holzminden, he entered the University of Göttingen in 1828 and received the doctorate two years later, presenting a Latin thesis upon different types of hygrometers. Bunsen spent the winter of 1832–1833 in Paris, and afterward traveled quite extensively, making longer stops in Berlin and Vienna. The year 1834 found him established as a docent in

264

ROBERT WILHELM
BUNSEN
1811–1899

MARCELLIN
PIERRE EUGÈNE
BERTHELOT
1827–1907

the University of Göttingen. In 1836 he succeeded Wöhler at Cassel, and three years later accepted a professorship at Marburg, which he retained till 1851. In that year he made a brief change to Breslau and then in 1852 accepted the professorship at Heidelberg which he retained till his retirement from active service in 1889. He died there August 16, 1899.

Cacodyl.—As soon as Bunsen was settled at Cassel, he began some investigations upon the organic compounds of arsenic which would alone have assured him recognition. Many years before, a French chemist named Cadet had distilled arsenious oxide with potassium acetate and obtained a liquid of a terrible odor which was not only intensely poisonous but also spontaneously inflammable. It is not surprising that these properties protected the substance from further investigation for many years. Bunsen, however, now attacked the problem, and found that the chief component of this dreadful liquid was an organic compound of arsenic, and that it had many of the properties of a metallic oxide. We now write the reaction which accounts for its formation as:

$$4CH_3COOK + As_2O_3 = 2CO_2 + 2K_2CO_3 + \left(\begin{array}{c} CH_3 \\ As \\ CH_3 \end{array}\right)_2 O$$

In Bunsen's time the determination of organic structure was not possible, but he recognized in the complex $C_4H_{12}As_2$ what was essentially a complex metal, to which he gave the name of cacodyl, Kd, on account of the terrific odor of most of its compounds. With acids the oxide formed salts:

$$KdO + 2HCl = KdCl_2 + H_2O$$

the chloride, bromide, cyanide, etc., and when such a salt was treated with a metal like zinc, halogen was removed:

$$KdCl_2 + Zn = ZnCl_2 + Kd$$

and what in those days passed for the free radical was liberated. Of course we now know that the resulting compound, like dicyanogen, has twice the molecular weight of the true radical, but at the time this discovery was made, it was seized upon by Berzelius as one of the most important arguments ever furnished for the truth of the radical theory—ranking in this respect with the cyanogen of Gay-Lussac and the benzoyl radical of Liebig and Wöhler.

In the successful investigation of these substances Bunsen established his reputation once for all as a master of chemical manipulation, but an explosion of cacodyl cyanide cost him the sight of his right eye, and weeks of illness resulted from inhaling its fumes. From this time on Bunsen devoted himself exclusively to work in the inorganic field.

Bunsen Cell—Gas Analysis.—In 1841 Bunsen described a practical form of the zinc-carbon cell, introducing a very active carbon electrode to replace the platinum originally used by the physicist William Robert Grove. In 1845, Bunsen was commissioned, together with the Englishman Lyon Playfair, to study the process of English pig-iron production. He had previously, in 1838, given considerable study to this subject. With the aid of thermic data published by Dulong, Bunsen was able to show that only 15 per cent of the available reducing power of the fuel was utilized and the remainder was wasted in the form of carbon monoxide which could be utilized. At the same time the possibility of obtaining ammonium and cyanogen salts as by-products was pointed out. These studies led to a revision and expansion of the whole subject of gas analysis, which proved classic, and Bunsen's book *Gasometrische Methoden* (1857) is still a work of reference in this subject. More rapid methods have since been devised but none exceeded his in accuracy for many decades.

He studied the different parts of the non-luminous gas-flame and invented the burner that bears his name. By using the different parts of the flame, he was able to identify most of the common constituents of minerals and his book on *Flammenreaktionen* was published in 1866, with a second edition in 1886.

Geological Studies in Iceland.—In 1846 Bunsen spent three or four months in Iceland where he devoted himself to the study of the rocks, and took a great interest in the action of the geysers. Competent judges have referred to his work on the Icelandic rocks as laying the foundation of modern petrology, while his method of attacking the problem of geyser action seems of sufficient general interest to warrant a brief résumé here. Before this time most geologists had believed that the geyser water was volcanic. Bunsen, however, was able to prepare water like it in composition by boiling rain water with the local rocks, and came to the conclusion that it was really of surface origin. He also found that only the alkaline springs dissolved silica and only these formed geysers. A geyser according to Bunsen simply represents a deep tube or fissure in the earth in which alkaline water has settled and which is heated unequally by the hotter rocks around. In such a long narrow and nearly vertical tube there will be no free circulation of the water so that this will in general be considerably hotter toward the bottom than at the top. On the other hand, the pressure of the water column raises the boiling point of the water very markedly as the depth increases. By sinking self-registering thermometers at various depths into the tube, Bunsen found that a few minutes before the eruption the temperature at several places was very close to the boiling-point at that depth. If we now assume that this boiling-point is reached at any place the first effect must be to lift the water column above the point where steam is first formed. The pressure being once reduced, the water further down now finds itself heated far above its boiling-point, and bursts into explosive ebullition, until the whole mass is discharged violently into the upper air. The water of course gradually falls back into its basin, refills the tube and the process repeats itself as before. In cooling and drying also, the water deposits some of the silica it held in solution while superheated, and this accounts for the building up of the crater, and the silicious lining of the geyser tube.

The Photochemical Investigations.—The twelve or fifteen years just following 1850 probably represent the most productive of Bunsen's life. In 1854 he published a very fundamental treatise on iodimetry describing volumetric methods "of very general applicability," and not long after, in connection with his student Roscoe, he took up the quantitative study of the action of light upon chemical reactions. That chosen for especial study was the formation of hydrochloric acid from its elements. Hydrogen and chlorine were mixed in molecular proportions, and subjected in a specially designed apparatus to the action of light of known intensity for varying periods of time.

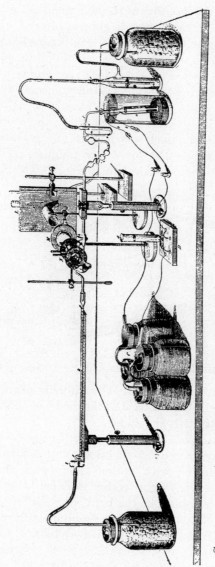

SOME OF THE APPARATUS EMPLOYED BY BUNSEN IN HIS PHOTOCHEMICAL INVESTIGATIONS

It was found that the quantity of hydrochloric acid formed was proportional to the intensity of the light and the time of exposure, and, what was perhaps of more general interest, that the light absorbed in passing through such a reacting medium was proportional to the chemical change produced, so that the photochemical absorption followed the same laws as ordinary absorption. Bunsen also called attention to a phenomenon which has not even yet been quite satisfactorily explained, namely the preliminary exposure which is required before the reaction acquires a constant velocity, and which must be repeated whenever action has been arrested for a few minutes. This he called the period of "photochemical induction." This brief descrip-

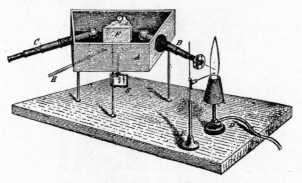

THE FIRST FORM OF THE SPECTROSCOPE

tion does no justice to the extent and quality of the work, which Ostwald has well characterized as the model of all that a physicochemical investigation should be.

The Spectroscope.—In 1854 Kirchhoff came to Heidelberg as professor of physics and he soon began to work with Bunsen upon problems connected with optics. For some time previously Bunsen had been paying attention to flame tests in qualitative analysis, and had been in the habit of showing that flames in which several elements are being simultaneously volatilized can conveniently be resolved by looking at them through a prism, when each color stands out separately. The narrower the flame the sharper the definition, so that the next logical step was to allow the flame to shine through a narrow aperture, to direct the rays by a telescope in a parallel stream upon a prism, to view the spectrum thus produced by another telescope, and to enclose the prism itself in a box to protect it from diffused light. The result was the spectroscope, an instrument which has added constantly to human knowledge from that day to this. In the hands of Kirchhoff it demonstrated the absorption of radiations by the vapor of the same substances which emit them, and in this way accounted for the dark Fraunhofer lines in the sun's spectrum by the presence of certain elements as gases in its atmosphere. Bunsen soon after applied it to the analysis of the water of certain springs, and the result was the discovery of the new elements rubidium and cesium, and the characterization of their important compounds.

Bunsen as a Teacher.—The above represent only a few of Bunsen's more celebrated investigations, but he is scarcely less well known for many characteristic and original tricks of manipulation and ingenious pieces of laboratory apparatus whose efficiency is equaled only by their extreme simplicity. To chemists it is almost superfluous to name them: the Bunsen burner, the battery, the ice calorimeter, the Bunsen valve (a slit in a rubber tube), the photometer (a grease spot on a piece of paper), all remind us of the ingenuity and practical sense of the master. Last but not least, Bunsen was a great teacher, rivaled only by Liebig and Wöhler in the number and distinction of the students whom he attracted to his laboratory. He was eminently practical and very slow to adopt new theories. His simplicity of character, fatherly interest in his students, and unbounded sense of humor made him no less beloved than admired by all. Tyndall has characterized him as the ideal university professor. It is recorded that in 1856 the following chemists of future eminence were at one time enrolled as students in his laboratory: Beilstein (of the great *Handbuch*), Lothar Meyer (of the periodic law), Quincke (long professor of physics in Heidelberg, and an authority on surface tension), Landolt (best known by his comprehensive *Tables*), Roscoe (of the Roscoe-Schorlemmer textbook), Volhard (whom students associate with two well-known analytical processes), and Adolf Baeyer (successor of Liebig in Munich and the hero of the indigo synthesis). At the same time Kekulé was a docent in the university. Here certainly must have existed a scientific atmosphere.

Berthelot.—Marcellin Pierre Eugène Berthelot was born in Paris, October 29, 1827, the son of a physician.   He early attended the *Collège Henri IV*, and in 1846 won a prize in philosophy open to the competition of students in all the *lycées* of France.

He next attended the *Collège de France* where he began the study of medicine, but gradually interested himself more and more in chemistry, coming under the influence of Pelouze, Dumas, Claude Bernard, Regnault and Balard.   He finally became assistant to the last named, and in this position was fortunate enough to find much time for his own researches.   In 1859, Berthelot was made professor at the *École Supérieure de Pharmacie*, a position which he held till 1876, although in 1860 he also accepted a professorship at the *Collège de France* which had been created especially for him and which offered opportunities for research altogether unequaled in France at that time.   A laboratory was set apart for his especial use, and the routine duties consisted of only forty public lectures a year, with no obligation to hold examinations, and perfect freedom to make the lectures whatever he chose.   As a matter of fact he made them largely accounts of his own researches.

Berthelot became a member of the Academy of Medicine in 1863, of the Academy of Sciences in 1873, and was made inspector of higher education in 1876.   Almost alone among scientific men he also reaped high political honors, being created a senator for life in 1881, minister of public instruction 1886–1887, and minister of foreign affairs from 1895–1896.   He died suddenly in Paris on March 18, 1907.

Organic Syntheses.—Almost the earliest of Berthelot's publications revealed the general tendency of his subsequent work. In 1851 he passed alcohol, acetic acid and other simple substances through hot tubes and by such pyrogenetic reactions prepared benzene, phenol and naphthalene.   A very indirect synthesis of acetic acid was already known, so that this reaction at once opened to synthesis whole classes of substances hitherto unattainable in this manner.

Ever since Wöhler's preparation of urea from ammonium cyanate in 1827, the preparation of isolated compounds from the elements had succeeded here and there; but these researches of Berthelot (which he soon extended further) at last began to justify the hope felt by every chemist that it may some time prove possible to prepare all the complex compounds met with in nature by laboratory processes. Berthelot devoted himself to the realization of this ideal with zeal, and it is worth recording that he was the first to use the word synthesis in this connection. One of his next successes was the preparation of the fats in glass by the action of glycerol upon the fatty acids. This formed a part of an extensive investigation of glycerol which resulted not only in the discovery of many important derivatives like the allyl compounds, but also in the recognition that this important substance is a tri-atomic alcohol. Berthelot expressed this in the form that glycerol stands to ordinary alcohol in the same relationship that phosphoric acid stands to nitric. We have already seen (page 222) how this idea was extended when Wurtz discovered the glycols. Meantime Berthelot's studies in the terpene series served to connect oil of turpentine with camphene and camphor, and work on the sugars interested him in fermentation. Here he discovered in yeast the *invertin* which has the property of hydrolyzing cane sugar, and he expressed the opinion that the transformation of sugar to alcohol was doubtless due to some other enzyme contained in the yeast. This suggestion, however, had to wait for nearly forty years before it was justified by Buchner's discovery of *zymase*.

Berthelot next continued his synthetic studies by verifying Faraday's observation that alcohol can be obtained from ethylene through ethyl sulfuric acid. Having also worked out his well known preparation of methane from carbon bisulfide, he obtained from the former first methyl chloride and then methyl alcohol, thus opening to the theoretical possibilities of synthesis all the substances which can be prepared from these two alcohols. This investigation occupied about ten years and the results were published in an important book *Chimie fondée sur la synthèse.*

Studies on Ester Formation.—After 1860 Berthelot took less interest in the development of pure organic chemistry, turning his attention more and more to the forces which govern chemical reactions in general. In 1862 there appeared a very famous paper published in collaboration with Péan de St. Gilles concerning the velocity of esterification. It was found that when an acid and alcohol are brought into contact, the reaction between them never reaches completion but stops at a definite equilibrium point, and it was further found that, at any moment, the quantity of ester formed is proportional to the products of the active masses of acid and alcohol present. This is, as we see, essentially our modern mass action law applied to a single reaction, and the statement of such a relationship in mathematical form represents one of the first efforts of its kind.

Acetylene.—Meantime Berthelot was continuing his synthetic studies by brilliant contributions to the chemistry of acetylene. Although not the discoverer of this substance, he gave it its present name, and established many of its singular properties, among others its preparation from the elements in the electric arc and its polymerization to benzene when strongly heated. This last observation led to the syntheses of many other complex hydrocarbons by pyrogenetic methods. Among these were styrene, naphthalene and acenaphthene.

Studies in Thermochemistry.—Even in his earliest work Berthelot had interested himself in the quantity of heat evolved or absorbed in a chemical reaction, but after 1869 he made a most extensive study of the subject with particular reference to the combustion of organic compounds in his calorimetric bomb, also including many other reactions, so that most of our data on this subject are due either to him or to Julius Thomsen of Copenhagen who also made studies of this kind his life-work. The investigation involved countless observations and an immense amount of computation. Among the results of general interest was a thorough confirmation of the important principle (not discovered by Berthelot) that in any chemical transformation the amount of heat evolved or absorbed by a given series of reactions depends only upon the initial and final states of the substances concerned and not at all upon the steps involved; thus if we start with hydrochloric acid, ammonia, and water at a given temperature, and end with a solution of ammonium chloride in water it makes no difference whether we first allow the dry gases to react, and then dissolve the product in water, or whether we dissolve the hydrochloric acid and ammonia separately in water and then mix the solutions.

Berthelot also derived from his researches a supposed law to which he attached great importance but which has not stood the test of modern criticism. This he called the *principle of maximum work*. It states that a chemical reaction always takes place with the production of those substances whose formation involves the greatest evolution of heat. Although this has been found to be thermodynamically unsound, it serves as a practical rule which holds true in a great majority of cases.

Work on Explosives.—During the Franco-Prussian war, Berthelot was a member of the scientific committee organized for the defence of Paris and became interested in explosives, dealing not only with the practical side, but also studying the nature of explosive reactions in general. The details can, of course, receive no adequate description here. One result, however, deserves mention. Berthelot studied with especial care the propagation of explosions in gas mixtures when these are confined in long tubes, and found that in such cases the velocity of transmission is independent of the pressure and of the diameter of the tube, being strictly characteristic for the gas mixture concerned. To this Berthelot gave the name of the *explosion wave*.

In 1883 a tract of land originally belonging to the palace at Meudon near Paris was placed at Berthelot's disposal, and he established there an annex to the organic laboratory of the *Collège de France* which he used as an agricultural experiment station, and during his later years spent much time there carrying on researches especially devoted to the nitrogen supplies of the growing plant.

Historical Studies.—In addition to all his chemical and political activities Berthelot still found time for original historical studies. He visited Egypt in 1869 to attend the opening of the Suez Canal, and the expedition served to stimulate his curiosity concerning the chemical knowledge possessed by the ancients, and the origin of alchemy. From this time on, as opportunity offered, he devoted much effort to the collection and translation of rare manuscripts, even those in Eastern languages, to the comparison and editing of alchemistic texts, and to the analysis of old coins and other utensils brought to light by the labors of archaeologists. His books, *Les Origines de l'alchimie* and *La Chimie au moyen âge*, as well as several other less known writings, give an account of his labors in this field. Indeed, Berthelot's literary productivity is no less remarkable than the great quantity of his experimental work, more than twenty-five imposing volumes having come from his pen in addition to his contributions to the scientific journals.

Mental Attitude.—Detractors have criticized his experimental work on the ground of lack of thoroughness and even of accuracy, but we have to remember that Berthelot was interested primarily in the larger features of the problems which he attacked. The isolated fact or observation he valued, not for itself, but for the light it threw upon the main question, and so he was unwilling to stop and establish the best conditions for every reaction, or sometimes even to verify his compounds by the most careful analyses. In fact, he sometimes took the liberty of genius, to rely on his intuitions, and he seldom had to regret his courage. Berthelot always brought an entirely original point of view to the solution of his problems, and this led to a disregard of the work of others which sometimes bordered on injustice. This independence expressed itself characteristically in his formulas. For one devoting himself to organic synthesis, the modern student is likely to think of our structural formulas as an indispensable help and guide; but Berthelot only adopted them in the last years of his life, recklessly using the old equivalents instead of the atomic weights and thereby attaining formulas essentially empirical, but modified in ways of his own in order to bring out special relationships which he wished to emphasize. There is no reason to dwell on these formulas, since no one else employed them, but they illustrate the peculiar combination of originality and conservatism in Berthelot's mind, and his innate aversion to the hypothetical element involved in all ideas of atoms and molecular structure. When a friend once told Berthelot that he need not take the atoms so seriously, that using them as aids to thought need imply no belief in their objective existence, he replied with a trace of bitterness, "Wurtz has seen them!"

This aversion to hypothesis was a part of the very philosophy which in Berthelot's case seems to have been the compelling inspiration of his work. In student days he formed an intimate and lifelong friendship with Ernest Renan and both became thoroughly imbued with the spirit of religious scepticism so common in France at that time, and expressed by the latter in his *Life of Jesus*. Berthelot, on his side, seems to have assumed the task of showing that all the remarkable transformations of the organic world are due to the play of simple chemical and mechanical forces acting in a mechanical way. As he himself expressed it, "It is the object of these researches to dō away with *life* as an explanation, wherever organic chemistry is concerned." Strange as such an aim now appears to us, and little as it would now seem to prove even were the whole contention conceded, we find in Berthelot an interesting and unusual case of a life producing a wealth of positive, constructive results when inspired by a spirit of negation.

Pasteur.—Louis Pasteur was born in Dôle, France, December 27, 1822. Not long after, the family removed to Arbois and there most of Pasteur's youth was spent. Having attended the colleges at Arbois and at Besançon, he became *bachelier ès lettres* in 1840 and *bachelier ès sciences* in 1842, being set down as *mediocre* in chemistry—another interesting commentary on academic standards. In 1843 he entered the *École Normale* at Paris where, three years later, he became assistant to Balard with opportunities for independent investigation. His first appointment was to the faculty of Dijon, but he soon exchanged this position for an assistantship in Strasbourg. In 1854 he was made professor at Lille and dean of the Faculty of Sciences, a position which he surrendered three years later to return to the *École Normale* in Paris, and with this institution he remained connected throughout practically the whole of his active life. Among other honors, he was made a member of the Academy of Sciences in 1866, of the Academy of Medicine in 1873, and of the French Academy in 1882. He died in Paris, September 28, 1895.

Work on Tartaric Acid.—Practically the first scientific problem which engaged the attention of Pasteur proved to be of far-reaching significance. In Balard's laboratory he had come in contact with Laurent, who interested Pasteur in the microscopic study of crystals. These studies led him to follow the work of Mitscherlich on arsenates and phosphates and to include in his observations the salts of tartaric and of racemic acids. According to Mitscherlich the double sodium ammonium salts of these acids crystallized in exactly similar forms and yet, in solution, the tartrate rotated the plane of polarized light to the right while the

LOUIS PASTEUR

1822–1895

Reproduced from the *Chemical Society Memorial Lectures*, by the kind permission of the Council of the Society.

racemate was optically inactive. A more thorough examination by Pasteur, however, showed that the crystalline forms were not exactly alike; that the tartrate showed certain hemihedral faces which occurred only on the right side of the crystal, whereas in the case of the racemate such faces appeared upon different crystals sometimes on one side and sometimes upon the other. It occurred to Pasteur to separate the right-handed from the left-handed crystals and to examine them separately with the polariscope. He now found that the right-handed ones were nothing else than the familiar tartrate, while the left-handed crystals represented the salt of a hitherto unknown acid, exactly like tartaric in all other respects, but rotating the plane of polarized light as much to the left as tartaric acid did to the right. Now the connection between optical rotation and hemihedral forms was not new. Hauey had observed the occurrence of hemihedral faces among quartz crystals and Biot had noticed that some specimens of this mineral rotate to the right while others rotate to the left. Herschel combined these observations showing that the geometrical form goes hand in hand with the direction of rotation. Pasteur's present observation was a distinct step in advance, for the tartrates rotate the plane of polarized light *in solution*, and it was soon to be discovered that optically active volatile organic compounds show the property even in the *gaseous* state. From this Pasteur drew the bold and correct conclusion that the molecule of such a compound is itself unsymmetrical.

He has left a pleasing account of the interest which Biot, then an old man, took in these researches:

The announcement of the above facts naturally placed me in communication with Biot, who was not without doubts concerning their accuracy. Being charged with giving an account of them to the Academy, he made me come to him and repeat before his eyes the decisive experiment. He handed over to me some paratartaric[1] acid which he had himself previously studied with particular care, and which he had found to be perfectly indifferent to polarized light. I prepared the double salt in his presence, with soda and ammonia which he had likewise desired to provide. The liquid was set aside for slow evaporation in one of his rooms. When it had furnished about 30 to 40 grams

---

[1] An earlier name for racemic acid.

of crystals, he asked me to call at the *Collège de France* in order to collect them and isolate before him, by recognition of their crystallographic character, the right and left crystals, requesting me to state once more whether I really affirmed that the crystals which I should place at his right would deviate to the right, and the others to the left. This done, he told me that he would undertake the rest. He prepared the solution with carefully measured quantities, and when ready to examine them in the polarizing apparatus, he once more invited me to come into his room. He first placed in the apparatus the more interesting solution, that which ought to deviate to the left. Without even making a measurement, he saw by the appearance of the tints of the two images, ordinary and extraordinary, in the analyser, that there was a strong deviation to the left. Then, very visibly affected, the illustrious old man took me by the arm and said, "My dear child, I have loved science so much all my life that this makes my heart throb."

The incident marked the beginning of a friendship which ended only with the death of Biot and proved of great advantage to Pasteur.

The idea of molecular structure in our modern sense was not developed at this time, so Pasteur was not in a position to refer back the asymmetry of the molecule to the particular atoms which are responsible as we do today. He did, however, account for the four forms of tartaric acid and worked out the three methods for splitting racemes which are still our main reliance in work of this kind. The method of mechanical selection we have already described, but Pasteur added two others. He saw that the combination of a right-handed acid, for example, with a left-handed base could not have the same properties as the compound of a left-handed acid with the same base, and acting on this idea he devised our present methods of adding to a raceme another active complex, usually involving salt formation. Pasteur also made the important observation that when *penicillium glaucum* grew in a racemate solution the right-handed form gradually disappeared, while the other was unattacked. This not only furnished a method frequently applicable for obtaining one component of a raceme, but it also demonstrated the important principle that optical opposites, in spite of their striking similarity in other respects, show marked differences as soon as physiological influences come into play.

Studies in Fermentation.—Work with microorganisms of this kind was destined later on to absorb all of Pasteur's activities. When professor at Lille he became interested in the troubles met with by a local distillery in fermenting beet sugar. The difficulty consisted in an undesired fermentation which was producing lactic acid. Study soon showed that during the process certain microorganisms appeared in the fermenting liquid which were foreign to a healthy alcohol fermentation, and that these, when placed in a fresh sugar solution, induced a renewed formation of lactic acid. The obvious conclusion was that the fermentation was *caused* by the organism. Familiar as such an idea seems to us, it was in direct contradiction to the general opinions of the time.

Although fermentative and putrefactive processes had long been familiar and one of them, alcoholic fermentation, had been practised industrially for centuries, next to nothing was really understood about the nature of the process, and this in spite of the fact that a good deal of evidence was available which might have been used for the solution of the problem. In the seventeenth century the microscope had become so far perfected that it was possible to observe the forms of yeasts and bacteria, but it was only in 1803 that L. J. Thénard ventured to declare that these organisms were the cause of the chemical action involved. While this made some impression at the time, the idea again lost ground, largely on account of the opposition of Berzelius and Liebig, whose tendency to dogmatize here had very unfortunate results. Neither Berzelius nor Liebig paid much attention to the fact that yeast is a living organism, though neither could be said to be ignorant of the fact. To Berzelius the action of yeast upon a sugar solution was a splendid example of *catalysis*, by which he understood rather more than we now ascribe to the word, regarding it as a kind of contact force. Liebig's theory was more elaborate. He reasoned that a substance is only stable when the amplitude of vibration of its atoms does not exceed a certain amount, for if these get beyond the range under which chemical affinity acts, the compound must obviously decompose. If now there be brought into contact with a reasonably stable substance another which is already undergoing putrefaction (so Liebig regarded yeast), then the escaping decomposition products of the latter act upon the atoms of the more stable one, as one tuning fork affects another of the same pitch, causing decomposition of the compound.

The view of Berzelius has been in a measure justified by recent investigation, for we now know that the yeast contains an enzyme, *zymase*, whose presence, rather than the vital processes of the yeast itself, brings about alcoholic fermentation. The theory of Liebig, however, was in reality only a crude attempt to picture the mechanism of the catalysis and it rested upon no adequate experimental evidence. It was, however, defended by its author with a vigor and obstinacy characteristic of the man, and inversely proportional to the strength of the argument—a fact which will hardly surprise any student of human nature.

Pasteur's experiments were conclusive. He showed that when fermentation occurs certain microorganisms abound in the liquid, that when these are introduced into an unfermented liquid of the same kind fermentation is at once induced, that the kind of fermentation depends upon the kind of microorganism, and finally, that when organisms are rigorously excluded no fermentation occurs.

Spontaneous Generation.—The support of this last proposition involved Pasteur in a long and bitter controversy upon the old subject of spontaneous generation which in one form or another had vexed the world for centuries. The observation that decaying matter usually abounds with all sorts of life is as old as the race, and in early days the assumption was naturally made that the animals were the product of decay, even as acute an observer as Van Helmont asserting that mice could be produced by mixing meal with dirty rags. We can forgive this to Van Helmont, but it seems well-nigh incredible that views not much less crude in principle could persist beyond the middle of the nineteenth century. It is true, of course, that modern believers in spontaneous generation confined their arguments to animals much smaller than mice, but philosophical controversies on the subject recurred with regularity, and were always especially bitter, because one side or the other invariably tried to make the topic a factor in religious discussion. Its irrelevancy here was abundantly shown by the fact that spontaneous generation figured alternately on both sides of the question. This was clearly seen by Voltaire. Those who recall the inscription above the door of the chapel at Fernay, "*Deo erexit Voltaire*," will remember that its author was sometimes willing to break a lance on the side of orthodoxy, and concerning the skeptics of his day who used the argument of spontaneous generation to justify their atheism he remarked pithily, "It is strange that men should deny a Creator and yet arrogate to themselves the power of creating eels."

Attitude toward Religion.—Unlike Berthelot, Pasteur's temperament was deeply though unaggressively religious and like Faraday (who was also a devout Christian) he never permitted doctrinal bias to influence in the slightest degree the inflexible accuracy of his experiments, realizing that natural science has certain limitations which it can never pretend successfully to pass. Its sphere is the observation and correlation of sense phenomena, whereas religious truths are not sense phenomena, and must be "spiritually discerned."

In his work on spontaneous generation Pasteur had to contend with quite as much prejudice (and even misrepresentation) as any of his predecessors, but he had what none of them had possessed, an irreproachable experimental technique, and his results showed with perfect finality that under any conditions hitherto obtainable in the laboratory no living cell is ever produced from any other source than another living cell. In the course of these investigations Pasteur had won so large an experience with microorganisms that his services were soon in demand wherever fermentation processes were involved, and he was even called to England, to prescribe for certain so-called "diseases" of wine and beer.

Work on Contagious Diseases.—He was, however, not content to stop with such achievements. The analogy between fermentation and contagious disease had attracted the attention of both physicians and chemists at a very early date, and Pasteur saw a magnificent opportunity for service by devoting his energies to researches along these lines. These probably constitute his best claim to greatness as a benefactor of the race, but we will not follow them in detail here, because they served to draw Pasteur more and more away from work in pure chemistry. Suffice

it to say that in 1868 he began the study of a disease among silk-
worms which practically saved that important industry for
France. About 1877 he commenced a similar and equally successful campaign against anthrax which was working havoc
among French cattle. In the eighties he undertook a no less
valuable study of chicken cholera and a similar disease among
swine, and about the same time he took up the study of hydro-
phobia by which he is perhaps most popularly known.

About 1888 the contributions of friends and philanthropists
made possible an enlargement of the scope of his work by the
foundation of the Pasteur Institute which still carries on the study
of contagious diseases in the spirit of its founder.

This institution, however, by no means represents the only
extension of his personal work.   His influence upon the succeeding
generation has been widespread, and Lord Lister, for example,
was proud to acknowledge that the antiseptic methods of surgery
which he introduced into English hospitals were a direct application of ideas received from Pasteur.   When we think of the lives
prolonged by these methods and of the triumphs of modern
bacteriology and serum therapy in preventing and combating
disease, we may well question whether any single human life has
rendered greater practical service to the race than that of Louis
Pasteur.

James Curtis Booth (1810–1887) was an important factor in the development of chemistry in the United States.   In 1832 he went to Germany to
study chemistry and worked in Wöhler's private laboratory in Kassel and
the next year worked with Gustav Magnus in Berlin.   He was particularly
interested in chemical analysis and in 1836 established in Philadelphia a
laboratory for instruction in chemical analysis and applied chemistry.
Within a few years, nearly fifty young men worked there, and many of them
became prominent analytical chemists, including John F. Frazer, who was
professor of chemistry at the University of Pennsylvania from 1844 to 1872,
and Thomas H. Garret, who later became his partner in the business of
making commercial analyses.   After 1881 the firm became Booth, Garrett,
and Blair and was well known for the high-grade analytical work done,
particularly with respect to iron, steel, and iron ores.

In 1849 Booth received a Federal appointment at the United States
mint in Philadelphia and held the office until his death.   He was frequently
consulted by the government on chemical problems, and it was due to his
influence that the iron and steel industry was subjected to control by chemical analysis.   The American Chemical Society was organized in 1876 with

John W. Draper (1811–1882) its first president. James C. Booth was president in 1883, 1884, and 1885. The second president of the society (1877) was John Lawrence Smith.

John Lawrence Smith (1818–1883) of Charleston, South Carolina, was graduated from the Medical College of South Carolina in 1840. He then went to Paris and studied under Dumas, but during a walking tour he happened to visit Liebig's laboratory in Giessen and, under the inspiration of Liebig, became a zealous and enthusiastic student of chemistry. In 1842 his work on the *Composition and Products of Distillation from Spermaceti* was probably the most elaborate work on organic chemistry that had been done up to that time by any American chemist. In 1840 he published a paper on the detection of arsenic in the body and means of counteracting its effects. He was sent to Turkey by the United States government to give scientific aid to a project of cotton cultivation and, as a result of his work there, published a paper on Turkish emery in 1850.

He had previously published considerable work on methods of analysis and usually carried with him in his travels sufficient chemicals and apparatus to make a chemical analysis wherever he might be. His method for decomposing silicates prior to determining the alkalies, by heating with calcium carbonate and ammonium chloride, has been in constant use since its publication in 1853. In 1854 he was made professor of medical chemistry and toxicology in the University of Louisville and stayed there until 1886, which was the longest time he ever stayed in one place. He had an ample income and was fond of travel. His work with Wolcott Gibbs on the cobalt mines was especially fine.

Just as there were two men by the name of Silliman who were well-known as chemists so too there were two scientists by the name of Gibbs, one working at Harvard College and the other at Yale.

Oliver Wolcott Gibbs was born in New York City in 1822 and received his bachelor's degree from Columbia University in New York in 1851. He served one year as assistant to Robert Hare at the University of Pennsylvania and in 1845 obtained the M.D. degree but never practiced medicine. Next he studied chemistry with Rammelsberg and with Heinrich Rose in Berlin and with Liebig at Giessen. In Paris he attended lectures by Laurent, Dumas, and Regnault, returning home in 1848. The following year he was appointed professor of chemistry in the College of the City of New York where he remained fourteen years. In 1863 he became Rumford Professor at Harvard College and had charge of the laboratory of the Lawrence Scientific School for eight years. He retired from active service at Harvard in 1887 but was professor emeritus until his death in 1908.

He did more than any one else to introduce into the colleges of the United States the German conception of research as a means of chemical instruction. He wrote no books, delivered no popular lectures, but published seventy-six important papers covering a wide range of subjects. Although distinctly an inorganic chemist he did some work on uric acid and its derivatives. He perfected methods of chemical analysis, particularly in gas analysis, developed the idea of residual affinities, which was later improved by Werner, and applied his theory to the complex cobaltic salts. He studied the analytical chemistry of the platinum metals and did some remarkable work on complex inorganic acids containing silicic or phosphoric acid combined with tungstic or molybdic acid. E. F. Smith characterizes his work in these words: "Gibbs was a pioneer, breaking pathways into a tangled wilderness; but the ways are now open and he who wills may follow."

Josiah Parsons Cooke was born in Boston in 1827, prepared for college at the Public Latin School, and was graduated from Harvard in 1848. He traveled abroad for a year and on his return was made tutor in mathematics at Harvard. In 1850 he became professor of chemistry and mineralogy, and he remained at Harvard until his death at Newport in 1894. When a boy he heard Silliman lecture at the Lowell Institute, which led him to fit up a chemical laboratory at home. He had, therefore, a working knowledge of chemistry when he entered Harvard. He continued his studies there very much by himself, chemistry being so poorly taught that he could hear only five or six fragmentary and rather disjointed lectures. In Paris he attended lectures by Regnault and Dumas.

Chemistry at Harvard was virtually in a state of collapse when he took hold of it and he raised it to the front rank. Cooke, from the first, believed in the laboratory method of teaching chemistry and soon induced the faculty to introduce an elective course on qualitative analysis. At his death there were sixteen courses given in chemistry and mineralogy, chosen by over three hundred students, taught by a staff of three professors, three instructors, and eight assistants. His work on the atomic weight of antimony in 1873, was a masterpiece. In the study of antimony and its compounds he introduced the crystallographic method. His ideas with respect to the numerical relations between atomic weights and the properties of elements foreshadowed the periodic system of Mendelejeff and Lothar Meyer. He published eight books and seventy-three papers on subjects ranging from pure science to religion. He was a brilliant and popular lecturer. His writings show a remarkably clear conception of physicochemical principles as far as they were developed at the time. He helped to make chemistry an exact and disciplinary science.

In France important developments took place which had a marked effect on chemistry. On the industrial side, the soda industry started greatly aided the production of soap and glass. In 1775, the French Academy offered a large prize for the best industrial method for making sodium carbonate from common salt. Many schemes were submitted, but the best was that of Le Blanc.

Nicolas Le Blanc (1742–1806) was a French physician and apothecary who was interested in chemistry. In his factory, which was built in about 1791, common salt was treated with oil of vitriol, and the resulting sodium bisulfate was heated with carbon and then with limestone. From the product, leaching with water yielded a solution from which sodium carbonate could be obtained. During the French Revolution Le Blanc's factory was confiscated, and the promised prize was never paid. The factory was returned to Le Blanc in 1800, but he was never able to recover his spirit and died in poverty, by his own hand. The soda process was developed more successfully in England after 1814, particularly by James Muspratt.

James Muspratt (1793–1886) had training as a druggist, and his eldest son, James Sheridan Muspratt (1821–1874), prepared in 1854–1860 an excellent *Chemistry Dictionary* which was translated into German and into Russian. The LeBlanc soda process was in use for over a century but was gradually replaced by the ammonia or Solvay process. The Le Blanc process had as by-products hydrochloric acid and bleaching powder, and these products helped to make it profitable. Sulfuric acid was needed, and Muspratt was the first to use pyrites as a source of the sulfur.

In France, excellent scientific work was accomplished by Carnot, Clapeyron, Regnault, Clausius, and Sainte-Claire Deville which proved of considerable importance in the development of physical chemistry.

Nicolas Léonard Sadi Carnot (1796–1832) was a French physicist who understood the true nature of heat. He left behind him notes on some of the best methods for determining the mechanical equivalent of heat. Carnot's principle that the efficiency of a reversible engine depends upon the temperatures between which it works is fundamental in the theory of thermodynamics. He developed what is known as the *second law of thermodynamics* in 1824, but the significance of Carnot's work was not fully recognized until pointed out by Lord Kelvin in 1848–1849. Carnot realized that it is the work that can be accomplished rather than the heat evolved that is a measure of chemical affinity. Carnot's work was tested by **B. P. E. Claperon** (1799–1864) who, together with the Swiss professor **R. J. E. Clausius** (1822–1888), derived a thermodynamic equation for *changes of state* which was of considerable importance in the development of physical chemistry.

Henri Victor Regnault (1810–1878) was a French chemist and physicist. After studying in France, he worked under Liebig and later became professor at Lyons. In about 1835 he did important work in organic chemistry; he studied the action of halogen on unsaturated hydrocarbons, the organic acids, and the alkaloids. He analyzed samples of air from various localities, made careful determinations of specific heats, studied the expansion of gases, and proved that Boyle's law held only for ideal cases; he also did excellent work in thermometry. Besides this, he was director of a porcelain factory.

The results of his later work were destroyed by fire, and his son was killed in the Franco-Prussian war. After these two misfortunes, he never recovered his courage and did no work of any consequence after 1872. He was the author of a four-volume textbook which was translated into several languages.

Henri Étienne Sainte-Claire Deville (1818–1881) was born at St. Thomas, in the West Indies, where his father was consul. He received the M.D. degree at Paris and began to teach almost immediately. He held positions in several places from 1841 to 1859 when he was made professor at the Sorbonne in Paris. He studied oil of turpentine and tolu balsam and discovered toluene. In 1849 he discovered N_2O_5 and in 1855 prepared aluminum by means of sodium.

With H. J. Debray (1827–1888), another professor in Paris, he worked on the preparation of pure platinum and was able to fuse platinum on a technical scale. He was interested in and improved the methods for the technical production of sodium, aluminum, and magnesium. With L. J. Troost he studied vapor densities up to 1400°, and with Wöhler he worked on the preparation of crystalline boron and silicon and studied the halide of boron and silicon. He studied the dissociation of steam, CO_2, HCl, and CO at high temperatures and worked out a scheme for the analysis of the platinum metals. With Debray he also worked on the thermic dissociation of $CaCO_3$ and showed that temperature alone, and not the quantities of CaO and $CaCO_3$ present, determined the extent of the dissociation. Horstman (1842–1929), who was professor at Heidelberg and is credited with being the father of chemical thermodynamics, pointed out that this was not in contradiction to the law of mass action, because the system was not homogeneous, and to this equilibrium between $CaCO_3$, CaO, and CO_2, the equation of state derived by Claperon and Clausius applies. Sainte-Claire Deville is best known for his work on "reversible action" and "dissociation." It is interesting to note that Cannizzaro used the work of Sainte-Claire Deville to explain the apparent failure of Avogadro's law in the vapor from heated ammonium chloride, but Sainte-Claire Deville himself could not see the application and wrote to Cannizzaro in protest.

Literature

Bunsen's complete works have been published by Ostwald and Bodenstein under the title *Gesammelte Abhandlungen von Robert Bunsen*, 3 vols., Leipzig, 1904. This contains some commemorative addresses, notably a German translation of that delivered before the Chemical Society of London by Sir Henry Roscoe and included in the *Chemical Society Memorial Lectures*. There is also a small volume of *Erinnerungen* by Debus, Kassel, 1901.

There is a paper on Berthelot in Sir William Ramsay's *Essays Historical and Chemical*, London, 1908, and an unusually complete biographical account by Graebe in the *Berichte*, vol. 41, p. 4805 (1908).

The best life of Pasteur is that by his son-in-law, Vallery-Radot. The last English translation was published by Doubleday, Page and Co. (Doubleday, Doran & Company, Inc.) of New York in 1916. Pasteur's account of his studies in molecular asymmetry may be found in the *Alembic Club Reprints*, No. 14.

The work of the early American chemists can be found in Edgar F. Smith's *Chemistry in America* and in Charles A. Browne's *Half Century of Chemistry in America*. The development of physical chemistry is covered in Partington's *Short History of Chemistry* better than in most short histories.

CHAPTER XVIII

ORGANIC CHEMISTRY SINCE 1860

The long controversies which ended about 1860 in the triumph of Avogadro's hypothesis and the vindication of the atomic theory had been fought out in the organic field, and had culminated in the establishment of the valence theory as the guiding principle in that branch of the science. This gave, perhaps, to organic chemistry a somewhat exaggerated importance— at any rate, the idea that chemical compounds could be visualized as groups of real atoms united by real bonds exerted a remarkable fascination, and young chemists in great numbers began to devote themselves to synthetic studies, attempting on the one hand to prepare from the elements the most complex products of nature, and on the other to make the greatest variety of new combinations in order to find the utmost limits of chemical affinity and molecular stability. The rise of the coal-tar industry and the possibility of preparing from this source so many compounds of practical utility was partly cause and partly effect of this great movement which is going on uninterruptedly at the present day.

If, however, we ask what direct contribution to the science as a whole has been made by organic chemistry since 1860 we can hardly give it so high a place. We must rather confess that this branch of the science has lived largely for itself and while it has, during that time, developed a real history of its own which is of fascinating interest to the specialist, its great historical service to chemistry culminated in the work of Williamson, Gerhardt, and Kekulé.

This special history of modern organic chemistry is far too important to pass over entirely in silence, but only those influences will be considered which yielded some new fundamental idea, or disclosed the constitution of whole classes of compounds of unusual interest. The first of these great advances was made through the theory of the aromatic compounds advanced by Kekulé in 1865.

Kekulé's Benzene Theory.—These substances had originally received this name on account of a peculiar odor possessed by certain representatives. Later it was found that most compounds so classified exhibited certain chemical properties in common, such as ease of nitration and sulfonation, and stability toward oxidizing agents. They also contained, as a rule, relatively more carbon than substances like alcohol or acetic acid. Their structure therefore caused particular difficulties, because the high percentage of carbon in comparison to hydrogen could hardly be accounted for save by a massing of multiple bonds entirely out of keeping with the saturated behavior of the substances concerned. Gradually it became clear that most of these compounds were closely related to benzene, and the constitution of this substance thus became of fundamental importance. At last it occurred to Kekulé that a consistent explanation was to be found in the assumption that the six carbons of benzene were arranged in a ring united by alternate single and double bonds, and with a hydrogen attached to each carbon. The constant study of the aromatic compounds in all the laboratories of the world during more than fifty years has only served to confirm this hypothesis, which may now be considered one of the most thoroughly tested generalizations of science. There is, therefore, a distinct interest in Kekulé's own account of how the idea first came to his mind:

I was busy writing on my textbook but could make no progress— my mind was on other things. I turned my chair to the fire and sank into a doze. Again the atoms were before my eyes. Little groups kept modestly in the background. My mind's eye, trained by the observation of similar forms, could now distinguish more complex structures of various kinds. Long chains here and there more firmly joined; all winding and turning with a snake-like motion. Suddenly one of the serpents caught its own tail and the ring thus formed whirled exasperatingly before my eyes. I woke as by lightning, and spent the rest of the night working out the logical consequences of the hypothesis. If we learn to dream we shall perhaps discover truth. But let us beware of publishing our dreams until they have been tested by the waking consciousness.

A still bolder extension of the idea of structure which purports to show the actual arrangement of atoms in three dimensions was made in 1874 by van't Hoff, later destined to acknowledged leadership in physical chemistry.

Van't Hoff.—Jacobus Henricus van't Hoff was born in Rotterdam, August 30, 1852. While at school he distinguished himself by a taste for mathematics and what proved to be a life-long admiration for the writings and philosophy of Byron, certainly a strange enthusiasm for one destined to spend his own life in tireless devotion to science. In 1869 van't Hoff entered the technical school at Delft without at that time having any very definite plans as to his future career. In 1871 he removed to Leiden and here decided to devote himself to chemistry. In consequence the winter of 1872–1873 was spent in Bonn where he began work, as his letters show, with an almost extravagant admiration for Kekulé. Both the work, however, and the personal relationship proved disappointing, and van't Hoff failed here to make any marked impression upon his teachers and fellow-students. The next year was spent with Wurtz in Paris where the atmosphere proved more congenial. Returning to Holland in 1874 van't Hoff took his degree at Utrecht late in the same year, and then accepted a position in the veterinary school of the same university where he remained for two years. While there he had occasion to give private lessons in chemistry to the director, who afterward related that his young teacher presented the subject in essentially the same spirit as if it were a chapter in mathematical physics—a point of view characteristic of the new era in which he was destined to play so important a part. The year 1877 brought a professorship in Amsterdam where van't Hoff was expected to teach geology and mineralogy as well as chemistry, but as time passed on he had opportunity to devote himself more and more to his special field of physical chemistry. Finally in 1896 he accepted a research professorship at Berlin with the right but without the obligation of teaching. He held this till his death in 1911.

By this time it will be superfluous to call the reader's attention to the fact that men destined to the highest eminence in science usually produce some work worthy of their best powers at a decidedly *early* period in their career. This was true in the

JACOBUS HENRICUS VAN'T HOFF
1852–1911

case of van't Hoff who in 1874, just before taking his degree, published a little pamphlet setting forth all the fundamentals of what we now understand under the designation of stereochemistry. A little later this grew into the well-known book, *La Chimie dans l'espace.*

Stereoisomerism.—We have already seen how Pasteur had shown that the differences between such substances as the right-handed and left-handed tartaric acids must be due to a lack of symmetry in the molecular structure of the compounds concerned, but since his time no progress was made toward a more definite localization of the asymmetry. Ordinary structural formulæ, superficially considered, suggested no difference between the isomers, and it seemed at first as if the problem could not be solved until a molecule was actually *seen.* Van't Hoff, however, as a student of Kekulé was familiar with very mechanical conceptions of the constitution of matter, and he reasoned that the equivalence of the four valences of carbon (so well attested by all manner of evidence) could only be interpreted structurally in the sense that they were arranged equidistantly upon the surface of the atom. This involved representing them by lines drawn from the center of the atom to the apexes of a circumscribed tetrahedron. Once this assumption is made it follows as a necessary consequence that when the four bonds connect a given carbon atom with four *different* elements or groups the molecular structure must be unsymmetrical, that two extremely similar isomers must exist for a single asymmetric carbon atom, and that the number of isomers must be doubled by every such additional atom. Van't Hoff tested his conclusions by going over the known optically active substances and showing that each of them contained at least one asymmetric carbon atom, and that when, by any chemical reaction, such carbon atoms were made symmetrical the optical activity disappeared. As in all such cases the literature showed a few apparent exceptions but more thorough experimental investigation showed that these substances also followed the rule.

Cis-trans Isomerism.—The idea of the tetrahedral arrangement of the valences of carbon also enabled van't Hoff to account for another entirely different type of isomerism which had already given trouble. If two carbon atoms are connected by a double bond free rotation of the atoms about a common axis is thereby rendered impossible, and when the other two bonds of each carbon atom are attached to dissimilar groups two isomers are possible, according to whether certain groups are on the same side (*cis*) or opposite sides (*trans*) of the double bond.

$$\begin{array}{ll}
\text{H—C—COOH} & \text{H—C—COOH} \\
\quad\|\| & \quad\|\| \\
\text{H—C—COOH} & \text{HOOC—C—H} \\
\text{Maleic acid (cis)} & \text{Fumaric acid (trans)}
\end{array}$$

Such molecules are not unsymmetrical and hence cannot be optically active; they differ also in the relative positions of their substituting groups, and hence it follows that they must differ in properties and stability.   This proved an admirable explanation for such isomerism as is observed, for example, in the cases of fumaric and maleic acids, of the two crotonic acids, of angelic and tiglic acids, and many more now familiar to every student of organic chemistry.

Extension of the Theory.—Van't Hoff's book was hardly published when it was attacked with the utmost violence by Kolbe, whose aversion to mechanical conceptions was well-known, and who did not hesitate to characterize the idea that the spatial arrangement of atoms in molecules could be determined as something "not far removed from belief in witchcraft and spirit rapping." From the start, however, the new idea enjoyed the powerful support of Wislicenus whose work did much to extend and verify its conclusions, as indeed has all organic work since that time; most conspicuously perhaps that of Emil Fischer on the constitution of the sugars.   The fundamental idea has also been extended with time to include other elements besides carbon.   In 1890 it was shown by Le Bel that when the five valencies of nitrogen are satisfied by five dissimilar groups, optical isomerism can be realized, and the same holds true for quadrivalent tin and quadrivalent sulfur.   Furthermore in the cases of trivalent nitrogen Hantzsch and Werner have made out a very strong case for something akin to *cis trans* isomerism in the case of the oximes and for the diazotates.

$$\begin{array}{llll}
\text{C}_6\text{H}_5\text{—C—H} & \text{C}_6\text{H}_5\text{—C—H} & \text{C}_6\text{H}_5\text{—N} & \text{C}_6\text{H}_5\text{—N} \\
\quad\|\| & \quad\|\| & \quad\|\| & \quad\|\| \\
\text{N—OH} & \text{HO—N} & \text{KO—N} & \text{N—OK} \\
\text{Benz }\textit{syn}\text{ aldoxine} & \text{Benz }\textit{anti}\text{ aldoxine} & \textit{Syn}\text{ diazotate} & \textit{Anti}\text{ diazotate}
\end{array}$$

Not long after the appearance of van't Hoff's pamphlet similar views were published by Le Bel. The two had been fellow-students in the laboratory of Wurtz at Paris, where both had thought out essentially the same idea, each without mentioning it to the other. It is pleasant to record that the question of priority in the matter cast no cloud upon their friendship.

Bivalent Carbon.—Historically the most important step in the transition from the type theory of Gerhardt to the structure theory had been the introduction of the methane type by Kekulé. This made the quadrivalence of carbon a cornerstone of the new philosophy. Nevertheless once the theory was well established, evidence began to accumulate that this quadrivalence is by no means universal. There had, of course, always been the glaring case of carbon monoxide which everyone was willing to overlook so long as it stood alone, but about 1892 the work of John Ulric Nef of Chicago and others began to show with increasing cogency that there were several types of organic substances, notably the isonitriles $RNC:$ and the fulminates $MeONC:$, where two of the bonds of carbon are apparently unemployed. The evidence is cumulative in character and therefore unsuitable for presentation here, but chemists are now for the most part well convinced that in such compounds carbon is actually bivalent.

Trivalent Carbon.—A more startling exception was first observed by Moses Gomberg of the University of Michigan in 1900. He had set out to prepare hexaphenyl ethane $(C_6H_5)_3C.-C(C_6H_5)_3$, by the action of zinc on triphenyl chloromethane $(C_6H_5)_3C.Cl$, when to his surprise instead of the inert compound which analogy led him to expect, he obtained a highly reactive substance of the same empirical composition which formed addition products with a great variety of substances, even absorbing oxygen from the air to form a stable peroxide. On account of these striking properties, and in spite of a molecular weight determination, Gomberg did not hesitate to ascribe to his substance half the formula of hexaphenyl ethane $(C_6H_5)_3C.$ and to give it the name *triphenylmethyl*. This conclusion seemed so unorthodox that universal interest was at once aroused, and many chemists came forward with attempts to show how the unusual phenomena observed might be accounted for in a more conventional way. As time has gone on, however, and especially since the remarkable work of Schlenk in 1910 upon the corresponding compounds of biphenyl, it has become increasingly apparent that, in solution at least, a carbon atom attached to three benzene rings has lost practically all affinity for another carbon similarly connected, and at the same time has acquired properties of marked unsaturation toward other substances. A whole class of such compounds are now known, and they furnish convincing proof that we here have to do with substances in which carbon is truly tervalent.

Tautomerism.—Another troublesome difficulty has lain in the fact that certain compounds apparently have almost equal claims to two structural formulas, some of their behavior being easier to explain on the one and some on the other hypothesis. The phenomenon is called tautomerism, and acetoacetic ester is the classic example, for it reacts sometimes as if it had the formula $CH_3.CO.CH_2.COOC_2H_5$ and sometimes as if its structure were $CH_3.C(OH):CH.COOC_2H_5$. It was doubtless the influence of physico-chemical considerations which led to the true solution of this difficulty, by assuming that in all such cases two substances actually are present (though perhaps in very unequal quantities) and in dynamic equilibrium with each other, that is, that they are mutually convertible with a high velocity, so that when one component is used up by a reaction the other is immediately transformed to take its place. The idea that acetoacetic ester was an equilibrium mixture had been made probable by the work of Brühl and others upon its optical properties, but a striking confirmation of this theory was furnished when in 1911 Knorr succeeded in isolating the two forms and measuring the velocity of their mutual transformation. Tautomerism then is really isomerism in which both substances are so rapidly convertible into each other that under ordinary circumstances it is impracticable to isolate either.

Special Researches.—Still more important, however, than any of these general discussions have been the great series of researches clearing up the constitution, relationships and syntheses of whole classes of compounds. The limitations of a work of this kind would hardly permit even an enumeration of them, to say nothing of any adequate appreciation. Among the greatest rank those of Emil Fischer upon the sugars carried on since 1883, upon the derivatives of uric acid from 1892, and upon the proteins since 1899, all especially important on account of the magnificent experimental work involved and secondarily on account of the physiological significance of the substances concerned. With these may be mentioned the work of Baeyer upon the constitution of benzene, and upon indigo, the latter being especially rich in the great number of subordinate problems in all branches of organic chemistry which it raised and for which it suggested solution. There must also be mentioned Victor Meyer's work upon the derivatives of thiophene beginning in 1883, and that of Wallach upon the terpenes which has progressed uninterruptedly since 1884. Last though by no means least comes the recent work of Willstätter upon chlorophyll which began in 1906.

The Coal-tar Industry.—An account of the development of organic chemistry would hardly be complete without some mention of the more important events in the history of the coal-tar industry. Up to the middle of the nineteenth century this tar had been an extremely unwelcome and troublesome by-product of the gas works. Use was found for some of it as fuel, some was used for the preservation of timber, and the lower boiling portions were employed more or less as solvents, but these uses afforded no complete or profitable employment of the material. Aniline was found in tar by Hofmann in 1843, and the discovery led this chemist to his extensive researches on amines. In 1845 his discovery of benzene in the tar made possible the preparation of aniline and similar bases in large quantities, and in 1856 William Perkin, a student of Hofmann, while studying the action of oxidizing agents upon crude aniline oil prepared a dye which he called *mauve*. Against the advice of his teacher (who thought he ought to devote his talents to pure science) Perkin withdrew from the Royal College of Chemistry and began the manufacture of this and other products upon a commercial scale. His example was soon followed by others. Fuchsin came upon the market in 1859, and between 1858 and 1866 the work of Peter Griess, another associate of Hofmann, upon the diazo compounds made possible the almost infinite combinations now known as the azo dyes. In 1867 Graebe and Liebermann showed by a fortunate reaction that alizarin, the coloring principle of the madder plant was really a derivative of anthracene and that it could be prepared economically from this source. This discovery had a twofold influence, for an unexpected use was now found for tar anthracene, and the large acreage in France which had hitherto been cultivated for madder was made available for the production of foodstuffs. Finally the work of Baeyer upon indigo bore such fruit in the hands of Heumann and the chemists of the Badische Company that by 1894 this important staple could be produced from naphthalene at a price permitting competition with the natural product, and somewhat later it was manufactured from this source in a quantity sufficient to meet the requirements of the world.

Although dyes have proved the most important products of coal tar industrially, countless other compounds, suitable for use as remedies, perfumes, explosives, and so forth, have been prepared from the same source. To the chemist the great interest of this industry lies in the fact that every step in its progress has resulted from the application of the highest class of scientific work to the problems concerned. It has proved a veritable triumph of mind over matter.

Emil Erlenmeyer (1825–1909) played an important part in the development of organic chemistry. He was the son of a German preacher and went to Giessen in 1845 to study medicine. Upon hearing Liebig's lectures he decided to study chemistry. He spent one semester at Heidelberg and, upon returning to Giessen, was unable to find a place in Liebig's laboratory, so he went to work under H. Will. The next year he was made an assistant and had fourteen students under him.

Erlenmeyer had four sisters and three brothers who desired to study, so in 1849 he refused an appointment at the university and went into business as an apothecary. In 1855 he sold the business and went back into chemistry at Heidelberg. There he came into contact with Kekulé and became an ardent exponent of Kekulé's views on the structure of organic compounds at a time when some, like Liebig, still clung to the dualistic theory and others advocated the inadequate type theory. Erlenmeyer was a very energetic worker and published about a hundred and fifty chemical papers, besides doing a great deal of other writing. He was particularly friendly toward beginners in chemistry. In 1859 he founded the *Zeitschrift für Chemie und Pharmazie* which he edited until 1869. In 1871 he became one of the editors of Liebig's *Annalen der Chemie und Pharmazie*.

Erlenmeyer discovered isobutyric acid in 1865, the constitution of naphthalene (1866), and the constitution of hydracrylic and lactic acids (1866). He explained the structure of lactones (1880) and synthesized tyrosine

(1883). In 1862 he recognized the existence of the triple bond in acetylene. He introduced the idea of valence in place of atomicity and started a book on the new theory of valence and carbon chains in 1864 which, like Kekulé's book started in 1861, was never finished. He was particularly interested in cinnamic acid, and his son, Emil Erlenmeyer, Jr., has carried on his father's studies along this and other lines. Erlenmeyer's ideas on molecules, atoms, volume, saturation capacity, and vapor density were clear and logical. He was interested in the work of Sainte-Claire Deville and predicted that the tetratomic atoms of sulfur, phosphorus, and arsenic would be dissociated if heated to a sufficiently high temperature.

Griess.—Peter Griess was born in Kirchhosbach near Cassel, Germany, in 1829 and, although he showed promise as a boy, had considerable difficulty in settling down to serious study at the German universities. After studying at Cassel, Jena, Marburg, Munich, and again at Marburg, he began to pay some attention to his studies in his twelfth semester and occasionally did some work in the chemical laboratory. In 1856 he obtained, with some difficulty, a recommendation from Professor Kolbe with which he obtained a position in the *Ohlersche Anilinfarbenfabrik*. Not long after that a careless worker accidentally set fire to the factory and destroyed it. Thus thrown out of a job, Griess returned to Marburg to work under Kolbe and became, instead of the carefree student, a model of industry astonishing his instructors. In the fall of 1858 A. W. Hofmann paid a visit to Marburg, and Kolbe succeeded in interesting him in Griess as a promising young man whose father was a simple man and could not afford to keep him at the university much longer.

Griess went to London with Hofmann as assistant in the Royal College of Chemistry. In 1862 he left the Royal College to work in a brewery. Here he worked six or seven hours a day in the laboratory and was not allowed to publish any of his results, but during his spare time he was perpetually at work in his own private laboratory on the reactions of diazo chemistry, which had interested him in Marburg and also at the Royal College. He died in 1888. He was a skillful experimenter, and his work of fundamental importance in the development of the dye industry.

Carl Schorlemmer (1834–1892) was born in Darmstadt, Germany. In 1853 he went to work as an apothecary and as such moved to Heidelberg. Here he came under the influence of Bunsen, so that he gave up pharmacy and went to Giessen to study chemistry under Will and Kopp. In 1859 he went to England as assistant to Roscoe, and in 1874 he was made professor of organic chemistry at Manchester which was the first chair of its kind in England. He worked on the aliphatic hydrocarbons and showed that what had been assumed to be "free methyl" was the same as ethyl hydride, which we now call *ethane*. He discovered a general method for converting a secondary into a primary alcohol and studied the boiling points of the paraffins and the constitution of aurin and suberone.

He published *Chemistry of Common Life* in 1874 and *Rise and Development of Organic Chemistry* in 1875. In 1877 the *Treatise on Chemistry*, which he wrote with his colleague at Manchester, Sir Henry Enfield Roscoe

(1833–1915), appeared in German, and the next year in English. This was the outstanding English treatise on chemistry for about fifty years. Schorlemmer was interested in social democracy and was a friend of Karl Marx. Throughout his life he sought to improve the lot of the workingman.

Rudolf Fittig (1835–1910) was born in Hamburg, the son of a teacher in a private school. In 1856 he entered the University of Göttingen where he worked under Wöhler, getting his degree in 1858. He was assistant to Wöhler for some time. He was made professor at Tübingen in 1869 and succeeded Baeyer at Strasbourg in 1876. He wrote a textbook in 1868, the eleventh edition of which was published in 1887. He was interested in the *Zeitschrift für Chemie und Pharmazie* (1865–1871) and helped edit Liebig's *Annalen der Chemie und Pharmazie* (1895–1910). There are credited to him and his students 399 papers on chemical topics.

He discovered the pinacone reaction (1859) and diphenyl (1862) and synthesized aryl hydrocarbons by a reaction now called the *Fittig reaction*, which he used first with Tollens in 1864 when he made toluene by allowing a mixture of bromobenzene and methyl iodide to react with sodium. He synthesized mesitylene (1867), discovered isophthallic acid (1867), and investigated complex salts, such as $K_4Mn(CN)_6$ and $K_3Mn(CN)_6$ (1868).

He worked on piperine, discovered phenanthrene, proposed the diketone formula for quinone, worked on unsaturated acids (1877–1904), discovered coumarone, synthesized α-naphthol, studied ketonic esters, discovered diacetyl, and showed the relationship of the γ-hydroxy acids and lactones.

Perkin.—William Henry Perkin was born in London in 1838 and entered the Royal College at London in 1853. He soon became, like Griess, an assistant to A. W. Hofmann. He spent his evenings experimenting at home. He became interested in the artificial production of quinine, and in the course of his studies, which were unsuccessful with respect to the desired end, tried the effect of treating aniline with potassium dichromate, obtaining a precipitate of aniline black from which he obtained the color known as aniline blue or mauve (*cf.* page 298). This can be reckoned as the start of the coal-tar color industry in England.

Perkin had a large share, also, in the introduction of artificial alizarin. About 1874 he abandoned the manufacture of dyestuffs and devoted himself to researches in pure chemistry. Among other things, he discovered the reaction depending on the condensation of aldehydes with fatty acids. He was knighted in 1906 and died in 1907.

Johannes Wislicenus (1835–1902) was born in a Lutheran parsonage at Klein-Eichstedt. The family was of Polish descent, and Johannes's father was very liberal in his religious views. In 1846, the family moved to Halle, but as a result of his radical views he was forced to flee to England in 1853. At that time, the eighteen-year-old boy had started studying at Halle, but he and the rest of the family followed the father to England, and they all decided to migrate to America. The first ship they took was badly damaged by a storm off the coast of Ireland so that they were forced to disembark, and on the second ship cholera broke out and thirty-six lives were lost.

WILLIAM PERKIN
1838–1907

302

In November, 1853, they reached Boston, and the antislavery movement made considerable impression upon them.

Wislicenus earned $10 in working up a hair tonic for a barber and obtained some other work at $9 a week.   He went to New York and became interested in an educational scheme which attracted some students, but unfortunately the promoter ran off with all the funds.   Wislicenus then went back to Boston and got a job at $6 a week, helping Professor Horsford make analyses at Harvard College.   He also became interested in the Mechanics Institute and taught there.

In 1856 the family went back to Europe and settled in Zurich, where there was sufficient religious tolerance.   Wislicenus heard lectures at Zurich but went back to Halle in 1857 as a student and private assistant to Heintz.   For a time his religious radicalism caused consternation on the part of the university, but he quieted down when he found that Heintz had to assume the responsibility.   He had trouble because of the Latin requirement since he had studed at a Realschule which did not prepare students for the university, but he got his degree, nevertheless, in Zurich and almost immediately began to teach chemistry and mineralogy.   He was promoted in 1861, became assistant professor in 1864, and full professor in 1867.   He was called to Basel in 1869 but declined.   In 1871 he succeeded Adolf Strecker at Würzburg and succeeded Kolbe in Leipzig in 1884.

The work of Wislicenus, together with that of Baeyer, Wallach, and others, placed the theory of the asymmetric carbon atom on a firm basis. At first he was very practical in his work, as he needed to earn money, but he was really an idealist.   He worked on aldehyde ammonia compounds, acetoacetic ester, glutaric acid, methyl-β-ketone, vinyl ether, vinyl acetic acid, and hydrazoic acid.   In 1874–1879 he revised the Regnault-Strecker textbook in two volumes.   Over one hundred papers bear his name in chemical literature, and he taught many students and did much to develop the theory of organic chemistry.

Baeyer.—Johann Friedrich Adolf von Baeyer was born in Berlin in 1835.   His mother was a Jewess and her son Adolf, according to Emil Fischer, showed the result of the amalgamation of the good characteristics and abilities of the Semitic and Germanic races.   When only twelve years old, he discovered a new double carbonate of copper and sodium, and his experiments with indigo the next year started his interest in this dyestuff.   After about twenty years of research, Baeyer later succeeded in making this vegetable dyestuff in the laboratory, which is regarded as one of the most brilliant pieces of synthetic work ever accomplished in organic chemistry.   Baeyer studied physics and mathematics at the University of Berlin, but his studies were interrupted by a year of service in the army, after which he went to Heidelberg

JOHANN FRIEDRICH WILHELM ADOLF VON BAEYER

1835–1917

to work under Bunsen. The latter, however, had then lost all interest in organic chemistry, which appealed to Baeyer, so that Kekulé became his real teacher, although he obtained his degree in 1858 at Berlin with a dissertation on *De arsenici cum methylo conjunctionibus*, which was undoubtedly suggested by Bunsen. In Heidelberg little opportunity was given to students who preferred to work under Kekulé, so Baeyer worked in a very primitive private laboratory, nearly losing his life in discovering the frightful arsenic monomethyl chloride. Soon after this, Kekulé was called to Ghent in Belgium, and Baeyer followed him there.

In 1860 Baeyer returned to Berlin, was unable to find place to work at the university, but obtained, through the influence of his father, a modest position at the Gewerbe Schule in Berlin where he remained twelve years. Here the laboratory facilities were good and Baeyer succeeded in accomplishing much important work on indigo and uric acid and in physiological chemistry. In 1872 he was appointed professor of chemistry at Strasbourg, where he remained three years, attracting such students as Emil Fischer. In 1875, after the death of Liebig, he was called to Munich. There he was able to live a life of ease up to his death in 1917. The work of Baeyer and of his pupil Emil Fischer did much to develop organic analysis and synthesis in Germany, not only with respect to the training of students, but especially in the development of chemical industry. Baeyer was a practical, empirical chemist rather than a theoretical dreamer.

Albert Ladenburg (1842–1911) was the son of a well-to-do lawyer. He studied at the technical school at Carlsruhe but was chiefly interested in literature, music, and hunting. At the age of eighteen he went to Heidelberg to study mathematics under Hess but became interested in physics and chemistry. He came under the influence of Bunsen, Kirchhoff, Carius, and Erlenmeyer. He studied at Berlin but came back to Heidelburg to get his degree. With his students he published about 276 papers. He wrote a *History of Chemistry* and *Lectures on the Development of Chemistry during the Last* 100 *Years* (1869). He worked under Kekulé in 1869 and helped develop the theory concerning the constitution of aromatic compounds.

He visited Frankland in England in 1865 and went to Paris to work under Berthelot but found Wurtz more friendly. He worked with Friedel and Crafts on silicon compounds and showed that silicon in its compounds resembled carbon. In 1867 he became privatdocent at Heidelberg and was called to Kiel in 1873. He published a comprehensive *Handwörterbuch*

in thirteen volumes in 1882–1896. He went to Breslau in 1889 and sometimes had as many as a hundred students studying chemistry there. He
proposed the prismatic formula for benzene (1869), synthesized optically
active coniine (1886), and worked on the constitution of other alkaloids.

James Mason Crafts was born in Boston, Massachusetts,
March 8, 1839. His boyhood days were spent under particularly
favorable surroundings, and his interest in science was stimulated
by the lectures of Agassiz, Cooke, and Rogers, and by personal
acquaintance with the last named, who was the founder and
first president of the Massachusetts Institute of Technology.
Crafts fitted up a laboratory in his own house and carried out
experiments there that he found described in Hare's *Chemistry*.
He attended the Lawrence Scientific School during its early
years and received the B.S. degree in 1858.

After studying another year at Cambridge, Massachusetts,
he went to Freiberg in 1859 to study mineralogy and mining
engineering, being one of the first Americans to study at that
famous School of Mines. At Freiberg, Crafts became interested
in chemistry, so he migrated to Heidelberg to work under Bunsen
with whom he became very friendly. Bunsen and Kirchhoff
had just begun their studies with the spectroscope, and Crafts,
while acting as Bunsen's assistant, showed that cesium was
present in the waters of Nauheim.

In 1861, Crafts went to Paris to work under Wurtz at the
École de Médecine where he remained four years. In 1865 he
returned to the United States, examined mines in Mexico, and
traveled in California. When Cornell University was founded,
he was made the dean of the chemical faculty where he developed
the laboratory method of instruction.

In 1870, Crafts became professor of general chemistry at
the Massachusetts Institute of Technology where he did much
to build up the chemistry department. In 1874, because of
ill health, he relinquished his work there, although he retained
the title of non-resident professor until 1880. Most of the time
from 1874 to 1891 was spent in Paris at the École des Mines
where he carried out, partly by himself and partly in collaboration with Friedel, a valuable series of investigations on ethers
and other organic compounds of silicon and on the well-known
aluminum chloride method of synthesizing organic compounds.

JAMES MASON CRAFTS
1839–1917

Crafts did so much important work in Paris that most German scientists thought him a Frenchman.

Crafts also did some work on the density of the halogens at high temperatures and his investigations into thermometry were so accurate and thorough that they are still regarded as classic. For this work he was awarded the Jecker prize of 2,000 francs in 1885 by the Paris Academy of Science, he was made Chevalier of the Legion of Honor by the French government, and in 1911 he was awarded the Rumford medal by the American Academy of Arts and Sciences.

In 1891 Crafts returned to the Massachusetts Institute of Technology, taking charge of the instruction in organic chemistry in 1893. On the death of President Walker in 1891, he was made chairman of the faculty and a few months later he was chosen president. He received the LL.D. degree from Harvard in 1898. He resigned from active duty in 1900 but retained his interest in chemistry, maintaining a research laboratory at the institute.

Although his scientific activities were frequently impaired by ill health, he did much to develop chemical and physical science in this country. He was extremely modest but always the gentlemanly scholar, generous toward those in need of help.

Jacob Volhard (1834–1910) was born in Darmstadt, the son of a lawyer. In 1852 he began to study in Giessen just before his fellow townsman, Liebig, left for Munich. He worked under Heinrich Will and in 1855, when only twenty-one years old, received the Ph.D. degree *"per magna cum laude."* He worked for one semester under Bunsen and then was assistant at Munich for two years. Both Liebig and Volhard were quick-tempered, which probably explains why Volhard soon withdrew and loafed for about a year. Then too he had typhoid fever, and after his recovery, he was unable to find congenial work. At this time, however, Hofmann happened to visit Darmstadt and Volhard's father told him that he had a brilliant son who had become a problem. So in 1860 he went to England to work under Hofmann as a "voluntary worker." He hadn't been there long before he got disgusted, threw away his apparatus and chemicals, and left the laboratory. Hofmann went to his room and in a very friendly way counseled him not to give up. Volhard accepted the advice but returned to Germany in 1861.

In 1862 he began work at Marburg where he received considerable inspiration and published work that aroused the admiration of Liebig. As a result, Volhard went back to Munich after a seven-year absence. In 1863 he was made privatdocent. In 1862, when the American student Ira Remsen came to Munich to work under Liebig, he was disappointed to be obliged to work under Volhard instead, but his disappointment was short-lived. In 1868, Volhard received a flattering offer from the university at Turin, in Italy, which he refused, and in 1869 he was made full professor of organic chemistry at Munich. In 1870 when Wurtz defined chemistry as a "French science founded by the immortal Lavoisier," Volhard joined vigorously in the German protest.

In 1871, owing to the illness of Liebig, Volhard took over the editorship of Liebig's *Annalen der Chemie und Pharmazie*, at first with his friend Erlenmeyer, who withdrew after a year, and retained this editorship until his death. There are about sixty-seven scientific papers published by Volhard, either alone or with his students. He wrote a book on qualitative analysis, which was published in English, with the help of Renouf of Johns Hopkins. In organic chemistry his syntheses of sarcosine (1862), creatine (1868), and thiophene (1885) and his work on cyanamide deserve special mention. In 1877, he was called to Königsberg but refused to go. In 1878, however, he accepted a call to Erlangen, and in 1882 he went to Halle.

The story of Volhard's life is of special interest because it was that of a brilliant young man who had considerable difficulty in getting started after winning his Ph.D. degree, and it looked for a time as if he would never amount to much as a scientist. Although classed as an organic chemist, his work on analytical chemistry was important. While working on cyanamide, he accidentally discovered the reaction of thiocyanate and silver ions and the Volhard method of titrating silver or halide, which is based on the fact that red ferric thiocyanate does not form until all silver ions in a solution have been precipitated as insoluble silver thiocyanate. This method is in common use today.

The Volhard method of titrating manganous ions with permanganate in a nearly neutral solution is also well known. His accurate gravimetric method for determining manganese as the anhydrous sulfate is still recommended. He took particular interest in methods for standardizing permanganate solutions, introduced the use of mercuric oxide as precipitant in quantitative separations and studied iodometric procedures. Among other things, he devised a form of absorption flask, a drying tube, and a ring burner.

Friedrich Konrad Beilstein (1838–1906) was one to whom innumerable chemists all over the world are grateful for the monumental work that he accomplished in cataloguing all the important data concerning carbon compounds in his *Handbuch der Organischen Chemie*. Of the fourth edition, which was started in 1918, there are now seventeen volumes, but, as commonly bound, it really consists of twenty-seven volumes which cost about $40 each at prevailing prices. The work started with notes that Beilstein probably arranged for his own use while at Göttingen from a desire to keep in touch with all the literature of organic chemistry. In 1881 the first edition of two volumes was published, and he did practically all of the editorial work without any assistance. In 1886 the second edition of three volumes was finished, and in 1900 the third edition was completed. From that time, the work passed out of Beilstein's hands and has been continued by the German Chemical Society. The book is brief but exhaustive in its summary of all work done in organic chemistry.

Beilstein was born in St. Petersburg, of German parents, and was a master of Russian as well as of German. As a youth he was precocious, and he was only fifteen years old when he went to Heidelberg in 1853 to study under Bunsen and only twenty when he received the Ph.D. degree in 1858. In 1855 he studied mathematics and physics besides working under Liebig at Munich and in 1856 went back to Heidelberg to work in analytical, inorganic chemistry, which he soon decided was not his field.

In 1857 Beilstein went to Göttingen and worked with Wöhler who was then in his prime, and here he associated with other chemists who later became famous. In the same year he went to Paris for a year with Wurtz. In 1859 he was assistant to Löwig at Breslau and in 1860 had a similar position under Wöhler at Göttingen, but was made privatdocent the same year. In 1865 he was made assistant professor. At Göttingen he was very active both as teacher and investigator. He became, together with Fittig and Hübner, editor of Kekulé's *Zeitschrift für Chemie und Pharmazie* and remained with it until 1871 when its publication ceased.

In 1865 he declined a call to St. Petersburg, but in 1866, when only twenty-eight years old, he became professor at the Technological Institute of St. Petersburg. He succeeded Mendelejeff and remained in Russia for thirty years. In 1881 he was made a member of the Russian Academy of Science, an honor which carried with it a suitable financial reward and opportunity for research, and was made professor emeritus in 1891. He spent his last years in Switzerland but frequently visited Germany. He was a genial companion, witty, and possessed of a remarkable memory. He never married, and his well-spent life was devoted to science with remarkable fixity of purpose. He liked to travel and loved music.

Beilstein's researches started with a study of cyanogen compounds and his doctorate was obtained as a result of a masterly study of murexide. He became interested in isomerism such as that of chlorotoluene and benzylchloride or of the chlorinated benzoic acids. He also worked with aliphatic compounds. As a manipulator he was less skillful than his friend Fittig, but his knowledge and understanding of the literature were far greater. In all he published about eighty-eight scientific papers.

Carl Graebe (1841–1927) was born at Frankfort on the Main and died there. His father started an import house in New York but was recalled to Germany in 1839 as American consul. In 1860 Carl went to Heidelberg to work under Bunsen and got his Ph.D. degree in 1862. The young man then went to Marburg to work under Kolbe but left him to work with Bunsen again. In 1864 he spent some time in technical work and thus became interested in dyestuffs. In 1865 he spent a half year under Erlenmeyer in Heidelberg but then went to Berlin to work with Baeyer at the Gewerbe Schule as assistant. It was during this period that he worked with Liebermann and synthesized anthracene. A German patent for producing this dyestuff was denied, but in England he was more successful, and the industry flourished until in 1900 as much as 2,000 tons were produced in 12 months.

In 1869 he spent some time in Mannheim but was in Leipzig from 1869 to 1870. From 1870 to 1875 he was at Königsberg but had to give up his work because of a nervous breakdown. He went to Zurich in 1876 and spent 2 years there without any regular work, but in 1878 he was called to Geneva and was very happy there until in 1906 he withdrew and went back to his hometown. As a result of the inflation after the World War he lost most of his money and received no pension, but his friends raised a fund so that his last years were free from want. In 1920 the first volume of his *History of Organic Chemistry* was published. Besides his important work with Liebermann on anthracene and alizarin, Graebe discovered acridin with Caro (1870), synthesized carbazole with Glaser (1872), and synthesized derivatives of quinoline and some acenaphthenes (1893).

Carl Liebermann (1842–1914) was born in Berlin and spent most of his life there. In 1861 he went to Heidelberg and worked under Bunsen, but the next year he returned to Berlin and worked for two years under Sonnenschein. In 1863 he went to Baeyer in the Gewerbe Akademie and was graduated in 1865. To please his father he took up industrial work for two years and at Mühlhausen learned about dyes. In 1867 he gave up his industrial work and went to work at Berlin under Baeyer where he profited by association with Carl Graebe, who had been made assistant there the previous year.

In 1869 he was called to Leipzig as privatdocent, but Baeyer gave him a similar position in 1870, and in 1873 he was made professor at the Gewerbe Akademie. He remained there until shortly before his death, but during this period (1882) the institution became the Technische Hochschule. He was called to Königsberg in 1877, and later to Kiel, but refused to leave Berlin. His work with Graebe on anthraquinone, alizarin, and phenathrene was of special importance for the development of the dyestuff industry. He worked on quercitrin and rhamnetin and discovered the so-called *Liebermann dyes*, which belong in part to the indophenols. He is also remembered for his work on the action of nitrous acid on phenols and secondary amines (Liebermann's reaction).

Remsen.—Ira Remsen was born in New York in 1846 and died at Carmel, California, in 1927. He studied in the public schools and in the Free Academy (now College of the City of New York) and was graduated from the latter in 1865. Two years later, he received the M.D. degree at the College of Physicians and Surgeons of Columbia University. He then went abroad to study in Munich under Liebig but worked under Volhard there. He next visited Göttingen where Wöhler advised him to work under Fittig. In 1870 he obtained the Ph.D. degree at Göttingen after which he served as assistant to Fittig who had been called to Tübingen. At Williams College, he was professor of chemistry and physics from 1872 to 1876. Feeling the need of a suitable textbook, he translated Wöhler's *Organic Chemistry* into English but soon began to write books for himself. His *Principles of Theoretical Chemistry*, published in 1876, was marvelously clear and was translated into German and Italian.

In 1876 he was called to Johns Hopkins as professor of chemistry. In 1879 he established the *American Chemical Journal* which he edited for many years and which was finally merged into the *Journal of the American Chemical Society*. Remsen served as president of Johns Hopkins from 1901 to 1912. He was a masterly teacher and an outstanding chemist. He was awarded at least six honorary degrees. His lectures were never dull, his logic was simple but effective, and he inspired many students. His eight textbooks were very successful, and he published many scientific papers, mostly on researches in organic chemistry. He had much to do in shaping chemical thought during the last half of the nineteenth century.

Victor Meyer was born in Berlin in 1848 and died in 1897, a suicide. Although Jewish by birth, he was brought up quite free from Jewish beliefs and ritual. He was eventually confirmed in the reformed Jewish church but married a Christian and brought up his children in this religion. His parents were not anxious to have him study chemistry but permitted him, in 1865, to attend the University of Berlin just after Hofmann had assumed the chair of chemistry there. He stayed there one semester and then went to Heidelberg and worked under Bunsen, hearing lectures in organic chemistry by Emil Erlenmeyer. He received his doctor's degree in 1867, at the age of nineteen, no research being required under Bunsen at that time. He became Bunsen's assistant and analyzed mineral waters for a year, meanwhile helping students to prepare for their examinations. Then he turned to organic chemistry and worked under Baeyer at the Gewerbe Schule in Berlin.

In 1871, he became professor of organic chemistry at the polytechnic school of Stuttgart, but the next year he was called to the Zurich Polytechnicum, where his students were often older than the professor. There he accomplished numerous researches in organic chemistry which were characterized by much origi-

VICTOR MEYER
1848–1897

nality, discovering, for example, thiophene in benzene (1882), which had not only been missed by other experimenters, but the indophenin reaction, due to the presence of thiophene, had been hitherto regarded as a characteristic test for benzene. In 1876 he began to reach into the field of physical chemistry and devised a new method for the determination of gas density in 1878. This convenient method enabled him to show that arsenious oxide vapors corresponded to the formula As_4O_6, that mercury and cadmium yielded monatomic vapors, and that halogen molecules dissociated into atoms on heating, a phenomenon which he continued to study up to his death.

In 1884 he published with the American F. P. Treadwell (born in Portsmouth, New Hampshire, in 1857, died in Zurich in 1918) *Tables for Qualitative Analysis*. In the next year, 1885, Meyer was called to Göttingen after the death of Hübner (1837–1854), the successor to Wöhler. Here he had so many students that the old laboratory became much too small, and it was necessary to build a new one. Meyer was one of the first to take up van 't Hoff's theory of the asymmetric carbon atom, and he became interested in the stereochemistry of nitrogen and the testing of the Hantzsch-Werner theory.

In 1888, Bunsen decided to retire from his professorial chair at Heidelberg and chose Victor Meyer as his successor. After some difficulties were overcome, Meyer was able to leave Göttingen for Heidelberg. There, during the next nine years, he carried out with his students many brilliant pieces of work, partly with gases, as in studying the equilibrium between hydrogen, iodine, and hydrogen iodide, but chiefly in the field of organic chemistry.

In 1892 he astonished the chemical world with his discovery of the iodoso compounds which showed great reactivity with respect to the ease with which the IO group changed to IO_2 (the iodo group). Soon after the discovery of *o*-iodobenzoic acid, he noticed what he called steric hindrance; benzoic acids with a substituent in the ortho position are esterified with difficulty, if at all, by treatment with hydrochloric acid in alcohol. Meyer's *Lehrbuch der organischen Chemie*, which he published with Paul Jacobson (1859–1923), is one of the best books of the kind ever published. Personally, Meyer was very attractive and his lectures were admired greatly. He overtaxed his strength, however, and during the last years of his life was often ill and frequently had to resort to drugs in order to sleep. Finally his nervous system was so shattered that he could stand it no longer and committed suicide. The accomplishments of this man, who died at the age of forty-nine, were remarkable, and he exerted a great influence upon the development of chemistry during the last half of the nineteenth century.

Emil Fischer was born at Euskirchen (Rhenish Prussia) in 1852 and died July 15, 1919. After leaving the Bonn Gymnasium in 1869, he was inclined to study mathematics and physics but this did not meet with the approval of his father. After trying for a year to make a good merchant out of Emil, the father decided that the young man was far too stupid ever to succeed as a merchant and only fit to study. Fischer worked some time at the University of Bonn, but Kekulé did little to increase Fischer's interest in chemistry; but at Strasbourg, under Baeyer, he became an enthusiast in organic chemistry. After taking his degree in 1874, Fischer served eight years as Baeyer's assistant at Munich. He was appointed to the chair of chemistry at Erlangen in 1882 and was called to Würzburg in 1885. Seven years later, he succeeded A. W. Hofmann as professor of chemistry at the University of Berlin, where he remained till his death. Fischer did not believe in merely projecting theoretical speculations but based his ideas, perhaps more than any other chemist, upon the results obtained in the laboratory. He devoted his life to the development of organic chemistry, and his work is characterized by originality, resourcefulness, and experimental skill. In his hands, no substance seemed too complex to admit of analysis and synthesis.

Such important classes of chemical compounds as the sugars and the proteins became easy to understand as a result of his work. The Fischer theory accounting for the so-called *Walden reversal* illustrates his insight, and, as a result of his work, the importance of stereochemistry was emphasized. During the World War his researches on carbon, rubber, constituents of coal tar, oils, fats, tannins, foods, etc., did much for Germany, although he never regarded the conflict as being waged in the best interests of the German people, as a result of which views

EMIL FISCHER
1852–1919

his social position was jeopardized.   It was, therefore, remarkable to find Fischer willing to do so much for his country during the war.   In 1875 he discovered phenylhydrazine and his work on rosaniline occupied his attention in 1878–1879.   His early work on uric acid was done in 1882–1884, and the later work on purin was begun about 1894.   The work on sugars was started in 1883 and the glucose synthesis completed about 1890.   His work on proteins dated from about 1899.   "His forte was to enter fields where others had but broken ground."   He was awarded the Nobel prize in 1902 and his laboratory at Berlin attracted to it a constant stream of brilliant students from all parts of the world.

Paul Ehrlich was born in 1854 near Breslau and died in 1915 at Frankfort on the Main.   He studied at the universities of Breslau, Strasbourg, Freiberg, and Leipzig and took examinations for the M.D. degree in his tenth and twelfth semesters.   His dissertation, written in 1878, was on the theory and practice of histological coloring.   Therein the twenty-three-year-old student of medicine made interesting deductions concerning the fixation of dyestuffs.   Ehrlich spent his entire life continuing his studies along these lines.   As a physician he was not interested so much in clinical practice as in the development of scientific medicine.   His side-chain theory—according to which similar compounds in the protoplasma of living beings possessed certain "side chains" in their chemical composition which were characteristic of the individual and had considerable influence upon life with respect to nourishment, poisons, and disease—has received considerable discussion.   He was connected with the Erste medizinische Klinik der Charité at Berlin and received the title of professor in 1887.   His work in his own private laboratory in Berlin attracted attention, and to further such studies he was called to Steglitz in 1896 and to Frankfort on the Main in 1898.   He may be called the father of *chemicotherapy*, his greatest discovery being salvarsan (606), which cures syphilis.   No medicinal remedy has ever been the subject of such thorough investigation.

Otto Wallach (1847–1931) was born at Königsberg, received his doctorate at Göttingen, and was made professor there in 1889.   He had served as assistant to Wichelhaus at Berlin and with Kekulé at Bonn, had worked for a time in an aniline works and was professor at Bonn from 1873 to 1876.   He was awarded the Nobel prize in 1919 in recognition of his achievements in organic chemistry and chemical industry as a result of pioneer work in the realm of alicylic compounds. He was well known for his work on terpenes. He wrote several books, published many papers, and had many Americans as students.

Ernst Beckmann (1853–1923) was born in Solingen and received his doctor's degree in 1878 at Leipzig. He worked at first as a pharmacist, then as assistant to Fresenius, but in 1890 was made assistant professor at Leipzig and full professor in 1897. He was a brilliant man and is known especially for his work in perfecting methods for the determination of molecular weights and for his discovery that ketoximes when treated with concentrated sulfuric acid, with phosphorus pentachloride in ether, or with benzene sulfonyl chloride are converted into acid amides, with substituents attached to the nitrogen atom. This is known as the *Beckmann transformation* and is due to a rearrangement of the atoms in the molecule, thus: $R-\overset{\parallel}{\underset{NOH}{C}}-R'$ becomes

$R-\underset{R'-N}{\overset{\mid}{C}}-OH$ or $R-\underset{NHR'}{\overset{\mid}{C}}=O$.

Ludwig Claisen (1851–1930) was born at Cologne, studied at Bonn and at Göttingen (1869–1874), then worked in the laboratory at Bonn (1872–1882). After this he spent several years in England. He was made privatdocent at Munich in 1887 and stayed there until 1890, when he was made professor at the Technischer Hochschule at Aachen. He stayed at Aachen until 1897, spent seven years at the University of Kiel, and after this worked with Emil Fischer at Berlin. He was a skillful manipulator and is known for the so-called *Claisen condensation* which serves for the introduction of an acid radical into esters, ketones, and aldehydes; sodium ethoxide or sodamide is commonly used as the condensing agent. An example of the Claisen reaction is the formation of sodium cinnamate from benzaldehyde and sodium acetate. He worked on aromatic ketonic esters, benzalcetone, and benzoylacetic ester and explained the synthesis of acetoacetic ester as due to the intermediate formation of an ortho compound. He synthesized pyrazole and isoxazole derivatives, carried out studies on tautomerism, worked on acetals and on rearrangements in *o*-acyl derivatives of ketonic esters. With respect to the keto and enol forms of such a substance as acetyldibenzoylmethane, he recognized the influence of negative groups.

Paul Sabatier (1854 ——) was assistant to Berthelot and obtained his doctorate in 1880. He was made professor at Toulouse in 1882 where he has remained in spite of a tempting offer to go to the Sorbonne. He was interested at first in physical chemistry, but his fame rests chiefly upon his numerous hydrogenation experiments which he carried out with his students, especially Senderens, Mailhe, and Murat. For this work he received the Nobel prize in 1912.

Eugen Bamberger (1857–1932) was born in Berlin and started to study medicine there in 1875. He spent a semester at Heidelberg and became interested in natural science. He returned to Berlin and studied chemistry

PAUL SABATIER
1854 ——

319

there from 1876 to 1880 and took his degree under Hofmann. He then worked under Rammelsberg at Charlottenberg and in 1883 went to Munich to assist Baeyer. In 1891 he was made assistant professor and in 1893 full professor of general chemistry at the Swiss Polytechnikum at Zurich. In 1904–1905 he was forced to give up teaching because of serious nervous trouble and, in spite of hospital treatment and operations, he lost the use of his right arm and suffered from severe headaches. He worked with an assistant in a private laboratory for some time.

Some idea of Bamberger's ability is shown by the fact that about 430 scientific publications bear his name. He had a keen sense of smell and a remarkable memory for odors as well as facts. He delighted in studying the mechanism of complicated reactions and worked with small quantities of material in small test tubes. He studied guanidine derivatives, polycyclic hydrocarbons, hydrogenation of polycylic aromatic compounds, benzimidazoles, isoquinoline, mixed azo compounds, diazo compounds, anthranil, and photochemical reactions. He discovered retene and pyrene, introduced the use of sodium in amyl alcohol as reducing agent, studied the reduction products of naphthylamines, cyanuric acid, cyanamines, the reduction of nitrobenzene to nitrosobenzene and phenylhydroxylamin, benzimide and dimethylaniline oxide, and the isomerism of nitroso compounds. From 1894 to 1900 he carried on a long controversy with Hantzsch on the structure of the diazo compounds.

Theodor Curtius (1857–1928) was born at Duisburg on the Rhine and studied philosophy and music at Leipzig. He was a baritone singer, sang in some concerts, and composed music. He became interested in chemistry and studied at Heidelberg, Munich, and Erlangen, where he received his degree in 1886. After serving in the army, he was made professor of chemistry at Kiel, and after two years went from there to Heidelberg (1901), to succeed Victor Meyer. He discovered diazoacetic ester, hydrazine, hydrazoic acid and its derivatives, pyrazoline derivatives, benzaldazine, and other aldazines besides the so-called *tetrazine* derivatives. He also worked on glycollic esters and on polypeptide. His method of obtaining amines from carboxylic acids, with intermediate formation of azide, isocyanate, and urethan, has proved useful in synthetic work and is known as the *Curtius reaction*. He was editor of the *Journal für praktische Chemie* where much of his work is to be found.

Arthur Hantzsch (1857–1935) was born at Dresden and obtained his doctorate in 1880 at Würzburg. In 1883 he was instructor at Leipzig but in 1885 was called to the Polytechnikum at Zurich. In 1933 he went to Würzburg but was in Leipzig as professor of chemistry from 1903–1927. Hantzsch has been called a fine example of the classicist with keen intellect, intuition, and critical power. With his students he published over five hundred papers on pyridine, coumarone, thiazole, hyponitrous acid, cyanuric acid, cyamelide, acid-base indicators, etc. With A. Werner, he studied the stereochemistry of nitrogen and the structure of oximes. He also studied the tautomeric behavior of phenylnitromethane and nitrophenols as pseudo acids, the properties of diazo compounds, the relation of light absorption to chemical constitution, and applied the modern physicochemical methods, particularly electrical conductivity, to organic chemistry.

Ludwig Knorr (1859–1921) was born near Munich, studied at Munich under Volhard (1878), at Erlangen under Fischer (1879), and at Heidelberg under Bunsen. He assisted Fischer at Munich (1880) and in 1882 followed Fischer to Erlangen where he took his degree. In 1885 he again followed Fischer, this time to Würzburg, and was made full professor at Jena in 1889. He published with his students about 115 papers. He studied pyrazolone and isopyrazolone and their derivatives and in 1887 discovered the important drug called antipyrine (phenyldimethylpyrazolone) which soon became industrially important.

His work on tautomerism (diacetyl succinic ester, acetoacetic ester, and acetyl acetone) led him to regard a tautomer as a substance which consists of an allotropic mixture of two forms in mobile equilibrium with each other. He devised a colorimetric method for determining the ratio of enol form to keto form in a tautometric mixture. He synthesized acetonylacetone, discovered aminoethyl ether, and worked on piperazine derivatives and alkaloids.

W. H. Perkin, Jr. (1860–1929), was born four years after his father's discovery of mauve, the first aniline dye. After two years at the Royal College of Science, he went to Germany at the age of nineteen and spent five years there working under Wislicenus at Würzburg and Baeyer at Munich. In 1887, he was made the first professor of chemistry at Heriot Watt College in Edinburgh and in 1892 went to Manchester to succeed Schorlemmer. At 1912 he accepted the chair of chemistry at Oxford as successor to Odling; here he did a great deal toward improving the methods of chemical research. Along with his scientific activities, he found time to indulge his love for music and played the piano well.

He synthesized polymethylene compounds, ethyl benzoyl acetate and derivatives, anthraquinone, indene and hydrindene and derivatives, di- and trimethyl glutaric acids and derivatives, camphor and derivatives, alkaloids, terpenes, brazalin, hematoxylin, harmine, harmaline, and isoquinoline derivatives. His work on polymethylene rings led to Baeyer's strain theory. Englishmen regard him as a greater chemist than his father and feel that he did not receive sufficient recognition outside of England.

Eduard Buchner (1860–1917) was born in Munich and died from wounds received in the war. He obtained his Ph.D. at Munich in 1888 from work under Baeyer. He was on the faculty at Kiel in 1893–1896 and was called to Tübingen in 1896. From there he went to the Berlin Agricultural College in 1898, then to Breslau in 1909, and finally to Würzburg in 1911. He was awarded the Nobel prize in 1907 for his important work in connection with alcoholic fermentation which he showed to be caused by an enzyme (ferment) contained in bran cells and not by the cells themselves. He published a book on this, *Die Zymasegärung*, in 1903.

Nef.—John Ulric Nef was born at Herisau, Switzerland, on June 14, 1862. When four years old, he was taken to the United

States where he received his education and did most of his scientific work. In 1880 he entered Harvard with the intention of eventually studying medicine, but he became so fascinated with chemistry and did such brilliant work that upon his graduation in 1884 he was awarded the Kirkland fellowship for study abroad. He went to Munich and at once came under the influence of Baeyer. It was undoubtedly the work of Baeyer on unsaturated valences of carbon in some of its compounds that had much to do with shaping Nef's later work. Under Baeyer, Nef studied compounds which show to a pronounced degree the phenomenon known as *tautomerism*. In 1886, Nef received the Ph.D. degree at Munich, his thesis being on the benzoquinone-carbonic acids.

In 1887, Nef became professor of chemistry at Purdue, but two years later he was called to Clark University where he remained until 1892. In that year he took charge of chemistry at the newly opened University of Chicago, and remained there until his death.

Nef was an ardent worker, a bold thinker, and one of the most brilliant organic chemists that this country has ever produced.

L. F. Jones[1] divides the important work of Nef into five periods. In the first period (1885–1891), Nef was engaged in the study of tautomeric compounds, especially of the keto-enol type, and of nitroparaffin salts. He concluded that the metal in the salts of these compounds was united to oxygen and that the free acids were hydroxyl compounds. In the second period (1891–1895), he began to study compounds containing bivalent carbon. He worked with isocyanides, fulminates, hydrocyanic acid, and acetylidene compounds. The third period (1895–1899) was occupied with the attempt to isolate methylene, CH_2, or some hydrocarbon containing bivalent carbon. During these years he developed theories concerning addition reactions and dissociation. These theories he applied during the fourth period (1899–1904) to the chemistry of esters of halogen acids, nitric acid, and sulfuric acid and to monatomic alcohols, ethers, aldehydes, acids, ketones, etc. The fifth and last period (1904–1915) was occupied chiefly with the study of the dissociation of sugars in the presence of oxidizing agents and of alkalies.

---

[1] *Proc. Am. Chem. Soc.*, pp. 44–72, 1917.

Nef's writings are hard to read, partly because they were published for the most part in German and largely on account of the originality of his theories.   In spite of these radical theories, it must be admitted that Nef was engaged in pioneer work and did much to develop organic chemistry in this country and to increase the respect of foreigners for the work done here.   During the summer of 1915, Nef suffered from heart trouble and after some weeks in a sanitarium at San Francisco, he was able to leave for Del Monte, but died suddenly at Carmel, California, on August 13, 1915.

Arthur Harden (1865 ——) who was awarded a Nobel prize in 1929, was born in Manchester, studied there under Sir Henry Roscoe and at Erlangen under Otto Fischer where he obtained his PhD. degree in 1888.   He was lecturer and demonstrator at Queen's College at Manchester for nine years, after which he was chemist at the British Institute of Preventive Medicine and professor of biochemistry at London University.   He obtained recognition as a result of his studies on the chemical effects of bacteria, especially with respect to enzyme action in the fermentation of sugars.

Johannes Thiele (1865–1918) was born at Ratibor in Upper Silesia and was a delicate youth, subject to fainting spells.   In the preparatory school, he became interested in chemistry but in 1883 went to Breslau to study mathematics.   In 1884 he went to Halle but was refused a place in Volhard's laboratory because he had never heard a lecture on chemistry.   He demanded an examination, however, and Volhard afterwards quoted the psalmist and said, "The stone which the builders rejected has become the head stone of the corner."

He became lecture assistant to Volhard who in many ways treated him like a son.   He obtained his degree in 1890 and in 1893 went to Munich as professor.   In 1902 he was called to Strasbourg and at the death of Volhard became editor of Liebig's *Annalen*.   He discovered semicarbazide, studied tetrazole derivatives, nitramide, derivatives of fulvene, guanidine derivatives, and unsaturated lactones and published about 150 original papers on chemical topics.

Victor Grignard (1871–1935) was born in Cherbourg, France, and studied mathematical science at Lyons.   He received his degree at Lyons in 1901 and returned there in 1906 after lecturing at Bésançon.   He was made professor at Lyons in 1908.   He was called to Nancy in 1909 but returned to Lyons in 1919.

He received the Nobel prize in 1912 for his development of the *Grignard reaction*, which was partly discovered by his teacher P. A. Barbier, and is of considerable importance in synthetic organic chemistry.   If a solution of an alkyl halide in ether is heated gently with metallic magnesium, an addition product or *Grignard reagent* is formed.   Thus, from CH_3I, the product is $CH_3.Mg.I$.   This addition product is very reactive toward water, alcohols,

VICTOR GRIGNARD
1871–1935

ammonia, acids, aldehydes, and ketones, and the Gringnard reaction is much used for the synthesis of hydrocarbons and various alcohols.

Fritz Pregl (1869–1930), head of the Institute of Medical Chemistry at Graz, Austria, deserves mention because he was the originator of the methods of quantitative organic microanalysis which have found widespread application all over the world.   Pregl was originally given a medical training but became specially interested in biochemical problems and did some work with K. B. Hofmann, Abderhalden, and Emil Fischer on bile acids, composition of proteins, and starch.   While studying the bile acids, lack of material made it necessary to give up the work or else invent methods for making accurate analyses with a few milligrams of substance.   By using a very delicate balance and by modifying the apparatus so as to measure small quantities accurately, he was able to devise methods which resulted in a marked saving of time and of material.   Students of all nationalities came to him in order to learn the special technique and enjoyed working with him.

Richard Willstätter (1872 ——) was born at Carlsruhe.   He received his doctorate at Munich in 1894 and began to lecture there in 1902.   He was made assistant professor in 1905 and was called to Zurich as professor in 1905 at the Polytechnikum.   In 1912–1915 he was director of the Kaiser Wilhelm Institute for Chemistry near Berlin but in 1915 went back to Munich.   He retired from the university in 1920.   He studied alkaloids and their derivatives, quinones, quinone-imines, lecithin, pyrones, chlorophyll, hemoglobin, the coloring matter of flowers, the assimilation of carbon dioxide by plants, and the action of enzymes.   He was awarded the Nobel prize in 1915 together with Sabatier.

Adolf Windaus (1876 ——) was born in Berlin and studied medicine in Frieberg.   He then went to Berlin and obtained the Ph.D. degree in 1899. He became an instructor at Freiburg in 1901 and in 1906 was made full professor, but he was called to the Kaiser Wilhelm Institute near Berlin, then to Innsbruck in 1913, and to Vienna in 1914.   In 1915 he succeeded Wallach as director of the laboratory at Göttingen.   He is best known for his discovery of vitamin D, and for his work on cholesterol, digitalis glucoside, and other cardiac poisons, colchicine, and imidazole.   He was awarded the Nobel prize in 1925 for his work on sterins and their relation to vitamins.

The discovery of the first vitamin was interesting.   A physicist, Hess of New York, found that cholesterol exposed to ultraviolet light had the power of curing rickets.   He turned to Windaus, as the foremost investigator of cholesterol, who assured him, after considerable study in which he was joined later by the physician Rosenheim of London, that it was not cholesterol that acquired the antirachitic power, but something present as impurity which he eventually found to be ergosterol, a phytosterol found in yeast. Windaus also studied the bile acids.

Heinrich Wieland (1877 ——) was born at Pforzheim in Baden and studied at Munich, Berlin, and Stuttgart, taking his degree from Munich in 1901.   He passed through the several grades at Munich and in 1913 succeeded Thiele as head of the chemical laboratory there.   In 1917–1918 he

was at the Kaiser Wilhelm Institute for Chemistry near Berlin and in 1921
he succeeded Gatterman at Freiburg.   But he was back in Munich in 1925
succeeding Willstätter.   He received the Nobel prize in 1927 in recognition
of his valuable work on the nitrogen compounds of organic chemistry,
especially the alkaloids, his work on the bile acids, and other contributions
in the field of biochemistry.   His work on hydrazines and free radicals containing nitrogen, such as $(C_6H_5)_2N$, and his studies on the mechanism of the
reactions that take place when halogen or a nitro group enters the benzene
ring are worthy of mention, as are his studies concerning the relationships
between aliphatic and aromatic compounds and, especially, his dehydrogena-
tion theory.   Previously, in studies of metabolism it had been generally
inferred that activated oxygen was of fundamental importance in life
processes.   According to Wieland, it is hydrogen that becomes activated in
respiration, and the function of the oxygen is merely to remove the activated
hydrogen.   Wieland has revised Gattermann's *Die Praxis des organischen
Chemikers*, which was first published in 1894, has gone through twenty-four
German editions, has been translated into English, Italian, and Russian, and
still remains a standard text for teaching beginners how to carry out work in
the organic chemistry laboratory.

Hans von Euler (1873 ——), whose full name is Hans Karl August Simon
von Euler-Chelpin, was born in Augsburg, Swabia, and studied physical
chemistry at Berlin, Göttingen, Würzburg, and Stockholm.   He worked
under Nernst and Arrhenius.   After obtaining his doctorate, he was
appointed in 1898 an instructor in physical chemistry at Stockholm, but his
activities have been distributed among inorganic, organic, and biochemistry.
His main interest seems to be in biochemistry and the chemistry of fermentation, for which he received the Nobel prize in 1929.   A glance at the latest
Decennial Index of *Chemical Abstracts*, which contains the titles of several
hundred papers published by von Euler and his students, impresses one with
the variety and multiplicity of his work.   He has explained the processes of
sugar fermentation on the basis of modern methods of physical chemistry.
He is well known for his important work with vitamins, and he has shown,
for example, that the carotin from beets is the most powerful of all known
vitamins.   He has written several books on such topics as *Qualitative
Analysis, Plant Chemistry, Chemistry of Enzymes, Chemistry of Yeast and
Fermentation.*

Walter Norman Haworth (1883 ——) was born in England and was a
pupil of W. H. Perkin.   After obtaining the degree of Doctor of Science,
he studied with Tammann and with Wallach at Göttingen and obtained the
Ph.D. degree in 1910.   Since 1920 he has been teaching at the University of
Birmingham.   He received the Davy medal in 1928, the Longstaff medal in
1933, and the Nobel prize in 1937.   His work on the sugars and vitamin C
(ascorbic acid) has been of special importance.   His formulation of sugars as
δ-oxides and cyclo-semiacetals has done much to clear up the chemistry of
carbohydrates.

Hans Fischer (1881 ——) was born at Höchst on the river Main and
studied chemistry and medicine at Lausanne and Marburg (1889–1904).

He received his Ph.D. degree at Marburg and in 1908 received the M.D. degree at Munich. He worked for a time at the Medical Clinic in Munich, then he went to Berlin to work under Emil Fischer, but he returned to Munich in 1911 and in 1912 began lecturing on internal medicine. In 1913 he succeeded Weinland at Frank's Physiological Institute, where he also lectured on physiology. In 1916 he succeeded Windaus as professor of medical chemistry at Innsbruck University, and the next year he had a similar post at Vienna. Since 1921 he has been professor of organic chemistry at the Munich Polytechnikum, as successor to Wieland.

The output of Hans Fischer and his students during the last fifteen years has been voluminous, but in a brief account of his own work he merely states that he is interested in the chemical constitution of blood and bile pigments and in the chemistry of pyrrole. His synthesis of hemin is of particular interest, and his work has helped to show that pyrrole compounds must play an important part in the constitution of blood and bile pigments. Fischer was awarded the Nobel prize in 1930.

Paul Karrer (1889 ——) was born in Moscow, but his parents were Swiss. He studied chemistry at Zurich under Alfred Werner and obtained his degree in 1911. For a year he was Werner's assistant, after which he went to Frankfort to work under Paul Ehrlich and stayed there six years. He became particularly interested in biochemical problems and organic arsenic derivatives. In 1918 he was assistant professor at Zurich and the following year was made full professor as successor to Werner.

Karrer has been interested in the study of polysaccharides, glucosides, vegetable pigments, and vitamins. He isolated vitamin A and showed its relationship to carotin (vitamin C or ascorbic acid) and to lactoflavin (vitamin B_2). Among his numerous publications is a large textbook, *Organic Chemistry;* an English translation of the fifth German edition of this work was made in 1938. He has received many honorary degrees and was awarded the Nobel prize in 1937.

Literature

There is an account of Kekule's life and work in the *Chemical Society Memorial Lectures.* His principal paper on aromatic compounds is in the *Klassiker,* No. 145, but the best idea of his contribution to organic chemistry is still to be derived from the first two volumes of his *Lehrbuch der organischen Chemie.* The third volume appeared much later and was essentially perfunctory.

Ernst Cohen's *Jacobus Henricus van't Hoff, sein Leben und Wirken,* Leipzig, 1912 is decidedly interesting. Van't Hoff's *La Chimie dans l'espace* has appeared in several editions and is still authoritative.

Readers interested in the recent development of organic chemistry are referred to J. B. Cohen's *Organic Chemistry for Advanced Students,* 2 vols., to Paul Karrer's *Organic Chemistry,* translated by A. J. Mee of Glasgow, or to *Organic Chemistry,* edited by Henry Gilman, *et al.* Portraits and brief biographical sketches of *The Nobel Prize-winners* have been published in Zurich, Switzerland, under that title; it is a beautiful book, but the English translation is not always correct.

Excellent biographical sketches, usually with portraits, of many prominent organic chemists are often printed in the *Berichte der deutschen chemischen Gesellschaft*. Prior to 1923, these sketches were to be found from the *Index of Subjects* under *Nachruf* or *Nekrologe*, but in later years they are in the *Table of Contents* under *Lebensbeschreibung* or *Nachrufe*. Reference to such sketches can be found in the annual subject index of the *Chemisches Zentralblatt*, under *Biographien und Nachrufe*, and in *Chemical Abstracts*, either under *Biographies* or under *Obituaries*.

CHAPTER XIX

INORGANIC CHEMISTRY SINCE 1860

In the last chapter, short biographical sketches were given of a few of the prominent organic chemists whose work, for the most part, has been published since 1860. Some of those chemists taught hundreds of students, many of whom were inspired to do better work and go further than their teachers. The advance in chemical knowledge has been rapid since 1860, and in the Third Decennial Index of *Chemical Abstracts* there are over two million entries. In 1938 alone there were over 65,000 papers published on chemical subjects.

It is impossible for any one person to evaluate properly all the work that is being done today, and what seems important to one chemist may be incomprehensible to another and not worthy of mention in the opinion of a third. In this chapter, some of the important work of the last eighty years will receive consideration, and the lives of typical chemists will be sketched, without any attempt at completeness. The conclusion must not be drawn that everything that is not mentioned is of minor importance. In fact, the most important work of recent years will be discussed in the textbooks in the various fields of chemistry and for that reason need not be emphasized here.

Analytical chemistry has been called the yardstick of the science, and modern chemistry differs from the older chemistry very largely because our present theories are based upon careful measurements. Although many of our best methods of analysis were in use in the eighteenth century, as is true of the separation of calcium from magnesium, the art of chemical analysis has made enormous strides toward perfection since 1860. To illustrate this, brief sketches will be given concerning the lives of Heinrich Rose, Karl Remigius Fresenius, Georg Lunge, Alexander Classen, Clemens Winkler, Frank Austin Gooch, William Francis Hillebrand, Edgar Fahs Smith and Frederick Pearson Treadwell.

329

Heinrich Rose (1795–1864) really does not belong to this period, but he wrote a comprehensive textbook on *Analytical Chemistry* which was published in 1829, and the sixth edition of which was translated into French in 1861. This book had a far-reaching effect upon the progress of analytical chemistry in the nineteenth century.

Rose was born in Berlin and studied under Klaproth[1] there. His grandfather, Valentine Rose, Sr. (1736–1761), was a Berlin apothecary who is remembered for his discovery of Rose's fusible metal, an alloy of bismuth, lead, and tin which melts at about 93°C. His father, Valentine Rose, Jr., was also an apothecary and proved in 1800 that "sulfuric ether," made by the action of sulfuric acid on alcohol, contains no sulfur. Gustav Rose, a brother of Heinrich, was a distinguished mineralogist and crystallographer. Heinrich Rose started to study pharmacy at Danzig, served in the campaign of 1815 as a soldier, studied under Berzelius in Stockholm, and was graduated from Kiel. He became privatdocent at Berlin in 1822, assistant professor in 1823, and full professor in 1835. He discovered antimony pentachloride and understood the mass-action effect of water upon it prior to the work of Guldberg and Waage in 1867. He studied the methods of analytical chemistry and improved them.

Karl Remigius Fresenius (1818–1897) was born in Frankfort on the Main and studied pharmacy at Bonn University in 1840. He went to Giessen in 1841 and was assistant to Liebig. He then became an assistant professor there in 1843, but two years later he accepted the chair of chemistry, physics, and technology at the Wiesbaden Agricultural Institute. In 1848 he became the first director of the chemical laboratory which he had persuaded the Nassau government to build at Wiesbaden. This laboratory became popular and has probably trained more analytical chemists than any other laboratory in the world. In 1841 he founded his *Zeitschrift für analytische Chemie* which still remains in the hands of the Fresenius family and is the leading journal devoted entirely to analytical chemistry. In 1841 he published the first volume of his famous textbook on *Qualitative Analysis*, and in 1846 he followed this with a volume on *Quantitative Analysis*. These books have been translated into several languages and were regarded as the best books on analytical chemistry for over sixty years. The seventeenth German edition of the first volume appeared in 1920 and contained 866 pages.

Georg Lunge (1839–1923) was born in Breslau and died in Zurich. His *Chemisch-technische Untersuchungsmethoden* is really a textbook on analytical chemistry, although Lunge was regarded as an industrial, rather than an analytical, chemist. Lunge was a recognized authority on the determination of sulfur in pyrite and on methods of standardizing acids. He received the Ph.D. degree at the University of Breslau in 1859, with a

---

[1] Martin Henry Klaproth (1743–1817) was considered the leading German chemist. He worked as an apothecary most of his life. He began to lecture in 1787 and was the first professor of chemistry at the University of Berlin, founded in 1810.

dissertation on *De fermentatione Alcoholica.* The same year he went to Heidelberg and worked under Bunsen and Kirchhoff. In 1860 he became chemist in a fertilizer factory in Silesia, and two years later he was making prussiate of potash, sal ammoniac, lead salts, and tartaric acid in his own plant. This he gave up and in 1865 became director of a chemical plant at Newcastle, England. There the Newcastle Chemical Society, which later became the Society of Chemical Industry, was founded, and Lunge became its president. In 1876 Lunge was called to the Polytechnischen Schule at Zurich, Switzerland, where he remained until 1907. He died in 1923.

Lunge's activity followed three distinct lines. (1) He was one of the best known teachers of industrial chemistry. (2) He was a skillful investigator of problems concerning chemical industry. (3) He was a voluminous writer. Prior to Lunge's time, most chemical factories were conducted by rule-of-thumb methods. Chemical receipts were treasured, and the theory underlying the chemical reactions involved was largely neglected. Lunge changed all this. His knowledge of chemical industrial processes was very broad, and he did much to improve them. His published writings number 675, including 86 books, some of them very comprehensive. Thus his four-volume book on *Chemischtechnische Untersuchungsmethoden* had reached its sixth edition in 1910, and his *Handbuch der Soda Industrie* comprised two volumes in 1879 and was enlarged in subsequent editions. His *Technical Chemists' Handbook* was revised by A. C. Cumming in 1930. His books appeared in English and French, as well as in German, and at least one of his very large works was written by himself in English, of which he was almost as good a master as of his native tongue. His work on methods of analytical chemistry led to the improvement of many standard methods and he suggested some new procedures. His work on tables of specific gravities of acids and bases in aqueous solutions is illustrative of his painstaking fidelity to details. His nitrometer for the gasometric analysis of nitrates is well known. His theories concerning the manufacture of sulfuric acid by the chamber process greatly improved our knowledge of this important industry. By his methods of instruction and by his work along many lines in the industrial field, Lunge accomplished much in harnessing chemistry to the service of mankind.

Alexander Classen (1843–1934) was born at Aachen and studied at Giessen and at Berlin. After obtaining his Ph.D degree, he worked for some time as an assistant and then in a private laboratory. In 1870 he was called to the Polytechnische Schule at Aachen to teach analytical chemistry. This became the Technische Hochschule, and Classen was made full professor there in 1882. In 1892 he became professor of electrochemistry. Classen and his students are best known for their work in establishing optimum conditions for the electrolytic determination of various ions. His *Handbuch der analytische Chemie, Theorie und Praxis der Massanalyse, Ausgewählte Methoden der analytischen Chemie,* and *Quantitative Analyse durch Elektrolyse* have been standard texts for over fifty years.

Our present theories concerning the chemistry of aqueous solutions is, to a large extent, the result of studies in connection with electrolysis. Electrolytic analysis furnishes a very exact method for determining many metal ions. By regulating the cathode potential it is possible to accomplish many electrolytic separations. As a result of the study of electrolytic potentials, an important method of electrometric analysis has been developed by which the end point of a titration is determined by a sudden change in cathode potential; these procedures are called *potentiometric titrations*. A recent modification has resulted in the so-called *polargraphic method* by which small quantities of impurity can be determined. By measuring the electrical resistance of a solution during a titration it is also possible to determine the concentration of electrolyte, and this gives us the *conductometric-titration* method. Thus, by measuring the temperature and electrical resistance of a solution of barium hydroxide before and after the combustion of a sample of steel in oxygen, the percentage of carbon in a sample of steel can be determined in about ten minutes, with the aid of a nomographic chart.

Clemens Winkler (1838–1904) began his studies at the Bergakademie, probably the oldest technical school in the world, at Freiberg, Germany, which is frequented by students from all parts of the world who are interested in mining. There he worked under Scheerer (1813–1875), who does not appear to have paid much attention to his students, although himself a good analyst of minerals. Winkler learned there to work on his own initiative, and his marked ability to make chemical problems clear was shown when his fellow workers came to him for advice. Much of the time he spent in analyzing new minerals brought to him by the mineralogist August Breithaupt (1791–1873). After two years at the Bergakademie, he wanted to study with Kolbe in Leipzig, but his father felt he needed him at home. He went to work in a color factory, but three years later, after his father's death, he became assayer for Pfannenstiel where he was kept too busy to accomplish much scientific research. He studied the properties of crystalline silicon and as a result of this research obtained the Ph.D. degree at Leipzig in 1864. In 1873 he succeeded Scheerer at the Bergakademie at Freiberg, remaining there the rest of his life, declining attractive calls to Dresden, Leipzig, Charlottenburg, and Göttingen. Soon afterward he persuaded the authorities to get Adolf Ledebur (1837–1906) to take over the lectures in metallurgy, and together these two men labored for many years.

Winkler, although a resourceful and skillful analyst, represents the careful, analytical type of scientist who is needed in every age. At a time when most young men with scientific aspirations in the field of chemistry were blinded with the marvelous advances taking place in organic chemistry, he elected to spend his life making careful analyses of inorganic material and later, when the physical chemists began to absorb most of the interest, he was regarded as conservative and old-fashioned. He published at least 125 papers in scientific journals and books on volumetric analysis and on technical gas analysis. The mineral winklerite was named after him by Breithaupt.

Winkler's interests lay entirely in the field of practical work rather than in the development of theories. He contributed valuable improvements to the methods of gravimetric, volumetric, and electrolytic analysis. His discovery of the element germanium, which proved to be the missing *ekasilicon* of Mendelejeff, was typical. Weisbach, the mineralogist, had discovered a new mineral argyrodite which he sent to Winkler to be analyzed. Repeated analyses of the mineral added up to only about 93 per cent, but Winkler did not give up the problem. After months of patient work he finally decided early in 1886 that a new element was present which, when present as oxide or sulfide, formed colloidal solutions with water and made its identification difficult. His determinations of the atomic weights of nickel and of cobalt are further proofs of his skill as an analyst. In attempts to learn more about the periodicity of the elements he prepared, for the first time, hydrides of magnesium, beryllium, lanthanum, cerium, zircon, and thorium. As by-product he found aluminum suboxide AlO. In publishing this work he made many theoretical and practical observations which inspired Hans Goldschmidt (1861–1923) to his important work on the reduction of metal oxides by aluminum. Winkler did a great deal also in developing the sulfuric acid industry.

Frank Austin Gooch (1852–1929) was born at Watertown, Massachusetts, he received the B.A. degree at Harvard in 1872 and the A.M. and Ph.D. degrees in 1877. Eleven years later he was awarded an honorary A.M. degree at Yale. He was an assistant to J. P. Cooke at Harvard and studied under Wolcott Gibbs and abroad until 1878. He served as analytical chemist in work for the tenth U. S. Census, the Northern Transcontinental Survey, and the U. S. Geological Survey and was made professor of chemistry at Yale in 1885, where he remained until his death. In the Kent Chemical Laboratory at Yale, Gooch and his students accomplished a great deal in the development of analytical chemistry. His crucible with the perforated bottom is known to every chemist. He showed originality in developing iodometric methods of volumetric analysis, and many other standard analytical methods were worked out or improved. He did considerable work in electrolysis with a rotating electrode. Besides writing many scientific papers he wrote at least five books. His *Methods in Chemical Analysis* (1912) and his *Representative Procedures in Quantitative Analysis* are worthy of particular mention.

William Francis Hillebrand (1853–1925) was born at Honolulu, December 12, 1853, the son of a physician. He was educated at Honolulu, at Oakland, California, and at Cornell (1870–1872). He studied six years in

WILLIAM FRANCIS HILLEBRAND
1853–1925

Germany, receiving the Ph.D. degree at Heidelberg in 1875. He also studied at the University of Strasbourg and at the Mining Academy at Freiberg. In 1879–1880 he worked as assayer at Leadville, Colorado, and was chemist for the U. S. Geological Survey from 1880 to 1908. From then until his death he was chief chemist for the U. S. Bureau of Standards. He was president of the American Chemical Society in 1906 and initiated the movement that led to the publication of the *Journal of Industrial and Engineering Chemistry.* He wrote several books on the quantitative analysis of rocks, besides contributing numerous papers to scientific journals. Hillebrand had an untarnished reputation with respect to accurate mineral analysis, and under him excellent work was accomplished at the Bureau of Standards in standardizing methods. His authoritative textbook, with Lundell, was published after his death.

Edgar Fahs Smith (1856–1928) was born at York, Pennsylvania. He was graduated from Pennsylvania College (now Gettysburg College) at Gettysburg in 1874. He went to Germany and studied under Wöhler and Hübner in Göttingen, obtaining the Ph.D. degree in 1876. In the same year he was appointed assistant to F. A. Genth in the Towne Scientific School of the University of Pennsylvania. In 1881 he was made professor of chemistry at Muhlenberg College in Pennsylvania and from 1883 to 1888 was professor at Wittenberg College in Ohio. In 1888 he was called back to the University of Pennsylvania to succeed Genthe as professor of analytical chemistry and remained connected with the university the rest of his life, retiring from active service in 1920. He was provost of the university from 1911 to 1920.

One of Smith's first literary labors was a translation into English of Richter's comprehensive books on inorganic and organic chemistry. Smith was a prolific writer and, besides publishing over two hundred scientific and historical papers, wrote twenty books. He enriched the literature of analytical chemistry, particularly with respect to electrolytic methods. His work on molybdenum attracted attention as well as his atomic weight determinations of palladium, molybdenum, selenium, tungsten, tantalum, columbium, boron, and fluorine. He had rare ability as a teacher and was a pleasing speaker, with an engaging personality. He was awarded nineteen honorary degrees.

Frederick Pearson Treadwell (1857–1918) was born in Portsmouth, New Hampshire, studied at Heidelberg and at Göttingen in 1875–1878 and, after obtaining his doctor's degree, worked as assistant to Bunsen from 1878 to 1881. Other Americans have acted as private assistants to German professors, but the career of Treadwell is remarkable because he went further. He was called to Zurich in 1881 and, after working through the various grades, became full professor at the Technische Hochschule there. His lectures on analytical chemistry were popular, and one of his students asked permission to publish his notes which encouraged Treadwell to write a *Kurzes Lehrbuch.* The book was issued in two volumes, one on qualitative analysis and one on quantitative analysis, and has been translated into several languages. His son, W. D. Treadwell, is a well-known analytical

EDGAR FAHS SMITH
1854–1928

chemist and is particularly interested in electrometric methods.   Most of the writings of this American were in German.

Chemistry in Russia.—In any English or German history of chemistry, the work of Russian chemists is likely to be neglected unless, like Wilhelm Ostwald, they have worked in another country and published their scientific papers in a language that most of us can read.   We have already discussed the work of Lomonosov, Mendelejeff, and here the lives of three other representative Russians will be outlined.   A Russian scientist is likely to be an extremely clever man, and many Russians have published the results of their work in German, or even in English, for they knew that only in this way would their work have an opportunity to effect the development of chemistry outside of Russia.   In the case of Mitscherlich it is doubtful whether Germans, as a whole, ever gave him full credit for his predictions with respect to the periodic table, for Lothar Meyer had similar ideas at about the same time.   Just as many Americans and Englishmen have studied in Germany, there are many Russian scientists who received their training there.

Nikolai Alexandrovitsch Menschutkin (1842–1907) was born in St. Petersburg.   He studied at the University there from 1858–1862 and then went to Tübingen, Paris, and Marburg but received his doctor's degree at St. Petersburg in 1869.   He taught there and was editor of the journal of the Russian Chemical Society.   Menschutkin published many papers, most of which had to do with organic chemistry, but in 1871 he published a book on *Qualitative Analysis* which was so good that it was translated into German and into English.

Boris N. Menschutkin (1874–1938), his son, was born in St. Petersburg and received his degree in 1895.   Since that time he has been teaching in Russia.   He has traveled in other countries and speaks several languages well.   Some of his historical studies, particularly with respect to the career of Lomonosov, have been published in English.   He has worked in the field of physical chemistry, in organic chemistry, and with molecular compounds, which are partly organic and partly inorganic.

Vladimir Nicolaevitch Ipatiev was born in 1867 at Moscow.   He has worked both with inorganic and organic substances and has published an enormous amount of work of high quality.   He has been specially interested in the hydrogenation of organic compounds and in the cracking of petroleum. He has received honorary degrees at St. Petersburg, Munich, and Strasbourg, has taught in St. Petersburg (Leningrad) at the university and at the Artillery Academy.   Since 1930 he has been professor of chemistry at

Northwestern University, Evanston, Illinois, and director of research for Universal Oil Products of Chicago, Illinois.

Atomic Weights.—One of the problems of the nineteenth century which attracted considerable attention was the exact determination of atomic weights. Great confusion prevailed in the early part of the century, and chemists were not at all agreed as to whether the atomic weight of oxygen was 8 or 16, and toward the end of the nineteenth century additional confusion was caused with respect to the choice of a standard for atomic weights. We have already seen how the Belgian chemist Jean Servais Stas developed accurate methods for determining atomic weights and for many years his values were by far the most reliable. During the latter part of the nineteenth century and early part of the twentieth, nearly, if not quite, all the gaps in the Mendelejeff periodic table of the elements have been filled and reasonably accurate values have been obtained for almost every atom, although, as we shall see in the next chapter, we now know that all atoms of a given element do not necessarily have the same atomic weight. To avoid confusion, an International Committee meets every year and carefully considers all work that has been done and agrees upon what seems to be the best value for the atomic weight of every element. The changes from year to year are now very insignificant in comparison with what they were toward the end of the nineteenth century. There are many chemists who have made accurate determinations of atomic weights since the time of Stas, but here only three will be mentioned—the Swiss, de Marignac, the American, Richards, and the Englishman, Aston.

Jean Charles Gallissard de Marignac (1817–1894) was born in Geneva, Switzerland. At the age of sixteen, he entered the École Polytechnique at Paris and also studied at the School of Mines for two years. After this he traveled in Scandinavia and Germany. In 1840 he went to Giessen to study under Liebig, but in spite of Liebig's enthusiasm for organic chemistry, de Marignac preferred the field of inorganic or mineral chemistry, although he did some work on phthallic acid. He went to work at the Sèvres porcelain factory but soon afterward received a call to the chair of chemistry and mineralogy at the Academy of Zurich, which became a university in 1878.

When only twenty-three years old, he began to study the rare earths. He discovered ytterbia and gadolinia and proved that tantalum is not the same as columbium (also called niobium). He was interested in crystallography, made many accurate analyses of minerals, studied diffusion, the specific heats, and expansion of salt solutions, and made patient, painstaking atomic-weight determinations of eighteen elements. To him the Swedish chemist Berzelius wrote, "I place the highest value on your experiments concerning atomic weights. The patience with which you repeat each experiment many times, the sagacity with which you vary your methods . . . and the conscientious manner in which you give the numbers dictated by the balance ought to assure for you the complete confidence of chemists."

Theodore William Richards.—Theodore William Richards was born at Germantown, Pennsylvania, on January 31, 1868, the fifth child of his parents. His father was an artist and his Quaker mother was a clever writer. The mother took charge of the boy's education until he entered Haverford College in 1882 as a sophomore. There he studied chemistry under Lyman B. Hall who, together with J. P. Cooke, a summer neighbor at Newport, Rhode Island, had considerable to do with interesting the lad in the study of science. After graduating from Haverford in 1885, at the age of seventeen, he decided to continue his studies at Harvard. There, however, a requirement in Greek had to be satisfied, but Richards, with the aid of his mother, was able to satisfy this requirement by six weeks of study. At Harvard he received the B.A. degree in 1886, the A.M. and Ph.D. degrees in 1888. Thus at the age of twenty he was the recipient of four college degrees. Subsequently he received honorary degrees from at least thirteen universities—Yale, Harvard, Cambridge, Oxford, Manchester, Princeton, Haverford, Pittsburgh, Pennsylvania, Prague, Christiania, Clark, and Berlin.

After being graduated from Harvard, he was awarded a traveling fellowship and studied in Germany under Jannasch, Victor Meyer, Hempel, and others. In 1889 he was appointed assistant in analytical chemistry at Harvard with which institution he remained connected until his death on April 2, 1928.

In 1894, Richards was offered the chair of inorganic chemistry at the University of Göttingen in Germany, where many Americans have studied. The offer was an attractive one since the laboratory facilities at Harvard were by no means adequate. One visiting Harvard at that time could not but wonder that Richards had been able to accomplish so much under the prevailing conditions. Richards was loyal to his alma mater and after careful consideration declined the call to Göttingen. He was then made full professor at Harvard, although only twenty-six years old. J. P. Cooke, with whom Richards worked as a student, was interested in atomic weights, and one of Richards's first investigations had to do with the determination of the atomic weights of hydrogen and oxygen. Prior to this time the atomic-weight determinations of Stas had been considered accurate but Richards, in checking over the work of Stas, was able to find errors. The atomic weights of no less than twenty-eight elements were determined by Richards and his students in the Harvard laboratories, and Richards came to be regarded as the foremost authority on atomic weights in the world. In 1907 he lectured in Berlin as exchange professor. Richards had an

Theodore William Richards
1868–1928

attractive personality, was pleasant to meet, and was interesting at all times as well as inspiring, although modest and unassuming. He played tennis and golf and was fond of yachting.

Besides the many honorary degrees already mentioned, Richards was the recipient of other honors in recognition of his outstanding ability. In 1910 he was awarded the Davy Medal, in 1911, the Faraday Medal, in 1912, the Gibbs Medal, in 1916, the Franklin Medal, and in 1914 he was awarded the Nobel prize, being the second American to receive this honor and the first American chemist. France awarded him the Le Blanc medal and the Lavoisier medal, and he was made a member of the Legion of Honor. He served as president of the American Chemical Society, the American Academy of Arts and Sciences, and the American Association for the Advancement of Science, besides being made the honorary member of many similar societies all over the world. He did much to develop accurate, analytical work and had a keen sense of the proper use of significant figures in computations. Hundreds of successful chemists received inspiration from him as a teacher, and among his well-known students were Hönigschmidt, who is now at Munich, and Gilbert N. Lewis, head of the chemistry department at the University of California.

Francis William Aston was born in 1877 and studied at the University of Birmingham. He was made an assistant professor there in 1909 and at Trinity College in 1910. He worked with J. J. Thomson at the Cavendish Laboratory. During the war of 1914–1917 he was technical head of the royal aircraft factory but returned to the Cavendish laboratory in 1919. He invented the "mass spectrograph" in 1919–1920 which is a modification of the method used by J. J. Thomson for the sorting out by means of magnetic and electrical fields the so-called *positive rays* produced by electrical discharges in gases. By this method of determining atomic weights, Aston showed that most of the elements are mixtures of what are called isotopes, *i.e.*, elements of different atomic weights but the same chemical properties. Thus in the case of chlorine, the recognized atomic weight of 35.46 is really the average weight of a number of elements with atomic weight 35 and another number of elements with atomic weight 37, but no single atom has the atomic weight 35.46. For this work Aston received the Nobel prize in 1922.

Chemistry in France.—During the last half of the nineteenth century, many Americans and Englishmen studied in Germany while very few studied in France. After the Franco-Prussian war, Germany advanced rapidly and exerted a powerful influence upon chemical thought throughout the entire world. The *Berichte der deutschen chemischen Gesellschaft* became the most important journal on organic chemistry; the *Chemisches Zentralblatt* was the most complete abstract journal; Fresenius's *Zeitschrift für analytische Chemie* was probably the best journal in

FRANCIS WILLIAM ASTON
1877 ——

analytical chemistry; Gmelin-Kraut's *Handbuch der anorganischen Chemie* and Beilstein's *Handbuch* were so comprehensive that most Americans and Englishmen felt that German
was the only language that they had to know in addition to the
mother tongue.   Then too, the effects of the French Revolution
and the Franco-Prussian war hampered the development of
science; and similarly, since the World War broke out in 1914 and
since all brilliant Jewish scientists were later expelled from
Germany, the development of chemistry in Germany has
received a tremendous setback.   Partly because of political
troubles, therefore, France seemed to be making little progress
in science, but in many ways the progress of Germany was over-
emphasized and France was neglected.   The monthly bulletins
of the French Chemical Society contain a great many important
papers, and one of the real reasons why French and Italian
chemistry of the nineteenth century has received so little attention in German, English, and American historical papers is
neglect on the part of the writers.   When Wurz in his *Dictionary*
defined chemistry as "a French science founded by Lavoisier,"
he antagonized foreigners and gave them an excuse to neglect
the work of Frenchmen.

Some very important chemical work has been done in France.
To illustrate this, attention will be given here to the work of
Raoult, Moissan, Le Châtelier, Becquerel, the Curies, and
Joliot.   They, as well as other French scientists, have done a
great deal to advance our knowledge of chemistry.

The Isolation of Fluorine.—As typical of the best inorganic
work of this period may be mentioned that of Moissan on the
isolation of fluorine and that of the same chemist upon the electric
furnace.   That some unknown element was present in the fluo-
rides was recognized by Lavoisier who put the radical of this
acid in his list of elements.   By this term, of course, he meant
not our element fluorine, but something corresponding to the
radical of muriatic acid, in harmony with his unfortunate theory
of the nature of such substances.   When Davy established the
elementary character of chlorine, fluorine began to appear in
the list of elements, but its isolation was delayed for many years.
It is so reactive that when by any operation, such as electrolysis,
it is for a moment set free, it attacks at once the walls of the

containing vessel, the electrodes, or the solvent, and so could not be isolated. Moissan, however, by using low temperatures and platinum electrodes was able in 1887 to prepare a little of the highly reactive substance, and in order to see it, he adopted the ingenious device of preparing vessels from transparent fluorspar, which of course is not attacked by the element. He carried on his experiments with such skill that he was able to make accurate determinations of most of the physical properties of this extraordinary substance.

The Electric Furnace.—Moissan also gave to chemistry an important piece of apparatus in his electric furnace. This is very simple in principle. Into a box of material extremely refractory to heat, usually lime, there are introduced two electrodes, usually of carbon, and between these are allowed to pass electric currents of great strength. The details differ according to whether the simple effect of heat or some reducing action is desired. With the hitherto unattained temperatures made possible by this furnace, Moissan was able on the one hand to reduce from their oxides many metals hardly obtainable in any other way and to prepare in quantity a large number of interesting carbides and other substances. Among these, calcium carbide, which is now prepared in this way on the large scale, has attained great practical importance, partly for the preparation of acetylene and partly for that of cyanamide, one of the more important of the newer fertilizers. Its formation also furnishes a means of obtaining nitrogen from the atmosphere, an important detail in modern national economy.

Raoult on the Freezing Point of Solutions.—The familiar phenomenon that salt water freezes at a lower temperature than fresh water first received serious attention from Blagden, an assistant of Cavendish, who studied the matter far enough to learn that, for solutions of the same compound, the depression of the freezing point is proportional to the concentration. Little further work was done until, in 1881, F. M. Raoult, then professor in Grenoble, made an extensive series of experiments along the same lines. These yielded the important additional information that for solutions of different substances in the same solvent, the depression of the freezing point was inversely proportional to the molecular weight of the solute, or, as Raoult expressed it,

"The quantities of different substances which depress the freezing point by an equal amount are those which the chemist calls molecular quantities." Not long after, Raoult found that an entirely analogous uniformity is to be observed in the elevation of the boiling point. These observations at once attracted the attention of organic chemists, who had hitherto possessed no reliable method for determining the molecular weights of non-volatile substances, and the technique of the determination as applied to such processes was much improved[1] by Beckmann. The results obtained by Raoult remained empirical, and, what was more serious, they showed numerous exceptions, most of which would be covered by the statement that in aqueous solutions of salts, as well as those of most acids and bases, the observed depressions of the freezing point (and elevations of the boiling point) were considerably greater than the rule required. What we now know as colloidal solutions, on the other hand, showed too little depression of the freezing point or elevation of the boiling point.

François Marie Raoult (1830–1901) was born at Fornes in France and became *aspirant répétiteur* at the Lycée of Rheims in 1853. After holding several intermediate positions, he was made professor of chemistry in Sens Lycée in 1862. There he prepared his thesis on the electromotive force of galvanic cells, with which he obtained his doctor's degree at Paris in 1863. In 1870, he was made professor at the University of Grenoble where he remained until his death. He found that the heat of reaction and the electromotive force do not correspond as they should if heat were a measure of chemical affinity. In 1878, he published his first paper on the freezing points of solutions and found that if 1 gram molecule of any substance is dissolved in 100 grams of a selected solvent (as benzene, acetic acid, etc.), the freezing point will be depressed equally. In 1884, he stated that, contrary to his expectations, the law did not apply to the solutions of salts in water. He studied the vapor pressure of non-aqueous solutions and showed that the molecular weight of a compound could usually be determined by the lowering of the vapor pressure as well as by the depression of the boiling point or elevation of the boiling point.

Henri Moissan (1852–1907) was born in Paris, studied in Frémy's laboratory, and attended lectures by Sainte-Claire Deville and by Debray

---

[1] Van't Hoff relates the following: "Being in Paris some years ago I asked Raoult's mechanician Baudin to furnish me with a thermometer just like that of Raoult. He, however, strongly advised me against this, remarking: 'The thermometer which Raoult uses is antediluvian!' Nevertheless, with this 'antediluvian thermometer' the world was conquered!"

Henri Moissan
1852–1907

346

(1827–1888). In 1879, he held a junior post in the Agronomic Institute at Paris and in 1886 he was professor of toxicology at the School of Pharmacy. In 1889 he was made professor of inorganic chemistry and later, in 1900, of general chemistry at the Sorbonne. In 1886, he succeeded in isolating the element fluorine by the electrolysis of a solution of potassium fluoride dissolved in liquid hydrofluoric acid at a low temperature. For this, and other brilliant work, he was awarded the Lacase prize in 1887 and the Nobel prize for chemistry in 1906. In connection with his experiments on the artificial production of diamonds, he developed the electric-arc furnace for obtaining high temperatures and with it prepared many new compounds, especially carbides, silicides, and borides, besides melting many substances which had been regarded as infusible. His most important writings were *Le Four électrique* (1897), *Le Fluor et ses composés*, and his *Traité de chimie minérale* in five volumes (1904–1906) which ranks as one of the best reference books on inorganic chemistry. He prepared uranium, tungsten, and vanadium with his furnace, studied the action of water on carbides, and obtained hydrides of calcium, sodium, and potassium, which he found to be nonconductors.

Henry Louis Le Châtelier (1850–1936) was born in Paris of a well-known family, for his father and brother were also prominent men. He finished his studies at colleges in France in 1872 and registered as a mining engineer. Two years later he was licensed to practice physical science. In 1877, after spending some time in Algeria, he became professor at the École des Mines where he had studied. He spent the rest of his life in Paris, where he lectured at the École polytechnique in 1882 and was made professor at the Collège de France in 1883. In 1887 he was made professor at the Sorbonne and the following year, professor of chemistry and metallurgy at the École des mines.

He began to study the mechanics of chemical reactions in 1888 to supplement the work of Berthollet, Sainte-Claire Deville, and Berthelot. He studied the laws of chemical equilibrium and the chemistry of solutions. From the laws of thermodynamics, he found that he could predict in which direction a reaction was likely to take place. In 1888 he stated that "if a system in physical or chemical equilibrium is subject to a stress involving a change of pressure, temperature, concentration, etc., the state of the system will automatically tend to alter so as to undo the effect of the stress." Thus, if a change of volume takes place as a result of a chemical reaction, then the application of pressure will tend to induce the formation of the compound or phase that has a smaller volume, or if the temperature is raised, that compound or phase which absorbs most heat is likely to be formed. This very important principle is known as *Le Châtelier's law.*

Le Châtelier did brilliant work as a scientist, teacher, writer, and editor. He made notable contributions to metallurgy, metallography, measurements of high temperatures, microscopy, ceramics, cements, chemical mechanics, and the theory of the combustion of gases. He showed how industrial problems should be attacked and pointed out the need for a closer union of pure and applied science.

HENRY LOUIS LE CHÂTELIER
1850–1936

In his study of cements he showed that good plaster of Paris consisted of $CaSO_4.\frac{1}{2}H_2O$, which he identified. He used the method of thermal analysis devised by Regnault and proposed a theory of the setting of hydraulic cements. In his study of gases, he determined temperatures of ignition, speed of propagation in explosions, and the explosive pressure. He studied the thermal expansion of glass and devised a sensitive dilatometer, and he studied carefully the complex reactions that take place in the production of ceramics. His study of metals and alloys was particularly noteworthy, and he made a daring prediction, which has been fulfilled, concerning the value of metallography to industry. Together with Osmond, he helped develop work with polished pieces of metal which he etched and examined under the microscope. From the appearance of the etched specimens he was able to obtain valuable information. Moreover, he was interested in the scientific management of industry as illustrated by Taylorism and translated Frederic W. Taylor's book into French. At the Sorbonne he had over three hundred students and during 1908–1922, directed the work of over one hundred graduate students.

Le Châtelier anticipated Haber with respect to the theory of making ammonia from the nitrogen of the atmosphere. He also made many practical applications of the phase rule of Gibbs and devised accurate platinum iridium couples for the measurement of high temperatures. In research work with his students he pointed out (1) the desirability of changing only one variable at a time, (2) the desirability of precise measurements with respect to every factor, and (3) the desirability of a defined objective for each step taken.

The *Revue de Metallurgie* was created by Le Châtelier about 1904, and he was editor of it until 1914. Besides his many scientific papers, he wrote books on metal alloys, steel, clays, and ceramics and acted as consultant in the manufacture of cement, steel, and synthetic ammonia. And with the advice of Sir Robert Hadfield, the Englishman, he recommended the use of helmets made of manganese steel for use in war.

The modern theory of atomic structure is based largely on the discovery of the electron and the facts of radioactivity. This will be discussed later at greater length, but, since we are now considering the work of French chemists, it is fitting to point out here that the discoveries of the radioactivity of uranium by Becquerel in 1896, of radium by Pierre and Marie Curie in 1898, and of thorium by Schmidt and by Mme Curie in 1898 led the Englishmen Rutherford and Soddy to the theory of atomic disintegration. Mme Curie herself was Polish but married a Frenchman and lived in France for the greater part of her life. Her daugher, Irène Curie-Joliot and her son-in-law Frédéric Joliot have also done much to increase our knowledge of the atom.

HENRI BECQUEREL
1852–1908
Reproduced from a photograph by the kind permission of Ch. Gerschel, Paris

Antoine Henri Becquerel (1852–1908) was born in Paris and, like his father, Alexandre Edmond Becquerel (1820–1891), and his grandfather, Antoine César Becquerel (1788–1878), was professor of physics at the Musée d'Histoire Naturelle in Paris. The grandfather had been interested in physical chemistry and the father had studied phosphorescent chemical compounds. When Roentgen published his work on X rays in 1895, he showed, among other things, that the rays made a fluorescent substance shine in the dark, which suggested an extension of the experiments of Niepce de Sainte-Victor who had noted that uranium salts could affect a photographic plate in the dark. Becquerel found that *all* uranium salts, whether phosphorescent or not, emit invisible radiations, which, like the Roentgen rays, darken a photographic plate and make the surrounding air a conductor so that the gold leaves of a charged electroscope lose their electrostatic charge and collapse. The radiations are now known to be of three kinds: (1) alpha rays, which are really helium atoms bearing two units of positive charge; (2) beta rays, which represent a stream of negative electrons; and (3) gamma rays, which represent a very penetrating radiation of extremely short wave length.

These radiations are sometimes called *Becquerel rays*, and the property is called radioactivity. The emission of the rays appears to be a permanent and abiding property of uranium and their constant emission indicates that the element is slowly undergoing a spontaneous decomposition. Radioactivity appears to be an infra-atomic property. For this work, Becquerel was awarded a Nobel prize in 1903 jointly with the Curies.

The Curies.—*Pierre Curie* (1859–1906) was born in Paris and eventually became professor of physics at the Sorbonne. He received his doctor's degree in 1895, and that year he married *Marie Sklodowska* (1867–1934), usually known as Mme Curie. They, their daughter Irène, and their son-in-law Frédéric Joliot have done outstanding work in the extension of our knowledge of radioactivity. This work is essentially physical, rather than chemical, in nature, but it is of fundamental importance to the chemist, and our present theory of the composition of the atom is dependent upon it. Marie Sklodowska was born in Warsaw where her father was professor of physics and mathematics. Marie received much of her education from her father and from work in his laboratory. She joined a secret society which organized evening classes for laborers and peasants that led to a "student revolt," after which Marie left her homeland. She spent some time in Austria but soon went to France, and in Paris she met Pierre Curie at the home of a Polish physicist. The interests of the two young people with respect to scientific,

MARIE SKLODOWSKA CURIE
1867–1934

IRÈNE JOLIOT CURIE
1897 ——

Frédéric Joliot
1900 ——

social, and humanitarian subjects led to that singleness of purpose that characterized the lives of both of them.   Her doctorate thesis on radioactive substances was considered one of the most remarkable theses ever presented in France.   She continued the work begun by Becquerel and tested nearly every known element, including thorium, of which the radioactivity was discovered independently by G. C. Schmidt, professor of physics at Münster.   She found that the activity of pitchblende, the most common uranium mineral, was about four times as great as was to be expected from the uranium content and by working up large quantities of the ore isolated a new element, which she called *polonium* in honor of her homeland; this is also known as *radium F*.   Later she discovered *radium*.   The late Wilhelm Ostwald in his autobiography wrote:

At my urgent request the Curie laboratory in which radium was discovered was shown to me.   The Curies themselves were away, traveling.   The laboratory was a cross between a barn and a potato cellar and if I had not seen the work bench with the chemical apparatus, I would have thought it a joke.

When, in 1903, Pierre Curie was urged to accept a decoration of the Legion of Honor, he wrote, "I pray you to thank the Minister and to tell him that I do not in the least feel the need of a decoration but that I do feel the greatest need for a laboratory."   Yet Mme Curie looked back upon the years spent in that dingy shed as the best and happiest of her life.

The Curies, Pierre and Marie, received the Nobel prize jointly with Becquerel in 1903, but after the death of Pierre (the result of being run over by a heavy dray), Mme Marie Curie received the Nobel prize for herself in 1920.   In 1935, her daughter Irène and her husband Frédéric Joliot also received the Nobel prize jointly.

After the death of her husband, Mme Curie succeeded him as professor of physics at the University of Paris.   In 1921 President Harding presented her with one gram of pure radium salt, and in 1929 President Hoover presented her with $50,000 raised by her friends in America to purchase radium for her laboratory at Warsaw.   Mme Curie died while her large book on radioactivity was in press. Her daughter has written a story of her life which has had an enormous popular appeal.

Irène Curie was born in Paris in 1897 and obtained her doctor's degree in 1925 as a result of studies on the alpha rays of polonium. She was well trained in mathematics and physics and served in the war as radiographer in hospitals. She married **Frédéric Joliot** in 1926. Her husband was born in Paris in 1900 and received his engineering diploma at the École de Physique et de Chimie de la Ville de Paris in 1923. He became assistant to Mme Curie in 1925 and in 1930 was made Doctor of Science. Much of the work done by Joliot has been accomplished with the aid of his wife and published jointly. In 1932 they discovered that atomic nuclei can be ejected from neutrons. In 1933 they determined the conditions for producing protons by gamma rays of great quantic energy, and in 1934 they succeeded in proving that the transmutation of elements is susceptible to chemical proof.

Chemistry in Sweden.—We have already seen that Berzelius (1779–1848), a Swedish chemist, did more than perhaps any one else to organize chemical thought in the first part of the nineteenth century. There have been quite a number of very capable Scandinavian scientists, but their work, unless published in French, German, or English, remains unfamiliar to most of us. Modern physical chemistry practically starts with the work of a Swedish chemist, Svante Arrhenius. Ostwald, who has sometimes been called the Father of Modern Physical Chemistry, received inspiration from reading about the work of Arrhenius. Another Swedish chemist, Theodor Svedberg, was awarded the Nobel prize in 1926 for his work on the physical chemistry of colloids. Both of these scientists have exerted an influence felt all over the world.

Arrhenius.—Svante Arrhenius was born near Upsala in Sweden in 1859 and died in October, 1927. He studied there and at Stockholm until 1884 when he received his degree at Upsala. In his dissertation and in a short paper which he published in 1887, he enunciated his theory of electrolytic dissociation which has since played such an important part in the theory of aqueous solutions. He worked with Ostwald in Riga, with Kohlrausch in Würzburg (1886), where he became acquainted with Walther

SVANTE ARRHENIUS
1859–1927

Ostwald and van't Hoff

Ostwald and Arrhenius

Nernst, with Boltzmann in Graz (1887), with van't Hoff in Amsterdam (1888), and with Ostwald again in Leipzig.   In 1891 he refused a professorship at Giessen, accepting a position in Stockholm instead, where he was made professor of physics in 1895, which position he held until 1905.   In 1905 he was awarded the Davy medal in London and in 1903 the Nobel prize. He wrote a number of books on physical chemistry, some of which were translated into other tongues.   His style was condensed and somewhat hard to read.

In 1884, when he had just completed his studies at Stockholm, Arrhenius presented to the Swedish Academy of Sciences a communication upon his recent work in electrolysis.   This contained some ideas which later investigation has shown to be erroneous or incomplete, but it may be said, in general, that he approached the subject essentially from the point of view of Clausius.   He concluded from his experiments that in any conducting solution only a certain proportion of its particles are really responsible for the conductivity, which in different solutions will be proportional to the relative quantity of such particles as compared to the rest.   At this time, Arrhenius made no attempt to differentiate these particles qualitatively from the other molecules in solution, but he assigned to every conducting solution a so-called *activity coefficient* to represent the proportion of its particles which took part in electrolysis.   When, now, the activity coefficients of Arrhenius were compared with the coefficients which van't Hoff had designated by *i* in his work on osmotic pressures, the two were found strictly proportional! In other words, the better a solution conducts the current, the more abnormally great is its osmotic pressure, or, as we have seen above, the more molecules it seems to have in a solution of given concentration.   Clearly this effect would be produced if the molecules were dissociated.

Ostwald on Affinity Constants.—An entirely independent argument, which spoke in the same sense, was next furnished by Ostwald, who had for some time been studying the so-called *affinity constants* of organic acids.   By this term was meant the strengths of the acids as measured by the velocity with which these substances catalyze the hydrolysis of esters or the inversion of sugar.   Ostwald had determined this constant for thirty or more organic acids and now measured their conductivity as well; he found his affinity constants were now proportional to the activity constants of Arrhenius.   This agreement is what must be expected if in any solution the ions exist ready-formed, for the more ions there are present, the greater must be the conductivity, the greater also will be the number of free particles and, hence, the osmotic pressure; and finally, since all acids catalyze hydrolysis, and since the effect must be due to the only thing that all acids have in common—the hydrogen ion—the more ions there are present, the greater must be the velocity of the hydrolysis.

Final Statement of the Theory.—On the strength of this unanimity, Arrhenius in 1887 promulgated the theory of electrolytic dissociation in essentially its present form and pointed out, in addition to the arguments already enumerated, that where dissociation is practically complete, as in the case of most salts, the physical properties of their solutions must be additive functions of the corresponding properties of the individual ions.   He showed that this is actually the case, not only for the properties already mentioned, but also for others like specific gravity and volume, refractive index, and capillarity.   He also showed how simply the new theory accounted for the hitherto puzzling fact that in dilute solution the heat of neutralization of strong acids and strong bases is the same.   If we accept the dissociation theory, the one thing which all these reactions have in common is the formation of undissociated water from the hydrogen ions of the acid and the hydroxyl ions of the base, the other ions remaining free.   The heat evolution then in all cases is the heat of this reaction:

$$H^+ + OH^- = H_2O$$

If, on the other hand, the acid or the base or both are weak (only slightly ionized), the heat effect is different.

Its Reception.—The new theory impressed most chemists as revolutionary, and while little could be said against the facts upon which it was based, yet it had to meet with a great deal of passive resistance. Its acceptance required a new mental attitude. Sodium chloride, for example, had always been considered an extremely stable compound, doubtless because it has a high heat of formation. The new doctrine, however, seemed to teach that we have only to dissolve it in water in order to decompose it into its elements, in spite of the fact that the chlorine reveals itself by neither its odor nor its color and the sodium does not evolve hydrogen with the water. These objections were, of course, chiefly the result of misunderstanding, since the chlorine ion, for example, is not the element, but an atom thereof plus a certain definite charge of electricity. In order to overcome such misunderstandings the three investigators most concerned in the establishment of the new theory, Ostwald, Arrhenius, and van't Hoff, formed a kind of offensive and defensive alliance for the propagation of the new faith. Perhaps the largest factors in the success achieved by the coalition were the foundation of the *Zeitschrift für physikalische Chemie* by Ostwald and van't Hoff in 1887 and the teaching and literary activity of the former during the next twenty years. As time has gone on, the belief in the theory of electrolytic dissociation has been strengthened. Studies with X rays indicate, moreover, that the ions are separated from one another, according to a symmetrical arrangement even in crystals before they are dissolved in water. It has been shown, also, that the ionization in solution is often more complete than was indicated by measurements of electrical conductivity, so that an *activity* factor has to be considered. Moreover, when salts are dissolved in water the ions formed are usually hydrated and not simple ions as we have often assumed.

Theodor Svedberg (1884 ——) was graduated in 1908 from Upsala where he was instructor in physical chemistry (1909–1912) and professor after 1912. He has published over fifty papers on physicochemical subjects, such as conductivity of solutions, electrical preparation of colloidal solutions, Brownian movement, etc. For this work he received a Nobel prize in 1926.

Chemistry in Holland.—Holland is a small country, but it has produced quite a number of brilliant chemists. Here the work of three great men only will be discussed, but their influence has been world-wide. These are van't Hoff, Roozeboom, and Debye.

Some of the work of van't Hoff has already been discussed in Chap. XVIII because he published in 1874 a little pamphlet on stereochemistry which has been of fundamental importance in the development of organic chemistry. He has been called the greatest physical chemist of his time. His work on osmotic pressure was extremely important.

Osmotic Pressure.—In 1748 Abbé Nollet tried the following experiment. He filled a small cylinder with alcohol, closed the mouth with a membrane so as not to include any air, and immersed the whole in water. He was surprised to see that water entered through the membrane until the latter was much distended, and on piercing it, the liquid "spurted about a foot," This seems to have been the first scientific observation of the phenomenon of osmosis, which we now interpret essentially as follows: In any solution the dissolved substance exerts a pressure against the surface of the liquid tending to expand it. In an ordinary vessel this is balanced by the surface tension and produces no visible effects. Animal and vegetable membranes, however, have the peculiar property of being permeable for water, but not for most substances dissolved in it. In an experiment like that of Nollet, then, the liquid can expand because the solvent can now enter through the membrane. The force causing this expansion we call the osmotic pressure, and we know that it depends upon the solute rather than the solvent because it varies with the nature and concentration of the former. Measurements of the magnitude of this force were at first difficult to obtain because natural membranes are not absolutely impermeable to the molecules of dissolved substances. Traube, however, by forming colloidal precipitates like copper ferrocyanide in the pores of clay cups, was able to prepare cells which fulfilled these conditions, and by their use in 1877 Pfeffer, then professor of botany at Bonn, made some quite accurate measurements of the force. He found it to be of an unexpected magnitude, a 1 per cent sugar solution, for example, exerting a pressure of about two-thirds of an atmosphere. The subject of osmotic pressure has always been of exceptional interest to physiologists and botanists because it plays an important role wherever there are cellular tissues, and plants owe to it their circulation and growth. In the early eighties Hugo de Vries of Amsterdam was making experiments upon the withering of plants. He found that, when placed in pure water, they showed a tendency to swell, whereas solutions more concentrated than those in the plant cell exerted a dehydrating action and the plants withered. Between these extremes it was possible to prepare so-called *isotonic solutions* which neither gave water to the plant cell nor took water from it, *i.e.*, they had the same osmotic pressure as the cell. De Vries prepared such solutions from a considerable number of different salts, and then made the important observation that these isotonic solutions, which he knew had the same osmotic pressure, all had the same freezing point.

The Contribution of van't Hoff.—In 1884, when the investigation had reached this stage, de Vries almost by accident communicated his results to van't Hoff, who at once saw their importance for physics and chemistry. He proceeded to work out the causal relationship which exists between osmotic pressure on the one hand, and vapor pressure, boiling point, and freezing point on the other. He then made an extensive study of the nature of osmotic pressure in general, and found that the relationships involved are far more simple than had been supposed. When a substance is dissolved in a liquid, its molecules exert against the surface of the latter a pressure which is not only analogous, but in most cases numerically equal, to the pressure which they would exert if the substance were a gas confined in the same volume. If, therefore, we write the equation of state for a gas:

$$PV = nRT$$

where P is the pressure, V the volume, n the number of molecules, T the absolute temperature, and R the so-called gas constant, the same equation holds for a substance in solution even to the numerical value of R.

There were, however, exceptions, and since the osmotic pressure determines the freezing point, these exceptions were the very ones already observed by Raoult, who had found, as we remember, that most salts and some acids and bases showed a greater depression of the freezing point than he could account for. This meant that their osmotic pressures were abnormally high, a fact which might be interpreted to signify that more molecules were present in the solutions of these substances than existing theories could account for. Van't Hoff had, at the time, no explanation to offer, but contented himself by writing the equation of state for such substances:

$$PV = inRT$$

in which i represented a constant dependent upon the nature of the individual substance. The equation appeared in this form in the now famous paper on the subject which he presented to the Swedish Academy of Sciences in 1885.

Hendrik Willem Bakhuis Roozeboom (1854–1907) was born in Alkmaar, North Holland. At the Hoogere Burgerschool he became interested in chemistry through his teacher Dr. J. D. Boeke. In the summer of 1875 he worked on soil analysis for van Bemmelen, another Dutch chemist, who is well known for his work on colloids while professor at Leiden. Roozeboom was ready to enter the University of Leiden in 1874, but lack of funds forced him to go to work. He worked in the laboratory of Dr. Mouton at The Hague and, as was the case with van Bemmelen, his employer was pleased with his work and felt sure that he had a future in chemistry. Mouton had a chemical factory which burned down in 1878, and Roozeboom was out of employment. He next worked as an assistant in the university laboratory at Leiden where he studied and passed his examination for the doctorate in 1882. The Dutch are often brought up under strict Calvinism so that when a youth becomes educated he is likely to lose his faith in religion. But with Roozeboom it was the opposite; the more he studied, the more religious he became.

One of Roozeboom's first scientific papers was on butyl bromide, but his later work was nearly all on inorganic salts. He published over eighty papers. He established the constitution of such hydrates as $SO_2.7H_2O$, $Br_2.10H_2O$, $HCl.2H_2O$, and $Cl_2.8H_2O$ and showed that what we often call ferric and aluminum hydroxides do not correspond to any definite state of hydration but are $Fe_2O_3.xH_2O$ or $Al_2O_3.xH_2O$. He studied the equilibria of various salt mixtures and in 1901 published an important book on *Heterogeneous Equilibrium*. Wilder Bancroft, the well-known American physical chemist, has said of him, "He has done more than any one else to show the importance and significance of the Gibbs phase rule." He wrote an important paper on *Iron and Steel from the Standpoint of the Phase Rule*. In 1896, Roozeboom succeeded van't-Hoff as professor at Leiden.

J. Willard Gibbs, Jr., as we shall see later, was a gifted American physicist who was not appreciated in his homeland. His writings were scarcely read and rarely understood by his American contemporaries, but we now realize, more and more, that he was a mathematical genius and his phase rule has become of fundamental importance in the study of mixtures and of alloys. Roozeboom's work and results obtained by the application of the phase rule made Gibbs famous in all countries.

Petrus Josephus Wilhelmus Debye (1884 ——) was born at Maastricht, Holland. He received a diploma in engineering at Aachen in 1905 and received his Ph.D. at Munich in 1908. He was assistant at Munich in 1906 and privatdocent in 1910. Then he was assistant professor at Zurich in 1911, professor of theoretical physics at Utrecht in 1912, professor of theoretical physics at Göttingen in 1914, and was called to Leipzig as professor and director of the physical chemistry laboratory in 1927. He has published over fifty scientific papers written in Dutch, German, and English. He published a book on *Polar Molecules* in English in 1929. Since 1930 he has been the principal editor of the *Physikalische Zeitschrift*. Debye received the Nobel prize in 1936, and since 1935 he has been Director of the Kaiser Wilhelm Institut for Physics at Berlin-Dahlen and professor at the University of Berlin. Debye studied the electrical moment of molecules and infra-molecular forces and helped to clarify our ideas concerning ions and molecules in solution. He showed that Niek Bjerrum, a Danish physical chemist (1879 ——) and professor at the Veterinary and Agricultural College of Copenhagen, was right in assuming total ionization of most salts in aqueous solutions and that the ions of a salt, such as NaCl, are situated in a solution in about the same relative positions as in the solid state, although they are farther apart and surrounded by a cloud which bears an electrical charge and exerts attraction and repulsion. The radius of the cloud is inversely proportional to the square root of the concentration. The ionic strength is determined by multiplying the number of ions of each sort by the square of their valences before adding them together. If the water which acts as solvent already contains ions of a foreign electrolyte, an ionic cloud of opposite sign can form around every ion as it leaves the solid phase and passes into solution. Bjerrum and Debye have shown that, although salts are almost completely ionized in solutions, the electrical conductivity is less than would be expected, because of the effects of the electric clouds.

A Czech Chemist.—Chemistry in Czecho-Slovakia has advanced to a very creditable state during recent years, and a number of very able men have worked at the university in Prague. The work of **Bohuslav Brauner** (1855–1935) deserves mention. He studied at Prague and also under Bunsen at Heidelberg and under Roscoe at Manchester. In 1881 he was a fellow at Owens College. In 1883, he was appointed lecturer and in 1890 professor of chemistry at the Czech University of Prague. He was particularly interested in modern inorganic chemistry and the perfecting of the periodic table of the elements. He obtained important results in determining the atomic weights of the rare elements. He worked on fluorescence (1877), the atomic weight of beryllium (1878–1881), chemistry of the rare earths (1882–1883), atomic weight of cerium (1885), volumetric determination of tellurium (1890), composition of certain metal chlorides (889), and on the preparation of large quantities of argon (1895).

Chemistry in Switzerland.—Several Swiss chemists have already been mentioned, but modern inorganic chemistry owes a great deal to the work of Alfred Werner whose "*Neuere Anschauungen auf dem Gebiete der anorganischen Chemie*" attracted the

attention of chemists all over the world and whose theory of
principal and subordinate valences prepared the way for our
present views concerning the electronic nature of valence.

Alfred Werner (1866–1919) was born in Alsace and was a German subject
from 1871. He received his diploma at the Polytechnicum in Zurich in
1889. Then he was assistant to Georg Lunge and was graduated from the
University of Zurich in 1890. He worked with Berthelot in Paris and
became lecturer at Zurich in 1892, assistant professor in 1893, and full
professor in 1895. He received a Nobel prize in 1913. He published nearly
170 papers and had charge of 200 doctorate theses with sometimes as many
as 25 graduate students working under him at one time. He was an inde-
fatigable worker and an inspiring teacher.

In 1892 Werner began the publication of a series of papers in
which he developed an entirely original conception concerning
the composition of the so-called *metal-ammonias*, which was
destined to have a marked, if at present somewhat indefinite,
influence upon our general conceptions of chemical combination.
It is a familiar fact that many salts of heavy metals, such as
cobalt, nickel, copper, chromium, iron, and members of the
platinum group, form addition products with ammonia in a
variety of proportions. Many of these compounds exhibit
striking properties, especially in the matter of color. Solutions of
copper salts in an excess of ammonia contain such complexes.
Long before Werner began his work a great number of these
compounds had been prepared and analyzed, but no one had
tried to consider them seriously from a single point of view, and
most of them were formulated in the helpless way in which we still
write salts containing water of crystallization.

Werner proceeded to tabulate the known compounds and to
prepare others so as to make his series complete, and he found
that the salts of a trivalent metal, *e.g.*, MeX_3, usually combined
with ammonia in all proportions from six to three, so that we have
in this case the series:

$$MeX_3, 6NH_3; \quad MeX_3, 5NH_3; MeX_3, 4NH_3; \text{ and } MeX_3, 3NH_3$$

If now we examine the chemical properties of these compounds,
certain remarkable relationships appear. In the first member
the whole of the acid radical is ionized. This can be shown by
the electrical conductivity, or by the fact that if X represents
a halogen the whole of it may be precipitated by silver nitrate.
In the second member, however, this is no longer the case. Here

(in $MeX_3,5NH_3$) only two-thirds of the acid is ionized, in the third member only one-third, and the fourth compound is a neutral substance which does not conduct the electric current. From these facts Werner drew the conclusion that in the first compound the three acid radicals were anions, while the metal and the six ammonias formed a complex cation. In the other members of the series, the acid radicals took their place successively with the ammonias in the metallic complex, finally forming the neutral compound, $MeX_3,3NH_3$. The series should then be formulated according to Werner as follows:

$$[Me,6NH_3]X_3; [MeX,5NH_3]X_2; [MeX_2,4NH_3]X; [MeX_3,3NH_3]$$

It was possible, however, to go further. Compounds with still less ammonia could be prepared if at the same time alkali salt were added, but now the metallic complex became the anion and the series could be completed as follows:

$$K[MeX_4,2NH_3]; K_2[MeX_5,NH_3]; K_3MeX_6$$

the last term representing a type of compound of which the well-known complex salt $K_3Co(NO_2)_6$ is a familiar example.

It will perhaps make these ideas more concrete if we tabulate here the compounds of the series beginning with $PtCl_4,6NH_3$ and their relative conductivities:

$[Pt,6NH_3]Cl_4$	522.9
$[PtCl,5NH_3]Cl_3$	unknown
$[PtCl_2,4NH_3]Cl_2$	228.0
$[PtCl_3,3NH_3]Cl$	96.75
$[PtCl_4,2NH_3]$	0.0
$K[PtCl_5,NH_3]$	108.5
K_2PtCl_6	256.0

Here, just as in the previous example, this method of formulating the metal-ammonias brings their composition into harmony with well-known series of complex salts, and makes the composition of the latter more intelligible. In most of these compounds, also, ammonia can be substituted, molecule for molecule, by water, and as the end members of such series we get familiar salts with water of crystallization, so that the theory throws some light even on that troublesome topic.

The Coordination Number.—In comparing the cobalt and platinum series just mentioned, the reader will have noticed that regardless of the valence of the metal, and equally regardless of the nature of the substituting groups, the so-called "inner sphere" (complex ion) consists of the metal and *six* other constituents. This number cannot be the valence of the metal but it does determine how many groups are spatially combined with it. Werner calls it the *coordination number*, and while in most cases this is six, in certain other well-known series it is four, and might so far as we know have some other value.

It will be seen that the new system is admirably adapted for use as a principle of classification, and indeed it rapidly became the basis of nomenclature and guide in research in the special field of the metal-ammonias where it originated. Werner, however, had been anxious from the first that his theory should represent something more than a series of types like Gerhardt's in which the most heterogeneous compounds might be classified on the basis of their empirical composition. Now just as the value of the structure theory in organic chemistry, as a picture of real conditions, lies in the fact that it explains isomerism, so in this new theory, if the grouping of ammonias and other radicals about a central metal atom represents a real spatial arrangement, then both structure isomerism and space isomerism should be observed, and this is the fact.

Stereoisomerism in Inorganic Chemistry.—In the first place it should make a difference whether a given atom is in the inner or outer sphere, *i.e.*, such a compound as $[CoCl,5NH_3]Br_2$ should differ from $[CoBr,5NH_3]ClBr$, and this is the case. But stereoisomerism is also possible. If six radicals are grouped about a central atom, two arrangements are possible, *viz.*, the hexagon or the octahedron. Werner decided in favor of the latter because two di-substitution products are observed, instead of three as in the case of benzene. These he formulated, for exam-

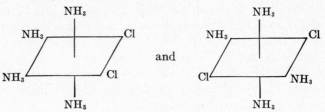

ple, as: which we see is a true case of *cis-trans* isomerism.

The realization of optical isomerism in this class of compounds was long delayed, partly because the preparation of compounds containing six different substituents offers experimental difficulties, but in 1911 Werner came to realize that it was not necessary to wait for the preparation of such compounds.   He found that three molecules of ethylene diamine $\begin{array}{l} CH_2 - NH_2 \\ | \\ CH_2 - NH_2 \end{array}$ could replace six ammonias in complex salts, each molecule connecting, as it were, two adjacent apexes of the octahedron. Now the study of an octahedral model reveals the fact that such

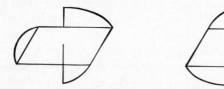

ions could occur in forms that are unsymmetrical mirror images of each other, and experiment has since shown that salts like $[Co,en_3]Cl_3$ (to use Werner's abbreviation) can be split into strongly rotating optically active components.   Ethylene diamine is itself inactive, but in order to meet the possible objection that the activity of the complex might be due to the carbons of that substance, Werner, in 1914, found an inorganic radical which could be substituted for the ethylene diamine, and was able to show that the resulting compound $\left[Co\left(\begin{array}{l} OH \\ OH \end{array} Co(NH_3)_4 \right)_3 \right] X_6$ was optically active though destitute of carbon.

Werner's views raise general questions of much interest. What, for example, is the significance of the coordination number? and what relation does it bear to the valence of the metal? Werner assumed that valence is more distributed than the representation by individual bonds can justly denote.   According to his usage, principal valences serve to connect atoms, while subordinate valences, usually represented by dotted lines, connect molecules.   These account for the rest of the attraction and are limited by the amount of space at the disposal of the substituents.   The future influence of these ideas upon the science is difficult to forecast. Werner himself worked out a theory of ammonium salts which is certainly far from satisfactory in its present form. Largely in consequence of his work, however, the ideas of partial, split, and subordinate valence are now frequently applied in both organic and inorganic chemistry, especially in formulating molecular compounds; and although there is as yet little consistency in their use, the idea is clearly destined to exert a considerable influence.

Germany and Austria.—The most striking development in the latter part of the nineteenth century was the rise of modern physical chemistry. Undoubtedly, Germany was the leader in this movement, and Wilhelm Ostwald did more than anyone else to develop it. The curious thing is that he had more American and English students than German. The remarkable strides made in industrial chemistry during the past twenty-five years have been due to the application of physical chemistry to the manufacture of chemical products, and this has progressed more rapidly in the United States than in Germany, where so many arts were kept more or less secret and handed down from father to son.

In one sense, physical chemistry is not modern. At all periods since the time of Lavoisier certain eminent investigators have preferred to devote their attention to the borderland between the two sciences. An early instance is that of Berthollet, who at the very beginning of the nineteenth century attempted to impress upon an inattentive world the important facts that the course of a chemical reaction depends not only upon the affinities involved, but also upon the masses of the reacting substances; that chemical reactions lead to states of equilibrium; and that the physical properties of the products, such as solubility and volatility, exert an important and sometimes a determining influence upon their course. We have seen how, unfortunately for Berthollet, he allowed his reasoning to lead him to conclusions which contradicted the law of definite proportions, with the result that not only were his conclusions discredited, but his point of view, so that discussions on similar topics remained unpopular for a long time.

Much of the work of Gay-Lussac, as well as that of Dulong and of Regnault, may be classed as physicochemical in the best sense,

and Bunsen's influence in this direction was preeminent, especially in his work on optics, on the spectroscope, and on the
influence of light upon chemical reactions. It is not surprising
that he was fond of saying, *"Der Chemiker der kein Physiker
ist, ist gar nichts!"* Kopp, the great historian of the science,
also did valuable work upon the physical properties of organic
compounds as functions of their constitution, which received
early recognition on account of its direct application to problems
of structure.

Other generalizations, too, which we are in the habit of associating almost exclusively with modern physical chemistry
really received attention and were accurately stated at a comparatively early day, at least so far as general principles were
concerned. This applies with especial force to the law of mass
action, which now ranks as one of the main foundation stones of
the science.

The Law of Mass Action.—In 1850 Ludwig Wilhelmy, then a
docent at Heidelberg, published a brief paper on the inversion
of sugar by acids in which, by means of the polariscope, he
studied the progress of hydrolysis with different acids, different
quantities of acid, varying temperatures, and varying amounts
of sugar, and worked out a mathematical expression for the
velocity of the reaction, which takes account of these factors
completely and correctly. He also pointed out that similar
studies upon other reactions of the same type must yield equations of the same form. This proved to be the case, but Wilhelmy himself received little credit, for by the time interest in
such problems had become general, his work was practically
forgotten. We have seen how Berthelot and Péan de St. Gilles
at about 1860 carried on an important investigation upon the
hydrolysis of esters, and expressed their results in the form that
at any moment the rate of reaction is proportional to the amount
of ester remaining undecomposed. On account of the prestige
of Berthelot, this work came to more general notice, and about
1863 two Norwegian scientists, Guldberg and Waage, being
impressed by the work of Berthelot, gave the idea more general
form, and in an extensive investigation they set forth the universal application of the law that the velocity of a chemical
reaction is dependent upon the products of the concentrations

of the reacting substances.   In their principal paper, published
in 1867, they express this as follows, in reasoning which sounds
characteristically modern:

If we assume that the two substances A and B change by double
decomposition into two new ones A' and B', and that under the same
conditions A' and B' can change into A and B, then neither the formation of A' and B' nor the re-formation of A and B will be complete
but at the end of the reaction there will always be present the four
substances A, B, A' and B', and the force which causes the formation
of A' and B' will be held in equilibrium by that which causes the formation of A and B.

The force which brings about the formation of A' and B' increases
proportionally to the affinity coefficient of the reaction

$$A + B = A' + B'$$

but it also depends upon the masses of A and B.   We have concluded
from our experiments that the force is proportional to the product of
the active masses of the two bodies A and B.   If we designate the active
masses of A and B with p and q, and the affinity coefficient with k,
then the force $= k.p.q.$

          *   *   *   *   *   *   *   *

If the active masses of A' and B' are p' and q' and the affinity coefficient of the reaction

$$A' + B' = A + B$$

equals k', then the force tending to re-form A and B equals $k'.p'.q'$.
This force is in equilibrium with the first and consequently

$$kp.q = k'p'.q'$$

By experimentally determining the active masses p, q, p' and q'
the relationship between the affinity coefficients can be found.   On
the other hand when this relationship is known the result of the reaction
can be calculated in advance for any chosen proportion of the four
substances at the beginning.

It is not perhaps superfluous to quote the closing paragraph
of this important paper:

Investigations in this field are doubtless more difficult, more tedious
and less fruitful than those which now engage the attention of most
chemists, namely the discovery of new compounds.   Nevertheless it

is our opinion that nothing can so soon bring chemistry into the class with the truly exact sciences as just the line of research with which this investigation deals.   All our wishes would be fulfilled if we might by this piece of work direct the permanent attention of chemists toward a branch of the science which since the beginning of the century has unquestionably been far more neglected than it deserves.

The Phase Rule.—It was much the same with the phase rule which, in recent times, has served such an excellent purpose in demonstrating the important relationships involved in heterogeneous equilibrium.   In this subject also the essential underlying principles were worked out abstractly by Willard Gibbs of Yale University as early as 1876.   Gibbs, however, was so indifferent to fame that he apparently did not care whether he was understood by his contemporaries, so that he not only called no attention to his results, but when it came to publication he buried them in the *Transactions of the Connecticut Academy.* Concerning the importance of the material there concealed, Ostwald has expressed himself as follows:

To give an idea of the significance of this work it suffices to say that a very considerable part of the laws and relationships which have in the meantime been discovered in physical chemistry and which have led to such an astonishing development of that field within the last decade[1] are found in this paper more or less thoroughly developed. The questions which concern the equilibria of complex systems are here treated with unexampled comprehensiveness and completeness; and in addition to the influences which are usually considered, such as temperature and pressure, there are also discussed the effects of gravity, elasticity, surface tension, and electricity.   Experimental research has only slowly begun to follow the paths whose goal and direction are indicated in this work, and a wealth of scientific treasures still await experimental treatment, though in many cases this would be an extremely simple matter.

In the fact of such conditions one must ask: Why did this work achieve no success commensurate with its importance?   Why, immediately upon its appearance, did not those effects follow which have since been attained in another way?   There are many answers.   Above all the blame must be laid to the uninviting form in which the author has recorded his results.   In a strictly mathematical manner, and with a text so concentrated that every page requires the active cooperation

[1] Written in 1896.

of the reader, the author takes us through his 700 equations, only seldom illuminating his results with any suggestive applications.

In short this paper by Gibbs must be classed with the *Statique Chimique* of Berthollet, which Ostwald himself once characterized as "much praised and little read."

The Theory of Electrolytic Dissociation.—For similar reasons interest in the physical side of chemistry did not become widespread until the theory of electrolytic dissociation was propounded by Arrhenius in 1887. This generalization, which found the world quite unprepared when it was first announced, nevertheless rested upon important chains of evidence which had been in process of development for a long time. These had to do with several widely separated departments of the science, and it was the service of Arrhenius to trace the connection between these facts and to weld them into a comprehensive whole. It will be well to trace the history of some of these movements in detail.

Hittorf's Work on Electrolysis.—Faraday's law rests upon the fact that whenever a current passes through an electrolyte the latter is decomposed, and for a given quantity of electricity certain definite quantities of the decomposition products appear at the electrodes in chemically equivalent proportions. Faraday rightly concluded that these components of the electrolyte are the carriers of the current and to these carriers he gave the name *ions*. He regarded them as formed by the current and would doubtless have explained the mechanism of the process in the terms of Grotthuss (see page 139), which were universally accepted at that time. Since the quantities of material appearing at the two electrodes are chemically equivalent, it was entirely natural, at the time when he wrote, that Grotthuss should have made the tacit assumption that both the anion and cation (to use words not current in his day) migrated with equal velocities. This was the universal assumption until, in 1853, Hittorf began a remarkable series of investigations in which he showed that this was not the case. He pointed out that if they wander with different velocities the fact must be susceptible of experimental proof by following the changes in concentration which take place about the electrodes.

Hittorf proceeded to test his conclusions by the electrolysis of a great number of salts under conditions which avoided mechanical mixing of the solutions and found that the ion velocities were as a rule unequal. To the ratios $\dfrac{u}{u+v}$ and $\dfrac{v}{u+v}$, where u is the velocity of the cation and v that of the anion, he gave the name *transference numbers*.

In addition to this valuable experimental work, Hittorf added important general discussions in which he pointed out that the ease of decomposition of electrolytes by the current is something which stands in no relationship to the heats of formation of the same substances from their elements, and that it takes place, in general, along the same lines of cleavage and into the same components which interact in double decomposition, and this he endeavored to emphasize by promulgating the dogma, "Electrolytes are salts." Hittorf's conclusions assumed, of course, that it was the electrolyte, and not the solvent, that carries the current, an assumption by no means universally shared by his contemporaries. If we follow out this idea, we see that in a dilute solution, when an ion has once been set free, it must be at a greater distance from another ion with which it may unite than from many molecules of the solvent, *i.e.*, it must be free during most of its transit. Hittorf did not emphasize this conclusion, but this made little difference historically, for his work, excellent as it was, was ignored on the experimental side and violently attacked on the theoretical one, so that it received no fitting recognition till many years later. Meantime certain theoretical speculations of Clausius began to exert some influence in the same direction.

Views of Clausius.—In 1851, Williamson, in a discussion of the mechanism of ether formation, had advanced the idea that in any chemical system atoms and molecules must always be in a kind of dynamic equilibrium, and that a molecule, instead of being a rigid structure always made up of the same atoms, is really carrying on a constant exchange with the corresponding atoms of neighboring molecules. Clausius in a paper published in 1857 found this idea useful in explaining the phenomena of electrolysis. He pointed out that if the molecules of an electrolyte were really rigid aggregates then we should expect that with a low potential difference between the electrodes no current would pass. When, however, the electromotive force attained a strength sufficient to disrupt these aggregates, a strong current should suddenly result. Experience contradicts these assumptions. There is no evidence that any current is needed to dissociate the molecules into ions. Except at very low potentials some current passes no matter how low the potential difference, and if this is increased, then the strength of the current increases proportionally in accordance with Ohm's law. Clausius felt that these facts could be made more intelligible by the application of an idea like Williamson's.

If we imagine a given potential applied between two electrodes immersed in a solution where an electrolysis is taking place, then, to quote Clausius:

A free part-molecule will no longer follow the irregular changing directions toward which it is driven by heat movements, but will alter the direction of its movements in the sense of the force now acting, so that among the movements of the positive part-molecules, although they are still extremely irregular, a certain definite direction will predominate, and similarly the negative part-molecules will move principally in the opposite direction. Furthermore, by the action of part-molecules upon whole molecules and of the latter upon each other those decompositions will be facilitated by which the part-molecules can at the same time follow the electric force in their motions, and these decompositions will take place more frequently, so that even in those cases where the position of the molecule is not so favorable that such a decomposition could take place spontaneously, yet the electric force can cause it to take place. Conversely decompositions by which the part-molecules would be obliged to move against the electric force would be made more difficult by the force and would take place more seldom.* * *It is easy to see that the influence which the electric force exerts upon the spontaneous but still irregular decompositions and movements of the molecules does not first begin when the force has reached a certain strength, but that even the smallest force acts in such a way as to modify these in the manner explained above, and that the magnitude of this action must increase with the strength of the force. The whole process agrees extremely well with Ohm's law.

The Contribution of Kohlrausch.—The next important contribution to this subject was made by Friedrich Kohlrausch (1840–1910), who was professor of physics at Göttingen, Zurich,

Darmstadt, and Würzburg.   Not long after the work of Clausius, he began an extensive series of experiments upon the conductivity of solutions.   Only slow progress was made at first because no really accurate methods were available.   When a solution is electrolyzed by a direct current, the polarization which soon takes place at the electrodes makes it almost impossible to obtain exact values.   Ultimately, however, this difficulty was overcome by the use of alternating currents, but it was not till 1876 that Kohlrausch published the important paper in which he fully confirmed the work of Hittorf.   Here he showed that for salts having a common ion, like sodium chloride and potassium chloride, the conductivities varied inversely as the transference numbers of the common ions in the two salts.   Using this datum he proceeded to demonstrate that every ion, regardless of the nature of the salt in which it was apparently combined, had a certain definite mobility, or relative migration velocity, which was the same for all combinations, so that the conductivity of a given salt could be calculated additively from the mobilities of the component ions.   These facts were in harmony only with the assumption that during electrolysis the ions were free throughout their course.   The modern theory of electrolytic dissociation, however, states that the ions exist ready formed in the solution, even when no current is passing.   Kohlrausch did not draw this conclusion, and in order to appreciate the evidence which permitted Arrhenius to draw it later, we must review the historical development of our knowledge concerning certain other properties of solutions (cf. pp. 344, 359–361).

Ostwald.—Wilhelm Ostwald (1853–1932) was born in Riga and entered the local Realschule in 1864.   Here he required seven years to complete the course to which most pupils devoted only five, but there is abundant evidence to show that this was not due to any lack of capacity, but rather to an altogether unusual versatility and a tendency to follow many lines of intellectual activity and self-instruction outside the curriculum.   This manifested itself in the collection of insects, the manufacture of fireworks, amateur photography (which then involved the difficult manipulations of the old wet process), carpentry, bookbinding, painting, and the equipment of a private laboratory where he could pursue chemical work beyond the point attainable in school.

In 1871, Ostwald entered the University of Dorpat where he at first devoted himself mainly to the frivolities of student life, but later settled seriously to work, and under the stimulus of a paternal warning took his degree within a space of time which none of his acquaintances then believed possible. In the same year (1875) he became assistant in physics at Dorpat, a position which he retained till called to a professorship at Riga in 1881. While there his physicochemical work, especially upon the affinity constants of acids, became widely known, and in 1887 he was made professor of physical chemistry at Leipzig. This date has a significance in the history of chemistry akin to that when Liebig was called to Giessen, for the work of Ostwald, Arrhenius, and van't Hoff was now attracting wide attention, and it served not only to win adherents for the theory of electrolytic dissociation, but also to arouse a latent interest in students the world over, who now began to realize that they wished to study chemistry from the physical point of view. These now flocked to Ostwald's laboratory in Leipzig, which became, as had been said of that at Giessen fifty years before, the factory for producing the world's supply of professors of physical chemistry. Accounts of those who studied there in the early days agree that the atmosphere was most inspiring. Laboratory conveniences were at first of the most meager description, but professor and students lived, as it were, together, and all ideas were shared in common. The field being practically new, important discoveries followed each other in quick succession, Ostwald himself being an example of tireless energy to all. In addition to the routine work of teaching, the supervision of research, the publication of results, and the editorial duties of the *Zeitschrift*, he found time to write many books, including the large *Lehrbuch* in six volumes, the *Elektrochemie* (a monumental historical study), numerous books illustrating different methods of teaching chemistry, and others dealing with philosophy, biography, and painting. He also has been a prominent agitator for reform in the German schools, as well as for the introduction of an international language, and he was a painter of acknowledged merit. It is small wonder that such a man should call his country house "Energie."

Ostwald's voluminous writings have extended his influence far beyond the walls of his laboratory and thus helped many a teacher to improve his own methods of introducing students to chemistry—a matter in which the author takes pleasure in acknowledging his personal indebtedness. In one point, however, Ostwald has worked against the tendency of the times. In his anxiety to remove from chemistry all superfluous hypothetical elements, he has systematically discouraged the kinetic point of view and has taught chemists to avoid all explanations of natural phenomena which involve the assumption of discrete particles, even the atoms of Dalton. Here, also, his influence has doubtless been a valuable corrective, but since the beginning of the present century, evidence has been constantly accumulating to prove the objective reality of the atom and the discontinuity of even important forms of energy like light and electricity, so that modern physics, which was practically free from corpuscular speculations when Ostwald began his campaign, has now gone over almost completely to that point of view.

Guido Bodländer (1855–1904) was born in Breslau, the youngest of fifteen children. He studied at the university there and obtained his degree in 1882 under the crystallographer Th. Liebisch with a thesis on the optical rotary power of isomorphous mixtures of the thionates of lead and strontium. He was assistant to Moritz Traube and studied the formation of hydrogen peroxide by oxidation with molecular oxygen. Then he was assistant at Bonn and at Clausthal and worked under Nernst in Göttingen. In 1898 he was made professor of physical chemistry and inorganic chemistry technology at the Technische Hochschule in Brunswick. He studied solid solutions (mixed crystals), solubilities of electrolytes, heats of formation, discharge potentials, the gold cyanide process, the Solvay process, and the contact method of making sulfuric acid, all from the standpoint of the physical chemist. He published about 68 scientific papers. Together with Abegg he helped clarify our ideas on valence.

Gustav Tammann (1861 ——) was born in Yamburg, Russia, which is about 68 miles southwest of St. Petersburg (Leningrad). He studied at Dorpat where there is a famous university founded by Gustavus Adolphus of Sweden in 1632. In 1669, the Russians under Peter the Great drove out the Swedes, but the university became strongly Germanic in spirit and sentiment until 1895 when it became thoroughly Russian. In 1918, however, Dorpat became a part of the new state, Estonia, and its name was changed to Tartu. From 1889–1903, Tammann was professor of inorganic and physical chemistry at Dorpat and from 1903 to 1930 professor at Göttingen, after which he retired. Tammann with his students published over three hundred papers. In 1896, while at Dorpat, he showed the similarity of melting-point and vapor-pressure curves. He studied the properties of glasses, which he regarded as supercooled solutions and also studied the effect of pressure on the conductivities of solutions of acids. He published the following books: *Ueber die Beziehungen zwischen den inneren Kräften und Eigenschaften der Losungen, Die Aggregatzustände,* and *Lehrbuch der Metallurgie.* He was editor of the *Zeitschrift der physikalischen Chemie.* He studied ice and its various forms and established equilibrium diagrams for many alloys, by thermic analysis. He was an outstanding physical chemist who did a great deal for the development of metallurgy with the aid of the Gibbs phase rule.

Hermann Walther Nernst (1864 ——), whose first name is rarely used, was born at Briesen in West Prussia and studied at Zurich, Berlin, Graz, and Würzburg. He received his Ph.D. at Würzburg in 1887. He received other degrees at Erlangen, Göttingen, and Oxford and was awarded a Nobel prize in 1920. He was assistant to Ostwald in Leipzig (1887) and then went to Göttingen (1890) where he was made full professor in 1895 and the head of the laboratory of physical chemistry there. He declined a call to Giessen in 1890 and one to Munich in 1894. In 1905 he was called to the University of Berlin and since 1922 has been President of the Physikalisch-technisches Reichsamt at Berlin-Charlottenburg.

He showed in 1889 that the electromotive force of galvanic cells could be explained in terms of a solution pressure of the metal electrodes as a result of which there is a tendency to send electrically charged ions into the solution, and this tendency is opposed by the osmotic pressure of the dissolved ions. From this and the fact that the osmotic pressure follows the

WALTHER NERNST
1864——

gas laws, he was able to show how the voltage of a metal against a solution of its ions changed with the concentration of the ions in the solution. The formation of positively charged ions from a metal corresponds to an oxidation, and all reactions of oxidation or reduction find a place in the table of oxidation potentials. Then from the Nernst rule, together with the law of mass action, one is able to predict how the oxidation or reduction reaction will be affected by changes in concentration and whether, under given conditions, an oxidation or reduction will take place. In 1889 Nernst also introduced the concept of the *solubility product* which applies to every reaction where precipitation takes place. He studied reaction rates, chemical equilibria, liquid crystals, the application of the laws of chemical equilibrium to toxins and antitoxins, specific heats at very low temperatures, and the determination of dielectric constants and their effects upon electrolytic dissociation.

Nernst had many American and English students and, like Tammann who succeeded him at Göttingen, he has had a very marked influence upon the development of physicochemical theory. In 1895 he published, with Schönflies, a book entitled *Einführung in die mathematische Behandlung der Wissenschaften* which shows what mathematics a chemist or physicist should know. His *Theoretical Chemistry from the Standpoint of Avogadro's Rule and Thermodynamics* has gone through several editions in English, as well as in German. Nernst was editor of the *Jahrbuch der Elektrochemie* and of the *Zeitschrift für Elektrochemie*. In 1920 he received a Nobel prize. He also wrote *Theoretische und Experimentale Grundlage der neuren Wärmesatz* (1918) and *Das Weltgebäude in Licht der neuren Forschung* (1921).

Georg Bredig (1868 ——) was born in Glogau, Germany, and received his Ph.D. degree in 1894 at Leipzig, where he worked under Ostwald. He then studied a year at Amsterdam. He received the M.D. degree at Rostock in 1919 and an honorary degree from Heidelberg. In 1910 he was made full professor at Karlsruhe. He has measured the ionization constants of weak bases (1894), pointed out the importance of amphoteric electrolytes (1898), and studied catalytic reactions, such as that of hydrogenation, particularly of colloidal platinum, and the poisoning of catalysts. He has been interested in the chemistry of colloids and in photochemistry.

Richard Abegg (1869–1910) was born in Danzig and studied at Tübingen, Kiel, and at Berlin. He worked under Hofmann in 1891 on organic chemistry, but then worked under Ostwald at Leipzig and under Arrhenius at Stockholm. He went to Göttingen in 1894 and was made professor there in 1897, but in 1897 he was called to Breslau. In 1900 he was offered a position in Christiania (Oslo) which he refused. In 1909 he went to the Technische Hochschule in Breslau and was placed in charge of a laboratory where he expected to be very happy, but he was killed the next year in an unfortunate balloon accident.

Abegg was a gifted physical chemist and started a very comprehensive *Handbuch* in which, as far as possible, the literature of inorganic chemistry was reviewed from the standpoint of the physical chemist. He developed, together with Bodländer, a very satisfactory valence theory which fits in nicely with our present ideas concerning electrons. According to Abegg, an element can vary from its lowest to highest valence only 8 units. Thus the members of the halogen group in the periodic table normally have a valence of −1, but oxidation gives to them valencies of +1, +3, +5, and +7. In the next family, with sulfur the lowest valence is −2, as in sulfides, and the highest +6, as in sulfates. Then in the nitrogen family, the lowest possible valence is −3, as in ammonia, and the highest +5, as in nitric acid. In terms of the electron theory, we say that the electrons present in the outside layer can be lost to some other element, or more electrons can be added and the limits are no electrons in the outer layer or 8. Thus, with sulfur there are normally 6 electrons present; it can accept 2 more and have a negative charge of −2, or it can give up all 6 of the outer electrons and assume a positive charge of 6 units. This corresponds exactly to Abegg's ideas.

Abegg worked on the freezing points of solutions (1894–1898), the dielectric constant of ice (1898), the polyiodides of the alkali metals (1906), and on electric potentials in non-aqueous solutions (1909). He distinguished between monopolar and heteropolar compounds (1906).

Friedrich Raschig (1863–1928) was born at Brandenburg on the Havel River. He studied from 1881–1885 at Berlin and in Heidelberg for a short period. He was assistant at Berlin for two years, and for three years he was chemist at the Badische Anilin und Soda Fabrik. He was particularly interested in the industrial preparation of nitrogen and sulfur compounds.

In May, 1891, Raschig had his own factory for the preparation of phenol. He discovered nitramide (1887) and chloramine (1907). He proposed a theory for the reactions that take place in the manufacture of sulfuric acid by the lead-chamber process (1887 and later), studied the sulfonic acids of hydroxylamine (1887), and worked out a method for the commercial production of hydroxylamine (1887). He studied nitrogen iodide and the thionic acids. He worked out a simple method for preparing large quantities of hydrazine from ammonia (1908) and discovered a suitable commercial method for making hydrazoic acid from hydrazine. The lead salt of hydrazoic acid, called *lead azide*, was used as a detonator during the World War and has displaced mercury fulminate quite generally.

Raschig was an authority on the technical production of phenol, and his researches showed originality. He devised new titration methods for quantitative analysis and proposed the precipitation of sulfuric acid with benzidine hydrochloride. The solubility of benzidine sulfate is about the same as that of barium sulfate, but the benzidine precipitate is soluble in caustic-soda solutions and behaves in titration as if it were free sulfuric acid. Raschig was very successful in solving technical problems.

Richard Zsigmondy (1865–1929) was born in Vienna and received his Ph.D. degree at Munich in 1889. He worked for about a year as private assistant to Prof. Kundt at Berlin and from 1893–1897 was at Graz. After this, he entered the employ of Schott and Gen in Jena where he worked on colored and turbid glasses. He left industrial work in 1900 and worked in a private laboratory in Jena for seven years. He did classic work with his ultramicroscope and studied colloidal gold and the purple of Cassius. He published numerous papers and a book *Zur Erkenntniss der Kolloide* which reached its fifth edition in 1925, the year that he was awarded a Nobel prize.

He was also awarded several medals and three honorary degrees. Zsigmondy did considerable pioneer work with colloids and pointed out that there was a gradual change from a condition of true solution to that of colloidal solution and to that of a suspension. In the case of the true solution the particles are extremely small, but it is more or less arbitrary where the line is drawn between that of a solution with very large molecules to that of a colloid with larger ones and finally to a suspension with still larger particles. He studied protective colloids and showed how common the colloidal condition is in everyday life, and also made use of ultrafilters. He was called to Göttingen in 1907 as assistant professor of inorganic chemistry and was made full professor in 1919.

Carl Bosch (1874 ——) was born in Cologne and obtained his Ph.D. degree in Leipzig for work done under Wilhelm Ostwald. He was the brother-in-law of Fritz Haber and helped him with the process for obtaining ammonia from the nitrogen of the atmosphere. Since 1899, Bosch has been in the employ of the Badische Anilin und Soda Fabrik. He has worked on synthetic indigo, barium cyanide, etc. The Nobel prize was awarded to him with Bergius for services in developing work under high pressures. Bosch ranks as an industrial chemist who obtained distinction by applying the principles of physical chemistry to his work.

Fritz Haber (1868–1934) was born in Breslau and studied at Heidelberg, Berlin, Zurich, and Jena, and during this time he worked as an unpaid assistant in chemical factories. He became assistant and lecturer at the Polytechnicum at Carlsruhe in 1894 and in 1906 was professor of physical chemistry and electrochemistry there. In 1911 he became head of the Kaiser Wilhelm Institute of Physical Chemistry and Electrochemistry near Berlin. Although, as we have seen, Le Châtelier anticipated some of the ideas for which Haber has often received credit, he is best known for the Haber process, which accomplishes the catalytic synthesis of ammonia NH_3 from hydrogen and nitrogen at high pressures. Willstätter has said of him, "His greatness lies in the conception of ideas of a scientific nature. The stimulation, the plan, the method are to him more important than the result. Creative work pleases him more than the completed task." Haber also worked on chemical equilibrium in flames, the electrolytic reduction of nitrobenzene, auto-oxidation, the synthesis of nitric oxide in the electric arc, and many other electrochemical problems. He has written several books of importance in chemical engineering and received a Nobel prize in 1918.

Friedrich Bergius (1884 ——) was born near Breslau, studied physical chemistry under Abegg and Ladenburg at Breslau and under Hantsch at Leipzig where he received his degree. He worked with Nernst in Berlin and with Haber at Carlsruhe.

FRITZ HABER
1868–1934

He was lecturer at Hannover in 1919 and in 1913 worked with Th. Goldschmidt at Essen. He studied the conversion of coal into a combustible liquid and the transformation of wood into a carbohydrate suitable for cattle feed. He now lives at Heidelberg. In 1931, together with Carl Bosch, he was awarded the Nobel prize for services with respect to the invention and development of high-pressure methods.

Emil Abderhalden (1877 ——) was born at Oberutzwil in Switzerland and received the M.D. degree at Basel in 1901. He worked under G. von Bunge and under Emil Fischer in Germany. It has already been pointed out that chemistry has progressed so rapidly and become so subdivided into separate fields that no one man can keep track of all chemical work. In a review written in 1937, Paul Walden pointed out that in 1887 only about 1200 papers were reviewed in a year in the *Zentralblatt*, but this had increased to over 60,000 in 1937. Remarkable advances have taken place in the field of physiological or biochemistry. The chemical reactions that take place in the living organism are now understood much better, and chemists are able by their laboratory technique to analyze small samples of the body fluids and thus obtain valuable information. Such work, however, is largely done in laboratories which are connected with hospitals, and the results of these researches are published in journals which do not come to the attention of most chemists. In any short history of chemistry, the field of biochemistry is almost entirely neglected, and it is left to the textbooks on biochemistry to recount the accomplishment.

Emil Abderhalden has been one of the most prolific writers on biochemical subjects and with his students he has published over two hundred scientific papers of merit. For some years he annually abstracted hundreds of papers on biochemistry for the *Chemisches Zentralblatt*. Since 1911 he has been full professor and director of the Physiological Institute of the University of Halle. His *Handbuch biologischer Arbeitsmethoden*, of which he was the editor in chief, is a large-sized book of thirteen volumes. His *Lehrbuch der Physiologie* (1925–1927) is in four volumes; his *Lehrbuch der physiologischen Chemie* contains 852 large octavo pages in its sixth edition (1931), and his *Biochemisches Handlexicon* (1911–1932) is in thirteen volumes. His writings are extremely interesting and stimulating.

Contributions of Physical Chemistry.—To students of the present day it is altogether superfluous to attempt any detailed account of the service that physical chemistry has done to the science as a whole. The ideas it has introduced now permeate all instruction in chemistry and make their influence felt in every department of the science. To inorganic chemistry, especially, has come the inspiration of a new point of view and a reawakened enthusiasm toward research. Dealing, as it does, with the influence upon chemical reactions of temperature, pressure, concentration, and catalysis, physical chemistry has given a new insight into the mechanism of all chemical change and made it possible to fix, as never before, the conditions most suitable for a given effect. There has resulted not only an enhanced accuracy in analytical procedure, but a universal improvement in laboratory technique. Industrial processes also have benefited universally, for physiochemical reasoning has in many cases made it possible to calculate in advance the most economical conditions of their operation. The contact process for the preparation of sulfuric acid is a beautiful example of this, but examples might be multiplied indefinitely.

Organic chemistry, too, has derived much benefit from physical chemistry. Prior to the World War of 1914–1918, the well-known American firm of E. I. Du Pont de Nemours of Wilmington, Delaware, was almost entirely devoted to the manufacture of explosives, but in 1938 explosives constituted only about 25 per cent of their products. Methods like that of obtaining ethyl alcohol from saw dust were known at about 1800, but it is only by taking advantage of the laws of physical chemistry that such a process can become profitable. The extent to which hydrogenated vegetable oils have replaced lard in cookery, the cracking of petroleum to produce greatly enlarged yields of gasoline, the manufacture of artificial silk and artificial rubber are but a few of the accomplishments of modern chemistry, and all these industries have found it necessary to employ men with a good, fundamental knowledge of physical chemistry. At the present time, the Du Ponts are erecting an eight million dollar factory for the production of a remarkable synthetic yarn. The actual chemistry of the various operations appears very simple on paper, but physical chemical principles must be followed for successfully carrying out each reaction.

The Rare Gases of the Atmosphere.—One of the most famous of modern researches in inorganic chemistry was that carried out by Lord Rayleigh and Sir William Ramsay which resulted in the discovery of several hitherto unrecognized components of the atmosphere. Nearly a hundred years before, Cavendish had, indeed, subjected a mixture of air with an excess of oxygen to the prolonged action of electric sparks and, after removal of the products of reaction and the excess of oxygen, had always found a residue which was not reduced in volume by further treatment of the same kind. This residue he estimated at about $\frac{1}{120}$ part by volume of the air originally employed. No one made any use of this observation, probably because later investigators had no real idea of how accurately Cavendish had worked, so that no question was raised as to the nature of the residue until Lord Rayleigh in 1893 called attention to the fact that nitrogen prepared from the air by removing the other known constituents is heavier than nitrogen prepared chemically in the laboratory, by about 1 part in 200, this discrepancy amounting to fifty times the experimental error of the determination. Four explanations suggested themselves. The atmospheric nitrogen might contain oxygen; the "chemical" nitrogen (from ammonia) might contain hydrogen; the atmospheric product might contain a heavier allotropic form of nitrogen (perhaps N_3) analogous to ozone; or finally it might contain a small quantity of an inert gas of higher specific gravity. The first two possibilities could be easily disposed of by mixing both kinds of nitrogen with oxygen and hydrogen, respectively, and again removing these contaminations. The specific gravities of the products were unaffected.

Argon.—Atmospheric nitrogen was then passed over glowing magnesium which absorbed by far the larger part forming a nitride, but left a residue little affected by magnesium, whose specific gravity was now perceptibly higher than that of the original nitrogen. When, by repeating the treatment, a gas had been obtained that was nineteen times as heavy as hydrogen, it was introduced into a Plücker tube, and its spark spectrum examined. This still showed the lines of nitrogen, but also a spectrum hitherto unknown which furnished convincing evidence that a new element was involved and not an allotropic form of nitrogen. There still remained the remote possibility that the new substance might in some way owe its formation to the processes devised for its isolation, and to settle this question atmospheric nitrogen was passed through a long series of porous clay pipes surrounded by a vacuum. The portion which diffused through the clay was found distinctly less dense than that which remained behind, showing that a heavier component must be present in the original air. Meantime two processes were worked out for preparing the new gas on a comparatively large scale. One consisted in passing atmospheric oxygen over magnesium mixed with lime, the other was an application of the principle of Cavendish in which the nitrogen was oxidized and the product absorbed. In this way it proved possible to obtain several liters of the new gas which was free from nitrogen and possessed the density 39.88 (O = 32). To this gas the discoverers gave the name *argon*, "idle," on account of its hitherto unexampled lack of chemical affinity. Nitrogen had hitherto been considered an inert gas, but this substance proved absolutely incapable of entering into chemical combination. Ramsay writes on this point:

The methods employed to prepare argon free from nitrogen—namely, by exposing the mixed gases to the action of oxygen in a discharge of electric sparks, and by passing them over red-hot magnesium— show that it cannot be induced to combine with one of the most electronegative of elements—oxygen, and one of the most positive—magnesium. It also refuses to combine with hydrogen or with chlorine when sparked with these gases; nor is it absorbed or altered in volume by passage through a red-hot tube along with the vapors of phosphorus, sulfur, tellurium, or sodium. Red-hot caustic soda, or a red-hot mixture of soda and lime, which attacks the exceedingly refractory metal platinum, was without action on argon. The combined influence of oxygen and an alkali in the shape of fused potassium nitrate or red-hot peroxide of sodium was also without effect. Gold would, however, have resisted such action, but would have been attacked by the next agent tried, viz., persulfide of sodium and calcium. This mixture was exposed at a red heat to a current of argon, again without result. Nascent chlorine, or chlorine in the moment of liberation, obtained from a mixture of nitric and hydrochloric acids, and from permanganate of potassium and hydrochloric acid, was without action. A mixture of argon with fluorine, the most active of all the elements, was exposed to a rain of electric sparks by M. Moissan, the distinguished chemist who first succeeded in preparing large quantities of fluorine in a pure state, without his observing any sign of chemical combination.

An attempt was also made to cause argon to combine with carbon by making an electric arc between two rods of carbon in an atmosphere of argon. It was at first believed that combination had taken place, for expansion occurred, the final volume of gas being larger than the volume taken; but subsequent experiments have shown that the expansion was due to the formation of some oxide of carbon from the oxygen adhering to the carbon rods. On absorption of this oxide by the usual absorbent, a mixture of cuprous chloride and ammonia, the argon was recovered unchanged.

*   *   *   *   *   *   *   *

Professor Ramsay has also made experiments on the action of a silent electric discharge upon a mixture of argon with the vapor of carbon tetrachloride; the latter decomposes, giving, not a resin, but crystals of hexachlorobenzene and free chlorine; but the volume of the argon was unchanged. It was all recovered without loss. Next the rare elements titanium and uranium have been heated to redness in a current of argon, with no alteration or absorption of the gas. And more recently, attempts have been made to cause argon to combine with the very electropositive elements, rubidium and cesium, by volatilizing them in an atmosphere of argon. Numerous experiments, in which electric sparks have been passed through argon cooled with liquid air between poles of every attainable element, have also been made, but without result.

*   *   *   *   *   *   *   *

These failures to produce compounds make it impossible to gain any knowledge regarding the atomic weight of argon from a study of its compounds, for it forms none.

The foregoing gives an excellent idea of the thoroughness with which this investigation was carried out. The difficulty regarding the atomic weight referred to in the last sentence was a very serious one, for the unusual properties of the new element made its position in the periodic table one of extreme interest. The molecular weight of argon was settled by its density as 39.88, but since it forms no compounds the only clue to the number of atoms in the molecule must be sought in physical constants. Fortunately one was available which had already been well studied in the case of known elements and which therefore furnished a reliable analogy. This was the ratio of specific heat at constant volume to that at constant pressure. In the case of all diatomic gases, like oxygen, hydrogen, and nitrogen, this ratio has a value closely approximately 1.4, whereas in monatomic elements (mercury vapor being the most convenient example) its value is 1.6. Furthermore, this is not a mere empirical coincidence, since arguments can be derived from the kinetic theory to show why such a difference must exist. The ratio of specific heats for argon was found to be 1.6 and the gas was therefore accepted as monatomic, a conclusion in harmony with its other properties, since a substance which combines with no other element would also be unlikely to combine with itself. The atomic weight therefore is equal to the molecular weight, 39.88, a figure very close to that of potassium.

Terrestrial Helium.—This left argon at first without analogies, but it was not destined to remain long unique. In 1868 during an eclipse, the spectrum of the sun's chromosphere displayed certain lines which could not be identified with those of any element known on the earth, and Lockyer and Frankland ascribed them to a new element to which, from the circumstances of its first observation, they gave the name of *helium*. Somewhat later William F. Hillebrand of the U. S. Geological Survey, on heating the mineral cleveite, obtained an indifferent gas which he described as nitrogen and which therefore received little further attention, until Ramsay in looking for compounds of argon, again prepared it, removed the nitrogen by magnesium, and then observed that the residual gas showed the spectrum of helium. Later the same gas was found in a number of other minerals, notably in monazite sand, where we shall have occasion to discuss its occurrence later, and also in the gases evolved by a number of mineral springs. The new element is, with the exception of hydrogen, the lightest gas known. Its other properties are practically those of argon, and its atomic weight, like its molecular weight, is 4.

Neon, Krypton, and Xenon.—By 1897 the existence of these two gases had convinced Ramsay that a whole new family of elements must exist of which argon and helium represented two members. A thorough search for others was therefore begun and ultimately crowned with success. Numerous minerals were first heated without result and the waters of mineral springs carefully examined, but these sources at first yielded, in addition to the well-known gases, only argon and helium. Finally the ele-- ments sought for were found in extremely small quantities in the atmosphere. The residue from boiling off a large quantity of liquid air was first fractionated and ultimately yielded another inactive gas which was named *neon*, "new," while a similar residue from crude argon yielded a still heavier substance of the same type which received the name *krypton*, "hidden." A particular interest attaches to this gas because the lines of its spectrum can be observed in the *aurora borealis*. At last, especially large quantities of liquid air were employed, and helium and another inert gas were found, and to the latter the name *xenon*, "stranger," was given. There is no opportunity here to describe the details of this investigation, but it should be said in passing that it represented the finest experimental work yet done with gases.

The relative quantities of these new elements which exist in the atmosphere are approximately as follows:

Helium	1 part in 245,300	by volume
Neon	1 part in 80,800	by volume
Argon	1 part in 106.8	by volume
Krypton	1 part in 20 million	by volume
Xenon	1 part in 170 million	by volume

It will be seen that there is a far smaller proportion of xenon in the atmosphere than there is of gold in sea water, and this gives some idea of the skill and patience required to isolate it in a pure state. The research was brought up to this point by 1900, and when the atomic weights of the new elements are compared, it is found that Ramsay's prediction of 1897 is fully justified. They constitute a natural family occupying a period of their own in the table of Mendelejeff where (having a valence of zero) they occupy an appropriate place next to the elements of valence one, and where their neutral properties form an appropriate transition from the most electropositive to the most electronegative elements. A selected portion of the table is here reproduced to emphasize these relations:

Hydrogen	Helium	Lithium	Beryllium
1	4	7	9
Fluorine	Neon	Sodium	Magnesium
19	20	23	24
Chlorine	Argon	Potassium	Calcium
35.5	40	39	40
Bromine	Krypton	Rubidium	Strontium
80	82	85	87
Iodine	Xenon	Cesium	Barium
127	128	133	137

Striking as these results are, the reader will notice that if the elements were arranged strictly in the order of their atomic weights the positions of argon and potassium would have to be reversed. This anomaly is outside the range of experimental error, and while by no means fully explained, it evidently is of the same kind which has long been observed in the relative positions of iodine and tellurium. We shall see later that new light has recently been thrown upon cases of this kind by the work of Mosely upon the atomic numbers.

Some English Chemists

Crookes.—William Crookes was born in London in 1832, entered the College of Chemistry in London at the age of sixteen, and became Hofmann's assistant there in 1851. The year previous he had obtained about 5 kilograms of a precipitate containing selenium from a German sulfuric acid plant, and his first published work was concerning the cyanide of selenium which he obtained from it. In 1859 he discovered thallium in these same residues. In 1871 he published his *Select Methods in Quantitative Analysis*. Crookes's work on the atomic weight of thallium, leading to a value 204.04 compared to 204.4 which is accepted at present, occupied several years and served as a model for later work.

Noticing the anomalous behavior of the balance when weighing substances, he constructed a radiometer which he at first regarded as a machine that transformed light into motion, but he later learned that it depended upon thermal effects. Much of this work was done in evacuated tubes and this led to his famous experiments on the phenomena produced by the discharge of electricity through highly exhausted tubes.

He developed a theory of "radiant matter" which eventually resulted in the modern electronic theory. Crookes founded the *Chemical News* in 1859 and published it until his death. His work on the rare earths is worthy of mention as well as his studies with radioactive elements. During the last years of his life he became interested in spiritualistic manifestations. He died in 1919.

Roscoe.—Sir Henry Enfield Roscoe was born in London in 1833 and studied at University College in London under Graham and Williamson. He went to Heidelberg and worked under Bunsen at Heidelberg (1855–1857). In 1857 he succeeded Sir E. Frankland in the chair of chemistry at Owens College, Manchester, where he remained thirty years. From 1885 to 1895 he was a member of Parliament and was keenly interested in education. While working under Bunsen he made mineral analyses that required great skill. In 1867 he studied vanadium and its compounds and showed that vanadium is an element related to nitrogen and that its oxide with the highest valence is V_2O_5, and not VO_3 as Berzelius thought. He was interested in spectrum analysis but did very little research in this field. He studied the chemistry of columbium (niobium), tungsten, uranium, and perchloric acid. He studied the solubility of ammonia in water and constant boiling mixtures of solutions of acids and bases. He wrote *Lectures on Spectrum Analysis* (1869), *Treatise on Chemistry* (with Schorlemmer), (1877–1892), *The Use of Dalton's Atomic Theory* (with A. Harden) (1898), and an *Autobiography*. The Roscoe and Schorlemmer treatise was unquestionably the most complete textbook on chemistry in English and has been regarded as authoritative.

Lord Rayleigh.—John William Strutt (1842–1919) (Lord Rayleigh from 1873) was an English physicist who was on the staff of Cambridge University from 1879 to 1884 and at the Royal Institute of Great Britain from 1887 to 1904. His interest in Prout's hypothesis that all atoms were really polymers of hydrogen, led him to determine accurately the density of gases. He tried to determine whether the atomic weight of oxygen was exactly sixteen times that of hydrogen and in 1892 announced that oxygen had the atomic weight 15.882 if hydrogen is taken as the standard, thus refuting Prout's theory.

In the course of his work he determined the density of nitrogen and discovered that the density of nitrogen prepared by the oxidation of ammonia was always about 0.5 per cent less than that of nitrogen obtained from air. Then Sir William Ramsay asked permission to perform some experiments and found that from nitrogen obtained from air about one-eightieth of the original volume could not be absorbed by red-hot magnesium, and the residual gas was about $^{15}\!/_{14}$ as heavy as nitrogen. Thus argon was discovered. Lord Rayleigh, like Sir William Crookes, was interested in the study of abnormal psychic phenomena. He received the Nobel prize in 1904 as well as many other honors.

Ramsay.—Sir William Ramsay was born in Glasgow in 1852. At the age of fourteen he began to study at the University of Glasgow. While playing football, he broke his leg, and during the time he was confined to the house he read Graham's *Chemistry* in order to find out how to make fireworks. He began to study science at the university in 1869. The next year, although only eighteen years old, he went to Germany to work with Bunsen but obtained his doctorate under Fittig in Tübingen, after two

SIR WILLIAM RAMSAY
1852–1916

SIR JAMES DEWAR
1842–1923

years' study.   He went back to Glasgow and was connected with the university until 1880, working with pyridine bases for the most part, but also doing physicochemical work in studying the dissociation phenomena of metal hydroxides and the heats of formation of organic substances during the last two years there.

In 1880 he was called to the chair of chemistry at University College in Bristol and was made director in 1889, although only twenty-nine years old. Here his work was chiefly along physicochemical lines.   He was called to University College in London to succeed Williamson in 1887.   In 1894 he began his famous work on the gases of the atmosphere which ended in the careful study and identification of the whole family of rare gases—helium, neon, argon, krypton, and xenon.

He was uncommonly sharpsighted and remarkably skillful in manipulation.   He was known internationally and was personally attractive.   He was friendly with Wilhelm Ostwald and Emil Fischer and helped to train a number of brilliant investigators.   He died in 1916 after suffering caused by his work with radium emanations.   Besides being an eminent scientist he was a scholarly gentleman, speaking at least five languages.

Sir James Dewar (1842–1923) was a British chemist and physicist who was fond of music and made violins.   He studied under Playfair at Edinburgh and became his assistant.   He also worked with Kekulé.   In 1875 he became professor of experimental philosophy at Cambridge, and two years later he succeeded J. H. Gladstone as professor of chemistry at the Royal Institution in London.   He won the Rumford medal in 1894 and was knighted in 1904.

His early papers are on organic chemistry.   Later he measured high temperatures and studied the chemistry of the electric arc and the physiclogical effects of light and also worked with the spectroscope.   His studies on the liquefaction of the so-called *permanent gases* began in 1874 with a paper on the *Latent Heat of Liquid Gases*.   In 1891 he described a machine for producing liquid oxygen in large quantities, and he showed that liquid oxygen and liquid ozone are magnetic.   In 1892 he described a vacuum-jacketed vessel which was suitable for handling liquefied gases.   This was the Dewar flask and served as a model for the well-known *thermos bottle*. He studied the properties of the carbonyls of nickel and iron and also the properties of thin films.   He was a scientist possessing great manipulative skill and for his work with gases was awarded a Nobel prize.

RADIOACTIVITY; ITS INFLUENCE ON THE ATOMIC THEORY

The last years of the nineteenth century witnessed some remarkable developments in the science of physics which have deeply affected many fundamental conceptions hitherto considered within the province of chemistry, such as the nature of the atom and the ultimate composition of matter.   These developments were associated with the discovery and study of certain new and altogether unusual types of radiation.

The X Rays.—As early as 1879 Sir William Crookes had passed electric currents of high potential through tubes containing gases at exceedingly low pressures—so-called *vacuum tubes*—and had observed that under these circumstances rays are emitted from the negative electrode or cathode which differ markedly from any hitherto studied.   They proceed in straight lines from the cathode but show the remarkable property of being deflected by a magnet, which would seem to indicate that they represent a stream of minute material particles.   These phenomena remained isolated for some time.   In 1895 Roentgen found that when the cathode rays impinge upon a solid, a new kind of ray is generated, which now penetrates the glass walls and proceeds into space, producing effects then altogether novel but now recognized as common to most of these new types of radiation. They cause, for example, various substances like zincblende, willemite, barium platinocyanide, etc., to fluoresce; they affect the photographic plate in a manner similar to the action of light; they traverse opaque media; and they ionize gases.   By this is meant that gases through which these rays pass become conductors of electricity, so that if such gases are introduced into an electroscope the latter loses its charge, and the relative velocity with which this occurs may be used as a measure of the relative ionizing effect of different types or sources of rays.

Radioactivity.—This new form of radiation received the name of *X rays*, and the fact that indirectly they made it possible to "see through" objects hitherto considered opaque excited the greatest popular interest.   No one, however, realized that their discovery had any important bearing upon chemical problems until in the following year Henri Becquerel discovered a somewhat similar type of radiation which proceeded from an entirely different source.   Becquerel came of a family long eminent for its contributions to the study of fluorescence and had himself lived up to the family tradition.   The formation of X rays from cathode rays in the vacuum tube and the fluorescence of the glass always observed in the latter suggested to Becquerel that fluorescent substances might possess the property of making a similar transformation of light waves.   His first experiments served to strengthen that belief. A uranium salt was exposed to the sun's rays while resting upon a photographic plate wrapped in black paper to protect it from the light. When the plate was afterward developed, the portion under the uranium salt was found to have been affected. On one occasion, however, when all other conditions had been the same, an accident prevented the exposure of the uranium salt to light. Nevertheless the plate exhibited the same effects as before, showing that uranium salts continuously emit rays capable of affecting the photographic plate even when not exposed to light. This fact was confirmed by experiments upon a great variety of uranium compounds. All showed the action, and its intensity was found proportional to the percentage of uranium in the substance. A puzzling exception was observed in the case of pitchblende from Joachimsthal—the mineral which had hitherto served as the chief source of uranium preparations. This mineral exhibited an activity several times greater than that of metallic uranium, showing that it must contain some other substance more highly radioactive than the latter. Mme Sklodowska Curie, at the suggestion of Becquerel, now undertook the chemical examination of the pitchblende (which is very complex) in order to find this especially active component.

The Discovery of Radium.—The first material which showed the property in a higher degree than uranium was a substance resembling bismuth, to which Mme Curie gave the name of *polonium* in honor of her native country. It has not even yet been obtained in a state of purity. A little later she discovered among the alkaline earths a new element which possessed the property of radioactivity in an especially high degree. It closely resembled barium but could be separated with some difficulty from the latter by the fractional crystallization of certain salts. To this new element was given the highly appropriate name of *radium*, and its purification was finally pushed to a point which justified a determination of the atomic weight. This yielded the value 226 and entitled the new element to a vacant space in the periodic table just below barium, which is also in harmony with its spectrum and chemical properties.

The properties of radium are remarkable. Its salts are self-luminous, and constantly give off radiations producing effects similar to those of X rays.　It was found that these rays were given off continuously with undiminished energy, and not only were rays emitted but heat—a gram of radium evolving 133 calories per hour.　When the character of the radiation was more thoroughly studied it was found that three distinct classes of rays could be distinguished.　These are still spoken of as the α, β, and γ rays.　Of these, the α rays are the least penetrating and have least action upon a photographic plate, while, on the other hand, they are the most potent in ionizing gases.　The γ rays are the most penetrating and in their character most resemble X rays.　The β rays, however, are identical with, or closely allied to, the cathode rays of the Crookes tube, though they have a higher velocity.　They carry a negative charge and are deflected by a magnetic field.　The γ rays are not deflected, and the α rays but slightly.　In the latter case, however, the deflection is in the opposite direction, showing that these rays carry a positive charge.　Their essential nature will be discussed later.

Rutherford's Work on Thorium.—The subject of radioactivity entered upon a new stage when, in 1900, Sir Ernest Rutherford, then professor in Montreal, began an intensive study of the radioactivity of thorium, the only previously well-known element, except uranium, which had thus far shown the property.　Acting upon the observation of Owens that some of the effects produced by radioactive products were modified by currents of air, Rutherford found that air which had been passed over an active thorium preparation had itself acquired activity, but that this activity decayed rapidly with the time in accordance with the equation:

$$\frac{I_t}{I_0} = e^{-\lambda t}$$

where I_0 represents the initial intensity, I_t intensity at the time t, e the base of natural logarithms, and λ a constant characteristic of the substance.　It has since been found that all radioactive materials follow this law of gradual decay, and it is perhaps the most important single generalization in the subject of radioactivity.

The experiments showed that thorium was continually producing an extremely attenuated but highly radioactive gas, and to

ERNEST RUTHERFORD
1871——

this Rutherford applied the name *thorium emanation*. He
found that when the gas is retained for some time in any vessel
the walls of the latter become coated with active material.
This he called the *radioactive deposit*. It exhibited some remarkable properties. If a negatively charged wire was suspended
in a vessel containing the emanation, all the deposit was concentrated upon the wire. The quantity of material was so
small that it could be recognized only by its activity, but that
it was a solid adhering to the wire seemed amply proved by the
fact that it could be driven off by heat, or removed by rubbing
with sandpaper. Still another substance, therefore, had been
formed by the decomposition of the emanation, activity and
period of decay were different from the latter.

In 1902 Rutherford and Soddy pointed out another decomposition of thorium compounds of a somewhat analogous character.
When a solution of thorium nitrate, for example, is precipitated
by ammonia, the hydroxide thrown down, when filtered and
dried, is found to be almost inactive. If the filtrate, however, be
evaporated to dryness and the ammonium nitrate expelled by
heat, an extremely small residue is left which possesses almost
the whole activity of the original preparation. At the end of
about a month, however, this has been practically lost, while that
of the precipitated thoria has by this time regained nearly all
its original value. Subsequent investigation has shown that
the changes just mentioned are in reality a good deal more complex, but these experiments sufficed to prove that radioactivity is
accompanied by the formation of new material. Any single
process, therefore, cannot be of infinite duration.

The Theory of Atomic Disintegration.—On the strength of this
evidence Rutherford and Soddy in 1902 advanced their theory
of atomic disintegration, which thus far has accounted for all
observed phenomena and is the present working hypothesis of the
subject. Its fundamental principles may be stated as follows:
The chemical atom is not to be regarded as an impenetrable
and indivisible point, but as an extremely complex structure, and
the forces which determine the relations of its component parts
are incomparably greater than any which obtain in chemical
combination between the atoms. The atoms of a substance
which we call radioactive are unstable and manifest this insta-

bility in the peculiar manner that certain ones (determined solely by the total number present) decompose explosively every instant, throwing off with great velocity the material composing the various kinds of rays above described and leaving behind a new chemical element with properties of its own, which may or may not include radioactivity.

Formation of Helium from Radium.—Since radium occurs only in minerals containing uranium, this theory made it probable that radium is a product of the latter, and since most active minerals, such as monazite sand, contain helium, this might be looked upon as one of the products of such activity. The latter point was established beyond question in 1903 when Ramsay and Soddy undertook a thorough study of the radium emanation. This material is a true gas obeying Boyle's law. It can be separated from other gases, condensed to a liquid, and frozen. Its atomic weight, as determined from its density by Ramsay, is 222. He classified it in the argon group and named it *niton*. The most striking observation made by Ramsay and Soddy was that when this gas has been kept for some days it disappears and helium appears in its place. This discovery, which represented the first known production of one element from another, seemed a realization of the dreams of the alchemists, and aroused a popular interest almost equal to that excited by the discovery of the X rays. The experiment was soon successfully repeated in several laboratories.

In the same year Rutherford pointed out that helium could not well be the only decomposition product of radium, as indeed was improbable, because the radium emanation, like that of thorium, also yielded an *active deposit*, which probably represents the greater portion of the products of decomposition. Rutherford suggested that the α rays emitted by the emanation, as well as other radioactive substances, might really consist of electrically charged atoms of helium. In 1909 he was able to prove this by an extremely ingenious experiment. Some of the radium emanation was sealed into a tube of glass so extremely thin that α rays could penetrate it with considerable ease. This tube was then placed inside another which was attached to a spectrum tube. The outer tube was then evacuated. After 2 days its contents showed the principal lines in the spectrum of helium, and after 6 the spectrum was complete. As a control a similar experiment was tried in which the inner tube was filled with helium instead of the emanation. None of this, however, penetrated to the outer tube.

Meantime it had been shown that many other radioactive changes take place with evolution of α rays, and it follows from this, that the production of helium is not a particular property of the radium emanation but is a frequent accompaniment of perhaps the majority of such changes.

Effects Produced by Single Atoms.—For our general conception of the nature of matter it is, perhaps, of still greater interest to know that the evolution of helium in such changes is discontinuous and consists of the expulsion of discrete particles. It has been found possible to prove this by direct observation. α rays cause the gases through which they pass to conduct electricity, and Rutherford and Geiger succeeded in devising an "ionizing chamber"[1] in which it was possible, when high voltages were employed, to detect the slightest currents by the movement of an electrometer needle. Now when a small portion of the α radiation of a weakly active preparation was allowed to enter the chamber, the entrance of each particle gave rise to a ballistic throw of the needle, so that the number of particles entering in a given time could be accurately counted. Had the radiation represented a continuous stream, the needle would, of course, have shown only a constant deflection.

Essentially the same results were obtained in another way. When radium was first discovered, Sir William Crookes found that the luminescence which it produces upon a screen of crystalline zinc sulfide is really made up of scintillations, apparently caused by particles expelled from the radium striking the crystals, and this led him to construct the familiar piece of apparatus known as the *spinthariscope*. Now if in an experiment like that described above we replace the ionizing chamber by such a zinc sulfide screen or by a diamond, it is possible, with the aid of a microscope, to count the scintillations in a given time. The two methods give very concordant results. From either, the number

---

[1] An ionizing chamber consists of an enclosed space between two parallel plates charged at a high potential difference. No current passes, however, unless the air between the plates becomes ionized.

of particles evolved from any preparation in a given time can be calculated. If we know the total charge carried by the rays during the same time, we have the data for determining the charge carried by each particle, an important constant in radio-activity work.

Mass and Dimensions of the Atom.—Some years before these determinations were made, J. J. Thomson, C. T. R. Wilson, and others had made extensive studies of the conduction of electricity through gases in the Crookes tube and similar forms of apparatus. They came to the conclusion that both the positive and nega-tive current are carried by minute particles, and that both sets of particles carry a charge of equal magnitude (the same as that which is carried by the hydrogen ion in electrolysis). But they concluded that the masses of the two kinds of particles differ widely, those carrying a positive charge being of atomic magni-tude, whereas those carrying the negative current (in the cathode ray) have a mass only $\frac{1}{1,000}$ of that of the hydrogen atom. We now call the latter particles *electrons*. Applying the same reasoning to the results of their own experiments, Rutherford and Geiger concluded that the α rays expelled by radioactive material consist of atoms of helium, each of which bears two unit charges of electricity. Making this assumption, they were able to predict with accuracy the volume of helium which should be evolved by a gram of radium in a year and thus to furnish an extremely simple and convincing proof of the relationships assumed. Rutherford writes:

The determination of the number of α particles emitted by radium and of the value of the unit charge allows us at once to deduce values of a number of important atomic and radioactive magnitudes. If e be the unit of charge carried by the hydrogen atom in electrolysis, and n the number of atoms in one gram, it is known from Faraday's experiments that $ne = 9647$ electromagnetic units. Since $e = 4.56 \times 10^{-10}$ electrostatic units, or 1.55×10^{-20} electromagnetic units, the value of n is at once determined. From this it is a simple matter, assuming Avogadro's law, to deduce the number of molecules in one cubic centi-metre of any gas at standard pressure and temperature. For conven-ience some of the more important atomic and radioactive constants are as given in the following table:

Charge carried by the hydrogen atom......... 4.65×10^{-10} e.s. units
Value of e/m for α particle................... 5070 e.m. units
Charge carried by the α particle.............. 9.3×10^{-10} e.s. units
Number of atoms in one gram hydrogen....... 6.2×10^{23}
Mass of an atom of hydrogen................ 1.6×10^{-24} gram
Number of molecules per cubic centimetre of
   any gas of standard pressure and temperature. 2178×10^{19}

With the aid of these data, it is possible to deduce at once the rate of production of helium from any substance, for example radium, for which the number of particles emitted per second has been determined. It is known that one gram of radium in equilibrium produces 13.6×10^{10} atoms of helium per second. Dividing by the number of atoms of helium in one cubic centimetre, this corresponds to a production of helium of 4.90×10^{-9} cc. per second or 158 cubic millimeters per year. It will be seen that this calculated value is in close agreement with that determined experimentally. Such a close concordance between calculation and experiment affords strong evidence of the essential correctness of the data on which the calculations are based.

Structure of the Atom.—The force of this reasoning as an argument for the objective reality of the atom may perhaps be better appreciated if we abandon for the moment the historical point of view, and consider the question as a problem to be solved by the experimental data now available. The quantities susceptible of direct measurement are the number of particles evolved by a given weight in a given time, the total charge carried by a given number of particles, the total quantity of electricity transported by the radiation of a given amount of radium in a given time, and finally the total quantity of helium evolved. From these data a simple calculation gives the number of particles present in a cubic centimeter of helium. There remains only the question whether these particles are really the chemical atoms, as we have hitherto understood that term. When we find that the number, dimensions, and charges carried by such particles agree entirely with the figures obtained by physicists using more indirect methods, there can no longer be much doubt as to the reality of the atom and probably of the electron. This certainty has naturally stimulated speculation concerning the structure of the atom itself. The phenomena of radioactivity would seem to indicate that electrons and atoms of helium are its most important components, but others may possibly be involved as well. There is as yet very little agreement between individual theorists in such matters. Physicists seem inclined to think of the atom as a highly dynamic complex, analogous to a planetary system, while chemists for the most part favor some conception which will permit close packing of the atoms in the molecules of solids.

The electron, too, is assuming a more and more important place in the chemical vocabulary. It not only appears in modern explanations of electrolysis and of metallic conduction, but chemical combination is frequently interpreted as the transfer of one or more electrons from one atom to another, the residual force which still binds the wandering electron to its original atom acting as a bond of valence. This leads naturally to electronic conceptions of valence in general. Several hypotheses of this kind have been suggested which doubtless contain elements of truth, but in organic chemistry, where the valence theory is most important, they have as yet hardly demonstrated their usefulness.

Radioactivity and Cosmogony.—Another topic which is of great general interest, but which hardly pertains to our subject, is the influence which the discovery of radium has had upon the fundamental conceptions of geology. The amount of heat which is continually evolved by radium is enormous in proportion to its bulk; the amount emitted by a cubic centimeter of the emanation in the course of its complete transformation is approximately ten million times as great as that evolved in the combination of the same volume of oxygen and hydrogen. Radioactive materials are, however, widely distributed in the earth's crust, and probably in its interior, so that the total heat which they evolve must compensate in large measure for that continually lost by radiation. In consequence, our previous conceptions concerning the earth's period of cooling must certainly be revised. It is easy to see that much more time can now be allowed for the processes of plant and animal evolution, as well as for other geological transformations. Furthermore the rate of transformation of radioactive elements when in equilibrium with each other is now so accurately known, that the minimum age of an active mineral can be calculated from its composition with a good deal of certainty.

In some cases the results are as high as sixteen hundred millions of years.

The Products of Radioactive Disintegration.—From the chemical standpoint there is greater interest in certain researches carried on simultaneously with those just described which had for their object the discovery of new kinds of radioactive material. These, for the most part, had to be sought in the transformations of elements already known. Here it was soon found that many products at first deemed homogeneous, like the *active deposit*, really represented mixtures of several substances passing consecutively into each other. The relationships involved seemed at first sight hopelessly complex, but by applying the law of decay, it became possible to recognize the activities of different elements even when they were superposed. In this way elements were discovered whose "period of average life" had sometimes to be reckoned in seconds. This constant varies widely. For radium it is 2,440 years; for the emanation, 5.55 days; and for uranium it is millions of years. In all, about thirty radioactive elements have been discovered, each of which belongs to one of three series or families. The first comprises the products of disintegration of uranium and contains radium and polonium; the second series is formed by the decomposition of thorium; and the third is derived in the same way from actinium, a natural radioactive element allied to lanthanum, which was discovered by Debierne in 1899. There is some reason to suppose that all three of these series end in ordinary lead, but this has not yet been proved.

The Mechanism of Radioactive Change.—Especial interest attaches to the mechanism of the process by which one of these elements is formed from another. We have seen that radioactive change is almost always accompanied by the evolution of three kinds of rays. Of these we know that the α rays are charged atoms of helium. Physicists who have made accurate comparison also tell us that the β rays are identical with cathode rays and consist of electrons, while the γ rays are probably of secondary origin, being produced whenever α or β rays impinge upon matter. They are similar to X rays and contain no material particles. An atom, then, loses either an atom of helium or an electron, according to whether in a given change it emits an α or a β particle, and it seems to be the rule that in any single transformation only one such loss occurs. The resulting uniformity is extremely simple. When an element loses an atom of helium it must, of course, lose four units of atomic weight. It also loses two units of valence, and the new element which results occupies a position in the periodic table preceding by two that of the parent element. This is admirably illustrated by radium. This element belongs to the alkaline earth group and is closely analogous to barium, having an atomic weight of 226 and the valence 2. It emits α rays and goes over to the emanation. This has the atomic weight 222. It has the valence 0 and finds an appropriate place in the periodic table in a vacant place below xenon, in the family of the inert gases. If, on the other hand, the original element loses an electron (β radiation), no change of atomic weight is involved, but the properties of the resulting element entitle it to a position in the table one point beyond that of the parent.

The Isotopes.—It will occur to the reader that any general application of these laws must result in assigning to some of the newer radioactive elements positions in the periodic table which are already occupied. Marvelous as it seems on the basis of our previous conceptions, this does not make the slightest difference! In spite of the distinguishing property of radioactivity, and in spite of a difference in atomic weight which may in some cases amount to several units, the two elements are alike in their properties, both physical and chemical, except radioactivity, and where sufficient quantities are obtainable to make the experiment, it has been shown that when they are once mixed, no separation is practicable. Substances which stand in this relation are said to have the same *atomic number* and are called *isotopes.*[1] Furthermore there seems to be no necessary limit to their number. Ordinary lead appears to have no less than four.

The simplicity of the relationships above described was shown in the work of Fleck, Russell, and Fajans in 1913. By their aid it is obvious that the properties of any radioactive element, no matter how short-lived, can be readily foretold if we know the position

[1] Isotopes differ slightly, of course, in properties depending directly upon mass, such as rate of diffusion. Harkins and R. S. Mulliken have utilized this fact to separate mercury into portions of appreciably different density.

of its parent in the periodic table, and the kind of radiation by which its formation is accompanied. This determines the position of the new element in the periodic system. If this position is already occupied, the properties of the new element will be identical with those of the present occupant. If it is vacant, the properties of the new element can be predicted with the usual degree of certainty from what is known of the other members of the same group.

X-ray Spectra.—Such a discussion as that upon which we are engaged would be incomplete without an account of certain recent studies of X-ray spectra which have thrown unexpected light upon both the arrangement of atoms in crystals and upon the relationships of the periodic system.

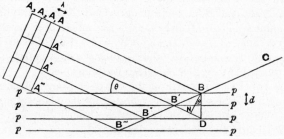

DIAGRAM ILLUSTRATING THE MECHANISM OF X-RAY REFRACTION

The stimulus to these investigations began with an observation made by von Laue in 1913. He found that when a narrow pencil of X rays is allowed to pass through a crystal, and then to strike perpendicularly upon a photographic plate, a dark central shadow is formed by the beam at the point of contact, but this is surrounded by symmetrically arranged dots which were recognized by Laue as due to diffraction. Now, ever since the discovery of the X rays, a dogma had prevailed to the effect that they could be neither reflected, refracted, nor diffracted. The fact is, however, that no diffraction grating can be efficient unless the spacing of its lines is of the same order of magnitude as the wave lengths of the vibrations concerned. Now X rays have wave lengths approximately only one ten-thousandth that of sodium light. This would require a grating the distance between whose lines was as small as that between the mole-

cules in a crystal.   It therefore occurred to W. H. Bragg of Leeds
and W. L. Bragg of Cambridge to use these spaces between molecules for this very purpose, and they found by experiment that
when a beam of X rays strikes at an angle upon the face of a
crystal, a kind of reflection occurs in which several surface
layers take part.   It is somewhat analogous to the way in which
an opalescent substance reflects light.   What happens is best
stated in their own words:

Let the crystal structure be represented by the series of planes p,p,p;
d being their common distance apart or "spacing." A,A_1,A_2,A_3,
. . . are a train of advancing waves of wave length λ. Consider
those waves which, after reflection, join in moving along BC, and
compare the distances which they must travel from some line such as
AA'' before they reach the point C. The routes by which they travel
are ABC, $A'B'C$, $A''B''C$, and so on. Draw BN perpendicular to
$A'B'$. Produce $A'B'$ to D, where D is the image of B in the plane
through B'. Since $B'B = B'D$, and $A'N = AB$, the difference between
$A'B'C$ and ABC is equal to ND, that is, to $2d \sin \theta$. Similarly, $A''B''C$
is greater than $A'B'C$ by the same distance and so on.

If DN is equal to the length of the wave, or is any whole multiple
of that length, all the wave trains reflected by the planes p,p,p, are in
the same phase and their amplitudes are added together. If DN
differs but slightly from the wave length, say by a thousandth part,
the many thousand reflections bear all sorts of phase relations to each
other, and the resultant amplitude is practically zero. We see, therefore, that when a monochromatic wave train is allowed to strike the
face of the crystal, it is only when the glancing angle has certain values
that reflection takes place. These values are given by

$$\lambda = 2d \sin \theta_1$$
$$2\lambda = 2d \sin \theta_2$$
$$3\lambda = 2d \sin \theta_3, \text{ etc.}$$

The reflection at the angle θ_1 is called the reflection of the first order,
that at the angle θ_2 reflection of the second order, and so on.

If the crystal is slowly turned round in such a way that the glancing
angle steadily increases, in general there is no reflected beam. But
as the angle assumes the values θ_1, θ_2, θ_3, there is a reflection of the rays.
Passing now to another face of the crystal which has a different spacing,
d', the monochromatic rays will only be reflected when

$$\lambda = 2d' \sin \theta_1$$
$$2\lambda = 2d' \sin \theta_2, \text{ etc.}$$

If, therefore, we measure the angles θ_1, θ_2, θ_3, at which reflection occurs, it gives us a relation between λ, the wave length, and d, the constant of the grating. By employing the same crystal face the wave lengths of different monochromatic vibrations can be compared. By using the same wave length, the distance d can be compared for different crystals and different faces of the same crystal.

The Atomic Structure of Crystals.—To test this reasoning the authors constructed an X-ray spectrometer. In its arrangement this resembles a reflecting goniometer, but the rays, after being reflected by a crystal, pass into an ionizing chamber where their intensity can be measured by the conductivity which they impart to the gas it contains. It is clear that if a given radiation consisted of vibrations of all wave lengths, there would be some ionization in the chamber for every position of the crystal. This would correspond to a continuous spectrum. If, on the other hand, the radiation consisted of a few monochromatic rays, then at certain angles a marked increase of ionization would suddenly result. When plotted, these would correspond to a line spectrum. As a matter of fact, there are both effects. There is a weak and characterless continuous spectrum, and, at certain angles, there are groups of two or three lines which are usually close together and which are characteristic of the source of the rays. It will be remembered that in the ordinary X-ray bulb the cathode rays generate the X rays by striking a tilted plate of metal, usually platinum or tungsten, which is called the anticathode. Now it has been known for some time that anticathodes of different material produce different kinds of rays, and Barkla, using a great variety of anticathodes, has found that the resulting rays differ widely in their coefficients of absorption. In the experiments of W. H. and W. L. Bragg it is clearly demonstrated that they have different spectra, and from this can be drawn some remarkable conclusions concerning the atoms which emit them. Before discussing this latter point, however, we must come back to the fundamental equation:

$$\lambda = 2d \sin \theta.$$

This obviously contains two unknown quantities, λ and d, but we have some data for determining at least the order of magnitude of the latter. If we know the mass of an atom of hydrogen (page 405), the molecular weight of the substance, and its density, it is an easy matter to calculate the average space occupied by each molecule. To get an accurate measure of the wave length, however, it is necessary to have a more accurate value, since in a crystal it is to be expected that the distances between particles will vary with the direction. It has proved possible to accomplish this by the study of crystals of simple chemical composition and highly symmetrical form. Rock salt which crystallizes in the cubic system is admirably adapted for the purpose. By a somewhat elaborate comparison of geometrical models too extensive to be repeated here, the Braggs prove that in the cubic system the structure of any crystal must conform to one of three space lattices, and they show that these can be distinguished by experiment, for if X-ray reflection be made on the principal crystal faces {100}, {110}, and {111}, the sines of the angles of first-order reflection will have different ratios in the three cases. These are:

$$\text{For the cube lattice, } 1:\sqrt{2}:\sqrt{3}$$

$$\text{For the cube-centered lattice. } 1:\frac{1}{\sqrt{2}}:3$$

$$\text{For the face-centered cube lattice, } 1:2:\frac{\sqrt{3}}{2}$$

Now it happens that KCl, NaCl, FeS and CaF_2 all crystallize in the cubic system and their space lattices are such that in each case one-half of a molecule is associated with what may be designated as the "unit cube." In any of these cases, therefore, the spacing between the particles can be found from the equation:

$$(\tfrac{1}{2}M)m = \rho(d^3{}_{(100)})$$

in which M is the molecular weight, m the mass of an atom of hydrogen, ρ the density of the crystal, and $d_{(100)}$ the space between the layers of particles parallel to the crystal face {100}. When the values of d obtained in this way from all four of the substances mentioned are substituted in the fundamental equation we obtain the same value for λ, which is a valuable check upon the correctness of the assumptions involved.

It has been pointed out above that with X rays of a given wave length it is possible to investigate the structures of various crystals by determining the depth between layers parallel to known crystal faces. Several investigators are now carrying on this work and have obtained interesting results. It is found, for example, that the reflection of the rays is a function exercised by the atoms of each element separately, regardless of the com-

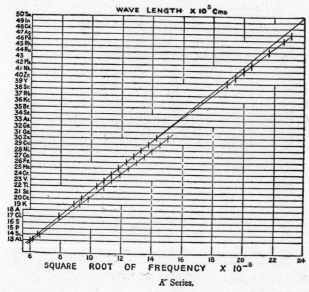

K Series.

RELATIONSHIP OF X-RAY SPECTRA AND ATOMIC NUMBERS

Reproduced from W. H. and W. L. Bragg's *X-rays and Crystal Structure,*
by the kind permission of the authors and of G. Bell and Sons, London.

pounds in which they are combined, so that the arrangement of the atoms of a given element in a crystal can be studied independently of the other atoms present, just as a geometrical figure (to use Bragg's illustration) may be used to connect the recurring points of a wall-paper design, without regard to the other details of the pattern. This has sometimes been expressed in the form that in a crystal the molecule has no separate existence, since, in rock salt, for example, each atom of sodium stands in the same space relation to several atoms of chlorine. A still more important conclusions must be drawn from these studies.

In a crystal, the atoms must be rigidly fixed, or at least they cannot have the latitude of vibration which has hitherto been assumed for all states of aggregation. This is particularly interesting, because T. W. Richards from his work on compressibility, and Pope and Barlow, from considerations of structure, have each come to the conclusion that in the case of solids at

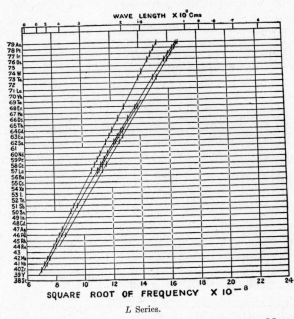

L Series.

RELATIONSHIP OF X-RAY SPECTRA AND ATOMIC NUMBERS
Reproduced from W. H. and W. L. Bragg's *X-rays and Crystal Structure*, by kind permission of the authors and of G. Bell and Sons, London.

least, the atoms must be close-packed. There is as yet, however, little agreement between these investigators concerning matters of detail.

Mosely's Work upon the Atomic Numbers.—To the chemist there is still greater interest in some work carried out by Mosely in 1913 and 1914 in which he made a comparative study of the X rays derived from different sources. He constructed anticathodes of every element for which this was practicable, and, employing the same type of apparatus as Bragg, determined the wave lengths of the different lines emitted. When the results are graphically compared, a surprising regularity becomes apparent. If the atomic numbers are plotted against the square roots of the vibration frequencies (reciprocals of the wave length) of corresponding lines, the resulting curve is almost a straight line, upon which the different elements appear at equidistant points. This gives an entirely independent check upon the order of elements in the periodic system and possesses certain advantages over every other periodic function hitherto studied. The results are reassuring. Three conclusions stand out prominently, and are worth emphasizing: first, the order of the existing elements is the same as that already adopted on the basis of chemical analogy, even where this contradicts the strict order of the atomic weights, as in the case of argon and potassium; second, the elements of the rare earth group all find separate places upon the curve, are therefore entitled to similar recognition in the table, and cannot all be grouped in one place as has been done by some theorists; third, the fact that the elements in this arrangement are equidistantly spaced shows more clearly than has hitherto been possible exactly the number of new elements whose discovery may be expected and their character. As a matter of fact there are now but two vacant spaces (85 and 87), so that the discovery of many more kinds of elements need not be looked for. This of course places no limit upon the possible number of isotopes, for these all have the same atomic number.

The most important of these conclusions is the first mentioned, which shows us that while they run closely parallel, the atomic number of an element is a more fundamental index of its quality than the atomic weight. This value must depend upon something closely allied to mass but not identical with it, and we must now restate the periodic law in the terms: The properties of the elements are periodic functions of their atomic numbers.

Sir Thomas Edward Thorpe (1845–1925) was born at Manchester, studied at Owens College and then under Bunsen at Heidelberg. In 1870 he was made professor of chemistry at Anderson College, Glasgow, four years later at Yorkshire College, in Leeds, and in 1885 at the Normal School (now Imperial College of Science) in South Kensington, London. In 1894 he was made director of the government laboratories. He retired in 1890. His *Essays on Historical Chemistry* are attractive and interesting, but he is best known for his *Dictionary of Applied Chemistry*, of which the first edition was finished in 1890, and which was compiled with the help of other chemists.

He worked on the oxides of phosphorus and discovered P_2O_4 and P_4O_6 (with Tutton). He also discovered phosphorus pentafluoride, phosphoryl fluoride (with Hambly), and thiophosphphoryl fluoride (with Rodger). He studied critical temperatures and the viscosity of liquids besides making some accurate atomic-weight determinations. Together with Roscoe, he studied the compounds of vanadium.

Lord Rutherford (1871–1937) was born at Nelson, New Zealand, and studied at the University there. After this he spent some time in research at the Cavendish Laboratory in Cambridge, England. In 1898 he became professor of physics at McGill University in Montreal, Canada. In 1907 he had a similar post at Manchester, England, and in 1919 became professor of experimental physics at the Cambridge University, England, and also professor at the Royal Institute in London. Although a physicist, chemists have learned from his brilliant work of the existence of radioactive transformations, the structure of matter, and the nuclear nature of the atom. He received a Nobel prize in 1908 and was knighted in 1914 and made a baron in 1931 with the title Lord Rutherford of Nelson.

Frederick Soddy (1877 ——) was born at Eastbourne, Sussex, England. He was educated at Eastbourne College, University College in Wales, Aberystwyth, and Merton College, Oxford, where he received his degree in 1898. After two years of postgraduate work at Oxford, he went to Canada and from 1900 to 1902 was demonstrator at McGill University in Montreal, working with Rutherford on radioactivity. In 1902–1904 he worked under Ramsay at University College, in London, where he obtained helium from radium. From 1904 to 1914 he was lecturer on physical chemistry and radioactivity at the University of Glasgow and then spent some time at Aberdeen. In 1919 he became professor of inorganic and physical chemistry at Oxford. From his work with Rutherford, the theory of the disintegration of radio-active elements was obtained and his theory with respect to the existence of isotopes, or elements with the same number of electrons outside the nucleus of the atom and same chemical characteristics but different atomic weights has been confirmed by subsequent work. Soddy received the Nobel prize in 1921. He has written books on *Radioactivity* (1914), the *Interpretation of Radium* (1920), *Chemistry of the Radioactive Elements* (1914–1920), *Matter and Energy* (1912), *Science and Life* (1920), *Cartesian Economy* (1922), and *Inversion of Science* (1924).

James Walker (1863–1932) was born in Dundee, Scotland. He matriculated at the University of Saint Andrews in 1883, but it took him six years to satisfy the requirements. He eventually obtained the degrees D.Sc., Ph.D., and LL.D. He was inspired by Purdie's lectures and became his assistant. Then he went to Leipzig to work in organic chemistry under Wislicenus but became converted into a physical chemist by Ostwald and took his doctorate in physical chemistry in 1896. For 2 years he was on the staff of University College in London and helped detect krypton and neon. In 1898 he became professor at McGill University in Montreal where he emphasized the importance of physical chemistry. He went back to Scotland where he was profes-

sor at Edinburgh from 1908 to 1928.   With Purdie he did pioneer work on
the stereochemistry of lactic acid and the action of *Penicillium glaucum* on
ethoxysuccinic acid.   He studied the velocity of reaction between hydrobro-
mic and bromic acids and in 1904 made the interesting conclusion that union
of a solute with the molecules of the solvent was a necessary precursor of ionization, although it is not always true that ionization results.

Mosely.—Henry Gwyn Jeffreys Mosely was born August 23, 1887,
in Weymouth, a seaport and summer resort in the southern part of
Dorsetshire, England.   His father was professor of comparative
anatomy at Oxford and his grandfather had been a celebrated mathematician, physicist, and astronomer at King's College, London.   Mosely
graduated from Trinity College, Oxford University, with honors in
natural science, but he had also done brilliant work in the classics.
Upon graduating from Oxford he became associated with Ernest Rutherford at Manchester, who set him to work at finding out the number of
electrons emitted during the disintegration of radium and, after a
year of study, Mosely announced that, on an average, every atom of
radium produced but one electron.

Mosely next studied the life of an emanation of actinium which exists
such a short time after it is formed that special devices had to be constructed to detect it.   With K. Fajans, later professor of chemistry at
Munich, he determined that the average life of the emanation was less
than 0.002 second.

He next studied the limit to the strength of an electric charge on an
isolated body containing radium.   As radium loses negative electrons,
it becomes more and more positively charged.   Mosely was able to
increase the charge to above 100,000 volts until finally the radium
emanation withered away and disappeared.   Meanwhile Max von Laue,
of the University of Zurich, discovered that the crystals of salt could be
used as diffraction grating for X rays, the minute spaces between the
atoms of the salt crystal serving to produce with X rays a spectrum
similar to the solar spectrum, which is produced with coarser gratings,
from light which has much longer wave length than that of X rays.
By his studies with X-ray spectra Mosely was able to clear up the
difficulties encountered in the periodic classification of the elements.
He was able to assign to each element an atomic number, which is
presumably the same as the number of electrons that are outside the
nucleus of an atom of an element.   When these numbers are used in
place of the atomic weights, difficulties, such as that of iodine and of
tellurium, whose atomic weights do not correspond to the proper positions in the periodic table, disappear.   In Mosely's classification by
atomic numbers, the rare earths all find a place (57-91); there are ninety-

two possible elements, and of the elements which were then missing (numbers 43, 61, 72, 85, and 87) all but two have since been discovered.

The French chemist Urbain gave to Mosely an ore containing an unknown number of rare earths present in small quantities. In a few days Mosely made a report which confirmed the conclusions arrived at by Urbain as a result of twenty years of careful work. Mosely enlisted in the British Army during the World War and was killed in 1915 at Suvla Bay in the Dardanelles. All his epoch-making work was done during four years. Dr. Millikan of the California Institute of Technology has said: "Had the European War had no other result than the snuffing out of this young life, that alone would make it one of the most hideous and most irreparable crimes in history."

Some American Chemists.—Until the latter part of the nineteenth century, it was well known that chemistry in the United States was far behind Germany with respect to its scientific development. For postgraduate work in chemistry, a large proportion of American students went to Germany. The greater part of the chemicals used in research were imported from Germany, and it was difficult for manufacturers here to make materials as good or sell them as cheaply. Most American students who studied in Germany were impressed by the encyclopedic knowledge of the professors there, but the professors were impressed by the diligence and enthusiasm of the American students. Their training was, for the most part, less adequate than that of the German students from the preparatory schools (Gymnasia), but they were in a hurry to get the work done and did not waste time drinking beer and dueling, in the manner of some of the German students. The German system of giving the students freedom in selecting their subjects for study and of having the professors pay little attention to whether the students attend classes or not is successful in producing some brilliant minds but wasteful from the standpoint of efficiency.

The war of 1914–1918 accomplished a great deal toward making the United States more prominent in chemistry. It taught the manufacturer that it was worth while to have well-trained chemists in his employ, and the country as a whole became more interested in science. It became easy, relatively speaking, to interest capital in new chemical operations, and, as a result, there is greater utilization of recent advances in science here than elsewhere.   Foreign students, in large numbers, are now coming to the United States to study science, and they are impressed, not so much with the knowledge of the professors, as with the extent to which that knowledge is utilized in everyday life.   The love for scientific research on the part of students is getting to be almost commonplace on the part of the American student.   Here, only a few of the Americans who have helped in the progress of chemistry will be mentioned.   They are not necessarily the most prominent chemists, but their work is representative of that done in the United States.

Charles Frederick Chandler was born at Lancaster, Massachusetts, in 1836.   His father was a merchant in New Bedford.   After attending the high school there, Charles studied at the Lawrence Scientific School of Harvard University not being eligible for the college on account of the Latin and Greek requirements.   After finishing his studies at the scientific school, he decided to study abroad, going over as supercargo on a sailing vessel.   He worked for a time under Wöhler in Göttingen and then under Heinrich Rose, the well-known analytical chemist, at Berlin, serving him as assistant for one year.   He returned to Göttingen for his Ph.D. in 1856.   Later in life he received five honorary degrees.   On returning to the United States he heard that Professor Joy at Union College needed an assistant and applied for the position.   Joy wanted the assistant, but the authorities would not furnish the necessary funds.   Chandler, who had no false pride, worked as janitor for a year at a salary of $400 doing his janitorial duties early and late but teaching during the day.   The next year he was placed on the instructing staff and remained there from 1857 to 1864 when he was called to Columbia. There he helped establish the School of Mines at which he was professor for thirty-six years and dean for thirty-three years.   This was the first school of its kind in America.   Chandler helped build up the College of Physicians and Surgeons at Columbia and the New York College of Pharmacy where he was appointed professor and afterward president.   He applied his scientific knowledge to public welfare and was the first chemist of the New York Board of Health.   His work in connection with sulfuric acid manufacture, sugar refining, petroleum refining and in the illuminating gas industry justified his reputation of being one of the first, outstanding industrial chemists of the United States.

He invented assay ton weights which are now used all over the world. The ore is weighed in assay ton units, and the button of precious metal is weighed to the nearest hundredth of a milligram in the metric system, but the assayer knows at once how many troy ounces of metal are present in an avoirdupois ton of ore without any computation.   Chandler earned large fees as chemical expert, but much of his money he gave to needy students. He was a leading spirit in organizing the American Chemical Society and the Chemists Club of New York, did a great deal of editorial work, and published many papers. He died at East Hartford, Connecticut, in 1925.

Edward Williams Morley was born in 1838 in Newark, New Jersey, the son of a clergyman. As a boy, his health was delicate, and he was taught at home until he was nineteen. He began to read before he was three, began Latin at the age of six, Greek at eleven. When he was twelve he spent all his money for materials to use in chemical experiments and at fourteen was reading Silliman's textbook recently published. He received his B.A. degree at Williams College in 1860, studied at Andover Theological Seminary until 1864, but returned to Williams in 1863 for the A.M. degree. He afterward received five honorary degrees. From 1866 to 1868 he taught in a private school at Marlboro, Massachusetts, then was called to the ministry, preaching for a short time in a Congregational church in Ohio. In the same year (1868) he was made professor of chemistry in Western Reserve College at Hudson, Ohio, which afterward moved to Cleveland and was known as Adelbert College of Western Reserve University, where he remained until he retired in 1906. He was also professor of chemistry at Cleveland Medical College in 1873–1878. He died at West Hartford, Connecticut, in 1923. Morley was a tireless worker and very skillful in the laboratory. He published fifty-five scientific papers.

His work on the density of oxygen and of hydrogen and the determination of the ratio in which they combine was published in 1895 after twelve years of research and showed an accuracy never reached previously. The Michelson-Morley experiments with light, although negative in result with respect to the drift of cosmic ether in relation to the motion of the earth, led to the Einstein theory of relativity. Morley's work showed great attention to all details. He enjoyed arduous research work such as making difficult chemical analyses, was interested in teaching, and in his desire to keep up with the literature even went so far as to learn the Russian language.

J. Willard Gibbs, Jr., was really not a chemist at all, but his discovery of the phase rule is perhaps the greatest single contribution to physical chemistry in the nineteenth century. He was born in New Haven, Connecticut, in 1839, the only son and fourth child of Josiah Willard Gibbs who was professor of sacred literature in the Yale Divinity School from 1824 until his death in 1861. Josiah Willard, the son, was graduated from Yale in 1858 and, continuing his studies there, was appointed tutor in 1863, teaching Latin and natural philosophy. In 1866 he went to Europe where he remained until 1869, studying at Paris, Berlin, and Heidelberg. In 1871 he was appointed professor of mathematical physics at Yale, a position which he held until his death in 1903. Of his many publications, *On the Equilibrium of Heterogeneous Substances*, published in two parts in 1876 and 1878, was of fundamental importance. It was translated into German by Wilhelm Ostwald and into French by H. Le Châtelier. His notes on vector analysis, which were not published but given to students in 1881–1884 formed the basis of the textbook on *Vector Analysis* published by his former student E. B. Wilson in 1901. Gibbs died in 1903.

JOSIAH WILLARD GIBBS
1839–1903

Arthur Amos Noyes (1866–1936) was born in Newburyport, Massachusetts, a descendent of a family that settled there in 1635. His father was a lawyer and had the reputation of being an absent-minded scholar and philosopher. He gave to his son instruction in Latin, chess, swimming, rowing, and sailing. From his high school teacher, Oliver Merrill, he acquired an early interest in chemistry, and he used the family dining room for such experiments as making phosphine by the action of yellow phosphorus on boiling alcoholic potash, until a flask broke and damaged the carpet and law books which caused the parental edict that further experiments be confined to the attic or woodshed. He determined to study at the Massachusetts Institute of Technology, but lack of funds caused him to carry out all the work of the freshman year, except drawing, at home, and, as a result he entered the sophomore class with high standing. He was a good student but not very skillful in manipulation. During his senior year, he became interested in organic chemistry from the lectures of L. N. Norton. He received the B.S. degree in 1886 and the M.S. degree in 1887. He was at once appointed assistant in analytical chemistry and given full charge of a class of forty in qualitative analysis. During this period he became acquainted with two students, George E. Hale and Harry M. Goodwin, both of whom have become prominent in the field of physics. At that time, qualitative analysis was taught in the sophomore year, and students were required to use the large textbook by Fresenius which was unquestionably the best book on the subject. Noyes, while working with the students, thought it would be well to give them a short text containing everything that each student was supposed to know and nothing else. In 1892, therefore, he had printed privately a book entitled *Notes on Qualitative Analysis* which comprised 58 pages. The sixth edition of this book was published in 1915 and even today it is used all over the world.

In 1888, Noyes went to Leipzig to work in organic chemistry under Wislicenus, but as a result of Ostwald's lectures he soon became more interested in physical chemistry. He obtained the Ph.D. degree under Ostwald in 1890 and returned to the United States very enthusiastic and interesting everyone with whom he came in contact in the ionization theory of Arrhenius and the mass-action law of Guldberg and Waage. He was again on the staff of the Massachusetts Institute of Technology and taught organic chemistry and physical chemistry.

He ranked as instructor from 1892 to 1894, assistant and associate professor from 1894 to 1899, and full professor of theoretical chemistry in 1899 at the age of thirty-three. Then, in 1903, he was made director of the research laboratory of physical chemistry, which post he held for seventeen years. In 1907–1909 he was acting president of the Massachusetts Institute of Technology. From 1915 until his death, he was director of the Gates Chemical Laboratory at the California Institute of Technology. For several years he was professor at the two institutions, spending part of the year in California and part in Massachusetts. At both institutions he was a leading member of the faculty and a guiding spirit on all of the important questions that arose.

ARTHUR AMOS NOYES
1866–1936

Among the well-known scientists who were trained by Noyes are Willis R. Whitney, (who, became distinguished for his work at the General Electric Company) C. G. Abbot, the astrophysicist, W. C. Bray and G. N. Lewis of the University of California, C. S. Hudson, Yogoro Kato, C. A. Kraus, K. G. Falk, R. C. Tolman, W. D. Harkins, E. W. Washburn, R. B. Sosman, John Johnston, F. G. Keyes, and Linus Pauling.

From 1895 to 1901 he was editor of the *Review of American Chemical Research* which was started because it was felt that much of the work that was being done in the United States was not properly abstracted in the *Chemisches Zentralblatt*. The *Review* was first published in the *Technology Quarterly* but soon became a part of the *Journal of the American Chemical Society*. In 1907, it was thought best to make the *Review* more comprehensive and cover chemical publications all over the world, and thus our present *Chemical Abstracts* came into existence. William Albert Noyes, then in charge of chemistry at the University of Illinois, was editor of the *Journal of the American Chemical Society*, and it was largely due to his efforts that *Chemical Abstracts* was started. Because of the similarity in names, the part that A. A. Noyes played in starting an abstract journal has been overlooked by most writers. W. A. Noyes also wrote a textbook on *Qualitative Analysis* which helps add to the confusion. Both of these men have also served as president of the American Chemical Society, and the students of each feel that their "Doctor Noyes" was a wonderful man. The keen judgment of Dr. W. A. Noyes was shown by his selection of Austin N. Patterson, and later Evan J. Crane, as editors of *Chemical Abstracts*.

A. A. Noyes is best known from his books *Qualitative Chemical Analysis, The General Principles of Chemistry* (with M. S. Sherrill) in 1913, which became *Chemical Principles* in 1921, and *Qualitative Analysis for the Rare Elements* (with W. C. Bray) in 1927. This last work represents the results of about thirty years of labor. Besides giving a complete scheme of analysis for all the metallic elements, it includes the results of hundreds of experiments which were performed in developing the scheme. The procedure is long, and there are few colleges, if any, that are willing to devote so much time to qualitative analysis with their students. In the case of the scheme for the platinum metals and for the examination of the rare earths, better procedures are now known, but the book is, nevertheless, a masterpiece. Noyes also wrote *Laboratory Experiments on the Class Reactions and Identification of Organic Substances* (with S. P. Mulliken) (1899), *The General Principles of Physical Science* (1902), *Electrical Conductivity of Aqueous Solutions* (1907), and scientific papers on theoretical, analytical, and organic chemistry and on educational subjects.

Noyes himself was never a skillful experimenter, but probably no teacher of chemistry in the United States has inspired more students with a love for chemistry. He was not particularly successful in handling mediocre students, and sometimes his writings had to be read several times before they were understood, although he was a remarkably clear thinker. He received honorary degrees from the University of Maine, Clark University, the University of Pittsburgh, Harvard, and Yale. He was awarded the Willard

GILBERT NEWTON LEWIS
1875——

Gibbs medal of the American Chemical Society, was a member of the National Academy of Science, and served in the National Research Council. He never married. He was fond of poetry which he could quote from memory by the hour.

Gilbert Newton Lewis (1875 ——) was born in Weymouth, Massachusetts, but studied first at the University of Nebraska (1890–1893). He then went to Harvard and there obtained the B.A. degree in 1896, the A.M. degree in 1897, and the Ph.D. degree in 1899. In 1900 and 1901 he studied at Leipzig and at Göttingen in Germany. He has received honorary degrees from Liverpool (1923), Wisconsin (1928), Chicago (1929), and Madrid (1934). In 1896–1897 he taught at Phillips Academy while he was doing postgraduate work at Harvard. In 1899–1900 he was instructor at Harvard, and in 1904–1905 he was in the Philippine Islands, in charge of weights and measures. In 1907–1912 he was attached to Noyes's laboratory at the Massachusetts Institute of Technology with the title of assistant professor in 1907–1908, associate professor in 1909–1911, and full professor in 1911–1912. Since then he has been professor of chemistry and dean of the college of chemistry at the University of California.

Lewis's book on *Thermodynamics and Free Energy of Chemical Substances* (with M. Randall) (1923) is much used as a college text and has been translated into German. He also wrote on *Valence and Structure of Atoms and Molecules* (1923), *Anatomy of Science* (1926), *Magnetochemical Theory* (1922), *Extremely Dry Liquids, Magnetism of Oxygen, Valence and the Electron,* and on various other subjects, such as relativity, non-Newtonian mechanics, four-dimentional vector analysis, etc. In 1916 he proposed a simple model of the atom and has interpreted the Werner valence theory in terms of the electron. In his laboratory, considerable work has been done on the preparation of pure deuterium, the isotope of hydrogen. Lewis has a very attractive personality and the ability to talk impressively before large audiences. He and his associates have done a great deal toward developing chemical theory. Lewis was a major and lieutenant colonel during the war of 1914–1918 and has been awarded the Davy, Willard Gibbs, and Richards medals.

Edward Wight Washburn (1881–1934) was born at Beatrice, Nebraska. He was an honor student in the high school in Nebraska and, like A. A. Noyes, performed experiments at home but received little sympathy from his father when explosions took place. To start his studies at the University of Nebraska, he sold his pony and did a great deal of tutoring. After two years he transferred to the Massachusetts Institute of Technology and was allowed almost no credit for work done in Nebraska. He had to spend four years at Boston to get his B.S. degree in 1905. Three years later he received the Ph.D. degree.

At M.I.T. he at once attracted the attention of Arthur A. Blanchard, who has taught freshman chemistry there since 1900. To Blanchard and A. A. Noyes much credit is due for helping develop this brilliant scientist. He remained attached to Noyes's research laboratory until 1910 when he was called to the University of Illinois as assistant professor. In 1913–1916 he was associate professor, and full professor from 1916 on. At M.I.T. he came into close association with G. N. Lewis and R. C. Tolman as fellow students.

Washburn was a skillful manipulator and published over one hundred papers on physical chemistry and ceramics. His book *Introduction to the Principles of Physical Chemistry* has been popular. He was the acting chairman of the division of chemistry at the National Bureau of Standards (1918–1919) and editor in chief of the *International Critical Tables* (1922–1930). Perhaps his most notable work was that on preparing the isotope of hydrogen, deuterium, and "heavy water" by the fractional electrolysis of water (1931). Early in his work he applied the principles of thermodynamics and buffer action to the iodometric determination of arsenic and was the first to make accurate determinations of transference numbers. By nature, he was quiet, dignified, friendly, capable, and fair-minded. He was the recipient of the Hillebrand prize.

Irving Langmuir (1881 ——) was born in Brooklyn, attended school in Paris (1892–1895), studied at Stevens Institute, and was graduated from the Columbia School of Mines in 1903. He then studied at Göttingen under Nernst and obtained the Ph.D. degree there in 1906. Since then, he has received honorary degrees from Northwestern University (1921), Union University (1923), Edinburgh University (1921), Johns Hopkins University (1931), Columbia (1925), Kenyon College (1927), Princeton (1929), Lehigh (1934), and the Technische Hochschule in Berlin (1929). He was instructor in chemistry at Stevens Institute in 1906–1909, but since then he has been engaged in research at the General Electric Company laboratories in Schenectady, New York.

He has published many papers of fundamental importance in the fields of engineering, physics, and chemistry. Surface phenomena, catalysis, vacuum and low-pressure electrical discharges, atomic charges, and chemical valence have all engaged his attention. He developed the gas-filled tungsten lamp and has worked on atomic welding. He received the Nobel prize in chemistry in 1932 and has been honored with many medals (at least nine) for his achievements. Aside from chemistry, he is interested in outdoor sports; he introduced skiing at Göttingen, likes to sail on skates, at one time walked 52 miles in one day, and at the age of forty-nine learned to fly.

Harold Clayton Urey (1893 ——) was born at Walkerton, Indiana. He studied at the University of Montana and received his B.S. degree there in 1917, then as chemist, entered the employ of the Barret Chemical Company at Philadelphia and remained there about 2 years. He then returned to the University of Montana as instructor for two more years. After this he did post-graduate work at the University of California and received his Ph.D. in 1923 for work done under G. N. Lewis. This was followed by an appointment as *fellow* at the University of Copenhagen (1923–1924) where he worked under Niels Bohr. After this he was made an associate in chemistry at Johns Hopkins University where he stayed until 1929 when he was made associate professor of chemistry at Columbia University.

IRVING LANGMUIR
1881——

He was made full professor at Columbia in 1934, the year that he received the Willard Gibbs medal and the Nobel prize in chemistry.

The division of science into domains such as physics, chemistry, and mathematics is purely arbitrary. It is impossible to think of chemistry absolutely devoid of physics or mathematics, and the remarkable advances of chemistry during the last fifty years have been due to the proper mingling of these three domains. Practically all of the work done by Urey has been at the border line between physics and chemistry, and, in fact, his work is just as interesting to the physicist as it is to the chemist and might just as easily have been done by a physicist. He has worked on the structure of atoms and molecules, thermodynamics and the properties of gases, absorption spectra, isotopes, the kinetics of chemical reactions, Ramon effect, etc. He discovered deuterium, which is hydrogen with atomic weight just twice that of ordinary hydrogen and worked with Washburn in perfecting the electrolytic method for obtaining deuterium. In 1930 (with Ruark) he published a work called *Atoms, Molecules and Quanta*, and from 1927 to the end of 1936 he published twenty-six scientific papers. He has edited the *Journal of Chemistry and Physics* and published a paper on *Mathematical Requirements for Physical Chemists*.

INDEX

Numbers in **boldface type** indicate biographical notes.   Asterisks refer to illustrations.

A

Abderhalden, Emil, **385**
Abegg, Richard, **381**
Abel, 227
Academy of Plato, 9
Acetic acid, Glauber, 42
    substitution by chlorine, 197, 231
Acetyl theory, 192
Acetylene, 274, 344
Acid salts, 168
Acids, basicity, 202, 204, 216, 219
    nature of, views of Berzelius, 167, 187
        of Davy, 151
        of Graham, 203
        of Lavoisier, 100, 147, 186
        of Liebig, 205
    polybasic, organic, 204
Active deposit, 401, 402, 407
Activity coefficient, 359, 361
Adam, creation of, 21
    a reputed alchemist, 19
Adiophorus spirit, 175
Adrian de Mynsicht, 36
Affinity, chemical, idea of Bergman, 68
        of Berzelius, 168
        of Boerhaave, 55
        of Dalton, 116
        of Davy, 151
        of Geoffroy, 56, 68
    tables of, 56
Affinity constants of acids, 359
Agricola, 35, 36
Air, alkaline, 76
    dephlogisticated, 67, 68, 78

Air, experiments on, 76
    and fire, 72
    fixed, 66, 67
    inflammable, 67
    marine acid, 76
    neutral, 76
    phlogisticated, 67, 68, 78
    as primordial substance, 5
    pump, discovery, 46
    spoiled, 72
Alchemist, The, 26, 37
Alchemy, 3, 4, 15, 16, 17, 19, 20, 22, 29, 275, 402
Alchymia, 37
Alcohol, 35
Alembic Club Reprints, 62, 88, 111, 131, 154
Alizarin, 298, 301
Alkali metals, isolation, 145
Alkaline earth metals, isolation, 147
Alkaloids, studied, 176
Alloys, views of Berthollet, 107
Aluminum, discovery of, 178
Alums, dualistic idea of, 169
    isomorphism of, 164
American Chemical Society, organization of, 284
Ammonia, composition of, 76
    supposed oxygen content of, 146, 167
    synthesis of, 88
    type, 220, 238
Ammonium amalgam, 146
Ammonium chloride, synthesis by Priestley, 76
    vapor density of, 216, 243
Amontons, 122